NUCLEAR HEMATOLOGY

GEORG DE HEVESY
(*Nobel Prize for Chemistry, 1943*)

NUCLEAR HEMATOLOGY

Edited by E. SZIRMAI

DIVISION OF NUCLEAR HEMATOLOGY
MEDICAL SECTION
THE INSTITUTION OF NUCLEAR ENGINEERS
LONDON, ENGLAND

1965

ACADEMIC PRESS   New York and London

ACADEMIC PRESS INC.
111 Fifth Avenue, New York, New York 10003

United Kingdom Edition published by
ACADEMIC PRESS INC. (LONDON) LTD.
Berkeley Square House, London W.1

LIBRARY OF CONGRESS CATALOG CARD NUMBER: 65-22773

PRINTED IN THE UNITED STATES OF AMERICA

List of Contributors

Numbers in parentheses indicate the pages on which the authors' contributions begin.

J. ALEKSANDROWICZ (193), Third Medical Clinic, Academy of Medicine, Cracow, Poland

NICOLE ARDAILLOU (41), Laboratoire des Isotopes, Institut de Recherches Sur les Maladies du Sang, Hôpital Saint-Louis, Université de Paris, France

E. H. BETZ (357), Institute of Pathology, University of Liège, Liège, Belgium

H. DA COSTA (339), Atomic Energy Establishment, Medical Division, Radiation Medicine Centre, Tata Memorial Hospital, Parcel, Bombay, India

ALLAN J. ERSLEV (89), Charlotte Drake Cardeza Foundation, Jefferson Medical College Hospital, Philadelphia, Pennsylvania

HENRYK A. GAERTNER, Third Medical Clinic, Academy of Medicine, Cracow, Poland

PHILIP H. GEISLER, Deceased, (379) The Cardeza Foundation for Hematologic Research, Jefferson Medical College, Philadelphia, Pennsylvania

MIHÁLY GERENDÁS (55), Hungarian Academy of Sciences, Budapest, Hungary[1]

THOMAS J. HALEY (11,23,265), Laboratory of Nuclear Medicine and Radiation Biology, Department of Biophysics and Nuclear Medicine, School of Medicine, University of California, Los Angeles, California

IOULIOS A. IOSSIFIDES (379), The Cardeza Foundation for Hematologic Research, Jefferson Medical College, Philadelphia, Pennsylvania

GEORGES MATHÉ (275,339), Institut de Cancérologie et d'Immunogénétique, Hôpital Paul Brousse, Villejuif (Seine), France

YVES NAJEAN (41), Laboratoire des Isotopes, Institut de Recherches Sur les Maladies du Sang, Hôpital Saint-Louis, Université de Paris, France

F. R. PAULSEN (133), Department of Science, The Civic College, Ipswich, Suffolk, England

J. B. PINKERTON (1), Division of Nuclear Hematology, Medical Section, The Institution of Nuclear Engineers, London, England

[1] Formerly Director of The Research Laboratory of Electron Microscopy, Budapest, Hungary.

VOLKMAR SACHS (443), Blutspendezentraee, Hygiene-Institut der Universität Kiel, Kiel, Germany

HAROLD R. SCHUMACHER (89),[2] Charolette Drake Cardeza Foundation, Jefferson Medical College Hospital, Philadelphia, Pennsylvania

EDOARDO STORTI (171), Institute of Medical Pathology, University of Modena, Modena, Italy

SANDOR SZALONTAI (55), Research Institute of the National Blood Center, Budapest, Hungary

E. SZIRMAI (1,457), Division of Nuclear Hematology, Medical Section, The Institution of Nuclear Engineers, London, England[3]

UMBERTO TORELLI (171), Institute of Medical Pathology, University of Modena, Modena, Italy

JAN URBAŃCZYK (193), Third Medical Clinic, Academy of Medicine, Cracow, Poland

SUSUMU WATANABE (485), Research Institute for Nuclear Medicine and Biology, Hiroshima University, Hiroshima, Japan

[2] *Present address:* Department of Hematology, York Hospital, York, Pennsylvania.
[3] *Permanent address:* Adolf Kroner Strasse 11, Stuttgart, Germany.

Preface

This book is the first attempt to describe the present state of our knowledge of the field of Nuclear Hematology. The steadily increasing applications of radioactive substances in the biological sciences and medicine, in addition to the many new technological uses of atomic energy, have brought about a growing risk of damage to the hematopoietic system. It therefore seemed desirable in this volume to present comprehensive information on this subject for the benefit of investigators in the various practical and theoretical areas of biology and physics. The volume is primarily directed to experimental and clinical workers in physiology, internal medicine, hematology, oncology, and radiology, but it is hoped that it will also prove useful to graduate students as an introduction into this new and important field.

The chapters are arranged in two major parts. The first part (Chapters 1–9), in addition to a historical survey and a section on electron microscopy, includes discussions of those aspects of hematology which utilize labeling with radioisotopes for the study of the morphology, physiology, and pathology of blood cells and blood-forming organs. In the second part (Chapters 10–17), the pathology of the effects of radiation, including those following atomic explosions, is presented. Emphasis is placed on radiation damage to the blood and the hematopoietic system. The experimental work on prevention and treatment of radiation injury and the possibilities of clinical treatment are discussed.

The Editor is greatly indebted to the contributors, whose willing cooperation made this book possible, and wishes to express his appreciation for the assistance given by the staff of the editorial and production departments of Academic Press.

E. Szirmai

Stuttgart, Germany
September, 1965

Foreword

Owing to the ingenuity and generosity of Ernest O. Lawrence, radioiron was already widely used in the late thirties. Paul Hahn and his associates, among others, found in their pioneer investigations that conclusions can be drawn from the amount of Fe^{59} incorporated into the erythrocytes from an orally administered dose.

The importance of plasma iron was emphasized by Heilmeyer and Plötner 30 years ago. A decade after the availability of radioiron, Fe^{59} of high specific activity was produced, and it was now possible to inject such small amounts of labeled iron into the circulation that it did not exceed the binding capacity of plasma transferrin. It was now also possible to determine the time the individual iron atoms spent in the blood plasma and their transport rate into the bone marrow and other organs. Such determinations were first carried out in the Donner Laboratory and led to numerous results of great importance.

Many isotopes find extensive application in hematology: Fe^{59}, P^{32}, K^{42}, Cr^{51}, and ThB are used in the determination of blood volume, and Fe^{59}, C^{14}, Cr^{51}, and DFP^{32} in the determination of the life span of elements of the blood. Several of these isotopes are applied in the study of erythron formation.

The present volume contains discussions of the above-mentioned and numerous other applications of isotopes in hematology that will be of interest to the clinician, the radiologist, and the biochemist.

G. DE HEVESY

Stockholm, Sweden
September, 1965

Contents

CHAPTER 1

Introduction to Nuclear Hematology

E. Szirmai and J. B. Pinkerton

CHAPTER 2

Methods for Applying Radioisotopes to Hematological Problems

Thomas J. Haley

CHAPTER 3

Use of Radioactive Isotopes in Hematology

Thomas J. Haley

CHAPTER 8

Blood Cell Studies with Radioautography

Edoardo Storti and Umberto Torelli

CHAPTER 9

Metabolism of Blood Cells and Their Precursors

J. Aleksandrowicz, H. Gaertner, and J. Urbańczyk

CHAPTER 10

Acute Radiation Effects: Damage of Hematopoiesis

Thomas J. Haley

CHAPTER 11

Total Body Irradiation Injury: A Review of the Disorders of the Blood and Hematopoietic Tissues and Their Therapy

Georges Mathé

CHAPTER 12

Effect of Irradiation on Immunity

G. Mathé and H. Da Costa

CHAPTER 13

Chronic Radiation Effects: Damage of Hematopoiesis

E. H. Betz

CHAPTER 14

Effects of Radiations on the Coagulation of Blood

Ioulios A. Iossifides and Philip H. Geisler

CHAPTER 15

Nuclear Hematology and Blood Transfusion

Volkmar Sachs

CHAPTER 16

Problems of Bone Marrow Transplantation in Radiation Damage

E. Szirmai

CHAPTER 17

Nuclear Hematology: Based on Experience with Atomic Explosions

Susumu Watanabe

CHAPTER 1

Introduction to Nuclear Hematology

E. Szirmai* and J. B. Pinkerton

*Division of Nuclear Hematology, Medical Section,
The Institution of Nuclear Engineers, London, England*

I. Definition and History

Nuclear hematology, a term coined, as far as we know, by Szirmai (1954), comprises a wide field of various areas of hematology. It can be defined as the specific aspect of hematology which utilizes radioactive substances (isotopes) for the study of morphology, physiology, and pathology of the blood cells and blood forming organs, and explores the effect of radiation on the hematopoietic system and the peripheral blood.

This definition suggests the correlation of nuclear hematology with both experimental and clinical medicine. It is correlated with nuclear technology and its progress. The position of this new branch of hematological investigation on the crossroads of biology and medicine, nuclear physics and engineering characterizes its interdisciplinary nature and justifies the presentation of its various parameters.

Permanent address: Division of Nuclear Hematology, Medical Section, The Institute of Nuclear Engineering, Adolf Kroner Strasse 11, Stuttgart, Germany.

1

A glance at the Table of Contents will show the principal fields of endeavor which are subordinated to the general term *nuclear hematology*. It is evident that they represent the two main areas stipulated in the definition; as a rule they will be discussed separately, although a strict separation was not possible in all instances.

The pioneer work in the foundation of nuclear hematology is that of the Hungarian Nobel Prize winner of 1943 George de Hevesy, who introduced the use of isotopes as labels in biology and medicine, and especially in hematology.

The isotopes most frequently used in theoretical studies of the blood and employed therapeutically in blood diseases are listed in Table I of Chapter 3 of this treatise.†

A detailed description of the study of radioactive isotopes would far exceed this introductory chapter: only a brief summary can be given here. Many details can be found in special reviews and proceedings of symposia and meetings: "First International Symposium on Radioisotopes in Hematology" (Keiderling and Hoffmann, 1962); "Use of Radioisotopes in Animal Biology and the Medical Sciences" (1962), Vols. I and II; International Conference "Man and Technology in the Nuclear and Space Age—Nuclear Hematology" (Szirmai, 1962, 1963), and others.

The use of radioactive isotopes followed closely the progress of discoveries in the physical sciences. The early work in the first period of employment of isotopes was limited to uranium (U) and thorium (Th), although the isotopes of lead (Pb) and bismuth (Bi) were included during the period 1913–1933. The discovery of deuterium (H^2) initiated a second period (Urey, 1932). The availability of artificial radioactive isotopes due to the work of Frederic and Irène Joliet Curie (Curie, 1932) made possible the use of various elements having different degrees of radioactivity. This third period of the age of isotopes was followed by the discovery of tritium (H^3) by Devasos and Corney (1939), thus originating the fourth period of application of isotope tagging of biological structures. The specific usefulness of radioisotopes in the solution of problems in hematology forms the subject of the individual chapters of this treatise.

II. Studies Employing Radioactive Isotopes

A. In Hematology

The tagging of cells of the hematopoietic system and the peripheral blood is a predominantly morphological method by which cells and their

---

† The Atomic Energy Commission of the United States began to supply radioactive isotopes for use in research projects in 1947.

structures may be characterized and the results correlated with data available by means of light and electron microscopy. It is evident that the high sensitivity of autoradiographic techniques has proved to be useful for studying hematopoiesis, particularly for analyzing early phases in the development of the mature cell and for establishing the genealogy of the erythropoietic, leukopoietic, and thrombopoietic systems. Also important determinations of blood volume and blood clotting time have been considerably facilitated by studies with isotopes.

Incorporation methods using tagged nucleic acids or their pyrimidine and purine precursors raised studies from the morphological to the functional level and permitted interpretations in terms of metabolic processes.

Some of these techniques, combined with classical functional determinations using radioactive isotopes in the investigations of the functional dynamics of physiological and pathological hematopoiesis, may be called nuclear hematological functional diagnostic methods. Important work was carried out early by Hevesy (1923, 1961) who used radioactive isotopes C^{16}, P^{32}, H^3, or N^{15} in the morphology of blood cells and DNA determinations, and C^{14}, Fe^{55}, or H^3 in heroin determinations.

Elucidation of physiological functions in hematopoiesis was of great importance in giving rise to new concepts of pathological processes of the blood. Increased understanding of the pathogenesis of blood dyscrasias, pernicious anemia, polycytemia, and the different types of leukemia and lymphoma can be attributed to the use of radioactive isotopes. The most important studies employing radioactive isotopes in morphology, physiology, and pathology of hematology have been outlined by Hevesy (1923, 1961), Heilmeyer and Keiderling (1961), Rasković et al. (1964), Dragić et al. (1964), Bianchini and Rossi (1964), and Szirmai (1965).

B. IN OTHER FIELDS OF MEDICINE

It seems appropriate to mention here briefly the application of isotopes to other fields of biology and medicine, occasionally related to hematological problems. Hevesy (1923, 1961) discussed the use of radioactive isotopes with C^{16}, P^{32}, H^3, and N^{15} (DNA), in morphology, physiology, and diagnosis; Hevesy and Wagner (1930) and Hevesy and Nylin (1953) extended these studies to hydrogen, phosphorus, rubidium, caesium, strontium, barium, vanadium, cadmium, and other radioactive isotopes for diagnostic and therapeutic purposes.

Radioactive isotopes are employed in the study of the metabolism of mitochondria (P^{32} and O^{18}) in the physiology of muscles and as the biochemical basis of nerve activity, in studies on viruses and bacteriophages, and in immunology, genetics, microbial metabolism, and in studies on the metabolism of bones and teeth (C^{14} and S^{35}). In the review literature

mentioned previously (see Section I) details on these uses of isotopes will
be found. Special reference should be made to hypophysectomy by nuclear radiation, the local application of radioactive isotopes (in solution
and in solid form) in diagnosis of thyroid imbalance (I^{131}) and neoplasia,
and in the therapy of hyperthyroidism. Isotope technique is also used in
studies of purine and pyrimidine metabolism, in the metabolism of amino
acids and proteins, sterols and steroids, phosphatides, in the study of
vitamins (A, E, K, C, B_1, B_2, B_6 and B_{12}), in the biosynthesis of porphyrins, and in the synthesis of DNA and RNA. The value of isotope distribution in diagnosis of tumors (I^{131}, I^{132}, P^{32}, and K^{42}) and in therapy with
isotopes (I^{132}, P^{32}, As^{321}, and Y^{90}) is well known.

C. In Pharmacology

The techniques used in pharmacological studies with isotopes are very
similar to those used in hematology (described in later chapters of this
treatise). It is known that the use of isotopically labeled drugs has greatly
broadened the scope of pharmacological research. By this method it is
possible to study the distribution of almost any drug which can be
labeled in animal and human tissue, its concentration at active sites, or
its transformation in the body (Duggan and Elwood, 1961, and many
other authors). The possibility of radiation damage limits the amount of
labeled drug which should be administered in human experiments, but
the calculation of permissible dosages of isotopes has been discussed in a
publication issued by the U.S. National Bureau of Standards (1952). It
is important to know that the possible radiation damage from ingested
drugs may be considerably lowered by labeling the molecules with tritium instead of the more commonly used C^{14} (La Brosse et al., 1958).
The maximum permissible amount of tritium in the human body in general is about ten times that of C^{14}. Most of the available carbon-14 compounds range in specific activity from 1 to 5 millicuries per millimole.
Tritium can be introduced (Duggan and Elwood, 1961) into any position that would normally receive hydrogen in the reduction stage of a
synthesis.

All studies of the metabolism of drugs and toxic substances employing
isotopes may be broadly divided into two categories: direct technique
designed to follow the fate of labeled compounds in the intact body, and
indirect technique in which the effect of drugs upon the utilization of
essential metabolites or their metabolic fate is determined. Labeled
drugs therefore permit the study of absorption, transport, distribution,
excretion, metabolism and metabolic pathways. Intracellular distribution
of compounds can be assayed by microradioautographic techniques (Miller and Elliott, 1955).

III. Radiation Measurement and Units

For the measurement of ionizing radiation, we have different methods such as:

1. the ionization chamber;
2. the Geiger-Müller counter;
3. the proportional counter;
4. the scintillations counter or solution-scintillation counter.

Knowledge of radioactivity and the various forms of radiation is necessary in studying their effects on hematopoiesis. An element is said to be radioactive if it emits radiations. Every radioactive element has a decay half-life which is characteristic. Such half-lives may vary in length between a fraction of a second and many thousands of years. In nuclear hematology, it is also necessary to know that there are several kinds of radiation emitted by different substances, among them the three important types, α-, β-, and γ-radiations. The last has physical properties similar to those of X-rays.

The intensity of an ionizing radiation is measured in terms of its activity. The picocurie is often used as a unit of this activity. One picocurie is about 2.2 nuclear disintegrations per minute. The amount of energy absorbed by the tissue after the ionizing radiation enters the body is measured in rads. One rad is equivalent to an energy absorption of 100 ergs per gram of irradiated material at a fixed point. One millirad is one thousandth part of this. The biological effect of a definite radiation dose is the so-called "relative biological efficiency" and this has the same effect as a dosage of 250 kv X-radiation.

The dose unit of the relative biological effect is a rem (röntgen-equivalent man). This is the radiation dosage in rads, multiplied by the factor of relative biological effect for the appropriate radiation, e.g., the biological effective dosage of 1 rad of α radiation is equivalent to about 20 rem. All such data are important in nuclear hematology because only with such knowledge is it possible to understand the relationship between radiation effect and damage in experimental work and in the clinic.

IV. Radiation Damage, Protection, and Therapy

Radiation damage on the subcellular, cellular, and organ level, as well as the symptomatology and therapy of acute and chronic radiation injuries under the most common conditions of exposure, are described in later chapters of this treatise (Chapters 10–17). The extent and the severity of irradiation injury depends largely on the radiation dose and exposure time and frequency. The specific sensitivity of the hematopoietic organs, the sensitivity of the various cells, their state of maturity, their functional importance, and their regenerative potentiality are essential contributing factors. Differences between direct irradiation and the indirect damage produced by exposure to radioactive material by contamination will be considered in the individual chapters.

The theory of radiation damage is based on two hypotheses that differentiate between two possibilities. The direct or target theory states that an essential part of the cell is directly damaged by the ionizing particle resulting in malfunction and/or death of the cell. On the other hand, the indirect or ionization of water theory gives an easier and often better explanation of radiation injury. The large amount of water in the cytoplasm can give rise to oxidizing radicals when the energy of the ionizing particle is absorbed by the cell. The presence of oxygen in the cell results in even greater production of free radicals and greater damage. Both theories should be considered in the approach to radiation protection.

Physical means of radiation protection by shielding cannot be discussed here. [See International Commission on Radiological Protection (1959–1960).]

The knowledge of *chemical* protection against radiation is limited at the present time. Protective action against the hematopoietic type of damage or death has been reported for many compounds, but there is no good theoretical explanation for any of them. Chemicals such as pyrogens (Smith and Cheever, 1959), estrogens (Treadwell *et al.*, 1943), and bacterial endotoxins (Smith *et al.*, 1957) cause a rapid proliferation of cells by the blood-forming organs, but they are not as effective as the alkylaminothiols or the isothiuronium compounds. Radical traps such as amino oxides (Haley, 1963), can reduce radiation mortality by 50% in experimental animals, but these chemicals are not as effective as those previously cited. In their search for new radioprotectant chemicals, Doull *et al.* (1961) have screened over 1200 compounds of widely different structure but have not as yet obtained any compounds which are better than PAPP (*p*-aminopropiophenone), MEA (mercaptoethylamine), and AET (2-aminoethylisothiouronium bromide HBr.). This points out the difficulty, as Haley (1963) reported, of screening compounds in which death is used as the end point. Quinoxaline-1,4-di-*N*-oxide and anhydroerythromycine-*N*-oxide are compounds which are able to reduce the LD_{100} to an LD_{50} of whole body irradiation by interacting with the oxidizing free radicals produced by radiation and by acting as antibiotics to prevent bacteremia, but they do not protect the bone marrow. Bradford *et al.* (1957) have reported selective inter- and intracellular distribution for the mercaptoalkylguanidines. These compounds protect both the bone marrow and the intestine. Bacq *et al.* (1953) and van Bekkum and De Grooth (1956) stated that the N-alkyl substituted dithiocarbamates are also highly effective radioprotectants against acute hematopoietic radiation damage or death. But, as Haley (1963) reported, there is still a great need for new and better radioprotectant agents of low toxicity. Compounds such as cysteine, glutathion, and cysteamine are not adequate. These substances diminished only the leukopenia, anemia, and thrombopenia in the experimental animals.

There is no essential difference in the therapy of acute and chronic radiation damage. The principal therapeutic procedures dependent on the specific needs of the organism exposed to radiation are infusions of whole blood, specific blood cells (e.g., platelets), or plasma and transfusions of spleen and bone marrow tissue. The experimental basis of these measures and their practical uses are discussed in Chapters 19 and 20. Often the size of radiation dosage and interval between treatments must be adjusted so that the patient's condition does not deteriorate progressively. Supplementary therapy, e.g., with antibiotics, should be started before the patient's condition deteriorates and should be continued between treatments. This discussion of symptomatic treatment of the pathological changes caused by ionizing radiation applies particularly to regressive processes. Proliferative diseases as the delayed effect of exposure to radiation, particularly leukemias and tumors of the hematopoietic system, require conventional therapy based on the experience in the treatment of malignancies, including in some cases of chronic leukemia the administration of radioactive isotopes (P^{32}).

V. Conclusion

In this chapter the term *nuclear hematology* has been defined as a specific field of hematology which is methodologically, experimentally, and clinically closely connected with the development of nuclear science and nuclear technology. The new field retains, however, its relation to the principles of general medicine and may well become an integral part of the "nuclear medicine" of the future, which will comprise experimental and clinical medicine. In many instances our knowledge in these areas is incomplete, but it is hoped that on the basis of experience gleaned to date more and more of the yet unsolved problems will be elucidated in the future by the concerted efforts of all branches of science and medicine.

References

Bacq, Z. M., Herve, A., and Fischer, P. (1953). *Bull. Acad. Roy. Med. Belg.* **18**, 226.

Bianchini, E., and Rossi, V. (1964). *Nucl. Hematol.* **III**, 1.

Bradford, R. H., Shapira, R., and Doherty, D. G. (1957). *Federation Proc.* **16**, 157.

Curie, F. (1932). Cited in "Radioactive Isotopes in Physiology, Diagnostics and Therapy" (H. Schwiegk and F. Turba, eds.), 2nd ed., 2 vols. Springer, Berlin, 1961.

Devasos, T., and Corney, N. (1939). Cited in "Radioactive Isotopes in Physiology, Diagnostics and Therapy" (H. Schwiegk and F. Turba, eds.), 2nd ed., 2 vols. Springer, Berlin, 1961.

Duggan, D. E., and Elwood, O. T. (1961). In "Radioactive Isotopes in Physiology, Diagnostics and Therapy" (H. Schwiegk and F. Turba, eds.), 2nd ed., Vol. II, pp. 423–444. Springer, Berlin.

Doull, J., Pezak, V., and Brois, S. (1961). Radiation Screening Program Status Report No. 2. (August). Cited in "Radioactive Isotopes in Physiology, Diagnostics and Therapy" (H. Schwiegk and F. Turba, eds.), 2nd ed., 2 vols. Springer, Berlin, 1961.

Dragić, M. B., Hajduković, S. J., and Grujić, V. (1964). *Nucl. Hematol.* **III**, 13.

Dyke, C. D., and Lawrence, H. J. (1961). In "Radioactive Isotopes in Physiology, Diagnostics and Therapy" (H. Schwiegk and F. Turba, eds.), 2nd ed., Vol. II, pp. 697–702. Springer, Berlin.

Haley, Th. J. (1963). *Nucl. Hematol.* **3**, Sept.–Nov. issue, p. 3.

Heilmeyer, L., and Keiderling, W. (1961). In "Radioactive Isotopes in Physiology, Diagnostics and Therapy" (H. Schwiegk and F. Turba, eds.), 2nd ed., 2 vols. Springer, Berlin.

Hevesy, G. (1923). *Biochem. J.* **17**, 439.

Hevesy, G. (1961). "Das medizinische Prisma," Vol. 3. Boehringer, Ingelheim am Rhein, Germany.

Hevesy, G., and Nylin, G. (1953). *Circulation Res.* **1**, 102.

Hevesy, G., and Wagner, O. H. (1930). *Arch. Exptl. Pathol. Pharmakol.* **149**, 336.

International Commission on Radiological Protection (1959–1960). Committee Reports Nos. 2 and 3 (1 and 4 in preparation). Macmillan (Pergamon), New York.

International Conference and Symposium: "Man and Technology in the Nuclear and Space Age," Nuclear Hematology, Milan, Italy, 1962 and 1963.

Keiderling, W., and Hoffmann, P. (1962). In "Radioisotope in der Hematologie," 1st Intern. Symp. Schattauer, Stuttgart, Germany.

La Brosse, E. H., Axelrod, J., and Kety, S. S. (1958). *Science* **128**, 593.

Miller, J. W., and Elliott, H. W. (1955). *J. Pharmacol. Exptl. Therap.* **113**, 283.

Rasković, D., Hajduković, S. J., and Karanović, J. (1963–1964). *Nucl. Hematol.* **II**, 15.

Smith, L. W., and Cheever, F. S. (1959). *Proc. Soc. Exptl. Biol. Med.* **100**, 817.

Smith, W. W., Alderman, I. M., and Gillepsie, R. E. (1957). *Am. J. Physiol.* **191**, 124–193, 549.

Szirmai, E. (1954). *Plasma* **4**, 533.

Szirmai, E. (1962). *Nucl. Hematol.* **I**, 4.

Szirmai, E. (1963). *Nucl. Hematol.* **II**, 5.

Szirmai, E. (1965). *In* "The Use of Radioactive Isotopes in Hematology," Lecture, 3rd Congress Nuclear Hematology. Cited in *Nuclear Energy* (1964) **7**, 155 (Preliminary program).

Treadwell, A., Gardner, W. U., and Lawrence, J. H. (1943). *Endocrinology* **33**, 161.

Urey, T. (1932). Cited in "Radioactive Isotopes in Physiology, Diagnostics and Therapy" (H. Schwiegk and F. Turba, eds.), 2nd ed., 2 vols. Springer, Berlin, 1961.

"Use of Radioisotopes in Animal Biology and the Medical Sciences" (1962). Published for the International Atomic Energy Agency by Academic Press, New York (two volumes).

van Bekkum, D. W., and De Grooth, J. (1956). *In* "Progress in Radiobiology" (J. S. Mitchell, B. E. Holmes, and C. L. Smith, eds.), Vol. III, pp. 243–246. Thomas, Springfield, Illinois.

CHAPTER 2

Methods for Applying Radioisotopes to Hematological Problems

Thomas J. Haley[*]

Laboratory of Nuclear Medicine and Radiation Biology of the Department of Biophysics and Nuclear Medicine, School of Medicine, University of California, Los Angeles, California

I. Introduction

Originally, it was necessary for the individual investigator to obtain radioisotopes from the Oak Ridge National Laboratory, but recently several firms have established radiopharmaceutical laboratories for the preparation of exact dosage forms. These products contain the amount of tagged compound required to perform any given hematological test. Furthermore, these products may be obtained in calibrated sterile syringes ready for use. Naturally, it is necessary to apply the usual background determination and preparation of standards from the sample, but the over-all procedure is much simplified. Available isotopes include: I^{125}, I^{131}, P^{32}, Co^{60}, RISA (radioiodine serum albumin) with either I^{125} or I^{131}, Cr^{51}, DFP^{32}, and Fe^{59}. It is also possible to obtain many special

[*] This study was supported by Contract AT(04-1)GEN-12 between the Atomic Energy Commission and the University of California.

products for individual research projects. These materials include those tagged with S^{35}, H^3 and C^{14}, and they will be discussed further in the section on tagging of specific cells and cell types.

In the use of labeled compounds, it is necessary to bear in mind the possibility of whole-body radiation exposure and keep the administered dose below that which could result in tissue damage. Furthermore, the smallest dose consistent with accurate results will be beneficial to both the patient and the investigator, and in the latter case, assist in reducing the laboratory background. With these introductory remarks we shall now discuss specific application of radioisotopes to hematological problems.

II. Blood Volume Determination Methods

Blood volume may be determined with P^{32}, Cr^{51}, or I^{131}, and although the procedures are similar certain differences in technique make it necessary to describe the methods in detail.

Berlin et al. (1950) and Koster (1953) used the following P^{32} method. Fifteen milliliters of blood were withdrawn into a heparinized syringe. Five milliliters of blood were incubated at 37°C with 5 mc of isotonic $NaH_2P^{32}O_4$ with a pH of 7.3 for 2 hours. The red cells were washed three times with isotonic saline; they were centrifuged, and the supernatant was removed aseptically. A sufficient amount of the patient's plasma was added to the radioactive red cells to give a hematocrit reading of 40. One milliliter of this blood was injected into an anticubital vein. Another milliliter of this blood was placed in a 2-liter volumetric flask; water was added to the mark, and the flask was boiled (Standard). Fifteen minutes later, 5 ml of blood were removed from the opposite anticubital vein and placed in a dry oxalated tube. One-tenth milliliter of blood sample and 0.1 ml of standard were pipetted into aluminum planchets in triplicate and counted in a lead pig under a Geiger-Müller tube. The hematocrits were determined in Wintrobe tubes and corrected for a buffy coat. The total red cell volume (TRCV) was calculated as follows:

$$TRCV = \frac{cpm/0.1 \text{ ml Std.} \times 2000 \times \text{hematocrit}}{cpm/0.1 \text{ ml blood}}$$

$$\text{Blood volume (BV)} = \frac{TRCV}{\text{Hematocrit}}$$

$$\text{Plasma Volume} = BV - TRCV$$

It is necessary to remember that laking of red blood cells can cause inaccurate results and that the time between sampling and counting should not be prolonged, because the RBC lose 6% of their P^{32} per hour. The average TRCV in normal individuals is 29.9(22.8–35.8)ml/kg and the average plasma volume is 38.7(32.6–45.1)ml/kg.

Small and Verloop (1956) and Gray and Frank (1953) used the following Cr^{51} method. Thirty milliliters of blood were aspirated from an anticubital vein into a syringe wetted with ACD (anticoagulant acid citrate dextrose) solution. The blood was placed in a sterile glass bottle containing 30 μc of Cr^{51} as $Na_2Cr^{51}O_4$ plus ACD solution and it was incubated at room temperature for 10 minutes with occasional agitation. Fifty milligrams of ascorbic acid were added to reduce the final 10% of the Cr^{51} to a nonusable form. All but 8 ml of the red cell suspension was removed and injected intravenously into the patient. From the 8 ml remaining in the bottle, 1 ml was removed and diluted to 1 : 99 with distilled water and counted. A standard hematocrit was performed on 2 ml of the blood sample. The remaining blood was centrifuged and aliquoted and the radioactivity per milliliter of plasma was determined. The injected red cell activity was calculated as follows: Red Cell Activity = Diluted Red Cell Activity − Plasma Activity × (1 − hematocrit). Thirty minutes post-injection, a blood sample was withdrawn from the opposite arm and the counts per milliliter of RBC were determined, then the TRCV was calculated as follows:

TRCV = ml tagged blood injected × [cpm/ml blood − cpm/ml plasma × (1 − 0.98 hematocrit tagged blood)]/cpm/ml blood after mixing − cpm/ml plasma after mixing × (1 − 0.98 hematocrit patient's blood)/0.98 patient's blood

BV = Plasma volume + Red blood cell volume

The mean red cell mass in normal males is 30.3 ml/kg and the average plasma volume is 41.1 ml/kg, but there is some variability between laboratories so that each should derive its own average and range

Radioiodine-tagged serum albumin has been applied to the problem of accurate determination of blood volume (Storaasli et al., 1950; Kaplan et al., 1954; and Pritchard et al., 1952). A volume of stock solution was prepared so that it contained 100 μc I^{131}, and diluted to 50 ml with sterile saline containing 250 mg of human serum albumin. One milliliter of this solution was placed in a 500-ml volumetric flask and diluted to the mark with water. Three 1-ml samples of this solution were placed in glass tubes and counted in a scintillation well counter. These samples agreed within 1%. Using a calibrated 5-ml syringe, 5 ml of the diluted stock solution of RISA was administered intravenously to the patient, making certain that the syringe was flushed with blood so that all radio-activity was removed and gotten into the blood stream. Ten minutes later, 10 ml of blood were removed from the opposite arm and placed in an oxalated tube. It was gently mixed and a 1-ml sample was pipetted into three tubes and counted in the scintillation well counter to 6400 counts. The room background was determined similarly and calculated with the following formula:

$$\text{Background (BG)} = \frac{6400}{\text{time} \times 60}$$

The counts per second for each blood sample and each standard were determined; the crude counts per second were found as follows:

$$\text{Crude cps} = \frac{6400}{\text{time} \times 60}$$

$$\text{Corrected cps} = \text{crude cps} - \text{BG}$$

The values for the three samples of blood and the three samples of standard were averaged and the blood volume was calculated with the following formula:

$$\text{BV} = \frac{\text{ml RISA injected} \times \text{Ave. corr. standard} \times \text{dilution of standard}}{\text{Ave. corrected counts of blood}}$$

Plasma volume may be obtained if the blood is centrifuged to remove the cells.

III. Diagnosis of Anemia with Fe⁵⁹ and Co⁶⁰

The differential diagnosis of anemia can be readily accomplished with the use of radioisotopes as shown in Table I. The use of Cr^{51} has been discussed in an earlier section, so only the applications of Fe^{59} and Co^{60} will be described here. Early work by Dubach et al. (1946) showed the utility of Fe^{59} in the study of hemoglobin synthesis. Finch et al. (1949) followed iron metabolism and erythrocyte iron turnover in a

TABLE I

GUIDE FOR THE DIFFERENTIAL DIAGNOSIS OF ANEMIA

Anemia type	Characteristics	Isotope used
Hemolytic	Decrease RBC life span	$NaCr^{51}O_4$
Pernicious	B_{12} absorption failure	Co^{60} Vitamin B_{12}
Aplastic	Prolonged Fe turnover time	Fe^{59} globulin

similar manner. However, it was Huff *et al.* (1951) who developed the Fe^{59} technique of determination of plasma and red cell iron turnover into a practical procedure and applied it to hematological problems.

Fifty milliliters of blood were withdrawn from a fasting patient utilizing an iron-free syringe; the blood was allowed to clot, was centrifuged, and the serum was removed asceptically and placed in an iron-free test tube. Ten milliliters of this serum were saved for the determination of serum iron and iron-binding capacity (normal values—serum iron, 70 to 125 μg%, iron-binding capacity, 175 to 225 μg%). The remaining serum was incubated with 10 μc of Fe^{59} citrate, and then the Fe^{59} labeled serum was allowed to remain at room temperature for 30 minutes. Using a calibrated syringe, a measured amount of this serum was injected into the patient; 1 ml was retained for making a standard. The standard was prepared by diluting 1 ml to 500 ml with water and using 2 ml as a standard. Ten milliliters of blood were removed at 10, 20, 30, 45, 60, 90, 120, 180, 240, and 300 minutes after injection and placed in oxalated tubes. Triplicate samples of serum were counted from these specimens. Daily withdrawals of 10 ml of blood were made; the hematocrit and count were obtained in triplicate until the Fe^{59} concentration reached a plateau. Plotting of these data gave the iron utilization curve. By recording body weight in kilograms, hemoglobin, iron-binding capacity, and serum iron values, other iron metabolism may be obtained by calculation. The plasma iron $T_{1/2}$ (time when the iron disappearance curve reaches one-half the value at zero time) is obtained by plotting the counts per minute per milliliter of plasma against time on the first day on semilog paper and extrapolating back to zero time. The iron utilization curve may be obtained from the whole blood specimens that were collected. Many of the values involved in iron metabolism may be calculated with the following formulas:

$$\text{Plasma iron pool (mg)} = \text{plasma volume in ml} \times \text{serum iron in mg/ml}$$
$$(\text{Normal values} = 2.4 \text{ to } 4.6 \text{ mg})$$

$$\text{Plasma iron turnover rate (mg/day)} =$$
$$\frac{0.693 \times 60 \times 24 \times \text{serum iron (mg/ml)} \times \text{PV (ml)}}{T_{1/2} \times 1000}$$
$$(\text{Normal values} = 32 \text{ to } 52 \text{ mg/day})$$

$$\text{Plasma iron turnover rate (mg/kg/day)} =$$
$$\frac{\text{Plasma iron turnover rate (mg/day)}}{\text{body weight in kg}}$$
$$(\text{Normal values} = 0.46 \text{ to } 0.75 \text{ mg/kg/day})$$

$$\text{Daily iron pool turnover} = \frac{\text{Plasma iron turnover (mg/day)}}{\text{iron pool (mg)}}$$

(Normal values = 9.6 to 15.9) (RBC Fe uptake = 83 to 100% in 5 to 6 days)

RBC iron turnover rate (mg/day) = plasma iron turnover (mg/day) × per cent RBC uptake

(Normal values = 30 to 50 mg/day)

$$\text{RBC iron turnover rate (mg/kg/day)} = \frac{\text{RBC iron turnover rate (mg/day)}}{\text{weight in kg}}$$

(Normal values = 0.43 to 0.72 mg/kg/day)

$$\text{Total red cell iron (mg)} = \frac{\text{BV (ml)} \times \text{Hb (gm)} \times 3.4}{100}$$

(Normal value = 2450 mg)

$$\text{Red cell iron renewal rate (per cent daily)} = \frac{\text{RBC turnover rate (mg/day)}}{\text{Total red cell iron (mg)}}$$

(Normal values = 0.97 to 1.45%/day)

$$\text{Mean RBC life span (days)} = \frac{1}{\text{RBC iron renewal rate}}$$

(Normal values = 69 to 103 days)

The metabolic defect found in patients with pernicious anemia can be detected even during clinical remission of the disease when cyanocobalamin labeled with Co^{60} is administered (Heinle et al., 1952). The defect is characterized by inability of absorbing the same amount of ingested cyanocobalamin as a normal person because of a deficiency in intrinsic factor. The original method was based upon fecal excretion of the vitamin, but the newer, more-simplified method developed by Schilling (1953, 1955) follows urinary excretion after a "flushing dose" of nonlabeled material (Conley et al., 1951). It should be borne in mind, however, that such conditions as sprue, myxedema, pancreatic insufficiency, and liver disease can also produce abnormal values with this test.

The fasting patient is administered orally 0.5 μc of cyanocobalamin-Co^{60} plus 0.34 mcg of nonradioactive cyanocobalamin at 8:00 a.m. A light breakfast may be eaten 1 hour later. Two hours after administration of the vitamin, urine should be voided and then 1 mg of nonradioactive cyanobalamin is given by intramuscular injection ("flushing dose"). The 24-hour urine specimen is collected under toluene, and its volume and specific gravity is recorded. One liter of the urine specimen is placed in a 1-liter counting bottle. If the entire specimen is less than 1 liter, it should be made up to that volume. A standard for comparison is made by diluting 0.5 μc of cyanocobalamin-Co^{60} to 100 ml in a volumetric flask. Ten milliliters of this solution is diluted to 1 liter and placed in a counting bottle. The constant geometry of both bottles should be maintained while counting, and, if necessary, a background count should be obtained for correction of the final results. The per cent of recovered cyanocobalamin is calculated as follows:

$$\text{Counts recovered} = \text{Counts in 1 liter aliquot of urine} \times \frac{\text{urine volume}}{1000}$$

(In specimens of less than 1 liter, the counts obtained are the actual counts recovered.)

$$\text{Counts administered} = \text{Counts in standard} \times 10$$

Per cent cyanocobalamin recovered/24 hrs urine =
$$\frac{\text{Counts recovered} \times 100}{\text{Counts administered}}$$

(Normal values = 3 to 25%; Pernicious anemia values = 0 to 2.5%)

It must be stressed that the dose of both radioactive and nonradioactive cyanocobalamin is critical in this test because of the amount absorbed from the gastrointestinal tract when the amount of material exceeds 1 mcg. Furthermore, all positive tests should be repeated with "intrinsic factor" to obtain confirmation of the original results.

IV. Tagging Specific Cells

We have seen in a previous section that it is possible to follow erythrocyte life span with Fe^{59}. Other hematopoietic cells may be labeled in a similar manner using tritiated thymidine and cytidine and thus a more complete picture may be obtained of total hematopoietic activity. Cronkite *et al.* (1959) were among the first to study specific tagging of the DNA in bone marrow cells using tritiated thymidine (H^3Th). Rubini *et al.* (1960) have followed the metabolism and fate of the compound in man. They reported a rapid plasma clearance of H^3Th and an incorporation of the compound into DNA of proliferating cells beginning 1 minute after injection. Moreover, the process of labeling bone marrow cells was essentially complete within 10 minutes. Bond *et al.* (1962) have employed double labeling of bone marrow cells using H^3Th to label DNA and tritiated cytidine (H^3C) to label both RNA and DNA. The methods used by Bond *et al.* (1962) will be described in detail.

Suitable groups of animals were injected intravenously with 2 μc/gm of H[3]C and sacrificed serially at 1, 4, 8, and 12 hours, and at 1, 2, 3, 4, and 5 days. Other groups were given 0.5 μc/gm of H[3]Th and sacrificed in the same manner and at the same time intervals. The cleaned femurs and tibias were cut and the marrow cells dispersed in 0.9% NaCl solution. The total cell count was determined from an aliquot in a Coulter counter. The RNA and DNA content of the cells was determined chemically. The saline washed cells were centrifuged, then they were homogenized with 2% PCA (perchloric acid) in the cold for 2 minutes in a Potter-Elvehjen homogenizer. After washing once with 2% PCA, the cell residual was extracted with 10% PCA for 5 hours at room temperature with intermittent shaking. The cell residuals were washed with 10% PCA, then they were extracted with hot 10% PCA at 60° to 65°C for 2 hours. All clear PCA extracts were combined with their respective washes and measured for optical density at 260 and 280 mμ (2% PCA extract and RNA), and at 267 and 290 mμ (DNA extract). An aliquot of these extracts was used to determine the H[3] content using a liquid scintillation counter. (The H[3]Th data were used to correct for the DNA appearing in the RNA fraction). Bone marrow smears were made by the camel's hair brush technique of Burke *et al.* (1955) and half of the slides of the animals receiving the H[3]C were treated with PCA to remove selectively the RNA (Ogur and Rosen, 1950). The slides were prepared for autoradiography using AR10 (Kodak, Ltd., London) stripping film. The exposure times had to be uniform for each series of slides and varied from 14 to 28 days after which times they were developed and stained. A single individual should enumerate the number of grains per cell at random and all cells with three or more grains should be considered labeled. The chemically determined tritium activity is expressed at disintegrations/min/10^8 cells in the bone marrow suspension. This value is a constant times the specific activity because the average amount of nucleic acids or subfractions remains constant in the steady state. Grain counts are expressed as the average number of grains per total cells of all types, labeled or not (the fraction of cells labeled times the average number of grains/100 labeled cells). This value is a constant times specific activity, because the average amount of nucleic acid/100 cells of all types is constant.

The following *in vitro* method of Rubini *et al.* (1962) may also be used to study the incorporation of H[3]Th in bone marrow cells. Normal dogs were scarificed after pentobarbital anesthesia and transcardiac phlebotomy. The ribs were removed, and were cut into 4-inch lengths and chilled in ice. The rib bone marrow was expressed by squeezing with pliers. This marrow was washed into siliconized, chilled beakers using the autologous serum obtained at phlebotomy as the diluent. No labeling will occur in the cold so the cells were kept chilled until they were used but this never exceeded 2 hours. The chilled cells were filtered through four layers of gauze, and then an aliquot was counted in the Coulter counter so that suspensions containing 50 to 100,000 nucleated cells/m^3 could be prepared. The cell suspensions were prewarmed to 37°C and incubated with 1 μc of H^{3}Th for 40 minutes. Following incubation, smears were prepared on clean slides, air dried and fixed in absolute methanol for 20 minutes. Autoradiographs were prepared using either Kodak AR-10 stripping film, or Kodak NTB-2 or NTB-3 liquid emulsion. Controlled humidity (60 to 70%) and temperature (70°F) are essential, both during filming and development. After development, the autoradiograph was stained with Giemsa stain buffered at pH 5.75 and examined under oil immersion microscopy. Representative areas were examined to obtain 1000 nucleated cells, and grain counts were performed of each labeled nucleus of all labeled cells. Various DNA precursors may be studied to determine their effects on H^{3}Th incorporation.

V. Counting Equipment

Many types of counting equipment are available to the investigator for the precise determination of the concentration of labeled materials in the blood or specific cells, and only a limited discussion will be given here since each manufacturer furnishes instructions for the proper use of his particular product.

The well type scintillation detector permits high accuracy measurements of the liquid samples obtained in blood and plasma volume determinations with RISA. Red cell volume and survival time studies may be made with Cr^{51}; and pernicious anemia diagnosis may be accomplished with Co^{60}-labeled cyanocobalamin. The size of the detection crystal and the well itself determine the volume of sample to be counted as well as the dose of radioactive compound to be administered. The larger the crystal, the smaller the dose required for the same degree of accuracy. The use of an automatic sample changer is also desirable because more samples can be counted and there is a constant background.

For the determination of C^{14}- and H^3-labeled compounds, it is advantageous to use the liquid scintillation spectrometer. Those instruments that have an automatic background subtraction and low level sample rejection circuit are particularly effective. Equipment such as this also has a serial entry printout compatible with automatic data processing systems.

Other systems are available for scanning paper chromatograms and determining the distribution of separated cellular components such as

RNA and DNA. However, chemical separation procedures often are good enough to enable the samples to be counted directly without further separation.

VI. Autoradiographic Methods

The use of photographic emulsions to localize the site of deposition of radioactive isotope in a specimen has received wide application in biology and medicine. More information can be obtained when the specimen and the emulsion are in intimate contact. Resolution depends not only on grain size but on the respective thicknesses of the specimen and the emulsion and the distance between them. Selection of the particular emulsion and the technique to be used depends upon the nature of the radioactive emanation, the concentration of the radioactive substance and its rate of activity. The photographic effect of the β-particle is inversely proportional to its kinetic energy.

There are several types of plates and emulsions available for autoradiographic studies. Kodak Type A plates give high contrast for β and γ emitters. Type No-Screen is useful for β and γ emitters with low flux radiation where high sensitivity is required. Many types of nuclear track plates are available. Type NTB 3 is the most sensitive, responding to the lowest rates of energy loss. The tracks of β particles possessing energies of up to 0.2 MEV can be recorded with type NTB 2. While types NTB and NTA are much less sensitive, permeable base stripping film varies in its sensitivity. There is a variability in emulsion thickness with NTB 2; NTB and NTA have a thickness of 10 and 25 microns, and NTB 2 only has the latter thickness. On the other hand, liquid emulsions of most types are available for direct coating of the specimen slides. Applications of these photographic techniques will be discussed as will the newly developed type NTE. This latter type has been developed for greater resolution of the exact area and cell type by use of electron microscopic techniques combined with autoradiography.

Boyd (1955) published a monograph on the state of the art of autoradiography in 1955; other investigators (Arnold, 1954; Messier and Leblond, 1957; Joftes, 1963) have improved the autoradiographic technique to obtain better results. Joftes (1963) pointed out that, from a histological standpoint, many methods were available for the proper preparation of tissues. Fixation could be accomplished by freeze-drying, acetone, or other similar agents, while imbedding could be done with paraffin or water-soluble carbowax. The slides could be protected with celloidin, formvar, or nylon after staining and before application of the emulsion. This latter process protects the stained tissue and prevents it being affected by the photographic processing. However, in the case of tritium-tagged materials, it is better to omit the latter process to obtain better resolution. Although older methods for the production of autoradiographs called for apposition of the slide and the emulsion or mounting the specimen directly on the film, neither of them was as satisfactory as the use of stripping film or direct application of the emulsion to the slide.

In the stripping film technique, the nuclear emulsion is removed from its mounting, either glass or acetate backing, and floated on water. The specimen is then dipped under the emulsion so that the emulsion adheres to the specimen, and, on drying, it shrinks to cover the specimen. Resolution is excellent, and the radiographic image retains its original relationship with the specimen. However, the procedure is difficult and time consuming, and there is the possibility of the loss of radioactivity during processing. As a result, coating and dipping techniques were developed and the latter will be discussed in detail. The tissues should be rehydrated after deparaffinization to aid in obtaining a uniform emulsion coating of the specimen. This can be accomplished during the last stages of processing and while the nuclear emulsion is being warmed to 40°C. Thinner emulsion layer can be obtained by heating to 50°C, but, above that temperature, heat sensitization artifacts can occur and should be avoided. Groups of ten slides each should be dipped vertically into the well-stirred emulsion, making certain that the emulsion coats the slide at least 10 cm below the specimen. The slide is withdrawn and allowed to drain for 10 to 60 seconds, with the latter time being preferred, because the thinner emulsion layer results in a better resolution. The slide is allowed to dry for 10 minutes, then placed in a container charged with solid CO_2 and Drierite, and sealed. The sealing process reduces the moisture content to below 15% and eliminates the oxygen content, thus giving a better latent image. After sealing the container, it can be kept at room temperature or stored in a cold room for the time required for the development of the latent image. This varies considerably and exact exposure times become a matter of experience. Development of the autoradiograph is accomplished in the following manner: Kodak D 19 developer is used for 1 to 10 minutes; Kodak SB 5a stope bath is employed for 15 seconds; Kodak fixer is utilized for 2 times clearing time and washed for 0.5 to 1 hour. All solutions should be maintained at $18 \pm 1°C$. The tissues are now stained with hematoxylin, polychrome toluidine blue, metanil yellow, gallocyanin, lithium carmine, or alum cochineal. Care should be exercised to prevent overstaining of the gelatin. Joftes (1963) suggested the following staining procedure: The tissues are stained in 1% toluidine blue directly from the wash water for 30 seconds, then destained in 70% ethanol to the desired shade. They are dehydrated in two changes of 100% *n*-butanol and are cleared in three changes of Xylol. The preparation is cleared by soaking in $\frac{1}{2}$ Xylol and $\frac{1}{2}$ balsam for 1 to 24 hours and then is mounted under balsam. The prepared slides are then observed under both low and high magnification, and the number of silver grains per cell is counted. Checks should be made to eliminate any artifacts that might be present.

REFERENCES

Arnold, J. S. (1954). *Proc. Soc. Exptl. Biol. Med.* **85**, 113.

Berlin, N. I., Lawrence, J. H., and Gartland, J. (1950). *J. Lab. Clin. Med.* **36**, 435.

Bond, V. P., Feinendegen, L. E., and Cronkite, E. P. (1962). In "Tritium in the Physical and Biological Sciences," Vol. II, pp. 277–289, Intern. Atomic Energy Agency, Vienna.

Boyd, G. A. (1955). "Autoradiography in Biology and Medicine." Academic Press, New York.

Burke, W. T., Brotherston, G., and Harris, G. (1955). *Am. J. Clin. Pathol.* **25**, 1226.

Conley, C. L., Krevans, J. R., Chow, B. F., Barrows, C., and Lang, C. A. (1951). *J. Lab. Clin. Med.* **38**, 84.

Cronkite, E. P., Bond, V. P., Fliedner, T. M., Rubini, J. R., Brecher, G., and Quastler, H. (1959). *Ann. N.Y. Acad. Sci.* **77**, 803.

Dubach, R., Moore, C. U., and Minnich, V. (1946). *J. Lab. Clin. Med.* **31**, 1201.

Finch, C. A., Wolff, J. A., Rath, C. E., and Fluharty, R. G. (1949). *J. Lab. Clin. Med.* **34**, 1480.

Gray, S. J., and Frank, H. (1953). *J. Clin. Invest.* **32**, 1000.

Heinle, R. W., Welch, A. D., Schraf, V., Meachum, G. G., and Prusoff, W. H. (1952). *Trans. Assoc. Am. Physicians* **65**, 214.

Huff, R. L., Elmlinger, P. J., Garcia, J. F., Oda, J. M., Cockrell, M. C., and Lawrence, J. H. (1951). *J. Clin. Invest.* **30**, 1512.

Joftes, D. L. (1963). *J. Nucl. Med.* **4**, 143.

Kaplan, E., Puestow, R. C., Baker, L. A., and Kruger, S. (1954). *Am. Heart J.* **47**, 824.

Koster, B. (1953). *Am. J. Med. Technol.* **19**, 291.

Messier, B., and Leblond, C. P. (1957). *Proc. Soc. Exptl. Biol. Med.* **96**, 7.

Ogur, M., and Rosen, G. (1950). *Arch. Biochem.* **25**, 262.

Pritchard, W. H., Mac Intyre, W. J., Schmidt, W. C., Brofman, B. L., and Moore, D. J. (1952). *Circulation* **6**, 572.

Rubini, J. R., Cronkite, E. P., Bond, V. P., and Fliedner, T. M. (1960). *J. Clin. Invest.* **39**, 909.

Rubini, J. R., Keller, S., Eisentraut, A., and Cronkite, E. P. (1962). In "Tritium in the Physical and Biological Sciences," Vol. II, pp. 247–267. Itern. Atomic Energy Agency, Vienna.

Schilling, R. F. (1953). *J. Lab. Clin. Med.* **42**, 860.

Schilling, R. F., Clatanoff, D. V., and Korst, D. R. (1955). *J. Lab. Clin. Med.* **45**, 926.

Small, W. J., and Verloop, M. C. (1956). *J. Lab. Clin. Med.* **47**, 255.

Storaasli, J. P., Krieger, H., Friedell, H. L., and Holden, W. D. (1950). *Surg. Gynecol. Obstet.* **91**, 458.

CHAPTER 3

Use of Radioactive Isotopes in Hematology

Thomas J. Haley[*]

*Laboratory of Nuclear Medicine and Radiation Biology of the
Department of Biophysics and Nuclear Medicine, School of Medicine,
University of California, Los Angeles, California*

I. Introduction

Since 1939, when Lawrence (1939) first applied P^{32} to a hematological problem, the application of radioisotopes to medical problems has become widespread. To facilitate one's understanding of the magnitude of such activity, it is only necessary to examine Table I. It can be seen that both dynamic physiology and biochemistry have proved to be of great value in the solution of problems involving hematopoiesis, and have, in fact, given a partial answer to the question posed by Claude Bernard almost 100 years ago. He said: "Nous saurons la physiologie, lorsque nous pourrons suivre pas à pas une molécule de carbone ou d'azote, faire

[*] This study was supported by Contract AT(04-1)GEN-12 between the Atomic Energy Commission and the University of California.

son histoire raconter son voyage dans le corps d'un chien, despuis son entrée jusqu'à sa sortie." Autoradiographic as well as highly sophisticated scintillation counting techniques make it possible to study the most intimate and delicate processes of cell life. Thus, greater understanding of the biological processes involved in health and disease of the blood-forming organs and the distribution of the various hematopoietic cells in the body is now possible.

TABLE I

Isotopes That Are Useful in Hematology

Isotope	Half-life	Type of radiation	Energy (Mev)	Use
Na[24]	15.06 hours	β	1.39	Circulation time studies
		γ	2.75, 1.36	
P[32]	14.3 days	β	1.70	Erythrocyte labeling and phosphate metabolism
S[35]	87.1 days	β	0.17	Serum protein labeling
H[3]	12.46 years	β	0.018	RNA and DNA synthesis *in vivo*
C[14]	5568 years	β	0.16	Intermediate metabolism studies
Co[60]	5.27 years	β	0.31	Pernicious anemia studies
		γ	0.17, 1.33	
Fe[59]	45 days	β	0.46, 0.26	Iron metabolism
		γ	1.3, 1.1, 0.2	Hemoglobin synthesis
I[131]	8.08 days	β	0.6, 0.33, 0.25	Serum protein labeling and turnover time studies
		γ	0.64, 0.36	
Cr[51]	27.8 days	β	0.32	Erythrocyte labeling

II. Blood Volume Measurement

The use of P[32]-labeled erythrocytes in the determination of blood volume of patients was introduced by Hevesy and Zerahn (1942). Incubation *in vitro* allows the erythrocyte hexoses and trioses to bind the P[32] and after intravenous injection and adequate time for mixing, it is possible to calculate the red cell mass from a subsequently drawn blood sample. Although this procedure became standardized and was widely used, it has been superceded by techniques employing Cr[51] and RISA. The use of these γ emitters has simplified the counting technique.

Sterling and Gray (1950) first described the use of Cr[51] red cell tagging method. Incubation is done in a manner similar to the P[32] method, and the Cr[51] tag is more stable than the P[32] one; less than 1% are lost per day in the former compared to 6% per hour for the latter. Mollison and Veall (1955) showed that there was excellent agreement between the two procedures insofar as the red cell volume was concerned. A further extension of radioactive isotope tagging for measurement of blood volume occurred when Storaasli et al. (1950) utilized radioiodine serum albumin (RISA) for this purpose. The I^{131} is firmly bound to the serum albumin; there is little capillary leakage of the compound, and neither lipemia nor hemolysis interferes with the determination. Plasma volume is obtained by measuring the activity in the sample and applying the dilution formula. Furthermore, good correlation has been obtained with the Evans blue method (Zipf et al., 1955). Similar results have been obtained by Smolik et al. (1956) in their comparison of the Cr^{51} and RISA methods. Gurney and Bolt (1956) combined both methods of tagging, and by separate sequential determinations were able to measure both the plasma and the erythrocyte volumes. Kiever et al. (1957) applied the method to the accurate measurement of acute blood loss and replacement. They demonstrated that the hematocrit was inaccurate and did not reflect acute blood loss under such conditions, whereas red cell mass measurements indicated the presence or absence of active hemorrhage. Moreover, plasma volume coupled with venous hematocrit is more useful than the latter alone in evaluating blood loss and replacement. Wollheim and Schnieder (1958) obtained similar results with P^{32}- or Cr^{51}-tagged erythrocytes in their transfusion studies. A combination of Cr^{51} and Fe^{59} tagging was used by O'Brien et al. (1957) to study extravasation of red cells following severe macerating wounds. Their results suggested that there was a limit on the rate of hemoglobin degradation under such circumstances. Remenchik and Moorhouse (1957) used P^{32} and RISA to study blood volume changes in congestive heart failure and found that the RISA-measured intravascular volume was greater than that measured with P^{32}-tagged erythrocytes. Furthermore, both spaces decreased in size after diuresis.

One point which must be emphasized because it is critical to the use of P^{32}-tagged erythrocytes is the experimental conditions under which the erythrocyte becomes tagged with P^{32}. Yamada et al. (1954) critically examined the labeling process and found that the incorporation of P^{32} into the erythrocytes was maximal in whole blood in the presence of isotonic glucose and was followed in a decreasing order by whole blood without isotonic glucose, in isotonic glucose alone, and in physiological saline alone. Release of P^{32} from its erythrocytic binding can also adversely influence the results of blood volume studies. Ginski et al. (1956) showed that release of P^{32} from the erythrocyte was about twice as fast when incubation was carried out with electrochromatographically purified orthophosphate than when it was evaporated. Mollison *et al.* (1958) described a citrate-phosphate buffer method for preparing the erythrocytes for labeling. They also diluted the P^{32} with the buffer prior to addition of the cells, and, in this manner, were able to obtain 98% P^{32} uptake in 30 minutes at 37°C. It was suggested that the lack of competing anions resulted in an accelerated rate of uptake of the tag. Radatic and Ninkov (1959) also showed that uptake was greater in buffer solutions, and the maximal uptake occurred at pH 6.2.

A new labeling procedure employing diisopropyl fluorophosphate-P^{32} (DFP^{32}) has recently become available. Eadie *et al.* (1960) showed that DFP^{32} could be used to tag erythrocytes either *in vitro* or *in vivo*, and that two stages are involved in the tagging process. First, tributyrinase is inactivated and 40 minutes later cholinesterase is inactivated. Increasing the DFP^{32} concentration increases the amount irreversibly bound, but it results in a greater elution from the erythrocyte after administration. An additional advantage of the DFP^{32} method is the ease of interpretation of the erythrocyte survival time curves compared to similar ones obtained with Cr^{51}. Studies by Ernise and van Rood (1961) were confirmatory, and they suggested that of all the available blood volume determination techniques, the DFP^{32} method was the one of choice. The procedure can be used to study erythrocyte viability and life span, but the methods to be discussed in the next section will go into such techniques more fully.

III. Erythropoiesis and Heme Synthesis

Since the time Huff *et al.* (1950) first showed that Fe^{59} could be used to determine the rate of iron removal from the blood and its incorporation into hemoglobin, many other investigators have studied the mechanisms involved (Sharney *et al.*, 1955; Chodos *et al.*, 1957). Turnover of plasma iron is roughly proportional to erythropoietic activity, and it is increased in polycythemia and hemolytic anemias and is decreased in aplastic anemia. In leukemia, anemia is often seen, and Fe^{59} studies have shown that it is associated with decreased erythrocytic life span and a lack of a normal erythropoietic response. Pollycove and Mortimer (1956) have described a five-compartment system for *in vivo* iron transport and utilization based upon their mathematical analysis of plasma Fe^{59} curves. These calculations gave a quantitative estimation of the rate of hemoglobin synthesis. The dynamic aspects of erythrokinesis are most easily studied with Fe^{59}. The rate of disappearance of Fe^{59} from the plasma, its incorporation into erythrocytes, and its localization in the bone marrow, liver, and spleen can easily be assayed with appropriately columinated scintillation detectors strategically placed over the body (Spencer *et al.*, 1957). In disease states, such as myeloma, Larizza and Ventura (1957) found that the rate at which Fe^{59} left the circulation was increased as was tissue uptake. Mobilization in the bone marrow, liver, and spleen followed the usual pattern.

While studies on Fe^{59} uptake by the erythrocyte and on hemoglobin production are being undertaken, it is also possible to measure the life span of the erythrocyte. Within 7 to 10 days after intravenous administration of Fe^{59} between 90 and 100% of the element in the peripheral blood is in newly formed red cells. Sequential measurements of erythrocytic Fe^{59} have shown that the radioactivity remains constant for 100 to 120 days. Thereafter, a decrease occurs as a result of cell death, but, after a short time, the level again rises as the Fe^{59} is utilized in new erythrocytes. Pollycove *et al.* (1956) have determined the mean and entire life span distribution of an erythrocyte population in normals utilizing the above procedure. Borun *et al.* (1957) developed a new method for the estimation of the mean life span of aging erythrocytes. The Fe^{59} distribution in top, middle, and bottom layers of centrifuged blood indicates that these layers contain young, intermediate, and aged erythrocytes, respectively. Initially, the top layer contains the highest Fe^{59} content, but, between the fifteenth and ninteenth days post-administration of the isotope, the lower layer increases in Fe^{59} content only to decrease as the cells die, and the Fe^{59} is again made available for incorporation in new erythrocytes. At times, the use of Fe^{59} for studying erythropoiesis has been questioned (Najean and Boiron, 1959), but Berlin *et al.* (1957), after comparing the Fe^{59}- and C^{14}-labeling methods for estimation of erythrocyte life span with the Ashby differential agglutination technique, concluded that all three methods were in excellent agreement. Moreover, such studies can reveal abnormalities in erythrocytes which might not be apparent by use of older procedures. In a similar manner, the use of Cr^{51} labeling in red cell survival studies has proven valuable, although erythrocytes of all ages are labeled in distinction to the Fe^{59} and glycine C^{14} methods which label newly formed cells in the bone marrow (Ebaugh *et al.*, 1953). Using *in vivo* body surface counting technique, Jandl (1955) studied the fate of Cr^{51}-tagged erythrocytes in hemolytic anemia and reported that the radioactivity disappeared from the blood more rapidly than normal and concentrated in the spleen, indicating splenic destruction of the red cells. Hughes Jones *et al.* (1957) made similar observations on transfusion of incompatible blood cells, and Mollison (1958) suggested two elimination mechanisms to account for incompatible cell removal from the blood stream: rapid removal by the liver and a slower removal by the spleen. Utilizing a Cr^{51} tag, Miescher *et al.* (1958) pointed out that, in normal aging of erythrocytes, the bone marrow was an important site of destruction of such cells, Perrone *et al.* (1958) found that Fe^{59} labeling was a good technique for the evaluation of the survival of stored erythrocytes. With a similar technique, Vladimirov and Urinson (1955) observed that the rapidity with which transfused erythrocytes were destroyed *in vivo* was a function of the length of time they had remained outside the body. Moreover, even the shortest time affects many red cells and renders them fragile. When the Fe^{59} is released into the plasma, 20% is incorporated into the liver and 50% of this Fe^{59} into hepatic ferritin (Mazur *et al.*, 1960). Austoni and Ziliotto (1955), using Fe^{59} and cytoautoradiographic estimation, have shown that, in the erythrocyte series in the bone marrow, the nucleated cells have a maximal uptake at 3 hours followed by a decrease until the ninth hour, at which time the mature cells begin to take up the Fe^{59}. Their uptake reaches a peak at 24 hours.

Thus far, we have confined our discussion to the erythrocyte and the means for measuring both its activity and life span; now it is necessary to discuss the substance, erythropoietin, which stimulates red cell production. Jacobson and Goldwasser (1957) showed that erythropoietin regulates the number of erythrocytes in the peripheral blood as well as the hemoglobin content in blood. Furthermore, erythropoietin can increase the red cell mass, the rate of reticulocyte formation, and the rate of Fe^{59} incorporation into red cells. The work of Gurney *et al.* (1957) showed that anemic subjects had high blood levels of erythropoietin, and when the red cell mass approached normal values the blood level of erythropoietin promptly decreased. By the use of triple tagging with Fe^{59}, thymidine-H^3 and formate-C^{14}, Alpen *et al.* (1959) observed no direct effect of erythropoietin on erythroid DNA synthesis, cell cycle, or hemoglobin synthesis, and, therefore, concluded that the compound must have an indirect mechanism of action in increasing the red cell mass. Further investigation is indicated to determine the mechanism of action of this compound.

Of major interest in hematology is the manner in which iron is transported in the blood and its incorporation into the hemoglobin molecule. Neale (1955) used Fe^{59} to demonstrate the presence of a blood β-globulin fraction, transferrin, which binds iron and acts as a transport mechanism to carry it to the sites of active hemoglobin synthesis. Paoletti *et al.* (1958) showed that these plasma proteins transport and condition the iron for entry into the reticulocytes but do not themselves enter into these cells. The iron is not in ionic form when this transfer is made. Allen and Jandl (1960) studied *in vitro* the conditions for incorporation of protein-bound Fe^{59} or leucine-C^{14} into adult and fetal hemoglobin. The latter was able to be formed under relative hypoxic conditions, possibly because of adaptation to the fetal environment in which both oxygen and glucose are at a premium. Kruh *et al.* (1956) demonstrated that when glycine-C^{14} and Fe^{59} are incorporated into hemoglobin by the reticulocytes, the radioactive glycine is incorporated in a random manner. Schapiro *et al.* (1955) demonstrated the presence of two hemoglobins with different metabolisms. These differences existed before fractionation. Hemoglobin-B incorporated more Fe^{59} *in vivo*, while *in vitro* hemoglobin-A showed the following behavior. The isotope composition remained the same between the second and the seventieth days but was reversed during acute leukemia. Reticulocytes from anemia blood synthesize the hemoglobins at different rates, and, here again, there are differences between *in vivo* and *in vitro* synthesis. Similar results have been obtained by Merjering and Huisman (1960) insofar as Fe^{59}-tagged hemoglobin was concerned, but they also found more varieties of hemoglobin, namely: Hb-Ao, Hb-A^A, Hb-A^B, Hb-A^C, Hb-A$_2$, and Hb-F. It was also observed that part of the Fe^{59} fraction of Hb-Ao was transferred to Hb-A during the aging process. Gajdos-Torok *et al.* (1959) isolated an enzyme preparation from erythrocyte stroma which catalyzed the synthesis of heme in the presence of Fe^{59} and protoporphyrin. Bannerman *et al.* (1959) studied the incorporation of Fe^{59} and protoporphyrin-C^{14} into heme by thalassemic cells, and concluded that these cells had an inherent defect which impaired their hemoglobin synthesis. Resegotti (1957) used Fe^{59} incorporation into hemin to study the life cycle of granulocytes and lymphocytes, their mean ages were 8.8 and 145 days. Similar studies should be attempted on the other cells of the leukocyte series.

IV. Pernicious Anemia

Since Chaiet *et al.* (1950) first produced cyanocobalamin-Co^{60} (vitamin B_{12}), synthetic processes have developed high specific activity material that can be used to measure Co^{60} blood levels. Naturally, the total amount of Co^{60}-tagged vitamin administered must be kept within reason, because the material has a liver biological half-life of 1 year (Schloesser *et al.*, 1958). However, saturation of the body stores with unlabeled cyanocobalamin decreases the size of the test dose required so that only 1 to 2 μc of Co^{60} are necessary (Schilling *et al.* 1955). Pollycove and Apt (1956) compared absorption of cyanocobalamin-Co^{60} in normal subjects and patients with pernicious anemia. While the former absorbed 62 to 82% of the dose, the latter absorbed only 5 to 15%. This absorption technique is valuable in the diagnosis of Addisonian pernicious anemia in patients with achlorhydria receiving maintenance doses of liver or unlabeled cyanocobalamin without reinvestigation of their previous course. Heinrich and von Heimburg (1956) showed that the Co^{60}-tagged vitamin appears in the blood within 1 to 3 hours after administration and pernicious anemia patients have only 0.1 to 8.85% of the dose in their blood. Goldberg et al. (1957) made a similar study which indicated that pernicious anemia patients had a blood activity level of cyanocobalamin-Co^{60} of less than 0.12% of the administered dose, whereas normal subjects had 0.23 to 1.71% of the administered dose per liter.

Studies on other hematological disorders have been made with cyanocobalamin-Co^{60}. Miller et al. (1957) examined the plasma disappearance, tissue distribution, and excretion of the vitamin in normal subjects and in patients with myelogenous leukemia. Although some of the material accumulated in the liver, none was found in the spleen or leukocytes of the leukemic patients. It was also observed that plasma of patients with chronic myeloid leukemia could bind increased amounts of cyanocobalamin-Co^{60} in vivo, and this assisted in differentiating this disease from other leukemoid states. Heinrich et al. (1956) made similar observations on serum protein binding of the vitamin in myeloid leukemia and reported increased retention and decreased excretion. There is an elevated serum binding capacity for cyanocobalamin-Co^{60} in acute and chronic myelocytic leukemia, in polycythemia vera, and also in some cases of chronic lymphocytic leukemia and idiopathic neutropenia (Meyer et al., 1957). Further studies should be made in other blood dyscrasias to determine their influence on cyanocobalamin-Co^{60} absorption, transport, utilization, distribution, and elimination from the blood and other organs.

V. Cardiac Output, Circulating Fluid Volume, and Regional Circulation

The old Hamilton dye dilution technique for measurement of cardiac output has been modernized by Pritchard et al. (1955). By use of RISA and an external γ-ray scintillation detector on a large artery or over the heart itself, it is possible to determine the cardiac output by calculation, Huff et al. (1955) showed that the values obtained by this method were similar to those obtained by the Fick principle.

Sen et al. (1957) simultaneously studied blood volume and peripheral circulation by the use of RISA. The initial uptake of the RISA was rapid, but subsequently an equilibrium was established between the intravascular and the tissue concentrations of the labeled materials. Accurate results employing this technique have also been obtained by Abrams et al. (1957) and Bartolomei and Bianchi (1957). Gitlin (1957) pointed out that a dynamic equilibrium exists between intravascular and extravascular plasma proteins and that during cycling from the plasma to the interstitial fluid catabolism is taking place. These considerations can modify the results of prolonged vascular studies but will give information concerning the rate of catabolism of RISA in relationship to the size of the body pool of a given plasma protein. Improvements in the RISA blood volume technique with a reduction in the standard error per determination have been published by Franks and Zizza (1958) and Head and Tanz (1958). Moir *et al.* (1956) have used the early disappearance of RISA from the circulation to study the differences between normal and edematous subjects. There was no difference in disappearance time, but edematous subjects had longer mixing times. In their studies on diabetic subjects, Endovina and Pattavina (1961) found they had slower rates of diffusion of both NaI^{131} and RISA into the lower limbs. Geraud *et al.* (1960) have used the method for the evaluation of vasoconstrictor and vasodilator drugs and have pointed out its versatility under such circumstances. Radiosodium (Na^{24}) has long been used to study circulation times or circulation efficiencies (Kety, 1949; Friedell *et al.*, 1949), but it is difficult to interpret the results. Application of the technique of Dobson and Warner (1957) may assist in clarifying the situation. However, even with its inherent difficulties, the Na^{24} method has given good evaluations of the changes occurring in capillary permeability in rheumatism and infectious arthritis. The method as employed by Sigidin (1956) differentiated between various degrees of disturbed permeability. Barlow *et al.* (1957) compared the usefulness of Na^{24} and K^{42} in blood clearance studies and were able to make simultaneous determinations of cardiac output, circulation time, and distribution volumes for both isotopes. It appears that the K^{42} was handled differently from Na^{24} because the former traversed the capillary walls at twice the rate of the latter. The techniques also will allow the calculation of peripheral resistance if blood pressure is recorded. Bauman *et al.* (1957) pointed out that simultaneous studies of transcapillary exchange in the pulmonary vascular tree can be made with Na^{24}, K^{42}, P^{32}, and RISA. The three electrolytes passed into the pulmonary extravascular space during a single transit through the cardiopulmonary pool. Losses of all three electrolytes were greater in congestive heart failure. Another application of Na^{24} to the study of peripheral vascular changes has been reported by Widmer *et al.* (1959). With the scintillation detector technique, they were able to show that doses of catecholamines which caused threshold elevations in blood pressure delayed Na^{24} clearance from intradermal injection sites. There are other numerous applications of isotopes to the study of peripheral vascular problems, but the ones cited will give an understanding of both the utility and the difficulties to be encountered in such studies.

VI. Miscellaneous Applications of Isotopes in Hematology

Turco and Fiorina (1958) studied the incorporation of P^{32} into bone marrow cells *in vitro*. Chromatographic separation of deoxyribonucleic acid (DNA) and ribonucleic acid (RNA) indicated that in acute leukemia and polycythemia there was a tenfold increase in both DNA and RNA, but, in myeloma, only the latter was increased and then only moderately. Tanaka (1959) also studied the rate of DNA synthesis in bone marrow *in vitro* using both P^{32} and C^{14}-formate. His radioautographic method indicated preferential incorporation of the isotopes in immature myeloid cells and erythroblasts with the following order of decreased radioactivity: promyelocytes, myeloblasts, myelocytes, erythrocytes, and metamyelocytes. In a 24-hour culture, the lymphocytes, mature leukocytes, and erythrocytes gave negative activity uptakes. Cronkite *et al.* (1959) showed that thymidine-H^3 is taken up by the cell nucleus of bone marrow cells only during DNA synthesis preparatory to cell division. Bond *et al.* (1959) obtained similar results with both bone marrow and the mononuclear cells of peripheral blood. The radioautographs indicated that only premitotic cells incorporated the thymidine-H^3 in DNA. Gavosto *et al.* (1960) studied the incorporation of DL-leucine-H^3 and DL-phenylalanine-H^3 into bone marrow and found that the rates of incorporation were greatest with immature cells. Maximum incorporation occurred in erythroblastic elements as compared to granuloblasts. Eosinophils exhibited greater incorporation than neutrophils.

Dajani and Orten (1959) studied the utilization of glycine-2-C^{14} and acetate-1-C^{14} by the nucleated erythrocyte, and found that either substrate gave the same pattern in the formation of individual Krebs cycle acids. Rowe (1959) followed the simultaneous incorporation of orthophosphate-P^{32} and acetate-Me-C^{14} into the phospholipids of the erythrocyte. Chromatographic separation of the phospholipids showed that all fractions were labeled with both P^{32} and C^{14} with the cephalins containing the most activity followed by the lecithins and the sphingomyelins. Using only a P^{32} tag, Yoshikawa *et al.* (1959) found activity in both adenosine tetraphosphate and ribose phosphate isolated from erythrocytes. Gerlach *et al.* (1958) studied the intermediate phosphate metabolism of the erythrocyte with P^{32}. Fractionation of the organic phosphates indicated the following order of decreasing incorporation of the labeled phosphate: 2,3-diphosphoglyceric acid, ATP, ADP, fructose-1,6-diphosphate, triose phosphate, and orthophosphate. No labeled creatine phosphate was present. The authors concluded that their results indicated that ATP played the same role in erythrocytic phosphate metabolism as it did in other tissues. Kawai *et al.* (1956) found that heparin was superior to such anticoagulants as oxalate, citrate, or varidase when used in studying phosphate metabolism of the erythrocyte because the values obtained were similar to those found for defibrinated blood. Moreover, their results indicated that ATP was the precursor of ADP.

In vitro synthesis of high energy phosphates by the erythrocyte revealed that ATP is rapidly formed in whole blood and more slowly in washed cells, while creatinine phosphate is only formed in whole blood (Hofmann-Credner, 1955). Neither compound is formed in hemolysates. Corsini *et al.* (1958) demonstrated that phospholipid turnover in plasma could be determined with P^{32}. Glycine-C^{14}-labeled plasma proteins were studied in cases of polycythemia vera, secondary polycythemia, myelogenous leukemia, hemachromatosis, diabetes mellitus, and rheumatic heart disease with congestive failure. Beeckmans (1957) showed that the total plasma protein curves were similar in all cases. The globulin fraction activity was identical in different patients and showed the highest activity with a fall lasting 15 days, followed by a flattening of the curve. The albumin fraction had a half-life of 21 days in patients with diabetes mellitus, 28 days in patients with polycythemia vera, and 39 days in a case of rheumatic heart disease.

A unique method for the diagnosis of thyroid malfunction developed out of the observation that the erythrocyte uptake of I^{131}-labeled thyroid hormones varied with the state of thyroid activity in the patient. Although the method has the advantage of being an *in vitro* one in which only the red cells and not the entire body is exposed to I^{131} γ-rays, it has certain inherent difficulties. The amount of L-thyroxine-I^{131} or L-triiodo-thyronine-I^{131} uptake by the red cell is decreased in the presence of plasma (Crispell *et al.*, 1956). The process appears to be a physicochemical phenomenon not directly dependent on enzymatic processes of erythrocyte respiration (Crispell and Coleman 1956). Further studies by Crispell *et al.* (1957) indicated that it was the albumin fraction and not the γ-globulin fraction that inhibited erythrocyte uptake of labeled thyroid hormones. Hamolsky *et al.* (1957) pointed out that a 2-hour erythrocyte L-thyroxine-I^{131} uptake test showed an average uptake of 13.9% per 100 hematocrit for euthyroid subjects, 21.9% for hyperthyroid subjects, and 9.3% for hypothyroid subjects. Age, sex, or time of year did not affect the results, but propylthiouracil decreased the value. Robbins and Murphy (1959) achieved similar results and adapted the test to routine clinical evaluation of thyroid function. Another thyroid function test dependent upon P^{32} depletion in the erythrocyte has been described by Ermans (1958). Thyroid hormones appear to act directly on phos-

phate transfer in the erythrocyte because the exchange rate is high in
hyperthyroidism, intermediate in the euthyroid state, and lower in hy-
pothyroidism (Ermans and Bastenic, 1959).

The metabolism of leukocytes has also been studied *in vitro*. Winzler
et al. (1957) studied the rate of incorporation of formate-C^{14} into different leukocytes and found the rate increased in the following order:
normal, chronic lymphocytic, chronic granulocytic, and acute leukemic
cells. In the granulocytic cells, there was a linear inverse relationship
between the rate of incorporation and the relative cell maturity. In
chronic granulocytic cells, the specific activity of acid-soluble adenylic
acid was much higher than the protein-bound serine and the RNA
adenine and guanine. Harris (1959) utilized adenosine-H^3 and cytidine-
H^3 for studying the turnover of these compounds in RNA of macrophages. The observed half-life of nuclear RNA was less than 2 hours
while observed half-life of the cytoplasmic RNA varied between 5 and 7
hours. These findings indicate that only a small part of the nuclear RNA
could have passed into the cytoplasm during the experiment, unless it
was rapidly destroyed on entering the cytoplasm. There was a higher
concentration of RNA in the region of the nucleolus. Upon the basis of
his studies of adenine-8-C^{14}-labeled leukocytes, Hamilton (1956) concluded that leukemic lymphocytes survive longer than leukemic granulocytes and that large fragments of lymphocyte nucleic acids are reutilized. Further investigation of leukocytes tagged with adenine-8-C^{14}
or guanine-8-C^{14} with or without orotic acid-6-C^{14}, covering a period
of 300 days, served to confirm the previous results (Hamilton, 1957).
The blast cells and early myeloid cells of bone marrow take up S^{35}
rapidly without depression of the bone marrow (Lajtha and Oliver,
1955). Izawa *et al.* (1956) pointed out that the rapid metabolism of the
immature myelogenous cells enabled them to incorporate more S^{35} than
the mature cell, but the immature erythrocytes and eosinophils did not
exhibit this property. The megakaryocytes and the nuclei and protoplasm of lymphocytes and monocytes took up the S^{35}. Using a radioautographic technique and H^3-labeled DFP, Kurth *et al.* (1961) reported
the following decreasing uptake of the labeled material *in vitro:* myelocytes, metamyelocytes, and polymorphonuclear neutrophils. No label
was found in lymphocytes, eosinophils, and basophils. Granulocytes in
both blood and bone marrow were labeled after intravenous administration of DFP-H^3.

Luganova *et al.* (1958a, b) studied respiration glycolysis, phosphate
metabolism, and the renewal of proteins and nucleic acids using both
P^{32}- and C^{14}-labeled compounds. It was observed that aerobic glycolysis
constituted about 65% of the level possible in anaerobic conditions.

Under the latter conditions, resynthesis of complex phosphate compounds including ATP can be accomplished by these cells. Very rapid phosphate renewal is characteristic of the thrombocyte, but it contains only small amounts of RNA and no DNA.

Serum fatty acid protein synthesis and turnover time have been estimated by use of labeled compounds. Lipsky *et al.* (1955) studied the rate of incorporation of acetate-1-C^{14} into the fatty acids of the phospholipid and non-phospholipid fractions of the plasma. Since the synthesis and turnover of the latter was more rapid than of the former, it was suggested that the non-phospholipid fraction served as a major vehicle for fatty acid transport in the plasma. Armstrong *et al.* (1955) studied the persistence of labeled albumin and globulin in blood and found that turnover times in recipients was shorter than in the donors. They compared *in vivo* S^{35} labeling with *in vitro* I^{131}-protein labeling, and found that, after intravenous administration of the latter, more easily interpretable turnover data on plasma proteins were obtained. Berson and Yalow (1957) reported that production of myeloma globulin in a donor was two and one-half times the rate of production of serum albumin in normal subjects. In hypoalbuminemic edema, Kushner *et al.* (1957) found that the I^{131}-labeled albumin had a shortened turnover time, and the total exchangeable albumin pools were reduced to about one quarter of the normal range. This observation was interpreted as a failure of equilibrium between intravascular and extravascular albumin. The half-life of S^{35}-labeled serum albumin was shown to be 55 to 60 days compared to 9 to 11 days for globulin (Niklos and Poliwoda, 1954). However, Margen and Tarver (1956) pointed out that judgment must be exercised in such studies and that measurement of the serum albumin pool size is extremely important if accurate results are to be obtained. Moreover, the use of donor S^{35}-labeled albumin was not as accurate as the intravenous administration of S^{35}-methionine or cystine.

VII. Conclusion

It has only been possible to review briefly the application of radioisotopes to problems in hematology, but it can be seen that many isotopes have been used in attempts to elucidate both normal and pathological hematological conditions. The role of biochemistry and histochemistry in hematology is only in the beginning phases. More accurate radioautographic procedures will be developed, and quantitative determination of intracellular constituents based upon the amount of silver deposited at various radioactive sites may allow the calculation of the number of molecules involved in any given metabolic process.

REFERENCES

Abrams, B., Everson, T. C., Fields, T., and Kaplan, E. (1957). *J. Lab. Clin. Med.* **49**, 494.

Allen, D. W., and Jandl, J. H. (1960). *J. Clin. Invest.* **39**, 1107.

Alpen, E. L., Lajtha, L. G., and van Dyke, D. C. (1959). *Nature* **184**, 1228.

Armstrong, S. H., Jr., Bronsky, D., and Hershman, J. (1955). *J. Lab. Clin. Med.* **46**, 857.

Austoni, M. E., and Ziliotto, D. (1955). *Acta Med. Patavina* **15**, 10.

Bannerman, R. M., Grinstein, M., and Moore, C. U. (1959). *Brit. J. Haematol.* **5**, 102.

Barlow, G., Agersborg, H. P. K., Jr., and Overmann, R. R. (1957). *Circulation Res.* **5**, 419.

Bartolomei, G. G., and Bianchi, R. (1957). Minerva Nucl. **1**, 163.

Bauman, A., Rothschild, M. A., Yalow, R. S., and Berson, S. A. (1957). *J. Appl. Physiol.* **11**, 353.

Beeckmanns, M. L. (1957). *Acta Med. Scand.* **157**, 85.

Berlin, N. I., Beeckmanns, M., Elmlinger, P. J., and Lawrence, J. H. (1957). *J. Lab. Clin. Med.* **50**, 558.

Berson, S. A., and Yalow, R. S. (1957). *J. Lab. Clin. Med.* **49**, 386.

Bond, V. P., Fliedner, T. M., Cronkite, E. P., Rubini, J. R., Brecher, G., and Schork, P. (1959). *Acta Haematol.* **21**, 1.

Borun, E. R., Figueroa, W. G., and Perry, S. M. (1957). *J. Clin. Invest.* **36**, 676.

Chaiet, L., Rosenblum, C., and Woodbury, D. T., (1950). *Science* **111**, 601.

Chodos, R. B., Ross, J. F., Apt, L., Pollycove, M., and Halkett, J. A. E. (1957). *J. Clin. Invest.* **36**, 314.

Corsini, G., Guintini, C., Bacchini, M. F., and Bianchi, C. (1958). *Boll. Soc. Med. Chir. Pisa* **26**, 270.

Crispell, K. R., and Coleman, J. (1956). *J. Clin. Invest.* **35**, 475.

Crispell, K. R., Kahana, S., and Hyer, H. (1956). *J. Clin. Invest.* **35**, 121.

Crispell, K. R., Coleman, J., and Hyer, H. (1957). *J. Clin. Endocrinol. Metab.* **17**, 1305.

Cronkite, E. P., Fliedner, T. M., Bond, V. P., Rubini, J. R., Brecher, G., and Quastler, H. (1959). *Ann. N. Y. Acad. Sci.* **77**, 803.

Dajani, R. M., and Orten, J. M. (1959). *J. Biol. Chem.* **234**, 877.

Dobson, E. L., and Warner, G. F. (1957). *Am. J. Physiol.* **189**, 269.

Eadie, G. S., Smith, W. W., and Brown, I. W., Jr. (1960). *J. Gen. Physiol.* **43**, 825.

Ebaugh, F. G., Jr., Emerson, C. P., and Ross, J. F. (1953). *J. Clin. Invest.* **32**, 1260.

Endovina, I., and Pattovina, C. (1961). *Giorn. Gerontal.* **9**, 277.

Ermans, A. M. (1958). *Ann Endocrinol. (Paris)* **19**, 858.

Ermans, A. M., and Bastenic, P. A. (1959). *Nature* **183**, 679.

Ernise, J. S., and van Rood, J. J. (1961). *Brit. J. Haematol.* **7**, 382.

Franks, J. J., and Zizza, F. (1958). *J. Appl. Physiol.* **13**, 299.

Friedell, M. T., Schaffner, F., Pickett, W. J., and Hummon, I. (1949). *Arch. Internal Med.* **83**, 608.

Gajdos-Torok, M., Gajdos, A., and Bernard, H. (1959). *Sang* **30**, 459.

Gavosto, F., Maraini, G., Perrelli, G., and Peleri, A. (1960). *Boll. Soc. Ital. Biol. Sper.* **36**, 237.

Geraud, J., Bru, A., and Bes, A. (1960). *Compt. Rend. Soc. Biol.* **154**, 1647.

Gerlach, E., Flickenstein, A., Gross, E., and Lubben, K. (1958). *Arch. Ges. Physiol.* **266,** 528.

Ginski, J. M., Thomson, J. F., and Omachi, A. (1956). *Proc. Soc. Exptl. Biol. Med.* **92,** 43.

Gitlin, D. (1957). *Ann N. Y. Acad. Sci.* **70,** 122.

Goldberg, S. R., Trivedi, B. K., and Oliver, L. (1957). *J. Lab. Clin. Med.* **49,** 583.

Gurney, C. W., and Bolt, R. J. (1956). *Univ. Mich. Med. Bull.* **22,** 319.

Gurney, C. W., Goldwasser, E., and Pan, C. (1957). *J. Lab. Clin. Med.* **50,** 534.

Hamilton, L. D. (1956). *Nature* **178,** 597.

Hamilton, L. D. (1957). *Brookhaven Symp. Biol.* BNL-474 (C-25), 52–74.

Hamolsky, M. W., Stein, M., and Freedberg, A. S. (1957). *J. Clin. Endocrinol Metab.* **17,** 33.

Harris, H. (1959). *Biochem. J.* **73,** 362.

Head, C. J., Jr., and Tanz, R. (1958). *J. Lab. Clin. Med.* **52,** 289.

Heinrich, H. C., and von Heimburg, R. G. (1956). *Naturforschung* **116,** 113.

Heinrich, H. C., Erdmann-Oehlecker, S., Radel, G., Somner, L., and von Heimburg, R. G. (1956). *Clin. Chim. Acta* **1,** 326.

Hevesy, G., and Zerahn, K. (1942). *Acta Physiol. Scand.* **4,** 376.

Hofmann-Credner, D. (1955). *Arch. Intern Pharmacodyn.* **103,** 71.

Huff, R. L., Hennessy, T. G., Austin, R. E., Garcia, J. F., Roberts, B. M., and Lawrence, J. H. (1950). *J. Clin. Invest.* **29,** 1041.

Huff, R. L., Feller, D. D., Judd, O. J., and Bogardus, G. M. (1955). *Circulation Res.* **3,** 564.

Hughes Jones, N. C., Mollison, P. L., and Veall, N. (1957). *Brit. J. Haematol.* **3,** 2.

Izawa, T., Iwasaki, H., and Tomiyama, T. (1956). *Yokohama Med. Bull.* **7,** 64.

Jacobson, L. O., and Goldwasser, E. (1957). *Brookhaven Symp. Biol.* BNL-474 (C-25) No. 10, 110.

Jandl, J. H. (1955). *J. Clin. Invest.* **34,** 912.

Kawai, G., Masuda, M., Fujiki, N., Takino, T., Takeda, H., Fujii, T., Kato, M., Kozen, K., Ikeda, T., Fujita, M., Maebara, S., and Hosoda, S. (1956). *Radioisotopes* (*Tokyo*) **5,** 34.

Kety, S. (1949). *Am. Heart J.* **38,** 321.

Kiever, I. C., Tyor, M. P., and Ruffin, J. M. (1957). *Southern Med. J.* **50,** 1147.

Kruh, J., Dreyfus, J. C., Schapiro, G., and Padieu, P. (1956). *Compt. Rend. Soc. Biol.* **150,** 1119.

Kurth, D., Athens, J. W., Cronkite, E. P., Cartwright, G. E., and Wintrobe, M. M. (1961). *Proc. Soc. Exptl. Biol. Med.* **107,** 422.

Kushner, D. S., Bronsky, D., Dubin, A., Maduror, B. P., and Armstrong, S. H., Jr. (1957). *J. Lab. Clin. Med.* **49,** 440.

Lajtha, L. G., and Oliver, R. (1955). *J. Clin. Pathol.* **8,** 166.

Larizza, P., and Ventura, S. (1957). *Boll. Soc. Ital. Biol. Sper.* **33,** 320.

Lawrence, J. H., and Scott, K. G. (1939). *Proc. Soc. Exptl. Biol. Med.* **40,** 694.

Lipsky, A. R., McGuire, J. A., Bondy, P. K., and Mon, E. B. (1955). *J. Clin. Invest.* **34,** 1760.

Luganova, I. S., Seits, I. F., and Teodorovich, V. I. (1958a). *Doklady Akad. Nauk SSSR* **118,** 537.

Luganova, I. S., Seits, I. F., and Teodorovich, V. I. (1958b). *Biokhimiya* **23,** 405.

Margen, S., and Tarver, H. (1956). *J. Clin. Invest.* **35,** 1161.

Mazur, A., Green, S., and Carleton, A. (1960). *J. Biol. Chem.* **235,** 595.

Merjering, C. A., and Huisman, T. H. J. (1960). Protides Biol. Fluids, Proc. 7th Colloq. Bruges Belgium, 1959 pp. 71–78.

Meyer, L. M., Bertcher, R. W., and Cronkite, E. P. (1957). Proc. Soc. Exptl. Biol. Med. 96, 360.

Miescher, P., Berger, H., and Gilardi, A. (1958). Intern. J. Appl. Radiation Isotopes 3, 87.

Miller, A., Corbus, H. F., and Sullivan, J. F. (1957). J. Clin. Invest. 36, 18.

Moir, T. W., Pritchard, W. H., and Ford, A. B. (1956). J. Lab. Clin. Med. 47, 503.

Mollison, P. L., cited by Rosenthal, D. J., and Lawrence, J. H. (1958). In "Radiation Biology and Medicine," Chapter 20, pp. 471–521. Addison-Wesley, Reading, Massachusetts.

Mollison, P. L., and Veall, N. (1955). Brit. J. Haematol. 1, 62.

Mollison, P. L., Robinson, M. A., and Hunter, D. A. (1958). Lancet 1, 766.

Najean, Y., and Boiron, M. (1959). Rev. Franc. Etudes Clin. Biol. 4, 72.

Neale, F. C. (1955). J. Clin. Pathol. 8, 334.

Niklos, A., and Poliwoda, H. (1954). Biochem. Z. 326, 97.

O'Brien, W. A., Howie, D. L., and Crosby, W. H. (1957). J. Appl. Physiol. 11, 110.

Paoletti, C., Boiron, M., Tubiana, M., Truhaut, R., and Bernard, J. (1958). Sang. 29, 492.

Perrone, E., Puricelli, G., and Reverberi, S. (1958). Minerva Nucl. 2, 26.

Pollycove, M., and Apt, L. (1956). New Engl. J. Med. 255, 207.

Pollycove, M., and Mortimer, R. (1956). Clin. Res. Proc. 4, 51.

Pollycove, M., Elmlinger, P. J., Sarkes, L. A., Apt, L., and Ross, J. F. (1956). Clin. Res. Proc. 4, 79.

Pritchard, W. H., MacIntyre, W. J., and Moir, T. W. (1955). J. Lab. Clin. Med. 46. 939.

Radotic, M., and Ninkov, V. (1959). Bull. Inst. Nucl. Sci. "Boris Kidrich" 9, 199.

Remenchik, A. P., and Moorhouse, J. A. (1957). A.M.A. Arch. Internal Med. 100, 445.

Resegotti, L. (1957). Acta Physiol. Scand. 41, 325.

Robbins, L. R., and Murphy, M. E. (1959). J. Clin. Endocrinol. Metab. 19, 1292.

Rowe, C. E. (1959). Biochem. J. 73, 438.

Schapiro, G., Dreyfus, J. C., and Kruh, J. (1955). Ric. Sci. Suppl. 25, Giorn. Biochem. Italo-Franco-Elvetiche, 132.

Schilling, R. F., Clatanoff, D. V., and Korst, D. R. (1955). J. Lab. Clin. Med. 45, 926.

Schloesser, L. L., Deshpande, P., and Schilling, R. F. (1958). Arch. Internal Med. 101, 306.

Sen, H. K., Mukherjee, S. R., Roy, B., and Banerjee, S. K. (1957). Indian. J. Physiol. Allied Sci. 11, 115.

Sharney, L., Schwartz, L., Wasserman, L. R., Port, S., and Leavitt, D. (1955). Proc. Soc. Exptl. Biol. Med. 87, 489.

Sigidin, Ya. A. (1956). Klin. Med. 34, 22.

Smolik, E. A., Muether, R. O., Nash, F. P., and Konneker, W. (1956). Am. J. Clin. Pathol. 26, 1127.

Spencer, R. P., Mitchell, T. J., King, E. R., and Baesman, R. F. (1957). Am. J. Clin. Pathol. 28, 123.

Sterling, K., and Gray, S. J. (1950). J. Clin. Invest. 29, 1614.

Storaasli, J. P., Krieger, H., Fredell, H. L., and Holden, W. D. (1950). Surg. Gynecol. Obstet. 91, 458.

Tanaka, H. (1959). *Naika Hoken* **6**, 1124.

Turco, G. L., and Fiorina, L. (1958). *Minerva Nucl.* **2**, 192.

Vladimirov, G. E., and Urinson, A. P. (1955). *Ukr. Biokhim. Zhur.* **27**, 277.

Widmer, L. K., Capeller, D. V., and Staub, H. (1959). *Verhandl. Deut. Ges. Kreislaufforsch.* **25**, 104.

Winzler, R. J., Williams, A. D., and Best, W. R. (1957). *Cancer Res.* **17**, 108.

Wollheim, E., and Schneider, K. W. (1958). *Deut. Med. Wochschr.* **83**, 1117.

Yamada, I., Arie, T., and Okamura, S. (1954). *Igaku To Seibutsugaku* **31**, 255.

Yoshikawa, H., Nakao, M., Miyamoto, K., and Yanagisawa, I. (1959). *J. Biochem. (Tokyo)* **46**, 83.

Zipf, R. E., Webber, J. M., and Grave, G. R. (1955). *J. Lab. Clin. Med.* **45**, 800.

CHAPTER 4

The Physiopathological Study of Platelets by Means of Radioisotopes

Yves Najean and Nicole Ardaillou

*Laboratoire des Isotopes, Institut
de Recherches Sur les Maladies du Sang,
Hôpital Saint-Louis, Paris, France*

The use of radioisotopes for the physiological study of platelets is quite recent. The first attempts, following those of Julliard *et al.* (1952), were not successful, essentially due to the difficulty in isolating viable platelets. In the past five years, various techniques have been devised that have proved satisfactory. They were found to be valid since they all give the same maximum survival time for normal platelets, 8 to 12 days; this figure is the same as that obtained by other indirect nonisotopic methods.

Over a period of 5 years, experiments using isotopes have provided a number of facts. Within the scope of the present topics, we shall confine our discussions to the following points:

Criticism of labeling methods;

Existence of a well defined survival of the platelets or random destruction;

Site of platelet destruction;

Mechanisms of the thrombopenias in human subjects.

I. Critical Study of the Methods of Tagging Platelets

The four main methods used for tagging platelets each have their advantages. These are:

Chromate *in vitro* labeling;

Diisopropylfluorophosphate (DFP) *in vivo* labeling;

Phosphate *in vivo* labeling; the platelets being then isolated and injected to a receiver;

Tagging of the precursor cells of the platelets *in vivo* by means of radiosulfur.

A. *In Vitro* RADIOCHROMATE TAGGING

This method of labeling (Morgan *et al.*, 1955; Aas and Gardner, 1958; and Najean *et al.*, 1959), which is the most widely used, is not a new one. It is in fact an adaptation to the platelets of a method devised 5 years ago for the red cells. It has several limitations.

(1) The chromate is toxic. Since the yield in the tagging process is low, it is necessary to use a considerable amount of radioactivity in the platelet suspension; under these conditions one has to make use of a chromate having a high specific activity.

(2) Since the fixation of the isotope to the platelets is low, it would be necessary to wash the platelet button several times before injecting it; but this is not possible as the platelets are extremely fragile. So a single washing will be performed and hence nonfixed chromate will be also injected. In fact the free isotope does not fix itself on to the cells *in vivo* and is eliminated very rapidly in the urine (90% in the first 24 hours).

(3) The affinity of the erythrocytes for the chromate is stronger than that for the platelets. Hence it is important to isolate as far as possible the platelets that are to be labeled. In practice this separation cannot be carried out at a concentration of circulating platelets less than 80,000/mm.[3]. Therefore autotransfusion of labeled platelets in cases with considerable thrombopenia is impossible.

(4) Preparation of the platelets must be fast (less than 4 hours), and carried out in plastic or siliconed vessels. Centrifuging is done at 4°C. The platelets are suspended in a nonalkaline buffered solution

(Tyrode buffer solution at pH 6.5). According to certain authors (Aster and Jandl, 1964) the choice of the anti-coagulant is important; we found, like some other writers, that the survival time of platelets isolated from blood collected in ACD or EDTA is the same (Cohen and Gardner, 1962).

(5) The shape of the curve probably demonstrates a lesion of the platelets. One generally observes a definite initial disappearance of the platelets followed by their partial recirculation; furthermore, in normal recipients, at the peak of this recirculation, the percentage of circulating platelets is only 30 to 50% of the total injected activity.

(6) Finally the possibility of a spontaneous elution of the tracer has to be discussed. The graphs obtained are always curvilinear, but not necessarily exponential. In fact the published curves using other techniques are not perfectly straight. It is not possible to ascertain whether the curvilinear aspect of the curve is due to an elution of the chromium *in vivo*.

(7) An essential advantage of this technique is that it uses a gamma emittor, usable for external counting. Thus it is possible to study in man the site of the sequestration of platelets.

B. TAGGING *in Vivo* BY MEANS OF DIISOPROPYLFLUOROPHOSPHATE-32 (DFP)

The DFP combines *in vivo* with esterases on the surface of the cells and thus labels the erythrocytes, granulocytes, and platelets. Theoretically the cells are equally labeled whatever their age; the tracer is not eluted. After cell destruction the product becomes hydrolyzed in the form of diisopropylphosphate no more available for combination with esterases and is not reutilized; the cell is not injured by fixation of the DFP (Leeksma and Cohen, 1955; Pollycove *et al.*, 1958; Mizuno *et al.*, 1959). However, this method has certain difficulties.

(1) The DFP tags several different types of cells *in vivo*. Consequently the platelets have to be completely isolated in each sample before counting. The number of platelets has to be determined in each one of these samples in order to be able to calculate the actual variation in activity of a known quantity of platelets. The manipulations involved are time-consuming.

(2) Study of the site of the sequestration of platelets is impossible.

(3) DFP-32 is extremely unstable; it should be dissolved in sterile oil before injecting. The most suitable preparation seems to be a solution of DFP in propyleneglycol which can be injected intravenously; by this mean tagging is rapid; maximum activity is obtained in 2–4 hours. When the DFP is introduced by intramuscular injection, maximum activity is

obtained only after 20 to 40 hours. If the DFP is dissolved in saline, the slope of survival time curve is found to be curvilinear (Zucker et al., 1961); it is highly probable this curve reflects an elution of the phosphate, part of the tracer having been injected in the form of phosphate rather than as DFP (hydrolysis).

(4) Since only a small fraction of the DFP is used to label the platelets, it is necessary to give considerable doses (approximately 100 μc in adult patients).

(5) DFP is much more expensive than chromate. The cost price of a single experiment exceeds $20.

C. Tagging in Vivo with Phosphate; Subsequent Isolation and Infusion into Another Recipient

This technique devised by Adelson et al. (1957) consists in tagging the platelets by injecting therapeutic doses of phosphate: approximately 0.1 mc/kg in the case of man, 0.2–0.5 mc/kg for the rabbit. The blood is collected about three days later; the platelets are then isolated and injected in a receiver.

(1) The required dose of P^{32} is very high. Hence, the method is only really suitable for experimental purposes. This technique has been performed in man, using platelets of patients with polycythemia, treated with P^{32} (0.1 mc/kg).

(2) Only homotransfusion can be used with this technique.

(3) It is necessary to isolate the platelets before injecting them in a receiver. As in the case of radiochromate, some of the cells may become injured, whence the two consequences shown by the published curves (Ebbe et al., 1962): initial loss with recirculation after approximately 20 hours, and loss (even at the maximum of the curve) of a part of the labeled injected platelets.

(4) P^{32} does not label the platelets themselves but the phosphatides of the platelets. The obtained curve represents a survival curve of the phosphatides and not of the whole platelets (Grossmann et al., 1960). Platelets tagged in vivo with phosphate and then incubated in fresh plasma lose part of their tracer; the nonlabeled platelets, when placed in vitro in the presence of P^{32}, will take up an amount of the external tracer to their phosphatides (Grossmann et al., 1963). Active phosphatide metabolism in mature circulating platelets is a possible cause of error in interpreting survival curves.

D. In Vivo Labeling of Megakaryocytes with Radiosulfur

The use of sodium sulfate was proposed by Odell and Anderson (1959). There are two possible methods. In the first one, it is necessary to obtain a constant level of infused radioactivity in order to observe the curve of the increase in specific activity of the circulating platelets; this activity will reach its maximum when all the platelets originally present (nonlabeled) have disappeared; the time required to reach this maximum measures the maximum survival time of the platelets. Another method involves the injection of a single dose of S^{35}-sulfate; the specific activity of the platelets is found to increase (as a result of maturation from the megakaryocytes), then to decrease (which corresponds to the death of the labeled platelets). The time elapsed between the half-maximal points on the ascending and descending curves is a measure of the average lifetime of the platelets.

(1) These methods can only be applied experimentally because the injected dose is high (particularly in the case of the technique involving a constant pool of activity (Vodopick and Kniseley, 1963). The half-life of S^{35} is long (approximately 3 months).

(2) According to Odell (1960), the method involving a single dose of tracer is difficult to interpret, particularly because of the variation with time in the volume of the pool of tracer.

(3) The remarks made with regard to P^{32} labeling of phosphatides which might undergo their own metabolism are also valid in the case of S^{35}-tagging of mucosaccharides. The curve of its disappearance following a single injection is moreover exponential in form (Robinson et al., 1961) and the survival figures given by Odell are lower than those obtained with other techniques (Odell and Anderson, 1959).

It is necessary to bear in mind the limitations of these techniques before interpreting the physiopathological results obtained with one or another of these methods.

II. Survival Time of the Platelets

If the platelets have a definite time of survival, then the graph representing the rate of disappearance of labeled platelets should be linear; but if, on the other hand, destruction takes place randomly, then the curve representing their disappearance would be exponential. However, a curvilinear graph could be due to other factors than the random destruction of the platelets; there might possibly be an exchange of the tagged substance between the living cells and the surrounding plasma (P^{32}-phosphatides, S^{35}-mucosaccharides) or elution of the tracer (chromate).

The loss of platelets tagged with P^{32} appears to be exponential (Adelson et al., 1957) or, more precisely, the combination of a straight line with an additional exponential function (Ebbe et al., 1962). The loss of normal DFP-labeled platelets occurs in a linear manner, if the injection is given intravenously (Zucker et al., 1961), and if one excludes the initial portion of the curve (Mizuno et al., 1959); this fact was also observed in the case of the erythrocytes tagged with DFP. The loss of normal platelets tagged with radiochromate was first described as being linear (Baldini et al., 1960); in fact the slope is slightly curvilinear (Najean et al., 1959; Ebbe et al., 1962), but this may be due to experimental errors (Aster and Jandl, 1963).

It was observed that the survival of the platelets is between 8 to 12 days. If their destruction was to occur randomly, this maximum survival time would have no significance and survival of the platelets would have to be expressed by making use of the half-life curve or the daily renewal rate.

On the other hand, in cases of thrombopenia, it is often impossible to express the survival of the platelets by its maximum value. In the example given in Fig. 1 the maximum survival rate is 5 days (not highly

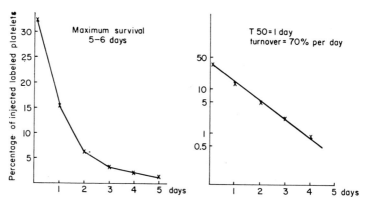

Fig. 1. Exponential slope of the survival of the CR⁵¹-labeled platelets in a case of idiopathic thrombocytopenic purpura.

decreased), but the curve is a perfect exponential one, and the rate of the platelets renewal is 70% per day (highly increased: normal values, 10 to 13% per day).

Several authors have attempted to prove that the platelets disappear because they are used *in vivo* for hemostasis; demonstration of decreased survival time in cases of thrombosis (Sacchetti et al., 1962) and increased survival time after treatment with anticoagulants (Adelson et al., 1961) support this opinion. However this type of disappearance of the platelets is not likely to occur in normal subjects for two reasons. The curve representing the disappearance of the platelets is approximately linear, so the platelets are not destroyed randomly, whereas destruction due to their utilization would be only at random. Furthermore, in cases of thrombopenia due to myeloid aplasia (Fig. 2) destruction of the platelets takes place at a normal rate; if the platelets were to disappear due to their utilization, the rate of their removal would be accelerated, since in this instance the needs would be the same as for a normal subject although the pool of usable platelets is highly decreased. In animals suffering from experimental aplasia, transfusion of platelets by crossed circulation also showed a normal survival rate (Lawrence and Valentine, 1947).

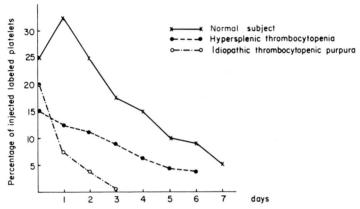

Fig. 2. Examples of survival curves (Cr^{51}-labeled platelets).

From the various experiments that have been carried out it is possible to draw the following conclusions.

(1) Platelets are destroyed in normal subjects by senescence in a linear manner. Hence, one can measure survival time and not just renewal rate. Moreover, as in the case of the erythrocytes, chemical changes occur in the platelets correlated to ageing (Löhr and Waller, 1959; Detwiler *et al.*, 1962).

(2) Except in certain pathological conditions, destruction is not due to utilization of the platelets. These particular cases are extensive thrombosis, and probably hemangioma with thrombopenia (Sutherland and Clark, 1962), although in the latter case the facts seem somewhat blurred; indeed, in several cases of this type a normal survival time was found (Blix and Aas, 1961), and also a paradoxical effect of splenectomy.

III. Site of Destruction of the Platelets

Part of the prepared and injected platelets is immediately entrapped; the graph of circulating radioactivity demonstrates this immediate removal (Fig. 3). The site of sequestration, partly temporary, seems to be chiefly hepatic and splenic in our experience. According to Aster and Jandl (1963), and Davey and Lander (1963), the trapping site is splenic. Other studies indicate that trapping is pulmonary (Maupin, 1957).

In point of fact, the essential problem is that of the site of destruction of the platelets in the normal state and under pathological conditions. This problem was studied in 385 different cases. Three different cases may be distinguished.

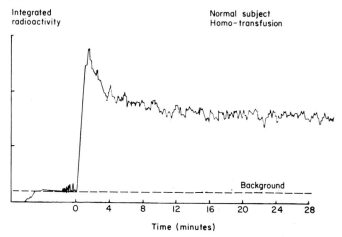

Fig. 3. Radioactivity over the precordial area during 30 minutes after injection of Cr⁵¹-labeled platelets in a normal recipient.

A. SITE OF PLATELET SEQUESTRATION IN NORMAL SUBJECTS

The experiments of Morgan *et al.* (1955) on normal subjects using platelets tagged with Cr^{51}, and that of Müller (1954) using platelets tagged with P^{32}, show that the platelet loss is essentially confined to the spleen. According to Aster and Jandl (1963) splenic activity changes little, whereas hepatic activity usually increases about 50% above the initial value, during the 8 days of the test.

We have studied sequestration of labeled platelets following their injection by means of daily measurements of the modification of radioactivity over the spleen area, the liver area, and the middle part of the right lung as compared to the radioactivity of the precordial area. The relative activity measured in this way over the liver and the spleen, in the normal subject, increases very slightly and almost in parallel (Fig. 4). Hence, there is only very slight hepatosplenic sequestration. We detected no pulmonary sequestration whatsoever. In cases of isoimmunization, the site of foreign platelets destruction was hepatosplenic or mainly hepatic.

B. SITE OF PLATELET SEQUESTRATION IN HYPERSPLENIC
   THROMBOCYTOPENIAS

The concept of hypersplenism, which is questionable in the case of idiopathic thrombopenic purpura, is certainly valid for some thrombopenias involving splenomegaly (Dameshek and Miller, 1946; Crosby, 1962). Several authors have demonstrated a normal or subnormal survival time of platelets in these cases (Hjort and Paputchis, 1960; Cohen et al., 1961; Najean et al., 1963). Few clinical and experimental investi-

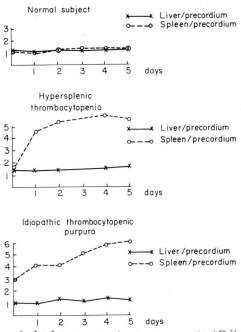

Fig. 4. Examples of platelet sequestration measurements (Cr⁵¹-labeled platelets).

gations have been devoted to the study of the site of sequestration of platelets in these cases; according to Aster, destruction is splenic in the case of slight thrombopenia with splenomegaly (Aster and Jandl, 1963); we studied 18 cases of thrombopenia of this type (Najean et al., 1963) and in all of them sequestration was extremely high and exclusively in the spleen (Fig. 4).

C. IDIOPATHIC THROMBOPENIC PURPURA (287 CASES)

In the case of idiopathic thrombopenic purpura, the results vary. In two-thirds of these cases the site of sequestration was mixed or predominantly splenic. There was no correlation between the site of sequestration, the length of the illness, the presence or absence of antibodies detectable by the antiglobulin consumption test (Dausset et al., 1961), or the extent of thrombopenia. Splenic platelet destruction was found more often in children than in adults. On the other hand corticotherapy was more efficient in cases with splenic destruction of the platelets than in the other cases.

TABLE I

EFFICIENCY OF SPLENECTOMY 6 MONTHS AFTER SURGERY

Site of sequestration	Number of cases	Rate of circulating platelets ($10^3/mm^2$)			
		> 300	150–300	80–150	< 80
Exclusively hepatic	5	0	1	2	2
Predominantly hepatic	5	1	1	3	0
Hepatosplenic	17	6	4	5	2
Predominantly splenic	19	5	10	2	2
Exclusively splenic	25	18	6	1	0
Total	71				

TABLE II

EFFICIENCY OF SPLENECTOMY MORE THAN 1 YEAR AFTER SURGERY

Site of sequestration	Number of cases	Rate of circulating platelets ($10^3/mm^3$)			
		> 300	150–300	80–150	< 80
Exclusively hepatic	4	1	0	1	2
Predominantly hepatic	4	0	0	2	2
Hepatosplenic	10	2	6	0	2
Predominantly splenic	10	3	4	2	1
Exclusively splenic	13	9	3	1	0
Total	41				

In 19 cases, splenectomy was carried out less than three weeks after the isotopic test; the actual amount of radioactivity present in the spleen was always much higher in those subjects whose splenic sequestration had been calculated high, than in those in which sequestration had been calculated as being mainly hepatic. It is a direct proof that the isotopic calculations were correct.

In cases where the test had been carried out several times at different stages during the course of the disease, it was always found that in different successive investigations sequestration always occurred at the same point (23 cases studied two times at an interval of more than one year). On the other hand we observed that the site of sequestration was the same in the same patient, if untreated, receiving steroid therapy, or recently spontaneously cured. This fact is apparently contradictory to that described by Aster and Jandl (1963) who suggested that the variations in the amount of antibodies caused a variation in the site of destruction of the platelets, as he previously demonstrated in the case of acquired hemolytic anemias in idiopathic thrombopenic purpura (Jandl et al., 1957).

There is a correlation between the efficiency of the splenectomy and the site of sequestration of the platelets in ITP. (Najean et al., 1964). These data are in Tables I and II.

IV. Rate of Decay of Platelets in Pathology

Isotope methods, particularly those involving the use of radiochromium, have made it possible to study the mechanism of thrombopenias. Several publications have been devoted to this subject (Cohen et al., 1961; Hjort, 1961; Najean et al., 1963).

It has been definitely proved that the survival time of platelets is normal in aplasias (Reisner and Keating, 1957). In 26 cases with thrombocytopenia due to medullary deficiency platelet survival time was normal.

In cases of thrombopenia with splenomegaly, the survival time of the autologous or homologous platelets is normal or subnormal: survival time more than 5 days (Najean et al., 1963). In most of the cases however, we did notice an anomaly: lack of the peak in the recirculation of the platelets at the 120th hour.

In cases of thrombopenic purpura that have been studied, a decrease in the survival time of the platelets was observed. According to our statistics, which at present cover 287 observations of idiopathic thrombopenic purpura studied at various stages of evolution, no exception to this rule was found. Strict parallelism exists between the rate of decay of the platelets and the degree of thrombopenia. The survival curve is exponential (Fig. 1) showing that destruction occurs randomly. The observation is only valid if one measures the survival time of the patient's own platelets or the survival time of foreign platelets provided the patient has not been previously transfused. Indeed, isoimmunization reduces the survival time of the platelets and in this instance decay occurs randomly (Borel et al., 1963).

The method involving the labeling of platelets is thus valid for diagnostic purposes. It will be helpful for the diagnosis of certain cases where thrombocytopenia is associated with anemia and leukopenia; platelet survival time will be normal in cases of bone marrow deficiency; it will be decreased in cases of idiopathic thrombopenic purpura.

✿ ✿ ✿

The use of different methods of labeling platelets could provide further data. Among the main investigations which have been carried out by means of these methods let us point to:

(1) The study of platelet groups and isoimmunization;

(2) The study of the significance of anti-platelet antibodies which are detectable by immunological methods;

(3) The study of methods of preservation of viable platelets, since it seems that the normal length of time in circulation is the only actually perfect test of cell integrity.

Therefore, one can assume that these methods have become just as necessary to the study of the physiology of platelets as the isotope methods applied to the erythrocyte population.

REFERENCES

Aas, K., and Gardner, F. H. (1958). *J. Clin. Invest.* 37, 1257.
Adelson, E., Rheingold, J. J., and Crosby, W. H. (1957). *J. Lab. Clin. Med.* 50, 570.
Adelson, E., Rheingold, J. J., Parker, O., Buenaventura, A., and Crosby, W. H. (1961). *Blood* 17, 267.
Aster, R. H., and Jandl, J. H. (1964). *J. Clin. Invest.* 43, 843.
Baldini, M., Costea, N., and Dameshek, W. (1960). *Blood* 16, 1669.
Blix, S., and Aas, K. (1961). *Acta Med. Scand.* 169, 63.
Borel, Y., Baldini, M., and Ebbe, S. (1963). *Blood* 21, 674.
Castaldi, P. A., and Firkin, B. G. (1963). *Austr. Ann. Med.*, 12, 333.
Cohen, P., and Gardner, F. H. (1962). *J. Clin. Invest.* 41, 1.
Cohen, P., Gardner, F. H., and Barnett, G. O. (1961). *New Engl. J. Med.* 264, 1294.
Crosby, W. H. (1962). *Blood* 20, 94.
Dameshek, W., and Miller, E. B. (1946). *Blood* 1, 27.
Dausset, J., Colombani, J., and Colombani, M. (1961). *Blood* 18, 672.
Davey, M. G., and Lander, H. (1964). *Brit. J. Haematol.* 10, 94.
Detwiler, T. C., Odell, T. T., and Mac Donald, T. P. (1962). *Am. J. Physiol.* 203, 107.
Ebbe, S., Baldini, M., and Dameshek, W. (1962). *Blood* 19, 537.
Grossmann, C. M., MacEwan, A. M., and Dilly, J. (1960). *Nature* 188, 950.
Grossmann, C. M., Kohn, R., anl Koch, R. (1963). *Blood* 22, 9.
Hjort, P. F. (1961). *Folia Haematol.* 6, 1.
Hjort, P. F., and Paputchis, H. (1960). *Blood* 15, 45.
Jandl, J. H., Jones, A. R., and Castle, W. B. (1957). *J. Clin. Invest.* 36, 1428.
Julliard, J., Maupin, B., Loverdo, A., Bernard, J., Colvez, P., and Lecomte, M. (1952). *Presse Med.* 60, 518.
Kissmeyer-Nielsen, F., and Madsen, C. B. (1961). *J. Clin. Pathol.* 14, 630.
Lawrence, J. S., and Valentine, W. N. (1947). *Blood* 2, 40.

Leeksma, C. H. W., and Cohen, J. A. (1955). *Nature* **175**, 552.

Löhr, G. W., and Waller, H. D. (1959). *Klin. Wochschr.* **37**, 833.

Maupin, B. (1957). *Rev. Franc. Etudes. Clin. Biol.* **2**, 72.

Mizuno, N. S., Perman, V., Bates, F. W., Sautter, J. H., and Schultze, M. O. (1959). *Blood* **14**, 708.

Morgan, M. C., Keating, R. P., and Reisner, E. H. (1955). *J. Lab. Clin. Med.* **46**, 521.

Müller, J. F. (1954). *Proc. Soc. Exptl. Biol. Med.* **85**, 420.

Najean, Y., and Ardaillou, N. (1964). *Semaine Hop. Paris* **40**, 395.

Najean, Y., Larrieu, M. J., and Bernard, J. (1959). *Rev. Franc. Etudes Clin. Biol.* **4**, 1071.

Najean, Y., Ardaillou, N., Caen J., Larrieu, M. J., Bernard, J. (1963). *Blood* **22**, 712.

Odell, T. T. (1960). *In* "Blood Platelets" (Henry Ford Hosp. Symp.) Little, Brown, Boston, Massachusetts.

Odell, T. T., and Anderson, B. (1959). *In* "Kinetics of Cellular Proliferation." Grune & Stratton, New York.

Pollycove, M., Dal Santo, G., and Lawrence, J. H. (1958). *Clin. Res. Proc.* **4**, 80.

Reisner, E. H., and Keating, R. P. (1957). *Proc. Soc. Exptl. Biol. Med.* **96**, 112.

Robinson, C. A., Bier, A. M., and Mac Carter, A. (1961). *Brit. J. Haematol.* **7**, 271.

Sacchetti, C., Boccaccio, P., Mora, L., and Ponassi, A. (1962). *Boll. Soc. Ital. Ematol.* **10**.

Sutherland, D. A., and Clark, H. (1962). *Am. J. Med.* **33**, 150.

Vodopick, H. A., and Kniseley, R. M. (1963). *J. Lab. Clin. Med.* **62**, 109.

Zucker, M. B., Ley, A. B., and Mayer, K. (1961). *J. Lab. Clin. Med.* **58**, 405.

CHAPTER 5

The Use of Electron Microscopy in General and Nuclear Hematology

Mihály Gerendás[*]

*Formerly Director of the Research Laboratory of Electron Microscopy,
Hungarian Academy of Sciences, Budapest, Hungary*

and

Sándor Szalontai

Research Institute of the National Blood Center, Budapest, Hungary

I. Introduction

Hematological research is nowadays shifting over to the investigations of *molecular dimensions* and to the study of the ultrastructure of the tissues and their pathological changes.

* Laureate of the Hungarian National Prize.

The resolution power of light microscopes has been limited. An object smaller than the wavelength of visible light cannot be studied with light microscopes. It therefore became necessary to use a radiation of shorter wavelength for the observation of submicroscopic dimensions (Gerendás, 1952; Leisegang, 1956; Haine and Cosslett, 1961; Wischnitzer, 1961; Breese, 1962; Ruska, 1963).

II. Techniques for Electron Microscopy

Preparations studied under the electron microscope must meet special requirements (Reimer, 1959; Pease, 1960; Kay, 1961). In general, preparations must be thinner than 0.05μ. As a rule, the preparations should not be thicker than ten times the details to be observed. This thickness, however, also includes that of the supporting films. In addition, the preparations should not be damaged by vacuum or by the mechanical and thermal effects of the electron beam. The reader is referred to the publications by Palade (1952, 1954), Guba and Sugar (1956), Bahr (1957), Lovas (1959), Tokuyasu and Okamura (1959) and Moore (1963), and to the books by Pease (1960), Boyd et al. (1961), Rhodin (1963), Siegel (1964), Kurtz (1964) for complete information.

III. Results of Submicroscopic Morphological Studies in Hematology

This problem has already been discussed in part by the following authors: Bessis (1950, 1956), Aleksandrowicz et al. (1955), Bloom (1955), Lindemann (1956), Jung (1957), Köppel (1958) Hollan (1959), and Szalontai (1962).

A. THE NORMAL HEMATOPOIETIC SYSTEM AND THE PERIPHERAL BLOOD CELLS

1. The Bone Marrow

The structure and the vascular bed of the marrow tissue have been studied with the electron microscope only by a few investigators (Pease, 1956; Weiss, 1959, 1960, 1961; Barta and Szalontai, 1963).

Zamboni and Pease (1961) remark: "Electron microscopists have tended to avoid bone marrow as an organ, although isolated cells have been studied repeatedly."

The submicroscopic structure of the fat marrow has been examined intensively by Weiss, as well as by Barta and Szalontai (1963). The great polygonal fat cells generally appear to be joined to each other by a membrane. Among the fat cells one can see cross-sections of collagenous fibers to which Weiss (1960) attaches importance in connection with the fat cells. Typical sinuses seem to be absent.

Fat cells are also found in the red marrow where they are situated singly or in groups having a direct connection with the hematopoietic cells. Near the flattened nucleus of fat cells, in the larger cytoplasmic area, some mitochondria can be observed. There are no RNA particles. After bleeding or hemolysis by phenylhydrazine, several transitional cells appear. The size of these cells is smaller than that of the fat cells. The cytoplasm has a looser structure and contains numerous vesicles. Besides small mitochondria, some star-shaped osmiophil particles, probably fat droplets, can be seen. The greatest part of the cytoplasm is filled with fat which in some cells is partly dissolved. The nucleus is watery; its density is hardly more than that of cytoplasm. The nuclear substance is equally divided and a zone of condensation can only be observed along the side of the membrane. According to Weiss (1961), these cells tend to form pseudopodia. Thus the cells resemble fat cells and also reticulum cells. Their appearance can be explained by fat phagocytosis of the reticulum cells or by the transformation of the fat cells into reticulum cells.

Important studies on the vascular system of the marrow have been carried out. It was shown that the structure of the sinusoids in red marrow differs from the structure of those in other organs (liver, spleen). Namely, the reticular cells which form the sinusoidal wall and their sheets lack an underlying basement membrane. The outer surface of the cytoplasmic lining is identical with the one adjacent to the lumen. Weiss (1961) has found only a structure reminiscent of the basement membrane in the vicinity of the fat cells. He traced this to condensation of the ground substance. A few collagenous fibrils can be seen in this discontinuous base material. The sinusoidal wall adjacent to the fat cells is generally complete, while it is fenestrated in the functioning bone marrow.

Because of the gaps of the endothelial lining and the loose contact of cytoplasmic sheets, Zamboni and Pease (1961) suppose that "there might be an 'open circulation'" in the bone marrow. But the authors mention that a much smaller quantity of protein is precipitated from the tissue fluid than from the plasma in the sinusoidal lumen. From this observation, however, the conclusion can be drawn that there is an effective separation.

On the basis of the latest findings, the theory of Doan et al. (1925) would appear to be unacceptable. According to this theory, the red cells are formed by the endothelial cells in the intersinusoidal capillaries. However, it was impossible to discover any intersinusoidal capillaries in the bone marrow with the electron microscope. Erythropoiesis, as well as leukopoiesis, take place in an extravascular way. Doan *et al.* (1925) studied the circulation and structure of the bone marrow mainly in fowl. Therefore, this discrepancy of observations is not necessarily caused by technical limitation (use of the light microscope). The evolution of hematogenesis should be taken into consideration. Doan's theory is supported by the fact that an intravascular development of red corpuscles was observed by Karrer (1961) in the liver of a chicken embryo with the electron microscope. On the basis of his observation, the blood cells of chickens originate from the endothelial cells, whereas extravascular erythropoiesis was found in the liver of a human embryo (Merker and Carsten, 1963).

The shape of the reticulum cells forming the walls of the sinusoid is variable. In the finely granulated, clear cytoplasm, one can see some mitochondria of different size. An extensive Golgi zone is found in the vicinity of the nucleus. According to the observations of Weiss (1961), the endoplasmic reticulum is well developed. Some smaller fat droplets are sometimes observed in the nucleus and more frequently in the cytoplasm. The chromatin generally accumulates along the nuclear membrane (Törö and Röhlich, 1961).

The structure of the infrequent fixed reticulum cells is slightly different. They are mainly found near the fat cells. Their borderlines are indistinct. The cytoplasmic protrusions penetrate among the hematopoietic cells. Sometimes they join with the nearest reticulum cell. In the loose-structured cytoplasm, several vesicles and Palade granules may be seen. The Golgi apparatus is well developed. Even the mitochondria are unusually big. The number of the tubules and vesicles of the endoplasmic reticulum is small. Sometimes larger and smaller indentations are also observed in the nucleus. According to Bessis and Thiery (1961a, b), the reticulum cell has been rounded off in the course of differentiation and a distinct borderline is developed. This distinct formed element can be identified with the hemocytoblast (Ferrata cell, myeloblast, stem cell), already known by observation with the light microscope. The big nucleus of the large-sized myeloblast occupies the greatest part of the cytoplasm. In the cytoplasm of the reticulum cells, numerous RNA particles, vesicles, and a less-developed endoplasmic reticulum are visible. The reticular-structured nucleolus is extremely large. Further direction of differentiation cannot be determined even on the basis of the submicroscopic structure of the pluripontential stem cell.

2. Erythrocytes

As this area has been extensively studied and described by Pease (1956), Bessis (1958a, b, 1960, 1961a, b), Policard and Bessis (1958),

Heilmeyer *et al.* (1962), Merker and Carsten (1963), Zwillenberg and Zwillenberg (1963), it will not be discussed here.

3. Granulocytes

The differentiation of the stem cell into the granulocyte is accompanied by typical morphological phenomena similar to erythroblastous transformation. The nucleus of the promyelocyte is mostly round and its contour is slightly ragged. The chromatin is condensed in the nucleus and is attached to the nuclear membrane. The nucleolus is of small size and low density. It is characteristic that the number of tubules and vesicles representing the endoplasmic reticulum increases significantly. A number of canaliculi widen and Palade granula can often be seen on their surface. The centrosphere is surrounded by the well developed Golgi apparatus. The aster advancing from the centriole situated near the outer membrane divides the Golgi zone here and there. The size of the mitochondria diminishes and they are generally oval or rod-shaped. A number of RNA particles can be observed scattered in the cytoplasm. In this period of development, granules appear which are well known from observations with the light microscope and are defined by panoptic coloring.

The neutrophil myelocyte is smaller. The relationship between the nucleus and the cytoplasm shifts more and more in favor of the latter. The chromatin granules seem to be arranged along the nuclear membrane. Occasionally one or two smaller nucleoli will be found (Tokuda *et al.*, 1961). Besides the round, slightly dense granules of 0.25μ size which are already observable in the cytoplasm of the promyelocyte and identifiable with the azurophil granules, a number of oval, more dense granules of about 0.15μ size, the so-called specific granules (neutrophils), also appear. These granules are enclosed within the membrane (Watanabe, 1957). The regression of the Golgi zone, the ergastoplasm, and the RNA granules begins in the myelocyte. Besides the characteristic transformation of the nucleus, the regression of the organelles is even more definite in the course of maturation. One can only see an abortive Golgi apparatus in the granulocytes having a segmented nucleus. In general, no nucleoli can be observed in the metamyelocytes, in the rod-shaped granulocytes, and in those having a segmented nucleus. In the lobulated nucleus, the chromatin is found along the nuclear membrane. Sometimes it is even traceable in the interlobular, thinned part. The oval granules prevail more and more in the cytoplasm. In some cases, the cytoplasm forms protrusions. When fixed, it immediately develops a smooth contour (Grey and Biesele, 1955; Goodman *et al.*, 1957).

The structure of the nucleus and the organization of the cytoplasm in the eosinophil granulocytes is similar to the submicroscopic structure of the neutrophil granulocytes. There is a remarkable difference between the size and structure of the granules. The size of the oval or round eosinophil granules is 0.5–1μ. In their interior, in the slightly dense, homogeneous matrix, one or more triangular, or disk-shaped osmiophil crystals can be observed. Watanabe (1957) proved, by means of a biconvex disk model, that the varying form of the crystalloids was a result of sectioning. In the eosinophil promyelocytes one can see a spherical vesicle with the marks of the crystalloid. In the course of further studies, it came to light that the crystalloid of the eosinophil granules was of lamellar structure. An alteration of osmiophil and clear striation can be observed (Sheldon and Zetterquist, 1955; Bargmann and Knoop, 1958).

The ultrastructure of the basophil granulocytes was studied by Goodman et al. (1957) and Braunsteiner (1959). Only Pease (1956) remarks that there are larger mitochondria in the basophil myelocyte that can even reach the size of the mitochondria in the myeloblast. Later, in the mature cell, only the granules show a difference. It is remarkable that the size and density of the granules in the basophil granulocytes are different. The shape of the granules is oval or irregular, or if the granules anastomose, polycyclic. Their inner structure changes according to the secretory cycle. It is dense and homogeneous in some of them, and lamellar in others. Grey and Biesele (1955) found a fine, reticular structure. Granules of similar structure can be observed in the tissue histiocytes (mastocytes) (Kelényi and Gógl, 1963).

4. Monocytes

The immature form of monocytes, the monoblast or histiocyte, is formed in the bone marrow, the lymph gland, and the connective tissue. In its large-sized nucleus, the nuclear substance is dispersed. One or more nucleoles can be seen. The Golgi zone is found in the nuclear indentation. The mitochondria are large and elongated. The cytoplasm of monocytes is slightly electron opaque compared to that of the granulocytes. In the cytoplasm of the mature monocytes, a number of vesicles and dense (azurophil) granules appear. The mitochondria become smaller (Low and Freeman, 1958; Jorke, 1963a,b). The nucleus is round or lobated. The chromatin, settled along the periphery of the nucleus, forms irregular fascicles. The numerous smooth-surfaced vesicles and tubules show the extension of the endoplasmic reticulum. The cytoplasmic membrane is characterized by a crenated contour.

5. Lymphocytes

The immature form of lymphocytes, the lymphoblast, probably descends from the reticulum cell. Its nucleus is round and the chromatin has a reticular structure. The nucleolus is large and spindle-shaped. In the cytoplasm there is an abortive endoplasmic reticulum. The Golgi zone is more developed than in the mature cells. The mature lymphocytes are recognized by the relatively large nucleus in which one often sees some deep incisions. The nuclear chromatin is more equally divided than in the other blood cells. A slight condensation may be observed. Its cytoplasm is uncommonly clear and contains some large mitochondria. The Golgi apparatus and the endoplasmic reticulum are abortive. In some of the lymphocytes, the "compound vacuole" can be found, in which there are numerous small, dense vesicles. RNA granules are observed here and there in the cytoplasm.

6. Plasmacytes

The origin of plasma cells is a problem discussed even today. Stoeckenius (1953) and Braunsteiner (1959) proved that after stimulation with antigen, ergastoplasm is formed in the nonphagocytic lymphoid or sessile reticulum cells of the lymph nodes. Within 24 hours the typical plasmacytes come into being. Jorke (1963a) regards those cells containing some ergastoplasm cisterns as plasmablasts. According to the observation of Amano and Tanaka (1956), on the other hand, the plasma cells are formed in the tissues from the adventitia cells of the small vessels.

The structure of plasmacytes is typical. The chromatin of the eccentrically settled nucleus appears in the shape of wheel spokes. It is characteristic that the pores are formed on the double nuclear membrane at the place of the density zone of nuclear substance (Wellensiek, 1957). There is a well-developed Golgi apparatus in the light area which is found close to the nucleus. The aster, originating in the centrosphere, is distinctly visible. It is striking that the cisterns of the ergastoplasm advance concentrically around the nucleus and, except for the clear space, fill the cytoplasm (Braunsteiner et al., 1953). In some places the lamellae of the ergastoplasm expand. In the cisterns of the rough-surfaced endoplasmic reticulum, a slightly electron-opaque reticular substance is usually visible. The dense granules observable from time to time can be identified as Russell bodies (Welsh, 1962). Several large-sized mitochondria are found in the cytoplasm.

7. Megakaryocyte-Thrombocyte System

This subject has already been thoroughly discussed by several authors, so it will not be necessary to go into details in this chapter (Feissly et al., 1957; Jones, 1960; Dalton et al., 1961; David-Ferreira and David-Ferreira, 1962; Schulz and Wedell, 1962; Jean et al., 1963; Rodman et al., 1963; Szalontai, 1963a,b).

B. Results of Functional and Morphological Studies

In the course of electron microscopic investigations, an old question was raised: how do the red cells get into the circulation? In order to examine this process, Bessis and Breton-Gorius (1960) experimentally induced hemolytic anemia in guinea pigs and rats which responded with increased erythrocyte migration. The authors established the fact that the erythroblasts and reticulocytes got into the circulation by means of leaf-like pseudopods. The diapedesis takes place through the opening at the same place where the endothelial sheets join. Thus their observation is in favor of an active cellular activity. Grasso et al. (1962) report a similar observation; they, however, raise the possibility that the vascular wall may disintegrate because of the pressure of the erythroid cells. Ackermann et al. (1961) consider the recession of the endothelial cell sheet as well. Yet, there is no doubt, that mature red blood cells are often visible among the cells in the active bone marrow. Zamboni and Pease (1961) demonstrated that the erythrocytes got into the sinusoid through the interendothelial gap. No protrusion was formed by the red blood cells. Besides, the authors detected that the diapedesis of the granulocytes could take place both at the joint of the endothelial cytoplasmic sheets and through the fenestration of the vascular wall.

The emigration of leukocytes was studied by Marchesi and Florey (1960), Williamson and Grisham (1961), and Marchesi (1961). The latter documented photographically the movement of the cells during diapedesis. Using a series of ultrathin sections, he showed that the granulocytes adhered to the interendothelial junction of the endothelial wall: they can also extend pseudopods between the outer cytoplasmic edges of the endothelial cells. The cytoplasmic substance accumulating in the pseudopods gradually enlarges the opening to make the passing of the larger, less plastic nucleus possible. The vascular wall remains intact after the leukocytic emigration. At the same time, the result of Marchesi's research disproves his former results, as well as the observation of Williamson and Grisham (1961), according to which the granulocytes can get into the connective tissue even through the cytoplasm of the endothelial cells.

The results of studies concerning phagocytosis are not conclusive. They probably vary according to the type of cells studied. Bessis (1961a) observed that the protrusions of reticulum cells engulf mature red cells and then incorporate them. The vacuole containing the erythrocytes finally splits into several smaller vesicles.

The granulocytes, according to the observations of Daems and Oort (1962), phagocytize even the precipitates of the antigen-antibody complex. The authors stated that the granules and mitochondria disappear after the incorporation of the homogeneous, electron dense substance. Vacuolization of the nucleus can be observed in some of the granulocytes.

Information was gained about phagocytosis by the monocytes from the work of Chandler and Hand (1961). They incubated an artificial thrombus in its own plasma and observed that the platelets had been phagocytized by the monocytes. In 24 hours several incorporated thrombocytes were already visible. The lysis of platelets, however, took place only on the sixth day.

The influence of erythropoietin on iron intake of erythrocytes was corroborated by Ladda (1962). He showed that the reticular cells in the bone marrow and in the spleen contained a considerable quantity of ferritin. It can be found sparsely in the cytoplasm and in the vacuoles. During a hypertransfusion, ferritin becomes traceable in the nucleus of reticular cells. At the same time, Ladda could not see any kind of internuclear ferritin in the histiocytes of control animals and of those hypertransfused but treated with erythropoietin.

The important part played by the plasma cells in the formation of antibodies is supported by study of submicroscopic morphological changes. Stoeckenius (1958) observed that after the intake of antigen, ergastoplasm is formed in the sessile reticular cells. Later the number of plasmacytes increases. The quantitative increase is shortly followed by structural changes. Among canals of ergastoplasm, there appears a substance of low density which gradually increases; cisterns also appear. The substance in the cisterns becomes thick and voluminous, and electron-dense spherules, the so-called Russell bodies, are formed (Welsh, 1960).

Protein formed in the plasmacytes can be given off in a characteristic way. Thiery (1959) and Stobbe (1960) demonstrated that the cytoplasm disintegrated into larger and smaller particles, then disappeared. This process has been designated by Thiery as *clasmatosis*. A more recent experiment of Thiery (1962) permitted examination of the mechanism of antibody formation. He observed in the lymph node and spleen of hyperimmunized animals that the macrophages containing ferritin had extended their protrusions among the plasma cells forming isles. The ferritin taken up by the plasma cells was accumulated in the vesicles of the Golgi zone. Thiery's observation makes probable the assumption of Braunsteiner (1959) that the decomposed antigen particles are transferred to the plasmacytes by macrophages.

C. Hemostasis and Coagulation of Blood

During the last decade, the results of physiological and biochemical work, as well as clinical observations, have made it more and more probable that the capillary system can not prevent the outflow of blood, even under normal circumstances. The majority of investigators explain the maintenance of vascular integrity by the hypothesis of continuous blood coagulation; others by the action of platelets.

The theory of continuous coagulation seemed to be supported by electron microscopic research. Fibrin fibrils were found by Levene (1955) in the intima of the human aorta and by Roos (1957) in the rat, using the replica method. This statement, however, is controversial because the majority of investigators of the submicroscopic structure of capillaries do not mention any particular fibrin films, while van den Hooff (1956) definitely denies their existence (Florey *et al.*, 1959; Bennett *et al.*, 1959).

The role of thrombocytes in maintaining vascular integrity was studied by Szalontai (1963b) with the electron microscopic pattern. He produced an increase of intravascular pressure in a healthy person without causing any petechial hemorrhage. In certain sections of the small blood vessels (capillaries, venules) the endothelial lining which forms the wall was unable to resist the increased stress. Both the separation of the inter-endothelial junction and the disintegration of the cytoplasmic lining of the endothelial cell might have occurred. It is peculiar that the thinned, aged endothelial lining disintegrated, while the endothelial cells, newly formed by amitosis, remained loosely joined. But injury of the vessels does not cause any bleeding because the platelets block the site of injury.

1. The Formation of the White Thrombus

Platelets have an important part in thrombosis and in those diseases accompanied by a prolonged bleeding time. Therefore, it is understandable that much research has been done on the formation of the platelet thrombus (Levene and Levene, 1957; Kjaerheim and Hovig, 1962; Poole *et al.*, 1963). In the course of these investigations, it was found that the platelets were accumulated near the damaged site of the vascular wall. There they adhered to the vascular wall and to one another. Kjaerheim and Hovig (1962) emphasize that the thrombocytes do not close the lesion of the vascular wall like a plug but like a capsule. It may be mentioned that Poole *et al.* (1963) observed the intravascular formation of the white thrombus.

It has already been shown with the light microscope that the platelets undergo morphological changes while performing their mechanical function (Witte and Schricker, 1958). The alterations taking place during the viscous metamorphosis can more thoroughly be studied with the electron microscope. The sticky metamorphosis of the thrombocytes initiates in the discontinuity of the limiting membrane (Rodman *et al.*, 1962). In a short time protrusions emerge and a loose aggregation of platelets occurs. At the same time, one can already observe the metamorphosis of the inner structure. In most platelets the granules become centrally packed forming a pseudonucleus (Parmeggiani, 1961; Castaldi et al., 1962; Scott et al., 1962; French and Poole, 1963). Some granules pushed out of the hyaloplasm and several thrombocytes having lost their organelles are also visible. In the loose aggregation, the platelets gradually approach each other, then amalgamate. Only by the resolving power of the electron microscope can it be proved that the membrane of the aggregated platelets is preserved. In fusion the volume of thrombocytes diminishes and the granules in the hyaloplasm seem to disintegrate. Finally, the fine-grained hyaloplasm limited by the membrane remains.

Hovig (1962, 1963a,b) studied the influence of those factors which cause the clumping of thrombocytes on the inner structure of the platelets. Adenosine diphosphate (ADP), thrombin, tendon extract, and collagen particles may equally give rise to the aggregation of platelets. The inner platelet structure, however, remains intact after giving ADP and collagenous particles subjected to ultrasonic or collagenase treatment.

2. The Process of Fibrin Formation

Thrombin, as is well known, plays a great part in the "polymerization" of fibrinogen into fibrin. The size of the thrombin molecules, according to the observations of Riddle et al. (1963), is between 80–100 Å. The size of the thrombin granules does not depend on the method of preparation and is not influenced by urea treatment. The prothrombin granules are slightly larger. The size of the nonchromatographed prothrombin is 90–120 Å. In the course of clearing, the form and size of granules may change.

The extensive research on the formation of fibrin clot can be explained by its physiological and pathophysiological importance (Hawn and Porter, 1947; Braunsteiner and Febvre, 1950; Haydon, 1957; Hall and Slayter, 1959). The problem was most recently thoroughly studied by Köppel (1962). In the drop preparation, as he pointed out, several (4 or 5) fibrinogen chains of about 220 Å size made up of round or oval nodules are visible before the beginning of the blood coagulation. He explains the difference in the measurements between the cleaned and the native blood fibrinogen by the adsorption of the plasma particles.

The first morphological manifestation of spontaneous blood coagulation is that the fibrinogen chains are connected to each other end-to-end. According to Köppel (1962), this slow process is significantly accelerated in the presence of thrombocytes.

The second phase of polymerization begins 15–20 minutes after the taking of blood. There appears a lateral and end-to-end junction of the fibrinogen bonds which developed in the first period. The fibrin fibrils reach a thickness of 1000–2000 Å. Their length, on the other hand, is beyond the bounds of measurability. In 30% urea solution, these fibrin fibrils do not dissolve. In this phase the transversal striation is easily traceable, especially in those fibrin fibers originating in the diluted plasma. One can identify the dense nodule forming the transversal striation (*Reliefquerstreifung*) with the fibrinogen molecule (D-striola) and the lighter, transparent section (T-striola) with the connecting plasma substance. An incision is visible in the T-striola (see Köppel, 1962).

In the third phase of polymerization, the fibrin fibrils unite into fibrin fibers through lateral junction.

3. *Fresh and Retracted Clot*

In ultrathin sections prepared after the emergence of a fibrin clot, the connection of the platelets and the fibrin fibrils were mainly studied by Kuhnke (1958), Rodman *et al.* (1962, 1963), Kjaerheim and Hovig (1962), and Szalontai (1963a). The results of the investigators do not agree. Some found that the fibrin fibrils adhered to the membrane of the thrombocytes; others traced the transverse section of fibrin fibrils in the platelets. In a fresh fibrin coagulum, longitudinally, transversally, and diagonally cut fibrin fibers are visible. Their cross-section is variable and can be brought into connection with the continuous emergence of the fibrin clot. A tendency toward grouping of the fibrin fibers is especially observed in the vicinity of the thrombocyte aggregations (Szalontai, 1964).

In the course of the retraction of a blood clot, a further junction of the fibrin bonds comes into play. The diameter of bonds may be 20 times thicker than the original fibrin fiber. According to the findings of Kuhnke (1958), the thrombocytes disintegrate during the development of retraction. Szalontai (1964), on the other hand, showed that the platelet membrane remains intact even after the retraction of a blood clot. The smaller aggregations come closer and closer together because of the retraction of the fibrin clot, and a large aggregate is eventually formed.

IV. Pathological Changes

It was only ten years ago that electron microscopic studies with ultrathin sections began in hematology. Considering the technical difficulties, such as the problem of embedding, fixation, and sectioning, this period has not been long enough for establishing and interpreting the ultrastructures in normal hematology. Nevertheless, there have been several attempts to become acquainted with and to explore more thoroughly these structures under pathological conditions.

A. IRON-DEFICIENT ANEMIA

Bessis (1958b) reported on utilization of iron in hematological disorders. According to his observations, a great quantity of ferritin is accumulated in the cytoplasm of erythroblasts in hypochromic hypersideremic anemia (hypochrome sideroachrestic anemia), thalassemia major, and saturnism. The ferritin molecules accumulate consistently in the mitochondria. But here the characteristic structure of ferritin disappears in a short time to form an amorphous, very dense mass of granules called *micelles ferrugineuses* by Bessis and Breton-Gorius (1959).

The disorder of iron incorporation was corroborated by Gautier (1961) in Cooley anemia and by Sorenson (1962) and Heilmeyer *et al.* (1962) in sideroachrestic anemia. The formation of the iron-micelles in mitochondria was traced back by Heilmeyer *et al.* (1962) to the decomposition of apoferritin. Its protein part is dissolved and makes the cohesion of the ferritin granules possible. It is probable that the last phase of heme synthesis takes place in the mitochondria and it may be lacking in the above disorders. In hemochromatosis, hemosiderin is found only in the reticulum cells.

Wolpers (1957) corroborated the earlier observations. In sickle cell anemia the red blood cells took on the typical shape on account of the peculiar arrangement of hemoglobin. He showed that big, empty spaces appeared in spite of the fact that no hemolysis took place in the meniscocytes. The *Stabstrukturen* extend and unite into thick fascicles. The space between the rodlet pairs widens.

B. ATYPICAL LEUKOCYTE REACTIONS

Attempts to determine the types of mononuclear cells observable in infectious mononucleosis was made by Braunsteiner *et al.* (1961), Paegle (1961), and Jorke (1963a). The results were ambiguous. Jorke found a varied picture in the peripheral blood. He observed several mature and some immature plasmacytes and a number of lymphoid cells. There were also some atypical cells with cytoplasm similar to monocytes and with a nuclear structure resembling that of lymphocytes. According to Paegle (1961), the majority of the cells may be classified as lymphocytes. He observed that the mitochondria of these cells are bigger and their shape variable. The basophilia of the cytoplasm can be explained by the accumulation of the Palade granules.

C. Hematoblastosis (Acute and Chronic Myelocytic and Lymphocytic Leukemias)

In the course of electron microscopic work on ultrathin sections, it was found that the malignant proliferation of the blood elements was characterized by structural deformations similar to neoplastic cells (Braunsteiner and Pakesch, 1960; Bessis and Thiery, 1961b, 1962a,b; Jorke, 1963b). It seems that in acute and chronic myeloic leukemia one can nearly always find a double population of cells: normal, or rather normal-like cells as well as immature, leukemic cells.

Sometimes one can see deep indentations on the relatively enlarged, irregular-surfaced nucleus of the leukemic cells. In some cells the nucleus seems to be lobulated because of these indentations. The nucleolus is hyperplastic, often very large with a varying structure. In some cases, the perinuclear space is enlarged. The Golgi apparatus is considerably larger than in the normal cells and its structure more vesicular. Sometimes the vesicles of the Golgi zone are connected to those containing granules. The number of the remarkably enlarged and often swollen mitochondria is generally increased. Characteristic is the asynchronism of the nucleocytoplasmic development. Besides mature granules, all stages of granule formation are present in the cytoplasm.

The electron microscope seems to be suitable for identification of those types of leukemia which are sometimes difficult to differentiate. Bessis and Thiery (1962a) emphasize, on the basis of their observation gained from many patients, that the number of stem cell leukemias is considerably smaller than was assumed on the basis of light microscopy of the bone marrow and the blood smear. When studying the submicroscopic structure, one can decide more accurately which cell type is involved in the disease.

Almost each phase of the fusion of azurophil granules preceding the emergence of the Auer rods can be made out. The fact that the "periodic" structure is already observable in some azurophil granules verifies this hypothesis. Thus the formation of the crystal begins rather early (Freeman, 1960). Besides the Auer bodies, a fibrillar structure located concentrically or in a semilunar shape, and consisting of parallel fibers is often visible. The fibrils surround a smaller part of cytoplasm containing several granules and mitochondria. But this fibril formation is occasionally found in abortive form also in one or two normal cells (Freeman and Samuels, 1958).

In chronic granulocytic leukemia, the nucleolus is often recognizable even in the metamyelocytes, besides the asynchronism of the nucleocytoplasmic development.

Peculiar intracytoplasmic and intranuclear formations are visible in the lymphoid leukemic cells as well. In some cells, a very large, spherical, transparent inclusion is found near the nucleus which indents the nucleus and extrudes the organelles. In a number of cells a very dense, prismatic crystal is seen. The form and size of these crystalloids which occur also in the nucleus are variable. Granules of different size and medium density may be visible in some of the cells, a mass of 150–200 Å size made up of dense granules in another. In the nucleus of some cells, the dense granules are surrounded by a lamellar structure.

Tokuda et al. (1961) described a remarkable observation. They studied the development of leukemia induced by acetylaminophenanthrene in animals. After an initial leukopenia a myeloid leukemia developed. In the hypoplastic bone marrow, the mitochondria in the cytoplasm of granulocytes were swollen and the vesicles of the Golgi zone enlarged. The surface of the nucleus became irregular. In the hyperplastic phase the tendency of mitochondria to aggregate was striking.

The results of electron microscopic investigations seem to corroborate more and more the earlier hypothesis that one must take into account the possible pathogenetic role of viruses in the spontaneous leukosis of animals or in leukemia induced by cell-free extract, perhaps also in human leukemia and hemosarcoma (Graffi and Fey, 1959; Dalton et al., 1961; Beard, 1962; Zucker-Franklin, 1963). Particles and microbodies, can be found extracellularly, in the cytoplasm, and in inclusion bodies. Their structure is almost identical with the structure of viruses observed in the leukosis of fowls and mice. Bessis and Thiery (1962b) found a structure reminiscent of viroplasm in reticulosarcoma.

We would like to add that we succeeded in tracing virus-like particles only in a few cases, especially in acute leukemia. To evaluate this finding, which is so rare in man, one must consider the observations made in experimental leukosis indicating the presence of only a small number of virus particles. It was found that in certain kinds of leukemia virus-like structures are not present in the pathological cells but are found in the megakaryocytes and platelets or in the reticulum cells (Tokuda et al., 1961). On the other hand, one cannot neglect the results of Danon et al. (1961). In the case of in vitro experiments, leukocytes and blood platelets are able to phagocytize the influenza virus.

D. ROLE OF PLASMACYTES IN THE FORMATION OF PATHOLOGICAL PROTEINS

A considerable quantity of paraprotein is accumulated in plasmacytoma (β- and γ-globulin; more rarely α-globulin; Bence-Jones protein) and in Waldenström disease (macroglobulin). In myeloma multiplex, it is striking that in the submicroscopic structure of plasmablasts deformations resembling neoplastic cells are recognizable besides the vast increase of plasma cells. In Waldenström disease the type of proliferative cells (lymphocytes?; plasma cells?) is not identified. It is certain that in the cytoplasm of these cells an expanded, organized ergastoplasm is visible. Consequently they have recently been placed by most of the investigators among the plasma cells (Stockinger, 1962; Brittin et al., 1963).

According to the observations of Bessis (1961a), only a few plasmacytes containing Russell bodies can be found in Kahler disease. On the other hand, one can see a great number of them in macroglobulinemia. In some cases inclusions are present in the nucleus of plasma cells. The structure of intranuclear inclusions is variable and they are generally surrounded by a membrane. Spherules of moderate density occur as well as those of great density. In the more electron transparent matrix, several bodies of different size and density resembling the Russell bodies are occasionally found. The significance of these inclusions is unknown.

Besides the accumulation of plasma cells, the frequent clasmatosis also indicates the hyperactivity of protein formation. But on the basis of the submicroscopical structure, it is impossible to state which plasma cells produce paraproteins and antibodies. Bessis found the paraprotein of a patient with myeloma to be of "periodic" structure. The macroglobulin seems to be a spherula of 500–1000 Å. It is surprising that neither the crystal structure nor the macroglobulin is found in the plasma cells.

E. Disorders of Hemostasis

Schulz et al. (1958) found in thrombopathia drumstick-shaped granules and giant granules in the majority of platelets. On the basis of the subsequent examinations, the granule anomalies seemed to be results of genetic injury and characteristic of the thrombopathy of the Willbrand-Jürgens type (Eriksson et al., 1961[1]). Such anomalies of granules as well as other changes are found also in thrombasthenia and other primary and secondary thrombopathies and, moreover, in hyperlipemia (Jean, 1961; Timaffy and Szalontai, 1963; Schulz and Wedell, 1962). According to Szalontai and Timaffy (1964), these anomalies of granules are the morphological manifestations of the phospholipid or lipoprotein formation which is connected with the formation of granules in thrombocytes and takes place in the peripheral circulation (Matter et al., 1960). In case of a functional injury of platelets, the number of "steatosis thrombocytes" increases as well.

Köppel (1962) studied this problem of insufficient formation of the fibrin clot in thrombopenia. He established that the fibrin fibers were more transparent and at the same time the outline of cross striation was

[1] See also Szalontai et al. (1962).

more definite. The D-striola can be transferred into the T-fascicle. It is peculiar that in the absence of fibrin-stabilizing factors due to urea treatment, the transversal striation of fibrin fibers disappears (Duckert *et al.*, 1961). Urea solution does not influence the transversal striation of the "thrombopenic" fibrin. Bang *et al.* (1962) studied the influence of the product of fibrinogen decomposed by proteolysis on the formation of fibrin. Several fibrin crystals and fibrin fibrils were formed. At some places the side-to-side junction of fibrin fibers did not take place. Even disintegrated fibrin products were incorporated into the fibrin net.

V. Changes Caused by Radiation Injury

From the latest studies by Cronkite and Bond (1960), it becomes clear that the radiation tolerance not only of the individual organs but also of the individual elements of the hematopoietic system is different (see Chapter 10). Nevertheless, there is a difference between the radio-resistance of the immature and mature cells (Wald *et al.*, 1962; Cottier and Jost, 1961). Chiefly the immature cells will be damaged. The only exceptions are the mature lymphocytes because the number of the mature or so-called small lymphocytes diminishes most rapidly under the influence of ionizing radiation (Hulse, 1959; Braun, 1963a,b). Moreover, it is known that in case of radiation injury, the ability of the cells to multiply ceases (Fliedner and Stodtmeister, 1962). Besides the lack of mitosis in case of irradiation in large doses, the direct cell-damaging effect prevails. The decrease of the lymphocyte number can be traced back to direct destruction.

A. Deformations Observed in the Structure of Blood Cells

1. *Early Effect*

The direct radiation injury of lymphocytes was observed with the electron microscope in the thymus, in the spleen, and in the bone marrow (Braun, 1963b; Bauer, 1962). Under the influence of whole-body irradiation in sublethal and lethal dose, significant deformations are visible in ten minutes. The double nuclear membrane of the small lymphocytes is enlarged in spots, and shrinkage of the nucleus sets in. In one hour a clear perinuclear space is formed in the major part of the cells as a result of the separation of nucleus and cytoplasm. In the nucleus the chromatin appears to be condensed in rough aggregates and the electron density of the nucleoplasm increases as a result of pyknosis. According to Cottier and Jost (1961), the nucleus becomes lobulated, vacuoles appear, and a part of the nucleoplasm escapes into the cyto-

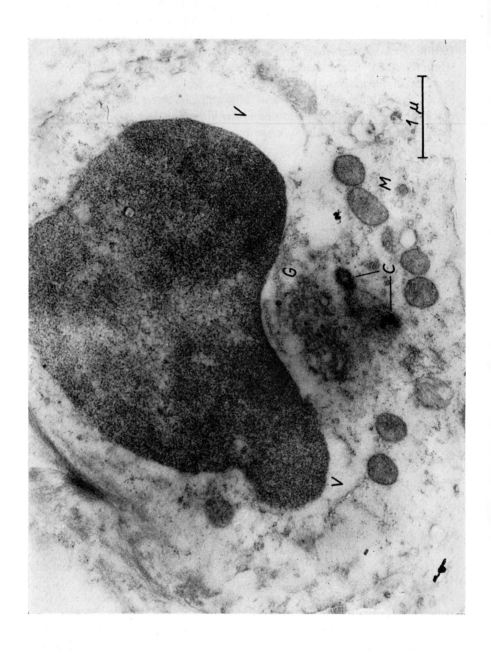

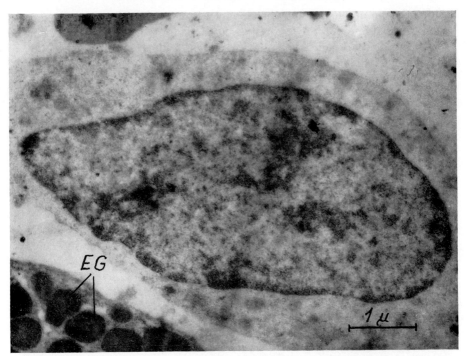

Fig. 2. Reticulum cell of human bone marrow, 60 minutes after 4060 rad Co⁶⁰ local irradiation. Alteration relating to cellular injury is visible only around the eosinophile granules (EG) in the left lower corner. Magnification: 18,000. (Authors' observation.)

plasm. In spite of such serious destruction of the nucleus the injury of the cytoplasm, with regard to the organelles, is negligible. Ten minutes after the irradiation the majority of mitochondria is totally intact (Fig. 1). Later the mitochondria increase in size. One can often notice the fragmentation of the inner cristas. The endoplasmic reticulum remains intact. Cottier and Jost (1961) observed the development of clear and darker areas caused by the uneven dispersion of the basic cytoplasmic matrix. The injury to the larger, immature lymphocytes takes place only after a larger radiation dose.

The reticulum cells are much more resistent (Figs. 2, 3, and 4) (Szalontai and Kiss, 1964). The activity of macrophages increases. Be-

Fig. 1. Lymphocyte from the thymus of the mouse 10 minutes after 800 r X-ray whole-body irradiation. A large gap (V) has been formed between the two nuclear membranes. The mitochondria (M), the Golgi zone (G) and the two centrioles (C) are intact. Magnification: 21,800. (From Braun, 1963b.)

sides the numerous phagocytized nuclei and nuclear fragments, many nonidentifiable inclusions are visible in the cytoplasm (Fig. 3). In some cases the double nuclear membrane is slightly enlarged. The slackening of the nuclear membrane is more frequently observed in the non-phagocytizing reticulum cells. The perinuclear cisterns may be connected with the greatly enlarged endoplasmic reticulum. The mitochondria are generally swollen and the inner cristas fragmented (Fig. 4).

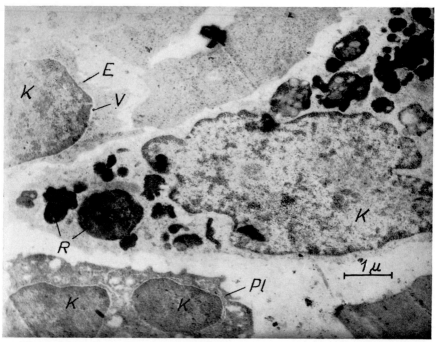

Fig. 3. Macrophage from human bone marrow, 60 minutes after 4060 rad Co⁶⁰ local irradiation. A clear zone (V) has been formed around the nucleus (K) of erythroblast (E) and of plasma cell (Pl). Phagocytized residues of cells (R) Magnification: 13,000. (Authors' observation.)

In the bone marrow similar changes take place under the influence of whole-body and local Co⁶⁰ irradiation (Bauer, 1962). Szalontai and Kiss (1964) found several sinusoidal fragments in ultrathin sections prepared from bone marrow punctates. This observation can be correlated with the results of the light microscopic findings of Fliedner and Stodtmeister (1962). As the authors stated earlier, the injury of the vascular system by X-ray exposure of bone marrow of rats is most striking. Edema and hemorrhages develop in a short time and the characteristic structure of red bone marrow changes.

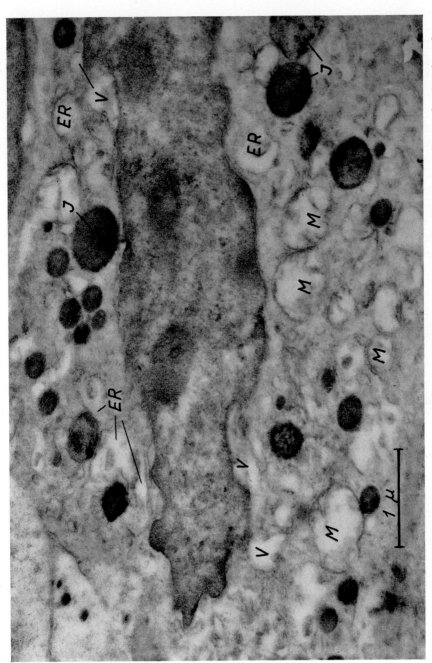

Fig. 4. Reticulum cell (mouse thymus) 10 minutes after 800 r X-ray whole-body irradiation. Small vacuoles (V) have been formed between the two nuclear membranes. The endoplasmic reticulum (ER) and the mitochondria (M) are swollen. Several inclusions (J) are visible. Magnification: 26,000. (From Braun, 1963b.)

In the course of electron microscopic investigation of sinusoidal fragments it became evident that the nucleus in the reticular cells forming
the capillary system of bone marrow had been separated from the cytoplasm because of shrinkage (Fig. 5). It was surrounded by a clear space.
The nuclear membrane was disrupted on the one side, and thickened on
the other. Slight damage also appears in mitochondria. The inner lamellar structure of the swollen mitochondria is hardly recognizable. The
structure of cytoplasm changes. Small blank spaces are visible in an
enlarged area near the nucleus as well as on several places in the membranes.

Early destruction in the granulocyte and the erythrocyte series can be
demonstrated. It is similar to the injury in lymphocytes. One hour after
radiation the nucleus of the immature and mature granulocytes (Figs.
6 and 7) and that of the erythroblasts is surrounded by a clear perinuclear area. Sometimes, especially in the case of immature red blood cells,
karyolysis is present. The density of cytoplasm often diminishes in the

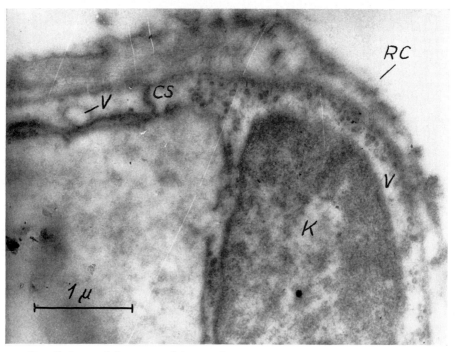

Fig. 5. Sinusoid fragment of human bone marrow, 60 minutes after 4060 rad
Co⁶⁰ local irradiation. Shrinkage of the nucleus (K), unequal division of the cyto-
plasmic substance (CS) and vacuole (V) formation is observed in a reticulum cell
(RC). Magnification: 27,000. (Authors' observation.)

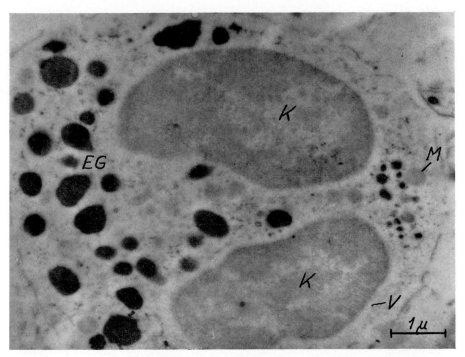

Fig. 6. Eosinophil granulocyte from human bone marrow, 60 minutes after 4060 rad Co⁶⁰ local irradiation. A clear space (V) has been formed around the nucleus (K) and the granules (EG). The mitochondria (M) are intact. Magnification: 14,800. (Authors' observation.)

granulocytes around the membrane of granules (Fig. 7). The mito-chondria are swollen and the inner lamellae are fragmented. In the nucleus of the erythroblasts, matting of the nucleoplasm is often ob-served. The signs of radiation injury described previously become visible in the basophile immature cells, infrequently in the lymphotic gland or in the germinoblasts and lymphoblasts. The plasma cells and the plasmo-blasts are far more resistent.

The cytological alterations observed in the days and weeks following the X-ray exposure have been investigated in ultrathin sections of the spleen by Scherer and Vogell (1958) and Stender (1963), as well as by Klug (1961). The published results are difficult to evaluate. Scherer and Vogell (1958) indicated the deviations only in the form of a table according to which the nuclear membrane of lymphocytes has thickened on the third day, while the inner crista system of mitochondria remains fragmented. On the seventh day the thickness of the nuclear membrane has returned to normal dimensions and only a few disintegrated mitochondria are visible. The findings of Klug (1961), on the other hand, differ essentially from the changes observed repeatedly in the first 24 hours. They cannot be reconciled with the results of Scherer and Vogell (1958). On the basis of their microphotographs, one cannot preclude the possibility that the alterations are not a result of direct radiation injury. Considering the observation of Braun (1963a,b), according to which newly formed lymphocytes appear in the thymus in 24 hours after ir-

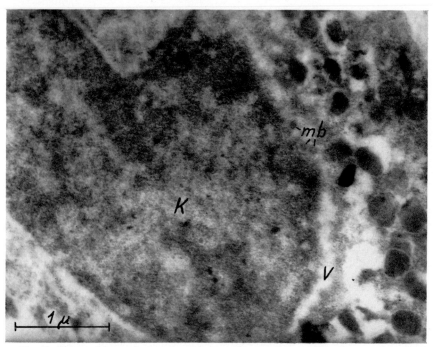

Fig. 7. Neutrophil myelocyte from human bone marrow, 60 minutes after 4060 rad Co⁶⁰ local irradiation. In the perinuclear clear zone (V) are microbodies (mb), and the cytoplasmic substance is less dense. Magnification: 26,000. (Authors' observation.)

radiation, it is conceivable that Klug (1961) demonstrates the new generation originated from the cells exposed to irradiation. Klug (1961) began his series of investigation on the third day after irradiation. He could not see in the spleen of the guinea pig any tendency to shrinkage in the nucleus of plasma cells, lymphocytes, and granulocytes. He claimed that the nuclear substance is irregularly dispersed. The nuclear membrane and the mitochondria are intact. He only found some difference between the size and structure of nucleoles, which are unusually large. Osmiophile and osmiophobe areas alternate in them giving them a

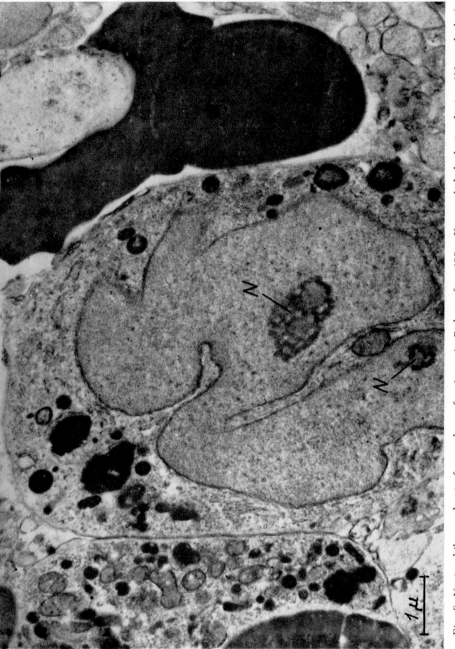

Fig. 8. Neutrophil granulocyte from spleen of guinea pig 5 days after 400 r X-ray whole-body irradiation (N—nucleolus). Homogeneous dispersion of nuclear substance. Magnification: 15,300. (From Klug, 1961.)

spongoid appearance. He generally found in the lymphocytes one nucleolus; in the plasma cells 1–3 nucleoli. Also he often found cells having nuclei, in which the nucleoli did not show any change. The author also detected the same changes in sections made 5 or 10 days later. The nuclear material was homogeneously dispersed (Fig. 8). The increase in density of nucleoli is even more remarkable in this nuclear substance (Fig. 9). It was surprising that he found nucleoli also in the granulocytes with segmented nuclei similar to those in lymphocytes (Fig. 10). Three weeks after irradiation there was no other change observed except for the relatively larger nucleolus. According to Klug the changes in the nucleus are due to the depolymerization of DNA.

Stender (1963) observed that following irradiation the chromatin of

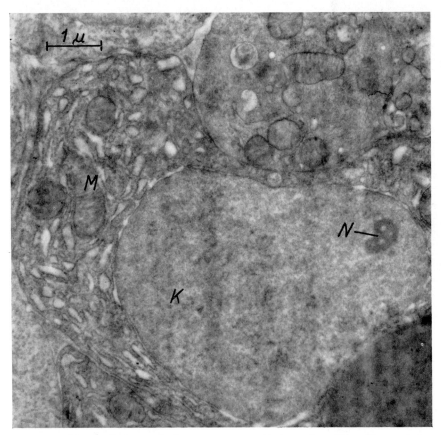

Fig. 9. Plasma cell from spleen of guinea pig 10 days after 4C0 r X-ray whole-body irradiation (N—nucleolus; M—mitochondria; K—nucleus). Magnification: 15,000. (From Klug, 1961).

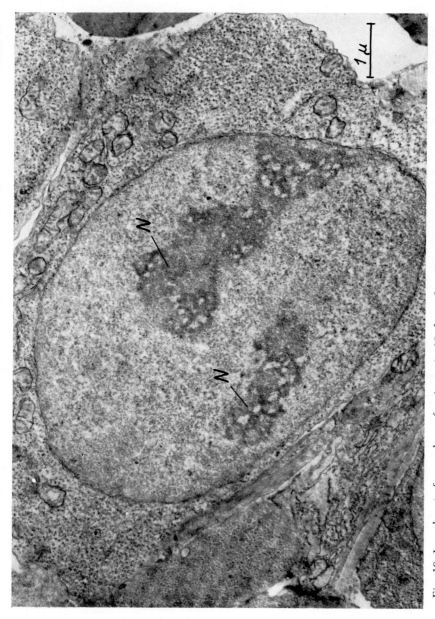

Fig. 10. Lymphocyte from spleen of guinea pig 18 days after 400 r X-ray whole-body irradiation (N—nucleoli). Magnification: 15,600. (From Klug, 1961).

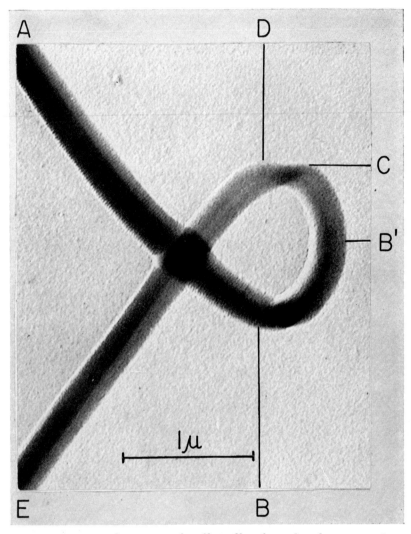

Fig. 11. The external structure of a fibrin fiber from thrombocytopenic human blood. Cross-striation ceases at the bending and torsion of fibrin fiber. From A to B the fiber adheres to the supporting film, the relief-cross-striation shows the usual pattern, with a period around 230 Å. From B to C the relief-cross-striation disappears and can be detected only between B and C. Torsion extends between C to D, here the relief-cross-striation disappears also. Between D and E the relief-cross-striation is hardly visible. Thirty minutes after bleeding. Fixation by OsO_4 shadowed by TiO_2. Magnification: 35,000. (From Köppel, 1962.)

the nucleus of some cells are arranged along the nuclear membrane and that the nucleolus is enlarged.

2. Late Manifestation

It is well known that leukemia can be brought on by ionizing radiation in animal experiments. The causative agent of leukemia, however, is still controversial. Parsons *et al.* (1962) found several virus-like particles in leukemic cells of irradiated RF mice. Therefore, he attributes the leukemia brought on by radiation to virus proliferating as a result of the blocking of immune processes. The work of Dalton *et al.* (1961), on the other hand, supports the primary leukemogenic effect of radiation. He could find virus particles neither in the myeloid cells nor in the mega-karyocytes of irradiated animals.

B. Results of Studies Related to Hemostasis

Cottier *et al.* (1961) produced local parenchyma and vascular injury through X-ray exposure of the hypophysis. White thrombi developed in a short time. Viscous metamorphosis of the platelets took place as under normal conditions. After irradiation heparinemia often occurs (Fiam and Resovszki, 1957). This biochemical observation can be correlated with the early injury and the disappearance of the granules of basophil cells. Furthermore, it is well known that 2–3 weeks after irradiation the number of thrombocytes significantly decreases. Köppel (1962) found the fibrin fibers in thrombopenia more translucent. However, the cross striation of the fibrin fibers was preserved (Fig. 11). In case of torsion or deflection of fibrin fasciculi, the disappearance of cross striation points to abnormal polymerization of the fibrin fibers.

References

Ackerman, G. A., Grasso, J. A., and Knouff, R. A. (1961). *Lab. Invest.* **10**, 787.
Aleksandrowicz, J., Blicharski, J., and Feltynowski, A. (1955). "Mikroskopia elektronowa krwinek." Panstwowe wydawnictwonaukowe, Warsaw.
Amano, S., and Tanaka, H. (1956). *Acta Haematol. Japon.* **19**, 738.
Bahr, G. F. (1957). *Exptl. Cell Res.* **12**, 342.
Bang, N. U., Fletcher, A. P., Alkjaersig, N., and Sherry, S. (1962). *J. Clin. Invest.* **41**, 935.
Bargmann, W., and Knoop, A. (1958). *Z. Zellforsch.* **48**, 130.
Barta, I., and Szalontai, S. (1963). In preparation.
Bauer, H. (1962). *Aerztl. Forsch.* **16**, 377.
Beard, J. W. (1962). *In* "Progress in Hematology" (L. M. Tocantins, ed.,) Vol. III, pp. 105–135. Grune & Stratton, New York.
Bennett, H. S., Luft, J. H., and Hampton, J. C. (1959). *Am. J. Physiol.* **196**, 381.
Bessis, M. (1950). *Blood* **5**, 1083.

Bessis, M. (1956). "Cytology of the Blood and Blood-Forming Organs." Grune & Stratton, New York.

Bessis, M. (1958a). *Blood* **13**, 410.

Bessis, M. (1958b). *Proc. 7th Intern. Congr. Intern. Soc. Hematol., Rome.* Grune & Stratton, New York (Publ. 1960).

Bessis, M. (1960). In "Handbuch der gesamten Hämatologie" (L. Heilmeyer and A. Hittmair, eds.), Vol. 2, Pt. 2. Urban & Schwarzenberg, Munich.

Bessis, M. C. (1961a). *Lab. Invest.* **10**, 1040.

Bessis, M. (1961b). In "The Cell" (J. Brachet and A. E. Mirsky, eds.), Vol. V, p. 163, Academic Press, New York.

Bessis, M. C., and Breton-Gorius, J. (1959). *Blood* **14**, 423.

Bessis, M., and Breton-Gorius, J. (1960). *Compt. Rend. Acad. Sci.* **251**, 465.

Bessis, M., and Thiery, J. P. (1961a). *Intern. Rev. Cytol.* **12**, 199.

Bessis, M., and Thiery, J. P. (1961b). *Nouv. Rev. Franc. Hematol.* **1**, 703.

Bessis, M., and Thiery, J. P. (1962a). *Nouv. Rev. Franc. Hematol.* **2**, 387.

Bessis, M., and Thiery, J. P. (1962b). *Nouv. Rev. Franc. Hematol.* **2**, 577.

Bloom, G. (1955). *Z. Zellforsch.* **42**, 365.

Boyd, J. D., Johnson, F. R., and Lever, J. D., eds. (1961). "Electron Microscopy in Anatomy," 296 pp. Williams & Wilkins, Baltimore, Maryland.

Braun, H. (1963a). *Strahlentherapie* **121**, 567.

Braun, H. (1963b). *Strahlentherapie* **122**, 248.

Braunsteiner, H. (1959). "Physiologie und Physiopathologie der weissen Blutzellen." Thieme, Stuttgart.

Braunsteiner, H., and Febvre, H. (1950). *Acta Haematol.* **3**, 174.

Braunsteiner, H., and Pakesch, F. (1960). *Acta Haematol.* **24**, 64.

Braunsteiner, H., Fellinger, K., and Pakesch, F. (1953). *Deut. Arch. Klin. Med.* **200**, 657.

Braunsteiner, H., Höfer, R., and Sailer, S. (1961). *Deut. Med. Wochschr.* **86**, 721.

Breese, S. S. (1962). "Fifth International Congress for Electron Microscopy." Academic Press, New York.

Brittin, G. M., Tanaka, Y., and Brecher, G. (1963). *Blood* **21**, 335.

Castaldi, P. A., Firkin, B. G., Blackwell, P. M., and Clifford, K. J. (1962). *Blood* **20**, 566.

Chandler, A. B., and Hand, R. A. (1961). *Circulation* **24**, 902.

Cottier, H., and Jost, L. (1961). *Proc. 8th Congr. Europ. Soc. Haematol., Vienna.* Karger, Basel (Publ. 1962).

Cottier, H., Roos, B., Rentsch, H., and Cronkite, E. P. (1961). *Blood* **18**, 797.

Cronkite, E. P., and Bond, V. P. (1960). "Radiation Injury in Man." Thomas, Springfield, Illinois.

Daems, W. Th., and Oort, J. (1962). *Exptl. Cell Res.* **28**, 11.

Dalton, A. J., Law, L. W., Moloney, J. B., and Manaker, R. A. (1961). *J. Natl. Cancer Inst.* **27**, 744.

Danon, A., Jerushalmy, Z., Kohn, A., and de Vries, A. (1961). *Proc. 8th Congr. Europ. Soc. Haematol., Vienna.* Karger, Basel (Publ. 1962).

David-Ferreira, J. F., and David-Ferreira, K. (1962). *Z. Zellforsch.* **56**, 789.

Dawson, J. M. (1954). *Proc. Intern. Conf. Elmi. London.*

Doan, C. A., Cunningham, R. S., and Sabin, F. R. (1925). *Carnegie Inst. Wash. Contrib. Embryol.* **16**, 163.

Duckert, F., Jung, E., and Shmerling, D. H. (1961). *Schweiz. Med. Wochschr.* **91**, 1139.

Eriksson, A. W., Hiepler, E., Jürgens, R., Lehmann, W., and Schulz, H. (1961). *Klin. Wochschr.* **39**, 32.

Feissly R., Gautier, A., and Marcovici, I. (1957). *Rev. Hematol.* **12**, 397.

Fiam, B., and Resovszki, P. (1957). *Honvedorvos* **9**, 101.

Fliedner, T. M., and Stodtmeister, R. (1962). "Experimentelle und klinische Strahlenhämatologie." Lehmann, Munich.

Florey, H. W., Poole, J. C. F., and Meek, G. A. (1959). *J. Pathol. Bacteriol* **77**, 625.

Freeman, J. A. (1960). *Blood* **15**, 449.

Freeman, J. A., and Samuels, M. S. (1958). *Blood* **13**, 725.

French, J. E., and Poole, J. C. F. (1963). *Proc. Roy. Soc.* **157**, 170.

Gautier, A. (1961). *In:* Heilmeyer, L., Merker, H., Mölbert, E., and Neidhardt, M. (1962). *Acta Haematol.* **27**, 78.

Gerendás, M. (1952). "Az Elektronmikroszkop." Mérnöki Tovabbképzö Intézet, Budapest.

Goodman, J. R., Reilly, E. B., and Moore, R. E. (1957). *Blood* **12**, 428.

Graffi, A., and Fey, F. (1959). *In* "Physiologie und Physiopatholgie der weissen Blutzellen" (H. Braunsteiner, ed.). Thieme, Stuttgart.

Grasso, J. A., Swift, H., and Ackerman, G. A. (1962). *J. Cellular Biol.* **14**, 235.

Grey, C. E., and Biesele, I. J. (1955). *Rev. Hematol.* **10**, 283.

Guba, F., and Sugar, I. (1956). *Proc. Electron Microscopy Conf., Stockholm* p. 131. Academic Press, New York.

Haine, M. E., and Cosslett, V. E. (1961). "The Electron Microscope." Spon, London.

Hall, C. R., and Slayter, H. S. (1959). *J. Biophys. Biochem. Cytol.* **5**, 11.

Hawn, C., and Porter, K. A. (1947). *J. Exptl. Med.* **86**, 285.

Haydon, G. B. (1957). *A.M.A. Arch. Pathol.* **64**, 393.

Heilmeyer, L., Merker, H., Mölbert, E., and Neidhardt, M. (1962). *Acta Haematol.* **27**, 78.

Hollan, S. R. (1959). *Blood* **14**, 203.

Hovig, T. (1962). *Thromb. Diath. Haemorrhag.* **8**, 455.

Hovig, T. (1963a). *Thromb. Diath. Haemorrhag.* **9**, 248.

Hovig, T. (1963b). *Thromb. Diath. Haemorrhag.* **9**, 264.

Hulse, E. V. (1959). *Brit. J. Haematol.* **5**, 278.

Jean, G. (1961). *Experientia* **17**, 428.

Jean, G., Racine, L., Marx, R., and Gautier, A. (1963). *Thromb. Diath. Haemorrhag.* **9**, 1.

Jones, O. P. (1960). *Anat. Record* **138**, 105.

Jorke, D. (1963a). "Lymphoidzellen des Blutes: Hämatologie and Bluttransfusionswesen," Vol. 2. Akademie Verlag, Berlin.

Jorke, D. (1963b). *Folia Haematol.* **81**, 30.

Jung, F. (1957). *Klin. Wochschr.* **35**, 44.

Karrer, H. E. (1961). *J. Ultrastruct. Res.* **5**, 116.

Kay, D. (1961). "Techniques for Electron Microscopy." Thomas, Springfield, Illinois.

Kelényi, G., and Gógl, A. (1963). *Morph. és Ig. Orv. Szemle* **3**, 270.

Kjaerheim, A., and Hovig, T. (1962). *Thromb. Diath. Haemorrhag.* **7**, 1.

Klug, H. (1961). *Radiol. Biol. Therap.* (*Berlin*) **2**, 301.

Köppel, G. (1958). *Z. Zellforsch.* **47**, 401.

Köppel, G. (1962). "Die Umwandlung des Fibrinogens in Fibrin." Schattauer, Stuttgart.

Kuhnke, E. (1958). *Arch. Ges. Physiol.* **268**, 87.

Kurtz, S. M. (1964). "Electron Microscopic Anatomy," 425 pp. Academic Press, New York.

Ladda, R. (1962). Exptl. Cell Res. 28, 595.

Leisegang, S. (1956). Elektronenmikroskop. In "Handbuch der Physik" (S. Flügge, ed.), Vol. 33. Springer, Berlin.

Levene, C. I. (1955). Lancet II, 1216.

Levene, M., and Levene, C. I. (1957). J. Clin. Pathol. 10, 200.

Lindemann, B. (1956). Strahlentherapie 101, 3.

Lovas, B. (1959). Z. Wiss. Mikroskopie 64, 95.

Low, F. N., and Freeman, J. A. (1958). "Electron Microscopic Atlas of Normal and Leukemic Human Blood." McGraw-Hill, New York.

Marchesi, V. T. (1961). Quart. J. Exptl. Physiol. 46, 115.

Marchesi, V. T., and Florey, H. W. (1960). Quart. J. Exptl. Physiol. 45, 343.

Matter, M., Hartmann, J. R., Kautz, J., De March, Q. B., and Finch, C. A. (1960). Blood 15, 174.

Merker, H. J., and Carsten, P. M. (1963). Blut 9, 329.

Möllenstedt, G. (1955). Optik 12, 441.

Moore, H. (1963). Tagung für Elektronenmikroskopie, Zürich.

Paegle, R. D. (1961). Blood 17, 687.

Palade, G .E. (1952). J. Exptl. Med. 95, 285.

Palade, G. E. (1954). Proc. Intern. Conf. Elmi. London p. 129.

Parmeggiani, A. (1961). Thromb. Diath. Haemorrhag. 6, 517.

Parsons, D. F., Upton, A. C., Bender, M. A., Jenkins, V. K., Nelson, E. L., and Johnson, R. R. (1962). Cancer Res. 22, 728.

Pease, D. C. (1956). Blood 11, 501.

Pease, D. C. (1960). "Histological Techniques for Electron Microscopy." Academic Press, New York.

Policard, A., and Bessis, M. (1958). Compt. Rend. Acad. Sci. 246, 3194.

Poole, J. C. F., French, J. E., and Cliff, W. J. (1963). J. Clin. Pathol. 16, 523.

Reimer, L. (1959). "Elektronenmikroskopische Untersuchungs- und Preparationsmethoden." Springer, Berlin.

Rhodin, J. A. G. (1963). "An Atlas of Ultrastructure," 222 pp. Saunders, Philadelphia, Pennsylvania.

Riddle, J. M., Bernstein, M. H., and Seegers, W. H. (1963). Thromb. Diath. Haemorrhag. 9, 12.

Rodman, N. F., Jr., Mason, R. G., McDevitt, N. B., and Brinkhous, K. M. (1962). Am. J. Pathol. 40, 271.

Rodman, N. F., Painter, J. C., and McDevitt, N. B. (1963). J. Cell Biol. 16, 225.

Roos, J. (1957). Thromb. Diath. Haemorrhag. 1, 471.

Ruska, H. (1963). Elektronenmikroskopie Das Medizinische Prisma 11, 1.

Scherer, E., and Vogell, W. (1958). Strahlentherapie 106, 202.

Schulz, H., and Wedell, J. (1962). Klin. Wochschr. 40, 1114.

Schultz, H., Jürgens, R., and Hiepler, E. (1958). Thromb. Diath. Haemorrhag. 2, 300.

Scott, J., White, J. G., Vernier, R., and Krivit, W. (1962). Federation Proc. 21(2), 66.

Sheldon, H., and Zetterquist, H. (1955). Bull. Johns Hopkins Hosp. 96, 135.

Siegel, B. M. (1964). "Modern Developments in Electron Microscopy." Academic Press, New York.

Sorenson, G. D. (1962). Am. J. Pathol. 40, 297.

Stender, H. S. (1963). *In* "Strahlenpathologie der Zelle" (E. Scherer and H. S. Stender, eds.). Thieme, Stuttgart.

Stobbe, H. (1960). *Schweiz. Med. Wochschr.* **90,** 1265.

Stockinger, L. (1962). *J. Cell Biol.* **15,** 131.

Stoeckenius, W. (1958). *Verhandl. Deut. Ges. Pathol.* **41,** 304.

Szalontai, S. (1962). *Magy. Belorv. Arch.* **15,** 233.

Szalontai, S. (1963a). *Haematol. Hung.* **3,** 213.

Szalontai, S. (1963b). *Magyar Haematol. Napok, Pécs.* (Congress)

Szalontai, S. (1964). "A vérlemezkék és a hajszálerek Kapcsolata." Thesis, Budapest.

Szalontai, S., and Kiss, B. (1964). In preparation.

Szalontai, S., and Timaff, M. (1964). *In* "Age with a Future" (P. Hansen, ed.), pp. 347–353. Munksgaard, Copenhagen.

Szalontai, S., Brasch, Gy., Nagy, I., and Rózsa, E. (1962). *Orv. Hetilap* **103,** 1990.

Thiery, J. P. (1959). *Rev. Franc. Etudes Clin. Biol.* **4,** 601.

Thiery, J. P. (1962). *J. Microscopie* **1,** 275.

Timaffy, M., and Szalontai, S. (1963). *Proc. 6th Intern. Congr. Gerontol., Copenhagen.*

Törö, I, and Röhlich, P. (1961). *Magy. Radiol.* **13,** 331.

Tokuda, T., Tsujimura, H., Ikeda, Y., and Miyaji, T. (1961). *J. Elektronmicroscopy (Tokyo)* **10,** 161.

Tokuyasu, K., and Okamura, S. (1959). *J. Biophys. Biochem. Cytol.* **6,** 305.

van den Hooff, A. (1956). *Lancet* **I,** 247.

Wald, N., Thoma, G. E., and Braun, G. (1962). *In* "Progress in Hematology" (L. M. Tocantins, ed.), Vol. III, pp. 1–52. Grune & Stratton, New York.

Watanabe, Y. (1957). *J. Electronmicroscopy (Tokyo)* **5,** 46.

Weiss, L. (1959). *Anat. Record* **133,** 439.

Weiss, L. (1960). *Anat. Record* **136,** 300.

Weiss, L. (1961). *Bull. Johns Hopkins Hosp.* **108,** 171.

Wellensiek, H. J. (1957). *Beitr. Pathol. Anat. Allgem. Pathol.* **118,** 173.

Welsh, R. A. (1960). *Blood* **16,** 1307.

Welsh, R. A. (1962). *Am. J. Pathol.* **40,** 285.

Williamson, J. R., and Grisham, J. W. (1961). *Am. J. Pathol.* **39,** 239.

Wischnitzer, S. (1961). *J. N. Y. Med. Coll. Flower Fifth Ave. Hosp.* **2,** 1.

Witte, S., and Schricker, K. Th. (1958). *Klin. Wochschr.* **36,** 1119.

Wolpers, C. (1957). *Klin. Wochschr.* **35,** 57.

Zamboni, L., and Pease, D. C. (1961). *J. Ultrastructure Res.* **5,** 65.

Zucker-Franklin, D. (1963). *Blood* **21,** 509.

Zwillenberg, H. H. L., and Zwillenberg, L. D. (1963). *Z. Zellforsch.* **60,** 313.

CHAPTER 6

Bone Marrow Kinetics

Harold R. Schumacher[*] and Allan J. Erslev

Cardeza Foundation, Jefferson Medical College, Philadelphia, Pennsylvania

I. Introduction

For the last century, the origin of circulating blood cells has been recognized as an extremely important biologic problem. The first major contribution was made by Neuman in 1868 when he described colorless nucleated elements in the bone marrow and stated that "the transition of nucleated cells to red corpuscles is effected by colored cells, the nuclei of which are either rudimentary or in a state of disintegration." His concept of the bone marrow as the sole organ of erythropoiesis was bitterly challenged but he received support from the great experimental pathologist Claude Bernard (1869) who pinpointed erythropoiesis to the dilated

[*] *Present address:* Department of Hematology, York Hospital, York,

capillaries of medullary tissue. With the advent of new staining methods introduced at the turn of the century by Ehrlich and by Pappenheim, studies of blood smears and tissue section led to finer definition of the morphology of cells in bone marrow and circulating blood. Definite cellular lines became recognized and it became accepted that the liver and the spleen were hematopoietic organs during fetal life while the bone marrow was the sole source of cells after the neonatal period (Michels, 1931). The major bone of contention was the ultimate origin of the cell lines. The first embryonic hematopoietic cells obviously must have arisen from a premordial stem cell, but did succeeding cellular generations originate from one common stem cell (monophyletic school) or did each cell line renew itself from a blast cell, solely committed to that line (polyphyletic school)? Much of the lively debate between Maximow, Ferrata, DiGuglielmo, Sabin, Downey, Naegeli, and contemporaries, concerning the origin of blood cells appears today somewhat outdated. The hotly argued data was almost entirely obtained from observation on embryos or tissue cultures and on nonmammalian animals. Most of the subsequent hematologists were satisfied to accept at face value the existence of multipotential stem cells variously called reticulum cells, hemohistioblast or RE cells, and then to forget about these nebulous cells and concentrate on the maturation and proliferation of the specific cell lines. Within the last decade there has been a renewed interest in stem cells. Yoffey has suggested that circulating lymphocytes are multipotential stem cells, Osgood has formulated a stem cell hierarchy, Lajtha has treated stem cell kinetics with computers, and the Brookhaven group has used painstaking isotope techniques in the study of these cells. We are still dealing with a hypothetical cell without definite morphological characteristics, but it seems that further study of the bone marrow with its continuously maturing population may lead to specific and general information on the origin of cells.

Cellular multiplication and cellular maturation were first subject to morphological studies after the introduction of the Romanofsky stains and of Ehrlich's brilliant cresyl stains for reticulocytes. Astaldi (1962), and Eigsti and Dustin (1955) employed mitotic indices in the quantitative study of blood cell formation, but it was not until the release of radioactive isotopes by the Atomic Energy Commission in 1946 that the dynamic study of bone marrow became of age. These isotopes have made it possible to study cellular production rates, life span, size of compartments or pools and destiny of individual cells. Hamilton, Cronkite, Yoffey, Craddock, Osgood, Quastler, and many others have studied the kinetics of cellular proliferation and have prepared models of one or more cell lines. It is the purpose of this chapter to review in a selective manner recent knowledge of kinetics of hematopoiesis gained by radiobiological techniques and to use this knowledge to construct tentative models of the production of bone marrow cells.

II. Radiobiological Techniques in the Study of Bone Marrow

A. LABELING

Measurements of the rate of disappearance, utilization, reutilization, and excretion of normal metabolic building blocks tagged with isotopes have been of great value in the study of bone marrow kinetics. If one utilizes a "uniform age" or "cohort" label, information is received primarily about intramedullary life span. Isotopes can also be used to tag substances which normally are not involved in cellular metabolism but nevertheless are capable of labeling blood cells. Examples of this are the chromate ion which will bind to sulfhydryl groups and diisopropylfluorophosphate which will bind irreversibly with certain intracellular esterases. In this tagging one utilizes an "all age" label and gains information about the intravascular lifespan.

B. SPECIFICITY OF LABEL

Almost all the radioactive chemicals used will label erythroid, myeloid, and thrombocytoid elements. Only radioactive iron is specific for one cell line, a fact which has facilitated the study of the kinetics of erythropoiesis. The study of myelopoiesis and thrombocytopoiesis have been impeded by the lack of specific labels and the extremely nonhomogeneous cellular population of the bone marrow. The cell lines have quantitatively different synthetic obligations and within each line the rate of synthetic activities change during the process of maturation. Attempts have been made to separate bone marrow suspensions into homogeneous fractions containing specific cellular elements at a uniform cellular age. Centrifugation with or without sucrose gradient has been used but no clear cut cellular separation has been accomplished. Freezing and hemolysis have also been employed in order to separate specific cellular elements, but again without much success. Long term cultures of bone marrow may lead to uniform cellular suspension but these cells are no longer capable of functioning as bone marrow cells and cannot be used to study the kinetics of this organ.

C. AUTORADIOGRAPHY

Probably the most exact way in which isotope studies can be related to specific cellular lines and specific cellular ages is radioautography. Tritium with its low energy beta rays has been found invaluable for this technique and a great number of studies on bone marrow have been reported with various tritium-labeled substances. Iron–59 has also been used for radioautography but its radiation is more penetrating making it difficult to pinpoint the origin of an atomic disintegration. Two techniques have been employed: coating with an emulsion or stripping with a fine grain photographic film. The "dipping" technique has the advantage of good contact and constant registry, but handling tends to increase fog and uniform thickness are hard to obtain. The "stripping" technique offers even emulsion thickness, constant registry, and excellent resolution, but the film tends to slip and the staining reaction may be impaired. The choice between the dipping and the stripping technique is at present a case of personal experience and preference (Comar, 1955).

III. Bone Marrow Kinetics

A. General Considerations

Blood cell production in the bone marrow can be divided into a stem cell pool and three differentiated cell series—the erythroid, the myeloid, and the thrombocytoid. Each of these can be subdivided into successive stages or pools (Fig. 1).

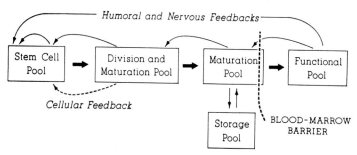

Fig. 1. General model showing normal hematopoiesis originating in the stem cell pool. The various humoral and feedback mechanisms are depicted.

The stem cell pool is a theoretical concept since its exact morphological equivalent has not been defined. However, it is difficult to conceive of a continuous renewal of blast cells without the existence of an undifferentiated precursor cell, the so-called stem cell. The division and maturation pool makes up about 33% of the active red bone marrow. All cells belonging here appear to undergo continuous maturation with regularly interposed divisions. Based on somewhat arbitrary morphological criteria this pool can be divided into several compartments (myeloblasts, promyelocytes and myelocytes or pronormoblasts, basophilic normoblasts and polychromatophilic normoblast or megakaryoblasts and promega-karyocytes).

B. MITOSIS

The cell cycle between two mitotic divisions is divided into a post mitotic rest period (G_1), a period of synthesis (S) a premitotic rest (G_2) and the mitotic period (M). The G_1 period is the major variable which may last months, as in liver cells, or a few hours, as in bone marrow cells. The other periods are believed to be constant. During the S period which lasts about 10 hours the DNA content doubles. In the G_2 period which lasts about 1 hour the cell does not synthesize more DNA but other processes occur preparing it for division. The mitosis itself takes about 0.5–1.5 hours and is divided into prophase, metaphase, anaphase, and telophase. It appears that ribosomal activities and cytoplasmic maturation proceed throughout the cell cycle. The sum of G_1, S, G_2, and M times (or the average duration from the termination of one mitosis to the termination of the next mitosis) is called the generation time (t_G). The mitotic index (M_1) is defined as the fraction of cells which morphologically are in the midst of a mitotic division:

$$M_1 = \frac{N^M \text{ (number of cells in mitosis)}}{N \text{ (number of cells in interphase)}} \tag{1}$$

It is obvious that the mitotic index becomes a function of the time spent in the different periods of the cell cycle.

$$M_1 = \frac{t_M \text{ (mitotic time)}}{t_G \text{ (generation time)}} \quad \text{or } t_G = \frac{t_M}{M_1} \tag{2}$$

The turnover time is defined by Leblond and Walker (1956) as the time taken for the replacement of all the cells in a given compartment and has usually been thought to be equal to the generation time. However, Killmann and co-workers (1963) have pointed out that this depends on how the compartments are separated. If the transition from one compartment to the next is sharp and follows a mitotic division, these investigators have used the term "heteromorphogenic division." If, however, the cell divides and maintains its morphological characteristics, they apply the term "homomorphogenic division." When compartments are separated by heteromorphogenic division the generation time which can be measured quite accurately from the mitotic index equals the turnover time and expresses the time spent in a given compartment. If the division, as appears more likely, is homomorphogenic the separation between compartments becomes much more indistinct and the turnover time or mean compartment time becomes difficult to determine.

When the cells have lost the ability to go through mitotic divisions they are passed into the maturation pool which is believed to represent 66% of active bone marrow. Here they continue to mature and at some point are released from or flushed out of the bone marrow to finish their maturation as circulating blood cells. Finally the fully matured cells enter the functional pool for the remainder of their life span.

Each pool is replenished from the preceeding pool except for the stem cell pool which must have a special cellular renewal system in order not to become depleted. Humoral and nervous feedback impulses are of importance to adjust the rates of cellular production to the peripheral demands. Intra- and extramedullary storage pools exist and participate in the adjustments between supply and demand. With the exception of the stem cell pool, these pools will be considered individually under the discussion of the three separate cell lines, the erythrocytic, the myelocytic, and the thrombocytic. The stem pool which may be multipotential will be considered first and related to all three cell lines.

C. Stem Cell Pool

1. General Considerations

It is usually assumed that the modern concept of bone marrow kinetics demand the existence of a self-perpetuating pool of undifferentiated stem cells. All other bone marrow cells exist in a state of relentless maturation and are believed not to be capable of continuous self-renewal. Suit and co-workers (1957) have shown by means of Fe^{59} radioautography that even the most immature pronormoblast will incorporate iron and synthesize heme. The continuous creation of new immature pronormoblasts from such cells would imply the existence of a division in which one of the daughter cells would continue maturation while its identical sister cell would lose whatever cytoplasmic heme had been accumulated by the mother cell and retrogress to an earlier immature stage. Such cellular de-differentiation has been described for cells involved in regeneration of the amphibian limbs (Konigsberg, 1963) and for viral infected mammalian cells (Ephrussi and Temin, 1960). It is certainly conceivable that absorbed iron and synthesized hemoglobin could be removed from maturing pronormoblasts by "reverse pinocytosis" in the Bessis complexes of nucleated red cells and reticuloendothelial cells. However, so far there is no experimental evidence to suggest that bone marrow cells can de-differentiate, and we have to assume the existence of a stem cell pool. This assumption is also supported by autoradiographic studies by Alpen and Cranmore (1959) showing a rapid decrease in the number of labeled pronormoblasts, a rate of decrease best explained by the entrance of un-labeled cells into the erythroid compartment, or in other words differ-entiation of stem cells. Our present problem is of assigning a specific morphological identity to the stem cells. Yoffey *et al.* (1959), resurrecting the old ideas of Maximow, solved this ticklish problem by assigning stem cell function to circulating small lymphocytes and postulating that these cells will, on demand, lodge in the bone marrow and transform to myelo-blasts, pronormoblasts, or megakaryoblasts. Studies by Gesner and Gow-ans (1962) have indicated that small lymphocytes can undergo transfor-mation to large cells but that these cells appear merely to be capable of producing more lymphocytes. Holub (1958) using diffusion chamber technique and Rebuck and Crowley (1955) using skin windows have also shown that lymphocytes can undergo transformation but only to other cells within the lymphoid family. Attempts to use pure suspension of lymphoid cells obtained from thoracic ducts or lymph nodes for radiation protection have not been successful (Gesner and Gowans, 1962) and do not support Yoffey's hypothesis of the multipotential possibilities of small lymphocytes. However, it appears that circulating blood does contain stem cell-like elements since buffy coat from peripheral blood can protect and recolonize radiated recipients (Goodman and Hodgson, 1962). These cells may be identical with the circulating cells Bond and co-workers (1958) have shown to be capable of DNA synthesis. The result of spleen shielding in Jacobson's (1954; cf. Jacobson *et al.*, 1957) classical studies could also best be explained by postulating that stem cells may be or may become part of the circulating blood. It is a possibility which is being studied intensively although most investigators still feel that the hematopoietic stem cell is a fixed bone marrow cell. Most recently Bessis has classified the hematopoietic stem cell into hemohistioblast which can differentiate into the hemocytoblast or the histioblast (Bessis, 1956b). The hemocytoblast can give rise to all cells except for the monocyte while the histioblast gives rise to monocytes and macrophages. Less ambi-tious classifications differentiate between non-phagocytosing reticulum cells, so-called stem cells, and phagocytosing reticulum cells. According to this classification the stem cell is a large cell with pale blue cytoplasm, a nucleus with an open structure of chromatin strands, and one or several deep blue, large nucleoli.

Whether or not this cell is multipotential or committed to one cell line alone is not known for certain. In a recent study Von Barta (1963) showed microphotographs which suggested that the same yellow bone marrow cell which was surrounded by normoblasts after prolonged ane-mia was surrounded by myeloid cells after the injection of pyrogens. Gurney *et al.* (1962) in their studies of stem cell kinetics in the polycythemic mouse also think that stem cells are multipotential, at least in regard to erythro- and myelopoiesis. They are not convinced that thrombopoiesis is initiated from the same stem cell since the pattern of platelet response to irradiation appears different from that of red cell response. The multicellular stimulation seen frequently in bleeding anemia and regularly in polycythemia vera and the over-all suppression seen in aplastic anemia are supporting evidence for the multipotential capacity of stem cells. However, definite conclusions probably will have to await the morphologic and functional identification of the stem cells.

The stem cell pool has two obligations, one homeostatic and the other functional. Its homeostatic obligation is to maintain a size that is fairly constant under normal conditions but capable of adjustment to meet changing requirements. Its functional obligation is to provide differentiated blast cells for blood formation.

2. Homeostatic Obligation

In order to maintain the stem cell pool at a constant size each cell lost from the pool through differentiation has to be replaced by a new cell. Osgood (1959) has suggested that this occurs through the employment of alpha-n division while Lajtha et al. (1962) suggest the existence of homeostatic signals within the pool controlling the pool size. In Osgood's nomenclature the alpha cells are primitive multipotential cells (stem cells) which maintain somatic genetic continuity and can, if needed, undergo self-replicating alpha-2 alpha divisions. The n-cells accounting for the majority of cells are on the other hand differentiated specialized cells with a finite life span and derived from the alpha cells. In response to a stimulus an alpha cell will divide (alpha-n division) creating an n-cell and a self-replacing alpha cell. However, studies have suggested that pronormoblasts are derived from the stem cell pool by means of cellular differentiation rather than by mitotic division (Erslev, 1959). This would mean that for each blast cell created the stem cell pool would lose one cell. This loss must in some way generate a signal which causes the division of another stem cell and the replacement of the lost member. Weiss (1955) has suggested that cells within a stationary pool liberate a repressor of cellular multiplication. The loss of a cell will diminish the amount of available repressor permitting a compensatory mitotic division. A similar scheme for the stem cell pool has been proposed by Lajtha et al. (1962). He suggests that a stem cell in the process of differentiation and departure from the pool will emit a signal which "triggers off" another stem cell to division. He also suggests that the signal emitted by one differentiating cell in some way only triggers one other cell to division. If a number of cells were triggered it is claimed that gross oscillations in the size of the stem cell pool would ensue. To a certain extent Lajtha bases this hypothesis on the assumption that a similar one-for-one cellular replacement occurs in the liver after partial hepatectomy. However, since it has not been resolved whether partial hepatectomy actually is followed by a single wave of mitotic activity or by a number of waves (Harkness, 1957) of decreasing magnitude, it is possible that stem cell replacement in the bone marrow follows a sine wave with dampened oscillations.

Regardless of the exact manner by which homeostatic autoregulation is accomplished, the stem cell pool appears to be kept at a constant size. Under conditions of a temporary decrease in the demand for cells the rate of stem cell differentiation and replacement is believed to be slow. Under conditions of accelerated production of blood cells the turnover in the stem cell pool increases. If the decrease in cellular production is sustained it is likely that the stem cell pool will atrophy with a contraction of red marrow and a "compensatory" spread of yellow inactive bone marrow. On the other hand, if the hematopoietic stimulation is prolonged the stem cell pool like other organs will probably hypertrophy. This will permit the expansion of active marrow into the long bones and into extramedullary sites. Whether this "hypertrophy" is accomplished by seeding of multipotential stem cells in new sites or by activation of dormant stationary stem cells is not known.

The effect of a reduction in the size of the stem cell pool has been dealt with theoretically by Lajtha et al. (1962) and experimentally by Gurney et al. (1962) and by Alpen and Baum (1962). Radiation has been employed primarily for this purpose since radiation is assumed to have little effect on differentiated bone marrow cells but a direct damaging effect on the stem cell pool. In a recent study Alpen and Baum (1962) have shown that rats repeatedly radiated would maintain a normal blood production despite an assumed progressive decrease in the size of the stem cell pool. This was interpreted as indicating a faster turnover in the remaining stem cells. At a certain point the hematocrit would decrease abruptly, suggesting that the few remaining stem cells could not turn over fast enough to support normal cellular production. Regeneration of a damaged and contracted stem cell pool is slow and may not be accomplished at all if the damage to the cellular genetic structure by radiation or radiomimetric chemicals is irreversible or self-perpetuating. However, regeneration of normal marrow stem cells is much more prompt. In radiated mice it takes about 5–7 days for the few transplanted bone marrow stem cells to recolonize all the bone marrow spaces (Iossifides et al., 1962). Conversely an artificially expanded stem cell pool produced by multiple, massive bone marrow transfusions into normal rats does not stay expanded for very long, but returns rapidly towards a normal size (Erslev and Gallo, 1963).

Consequently it appears that an efficient homeostatic mechanism exists which maintains the functional capacity of the stem cell pool at an optimal size by adjusting both the cellular turnover and the cellular mass to its functional obligations.

3. Functional Obligation

The study of stem cell function is obviously impeded by our inability to make a positive morphological identification of these cells. Recent studies indicating that erythropoietin acts specifically on stem cells hold the promise that we may be able to deal with them dynamically before we can recognize them morphologically. Erythropoietin is a hormone presumably liberated by the kidneys and transported in the blood stream bound to an inter-alpha plasma globulin. It is found in high concentrations in plasma under conditions of anoxic, anemic, or histiotoxic anoxia and its presence precedes increased erythropoietic activity, activity which cannot be distinguished from the accelerated erythropoiesis which follows tissue anoxia (Erslev, 1960b). Since there usually is a 2–3 day delay between the onset of anoxia or the administration of erythropoietin and the appearance of reticulocytes in the peripheral blood, it has been suggested that they work at an early stage of the erythroid development (Yoffey et al., 1959). Using completely different techniques, Erslev (1959), Alpen and Cranmore (1959), and later Filmanowicz and Gurney (1961), reached the common conclusion that erythropoietin acts on stem cells. In studies with colchicine, Erslev (1959) showed that this action does not involve a mitotic division but is best explained as a differentiation of a stem cell to a pronormoblast.

In studies in vivo on hypertransfused mice Gurney and Hofstra (1963) have used erythropoietin to "quantitate" the functional size of the stem cell pool. Hypertransfusion is employed to rid the bone marrow of maturing nucleated blood cells, and erythropoietin is administered to produce a single wave of erythropoietic activity. Then Fe^{59} is administered at the peak of this wave (50–60 hours later), and finally red cell Fe^{59} utilization is measured when it has reached a plateau (72 hours later). The response of normal hypertransfused mice can then be compared to the response of a mouse which in addition has received radiation, actinomycin D, etc., and the functional damage to the stem cell compartment can be assessed. So far the results have not been too informative but the approach is interesting and merits further work. In vitro studies of stem cell function using erythropoietin have been carried out by Erslev (1962b) and by Powsner and Berman (1962). These studies reveal that erythropoietin when added to bone marrow (2000 cells/cmm) suspended in a mixture made up by one-third serum and two-thirds tissue culture medium (M.E.M.) and incubated for 21 and 45 hours at physiological tp, pH, pCO_2, and pO_2 will accelerate the over-all cellular incorporation of iron and synthesis of heme. Erythropoietin was shown not to have any *in vitro* action on reticulocytes and to have a much more pronounced action on B.M. from hypertransfused rabbits than on bone marrow from rabbits with bleeding anemia. This could be best explained if erythropoietin *in vitro* acts primarily or exclusively on stem cells. There may be more stem cells in a hyperactive bone marrow than in the hypoactive bone marrow. However, the great number of iron-incorporating nucleated red cells in the active bone marrow would make it very difficult to detect the presence of a few newly created pronormoblasts while these few cells have a relatively much greater impact on the iron uptake of the hypoplastic marrow of a hypertransfused rabbit. The *in vitro* studies have so far not clarified the biochemical action of erythropoietin on stem cells or the homeostatic regulation which maintains the size of the stem cell pool. However, it is hoped that this *in vitro* approach may supplement the *in vivo* studies and become a useful tool in the study of stem cells. It seems likely that in addition to erythropoietin, cells can be differentiated to pronormoblasts through other mechanisms. Complete nephrectomy in men (Nathan et al., 1964) and rabbits (Erslev, 1960a) will not lead to erythroid aplasia despite the fact that erythropoietin generally is assumed to be produced by the kidney. Either erythropoietin or erythropoietin-like substances can be produced by other organs or the bone marrow may have a certain base-line rate of pronormoblastic renewal not regulated by erythropoietin.

Studies of leukopoietic and thrombopoietic substances have not progressed as far as similar studies with erythropoietin. It is not known whether these substances are involved in stem cell kinetics or merely are of importance in the maturation and release of leukocytes and platelets.

The stem cell pool offers a great challenge and the clarification of its morphology, function, and autoregulation would be of the greatest importance for an understanding of cellular growth and cellular renewal.

D. ERYTHROPOIETIC SERIES (FIG. 2)

1. General Considerations

The first cell which morphologically and biochemically can be recognized as belonging to the erythroid series is the pronormoblast. This cell will go through 3–5 sequential mitotic divisions with the nucleus grad-

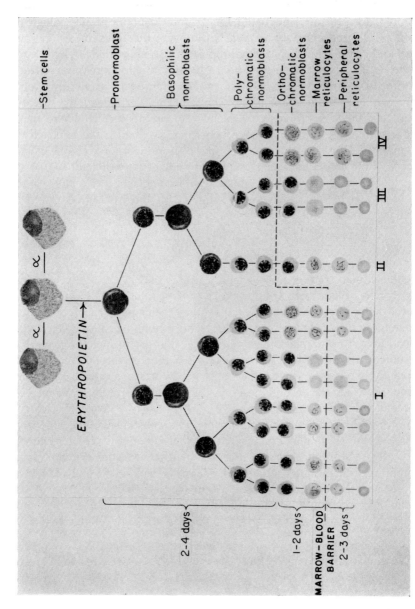

Fig. 2. Model of erythropoiesis showing bone marrow of erythrocytic precursors and their ultimate development and release into the peripheral blood as erythrocytes: (I) normal production; (II) production of macrocytes because of lack of division; (III) early loss of reticulum; (IV) late loss of reticulum.

ually becoming more pyknotic until it is incapable of further DNA or RNA synthesis and is extruded. Hemoglobin synthesis takes place concommitantly at a steadily decreasing rate until the last reticulin strand disappears and the cell becomes a mature adult red cell. Since the capacity to manufacture and carry hemoglobin is the major biochemical property which sets the erythroid cells apart from other bone marrow cells, it seems probable that the rate of maturation and multiplication of the immature red cells is closely related to the synthesis of hemoglobin (Lajtha and Oliver, 1962).

The exact process which leads to the differentiation of stem cells to pronormoblasts is not known but as discussed previously it seems to be initiated by the hormone erythropoietin. In some way erythropoietin must be capable of unmasking or de-repressing functional potentialities in the stem cells which lead to the assembly of α- and β-polypeptide chains, to the synthesis of protoporphyrin, and to the absorption of iron. By means of microspectrophotometric technique, Thorell (1947) had demonstrated hemoglobin in the earliest nucleated red cells and both Suit and co-workers (1957) and Alpen and Cranmore (1959) using Fe^{59} radioautography have shown iron uptake by even the most immature pronormoblast. From this stage on the three basic components of hemoglobin, globin, protoporphyrin, and iron are made available at independent but roughly synchronized rates. The DNA strands in the nucleus serve as a source of messenger RNA which presumably coats ribosomal particles and act as templates for the synthesis of α- and β-polypeptide chains (Burka et al., 1963). Globin synthesis probably takes place during all the phases of mitosis and will continue until the last ribosomal particle disappears from the maturing reticulocytes. Since the last template must have been synthesized prior to the extrusion of the nucleus from the orthochromatic normoblasts, the templates probably have a life span of about 3 to 4 days, the life span of the reticulocytes. In beautiful electron microscopic studies, Burka and Marks (1963) have shown that the ribosomal particles in early reticulocytes occur in clusters of five. As the cell matures and the globin synthesis decreases the clusters break up, suggesting that the active RNA template drapes itself over five ribosomal particles and strings them together. According to in vitro studies by Dintzis et al. (1958) and by Bishop and co-workers (1960), these strings will link together α- and β-polypeptide chains starting with the N-terminal of valine and proceeding at a rate of one completed chain approximately per 1.5 minutes (Burka and Marks, 1963; Dintzis et al., (1958).

Concommitantly protoporphyrin is produced by enzymes present in mitochondria. The biosynthetic sequence starting with pyridoxal-activated glycine and succinate-coenzyme A has been admirably reviewed by Harris (1963a). It will proceed until the mitochrondrial particles disappear from the maturing reticulocytes. The rate of synthesis of globin and protoporphyrin appear to run parallel although some workers feel that globin synthesis precedes protoporphyrin synthesis (Morrel *et al.*, 1958).

The third component necessary for the final assembly of hemoglobin is iron. Iron in the form of ferritin crystals can be incorporated directly from reticulum cells by means of pinocytosis (Bessis, 1959), but quantitative *in vitro* measurements of cellular iron utilization does not indicate that this process plays a significant role in the synthesis of hemoglobin (Erslev and Hughes, 1960). It has even been suggested that the pinocytosis described by Bessis actually is a "trophocytosis," an extrusion or removal of excess iron from nucleated cells (Harris, 1963b). Such a process is believed to take place in the spleen where siderocytes are "pitted" for their iron-staining granules (Crosby, 1959). The principal manner by which iron is incorporated into the nucleated red cells depends on a transferrin-cell membrane transport mechanism (Jandl, 1959). Transferrin molecules, each with two chelated ferric atoms, are specifically bound to binding sites on the cell membrane of immature erythroid cells. Here iron is unloaded and since iron enhances the affinity of transferrin for binding site (Jandl and Katz, 1961) the iron-free transferrin is replaced by fresh iron-containing transferrin. Iron released to the membrane will be bound to a new intracellular iron-binding protein (Allen and Jandl, 1960) and either be stored temporarily as ferritin or be transported directly to the site (?Golgi apparatus) where globin, protoporphyrin, and iron are assembled into hemoglobin molecules.

The cell membrane appears to lose its binding sites for transferrin at about the same time as the cell loses its ribosomal particles and its mitochondria, a timing which must be more than coincidental. It seems likely that the accumulation of hemoglobin in the red cells will influence both nuclear and cytoplasmic metabolism and possibly provide a negative feedback on synthetic activities (see below).

The synthesis of hemoglobin forms the basis for most studies on the kinetics of erythroid cells in the bone marrow. Morphologically hemoglobin is readily recognized and biochemically it is easy to isolate and crystallize. Protoporphyrin and globin can be labeled with a number of tagged amino acids, especially C^{14}- or N^{15}-glycine, and iron metabolism can be followed by using Fe^{59} and Fe^{55}. Radioactive iron is by far the most important tool since the kinetics of iron principally reflects the total synthetic activities of immature red blood cells. In addition, radioactive iron is bound irreversibly to protoporphyrin and will first be released when heme is catabolized after the death of the red cell. Two tests employing Fe^{59} have been used extensively to assess erythropoietic activity, iron turnover, and iron utilization (Pollycove and Mortimer, 1961; Bothwell and Finch, 1962). Tagged iron is cleared from the plasma at an exponential rate with 50% of the iron cleared in about 90 minutes. After the first 24 hours the slope changes and the remainder of the iron is removed at a much slower exponential rate. This second component of plasma clearing is probably caused by a feedback of iron from labile deposits on cell membranes or from intracellular ferritin. Using the initial clearance rate, the plasma iron concentration and the plasma volume, calculations can be made of the absolute amount of iron being removed from the plasma per unit time. This is referred to as the plasma iron turnover and is expressed in milligrams per 24 hours or per kilogram per hour or per 100 ml whole blood per 24 hours. In a normal adult man weighing 70 kg the plasma iron turnover is 0.0195 mg/kg/hour or 0.6 mg/100 ml of blood/hour. Assuming a normal blood volume of 5000 ml, a hematocrit of 45% and a red cell life span of 120 days, and knowing that there is 3.38 mg of iron per gram of hemoglobin (more conveniently: 1 mg of iron per 1 ml packed red blood cells) the theoretical need for iron in erythropoiesis would be about 0.01 mg/kg/hour or 0.4 mg/100 ml of blood/24 hours. The difference between the theoretical need for iron and the determined plasma iron turnover is caused by the fact that not all iron passing through the plasma is destined for the erythroid tissue. The fraction of iron which actually is incorporated into new cells can be determined by measuring the amount of radioactive iron in peripheral blood 1 to 2 weeks later. The percentage of administered radioiron accounted for in circulating red cells is called iron utilization and normally is between 70 and 90%.

Due to the existence of a labile iron pool with plasma feedback, the iron turnover and the iron utilization do not provide exact quantitative descriptions of hemoglobin synthesis. Under pathologic conditions, ineffective erythropoiesis (intramedullary destruction of nucleated red cells) (Haurani and Tocantins, 1961) and impaired iron reutilization (poor utilization of iron released from senescent red blood cells) (Haurani et al., 1963) make studies of iron metabolism even less quantitative. However, if these shortcoming are kept in mind, the tests are valuable adjuncts to our more routine kinetic measurements of erythroid activity: red cell count, reticulocyte count, and bone marrow differential count.

2. Division and Maturation Pool (Table I)

Pronormoblasts, basophilic normoblasts, and polychromatic normoblasts are capable of both multiplication and hemoglobin synthesis. The morphologic appearance of these cells depend both on cytoplasmic and nuclear maturity and on the phase of the mitotic cycle. The large, immature cell we usually recognize as a typical pronormoblast may actually be more mature than some smaller basophilic normoblasts because, as pointed out by Lajtha and Oliver (1962), it may be a premitotic cell with twice its regular complement of DNA.

The total mass of dividing nucleated red blood cells has been measured or rather estimated by a number of workers. Donohue et al. (1958) using Fe^{59} and bone marrow differential counts conclude that human bone

TABLE I

ERYTHROPOIETIC SERIES SIZE AND COMPARISON OF BONE
MARROW TIME PARAMETERS

Pool	Cell types	Number of cells $\times 10^9$ per kilogram body weight[a]	Generation time[b] (days)	Turnover time[b] (days)
Division and maturation pool	Pronormoblast	0.10	0.83	—
	Basophilic normoblast	0.48	0.83	—
	Polychromatophilic normoblast	1.47	1.25	—
	Total	2.05	—	—
Maturation pool	Orthochromic normoblast	2.95	—	2.07
	Bone marrow reticulocyte	5.00	—	1.67
	Blood reticulocyte	3.30	—	1–3
	Total	11.25	—	—
Functional pool	Mature red cells	330	—	120

[a]Data obtained from Donohue et al. (1958).
[b]Data obtained from Lajtha and Oliver (1960).

marrow contains about 5×10^9 nucleated red cells per kilogram body weight. How many of these are engaged in multiplication is difficult to assess. Lajtha and Oliver (1962) basing his estimate on theoretic consideration suggest that 45% of the cells or 2.25×10^9 cells per kilogram are capable of division while Reizenstein (1962) basing his estimate on observations gathered by Albritton (1955) suggests that it is 70% of the cells or 3.5×10^9 cells per kilogram body weight.

The generation times of the three maturation states within this compartment are usually calculated on the assumption that the divisions are heteromorphogenic, i.e., that each stage corresponds to one mitotic cycle.

Generation times of about 20 hours for each stage have been reported (Lajtha and Oliver, 1960) but other studies suggest a uniform generation time of about 12 hours (Stohlman, 1962). After reviewing the literature on the generation time for red cell precursors, Reizenstein (1962) recently concluded that the generation time for pronormoblasts was 2.4 hours, for basophilic normoblasts, 11.3 hours, and for polychromatic normoblasts, 28 hours. These unorthodox values are compatible with recent *in vitro* studies of bone marrow kinetics, but they need experimental confirmation. Estimation of the total transit time through the division and maturation compartment consequently ranges from about 60 hours to about 42 hours. Some cells undoubtedly go rapidly through the compartment with only few divisions. Both Suit *et al.* (1957) and Alpen and Cranmore (1959) have reported that 24 hours after the injection of Fe^{59} a few reticulocytes emerge with such a heavy labeling that they must have been derived almost directly from pronormoblasts without intervening divisions. Other cells may die in the bone marrow before final maturation in so-called ineffective erythropoiesis (Stohlman, 1962). Such intramedullary loss plays an important role under certain pathologic conditions but whether it actually takes place in the normal bone marrow has not been settled.

It has been postulated that there is an intricate balance between hemoglobin synthesis and nuclear ability to synthesize DNA and divide. According to Lajtha and Oliver (1962) a certain critical concentration of hemoglobin will initiate "nuclear pyknosis" and stop further cellular multiplication. If the hemoglobin synthesis is impaired as in iron deficiency more divisions will be possible before the critical MCHC (mean corpuscular hemoglobin concentration) has been attained resulting in microcytosis. On the other hand, if the hemoglobin synthesis is accelerated fewer divisions will be possible resulting in an early release of large cells (Stohlman *et al.*, 1963). The latter conclusion is partly based on the concept that erythropoietin accelerates hemoglobin synthesis, a concept which, however, is not generally accepted.

Studies by Erslev (1959), by Alpen and Cranmore (1959), and by Pollycove and Mortimer (1961) suggest strongly that the maturation and multiplication of nucleated red cells proceed at fixed rates not influenced by any physiological controlling mechanisms. The emergence of reticulocytes in response to an anoxic stimulus in rabbits was found not to be influenced by a subsequent hyperoxic suppression. The intermitotic time of nucleated cells was found to be the same in normal and in anemic dogs and calculation of mean effective erythron hemoglobinization time in various blood loss anemias of man was found to be constant. The lack of effect *in vitro* of erythropoietin on reticulocytes and nucleated red cells (Erslev, 1964b) also supports the contention that the metabolism of these cells is not physiologically adjusted to the peripheral demands for cells. These studies have provided much of the experimental basis for the now generally accepted hypothesis that erythropoietin acts primarily on stem cells.

In rats, however, erythropoietin appears also to influence the speed of maturation and the number of mitotic divisions of nucleated red blood cells. Linman and Bethell (1962) have repeatedly claimed that erythropoietin is made up by two substances: a heat-labile and ether-insoluble substance that regulates stem cell differentiation, and a heat-stable and ether-soluble substance that adjusts the speed of hemoglobin synthesis. More convincing and reproducible is the evidence presented by Stohlman (1961a), Gallagher and Lange (1962), Nagai (1962), and Nakao et al. (1962) showing that erythropoietin or acute anoxia will lead to the early release of large reticulocytes. Stohlman (1961b) has also shown that in rats these early macrocytes have a short life span and are replaced rapidly by successive crops of more normal cells. Although macrocytes with heavy reticulum are seen characteristically in humans after acute bleeding, there is no evidence that these cells are abnormal or have a short life span (Coleman et al., 1953). Rather than indicating a direct effect of erythropoietin on the rate of hemoglobin synthesis, it is conceivable that an acute erythropoietic stimulus will lead to increased growth pressure and local metabolic deficiencies resulting temporarily in the early release of defective, unfinished cells. It is difficult to understand that the early release of a few imperfect cells can be a useful adjunct to the many efficient cardiovascular measures used to provide oxygen to the tissues under conditions of acute anoxic or hypoxic anoxias, and that a physiological hormone should have such an effect.

The multiplication and maturation of nucleated red blood cells is dependent on an adequate supply of metabolic building substances and coenzymes but these are not involved in the physiological regulation of red cell production. Several hormones, specifically cortisone (Wintrobe et al., 1951), thyroxin (Waldman et al., 1962), and testosterone (Gardner and Pringle, 1961), have been shown to have an effect on the rate of red cell production. However, Gordon (1954) considers them modifying substances rather than primary regulators. Testosterone is a powerful erythropoietic substance in vivo but in vitro it merely increases the rate of iron incorporation and heme synthesis of immature red cells (Erslev, 1962). Recent studies have revived an old suggestion that the breakdown products of red cells, heme and protoporphyrin derivatives influence the rate of red cell production (Brown et al., 1963; Sanchez et al., 1963).

3. Maturation Pool

The maturation compartment includes the orthochromatic normoblasts and the intra- and extramedullary reticulocytes. The number of orthochromatic normoblasts is estimated between 1.5 and 2.75 $\times$ 10⁹ cells per kilogram body weight (Donohue et al., 1958; Reizenstein, 1962; Lajtha and Oliver, 1962). Marrow reticulocytes are about 5 $\times$ 10⁹ cells per kilogram (the same as the total number of nucleated red blood cells) and the circulating reticulocytes are about 3.3 $\times$ 10⁹ cells per kilogram (Donohue et al., 1958). The life span of circulating reticulocytes is between 1 and 3 days (Seip, 1953).

In view of a normal reticulocyte count of about 1% and a red cell life span of 120 days it is obvious that a number of red cells must emerge fully matured from the bone marrow. The reticulocyte count consequently depends on the release mechanism of cells from the bone marrow cavity. Two theories are usually cited to explain the control of this release. One is the growth pressure theory (Lamerton et al., 1959) and the other is the stickiness theory (Jandl, 1960). According to the first theory reticulocytes are kept inside the rigid bone marrow cavity until pressure from new, space-occupying nucleated red cells squeeze the more mature elements into circulating blood. Accelerated red cell production will not only increase the number of reticulocytes but also, because of increased growth pressure, release early reticulocytes (Heilmeyer's type 0, 1, and 2). In phenylhydrazine-induced hemolytic anemia the bone marrow has been shown to be completely depleted of marrow reticulocytes (Finch et al., 1959). On the other hand, decreased erythropoiesis is supposed to cause a decreased growth pressure and late release of reticulocytes. The second theory is based on the known clumping of nucleated red cells and reticulocytes. It has been suggested that the stickiness is caused by a protein coat of transferrin delivering iron to the cells (Jandl, 1960). As the cells mature the stickiness (?transferrin) decreases and the cells are ready to be washed out into the circulating blood. If reticulocytes are released too early they may impart a positive Coomb's test to blood (Sutherland et al., 1963). Such sticky reticulocytes may also be filtered out by the spleen and held there until they are fully matured.

These considerations of the release mechanism indicates the inherent difficulties in using the reticulocyte count as an absolute measure of red cell production. The same holds true for the 24 hour Fe⁵⁹ utilization test which depends both on the total mass of immature red cells and on the early or late release of reticulocytes from the bone marrow. However, both reticulocyte counts and 24 hour Fe⁵⁹ utilization are useful tests for a change in the rate of red cell production and their ease and convenience render them extremely valuable.

4. Functional Pool

The red cell mass consists of about 330×10^9 red cells per kilogram body weight, each with a life span of about 120 days. Red cell mass and red cell life span can be measured by a number of techniques but tagging with Cr^{51} is the easiest and most popular method. Chromate iron penetrates the red cell membrane in vitro and tags the β chain of the globin molecule. Tagging is promptly terminated by any reducing agent which changes the chromate ion into the nonpenetrable chromic ion. The rate of elution is about 1% a day but since the label is not reutilized, correction can easily be made depending on accurate assessment of red cell life span and red cell mass (Mollison and Veall, 1955).

As the red cells grow older the enzymatic dehydrogenase activity decreases and the production of ATP and reduced TPN and DPN fall off (Prankerd, 1961). ATP is necessary to maintain migration of sodium and potassium across the cell membrane and lack of ATP will decrease sodium pump activity and lead to osmotic swelling. The reduced nucleotides are necessary for maintaining heme-iron and the sulfhydryl groups of globin and cell membrane in a reduced state and their deficiency will lead to methemoglobin production, globin denaturation, Heinz bodies, and membrane weakening (Jandl et al., 1960; Jacob and Jandl, 1962). The aged cell will finally be taken up by the reticuloendothelial cells and catabolized, with iron reutilized for heme synthesis, with protoporphyrin excreted as bilirubin and globin returned to the amino acid pool.

The functional obligations of circulating red blood cells are undoubtedly involved in maintaining their number at a constant level. Red cells are created almost exclusively for the purpose of carrying oxygen from the lungs to the tissues. In order to provide the tissue with an optimal amount of oxygen for their metabolic activities, the total number of circulating red cells has to be adjusted both to the supply of oxygen in the lungs and to the demand for oxygen in the tissues. Such adjustments must be related to the adequacy of the oxygen transport and it seems most likely that tissue oxygen tension generates signals which regulate the rate of red cell production and thereby the number of circulating cells (Erslev, 1960b). Since a change in the rate of red cell production will tend to correct the alteration in tissue tension of oxygen which triggered the signals, we have the elements of a self-regulating feedback circuit operating between the tissues and the bone marrow. This circuit is obviously mediated in one direction by hemoglobin-bound oxygen. Recent studies have indicated strongly that it is mediated in the opposite direction by an erythropoietic hormone, the so-called erythropoietin.

The existence of this hormone had been suspected for many years, but it was not until 1950 that convincing experimental evidence for its existence was presented. In that year, Reissman (1950) demonstrated an accelerated erythropoietic activity in the bone marrow of the normal, well oxygenated parabiotic partner of a rat exposed to low atmospheric oxygen tension. This study suggested strongly the existence of a humoral erythropoietic substance and few years later Erslev (1953) demonstrated and partly isolated this substance, subsequently named erythropoietin. In 1955 Erslev suggested that the tissue tension of oxygen regulates the production of this hormone. This suggestion was later amplified by Jacobson et al. (1957), who showed that erythropoietin was released both when the supply of oxygen to the tissues was decreased and when the demand for oxygen was increased (thyroid medication or dinitrophenol). Evidence for a decreased release of erythropoietin under conditions of an increased supply of oxygen to the tissues (transfusion polycythemia or high ambient pO_2) or of a decreased demand (starvation or hypophysectomy) is indirect but quite convincing. Our present bioassay is too crude to measure subnormal values of erythropoietin but the end organ, the bone marrow, responds under these conditions as if the erythropoietin level was low.

Since the tissues have varying rates of oxidative metabolism and varying blood supply, they obviously must have varying tissue tensions of oxygen. Recent studies have suggested that it may not be the over-all tissue tension of oxygen but the tissue tension in one area, the kidney, which is of importance. In 1957 Jacobson and co-workers (1957) reported that nephrectomized rats do not respond to anoxia by releasing erythropoietin while ureter-ligated, equally uremic rats respond in a nearly normal manner. Many studies since then have confirmed and expanded this observation and it is generally accepted that the kidney releases erythropoietin in response to renal hypoxia. The juxtaglomerular apparatus has been implicated as the cellular source (Goldfarb and Tobias, 1963), but the evidence is still not quite convincing. It seems also almost certain that erythropoietin or erythropoietin-like material is released in small amounts from other tissues since nephrectomy in rabbits and man does not abolish red cell production completely (Nathan et al., 1964; Erslev, 1960a).

Erythropoietin is a relatively heat-stable, nondializable compound migrating with the mucoglycoprotein fraction in the inter-α-globulin region (Stohlman, 1962). It contains sialic acid and is inactivated by proteolytic enzymes. Using physicochemical methods, Borsook (1959) has estimated its molecular weight to be about 29,000 and neutron inactivation by Rosse et al. (1963) has suggested a weight of about 28,000.

So far no adequate biochemical or immunologic test for erythropoietin

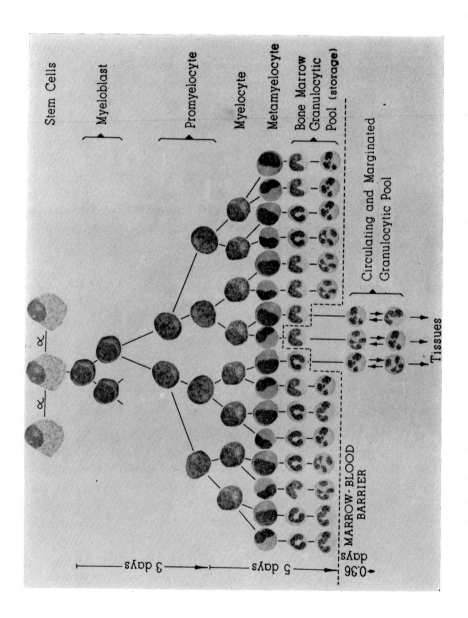

has been devised and its measurement depends on *in vivo* bioassay. A large number of bioassays have been proposed and used giving comparable but extremely crude data (Erslev, 1964a). At present the most important bioassays are in rats and mice rendered polycythemic. The polycythemia will suppress endogenous erythropoietin production, making it possible to recognize even small concentrations of erythropoietin in the test material. The 24 hour Fe^{59} utilization is generally used as the most convenient test for erythropoietic activity, although reticulocyte counts would be just as reliable.

In addition to maintaining the tissue tension of oxygen, it has been claimed that the circulating red cells produce other physical or mechanical consequences that provide a regulatory feedback to the bone marrow. The effects of viscosity have been suggested and, as mentioned above, the breakdown products of heme are believed to have some erythropoietic properties (Brown *et al.*, 1963).

E. MYELOPOIETIC SERIES (FIG. 3)

1. General Considerations

Of the several proliferation schemes for myelopoiesis, Osgood's alpha-*n* concept of cell division best fits the data of many investigators (Japa, 1942; Killmann *et al.*, 1962; Patt and Maloney, 1959; Cronkite *et al.*, 1960), although as pointed out by Lajtha (1962) no such division has ever been observed. In this scheme the stem cell divides and produces a myeloblast and another stem cell replaces itself. The myeloblast divides to produce two daughter cells which also divide (*n-2n* division) and yield four promyelocytes. The next two divisions produce sixteen cells (myelocytes) and a final division of these produce thirty-two cells (metamyelocytes) which are incapable of further division. This flow of cells agrees with the data of Killmann *et al.* (1962) who showed that the relative numbers of granulocytes in the marrow are 1 : 4 : 16 : 36 (myeloblast: promyelocyte: myelocytes: nondividing granulocytes). A serious objection to this scheme is that following irradiation the reduplication of a nonduplicating structure in the stem cell, "the *n* cell" results from the alpha-*n* division. Another objection raised by Brooke and Osgood (1959) was that chronic myelogenous leukemic leukocytes continued to grow in culture for extended periods of time. If myeloblasts, promyelocytes, and myelocytes were only capable of (*n-2n*) divisions, then no such apparent prolonga-

Fig. 3. Model of granulopoiesis showing the relationship between the bone marrow, the circulating granulocytic pool, the marginated granulocytic pool, and the tissues.

tion should take place. Osgood (1963b) has suggested that the myelocyte may be an alpha cell to explain these observations.

Glycolytic metabolism in leukocytes is predominantly aerobic, with oxygen consumption, glucose utilization, and lactic acid production significantly higher in normal mature leukocytes than in leukemic leukocytes. Glycogen is present in the neutrophilic, eosinophilic, and possibly the basophilic leukocyte but is apparently extremely low or absent in lymphocytes and monocytes (Astaldi *et al.*, 1952). Leukocytes possess a wide variety of enzymes: alkaline phosphatase, β-glucuronidase, nuclease, proteolytic enzymes, peptidase, lipase, esterase, amylase, adenosinase, catalase, acid phosphatase, cathepsin, arginase, glyoxalase, and lysozyme. Leukocyte alkaline phosphatase is capable of hydrolyzing phosphorus from a variety of phosphomonoesters. This enzyme has been shown to be much lower than normal in neutrophils of paroxysmal nocturnal hemoglobinuria and chronic myelogenous leukemia (Meislin *et al.*, 1959). Eosinophils and, to a lesser extent, basophils are rich in arylsulfatase. Hyaluronic acid ester and peroxidase are found in neutrophilic granules. Nucleotidase, an acid phosphatase, is ten times greater in granulocytic cells than in lymphocytes. Neutrophils may contain growth-activating substances (trephones) which are claimed to aid in blood coagulation. β-Glucuronidase has been demonstrated in neutrophils and eosinophils, but only a small amount appears in lymphocytes (Valentine, 1960). The sulfhydryl content of leukocytes is several times greater than in erythrocytes (Green and Martin, 1955). Half of the normal blood histamine is located in the basophils, one-third in the eosinophils, and approximately one-sixth in the neutrophils (Graham *et al.*, 1955). Lymphocytes, monocytes, erythrocytes, and platelets contain practically none. The specific granules of neutrophils appear to contain phospholipids, while the granules of the eosinophils contain protein surrounded by phospholipids, other lipid substances, deoxyribonucleic acid, arginine, and questionably, phosphorus, iron, tyrosine, and glycogen. The granules of basophils contain an acid substance closely resembling herparin which is bound by histamine.

Of great interest is the recent demonstration by Sbarra and Karnovsky (1959) that active glycolysis is necessary for phagocytosis. This finding and the studies of Cohn and Hirsch (1960a,b; Hirsch and Cohn, 1960), in which granule lysis and specific alterations in activity and distribution of enzymes were shown to follow phagocytosis, are starting to correlate much information on leukocyte metabolism and physiology. More recently Zucker-Franklin and Hirsch (1963) have shown by electron microscopy that phagocytosis takes place by discharge of the specific granules into phagocytic vacuoles within the cell's cytoplasm.

Leukocytes can be labeled by tagging a metabolic building block such as thymidine or formate (uniform age label) or by tagging a substance such as esterase not involved in cellular metabolism (all age label). Since tritiated thymidine is a DNA precursor, it is incorporated into all cells synthesizing DNA. This cellular incorporation varies with the cell type, the synthesis period, and the turnover time. The rate of triitiated thymidine incorporation decreases as the cell matures. After the bone marrow cells have been released to the peripheral blood, only a small number of monocytes (or lymphocytes) are capable of thymidine incorporation. Since formate is a simple molecule and serves as a precursor for specific positions in the purine ring, C^{14}-formate has been extremely valuable in tagging cells. In man, C^{14}-formate labels the purines in DNA and RNA, thymine in DNA, and to a lesser degree, the other pyrimidines in both RNA and DNA. Utilization of this compound tags cells which are engaged in both RNA and DNA synthesis. If the appropriate C^{14}-labeled precursors are utilized, it is possible to label efficiently and independently all four nitrogen bases of DNA in a given cell population. Since uridine is a nitrogenous base of only RNA, tritiated amounts of this compound may be utilized as an RNA percursor in cell labeling. One difficulty with this substance is the fact that methylation of the C-5 position will result in thymidine production and incorporation into DNA. Recent evidence suggests that leukemic cells contain a large amount of an enzyme capable of this conversion (Huennekens et al., 1963). Another problem is reutilization of labeled DNA. This phenomenon was first recognized recently, but may be of importance in the evaluation of data obtained with tritiated thymidine (Craddock, 1963). The all-age label most utilized is diisopropylfluorophosphate, which binds irreversibly with certain esterases in leukocytes and platelets. It has been utilized with great success in estimating the life span of the granulocyte.

2. Division and Maturation Pool (Table II)

The total marrow granulocytic pool has been estimated as 12.6×10^9 cells per kilogram (Donohue et al., 1958). Of this number, approximately 5.4×10^9 cells per kilogram are involved in cellular division and DNA synthesis. Morphologically, this includes all the cells in the marrow of granulocytic origin through the myelocyte. Table II demonstrates the comparison of the bone marrow time parameters (Cronkite et al., 1960b).

If the technique of autoradiography is employed after the intravenous injection of tritiated thymidine and serial bone marrow determinations are performed, much information concerning the division and maturation pool can be obtained. In one minute, label is detectable in granulocytic precursors. Groups of cells called hemohistioblasts, hemocytoblasts, reticulum cells, and myeloblasts had labeling indices from 35–93%. Promyelocytes had a labeling index of 76%, and myelocytes 68%. The percentage of labeled cells appeared to be constant for the first 3 to 5 days, but the grain count seemed to decrease in an exponential fashion. As the grain count approaches background, a second component of the curve appears, partly because whole grains are counted and the labeled population diminishes in size. From this experimental data, estimates of generation times for the cells in this compartment can be postulated. The generation time for myeloblasts is approximately 1.3 days. Promyelocytes give data with a great deal of scatter and only range values for generation times of somewhere between 1 and 2.5 days can be estimated. The large myelocytes start with 70% labeling and the grain counts diminish with a half-life of about 2.25 days. Small myelocytes start with a labeling index of approximately 20% which reaches a peak of 72% at the rate of 3.2% per

TABLE II

Myelopoietic Series Size and Comparison of Bone Marrow Time Parameters

Pool	Cell types	Number of cells $\times 10^9$ per kilogram body weight[a]	Generation time[b] (days)	Turnover time[b] (days)
Division and maturation pool	Myeloblast	—	1.32	—
	promyelocyte	2.6	1.0–2.5	—
	Myelocyte	—	2.33	—
	Total	2.6	—	—
Maturation pool	Metamyelocyte	2.7	—	0.92
	Bands	3.6	—	1.28
	Total	6.3	—	—
Bone marrow storage	Polymorphonuclear (bone marrow)	2.5	—	1.51
Functional pool	Circulating polymorphonuclear	0.31	—	0.4
	Marginated polymorphonuclear	0.35	—	—
	Intravascular polymorphonuclear	0.66	—	—
	Circulating eosinophils	0.0035–0.018	—	—
	Circulating basophils	0.0011–0.004	—	—

[a]Data obtained from Donohue *et al.* (1958).
[b]Data obtained from Cronkite *et al.* (1960).

hour. The grain count diminishes after maximum labeling with a half-life of 2.4 days. As the cells proceed through the compartment certain factors must operate that will regulate their release and division. According to Osgood (1958), release of cells may be controlled by absence of a short-range inhibitor of migration through the sinus wall produced by the most mature cell of the series which fails to return. The regulation of arithmetic and logarithmic division would be the production by the maturing cell of a series of inhibitors of each division at such a rate as to maintain an equilibrium concentration of this substance in the blood stream. Possibly, the secretory particles of Richter carry inhibitors also, secondary regulators of cell division represented by the various hormones, Menkin's factors, and regulators of the gradient factor, nutrient concentration, and blood flow. Craddock (1957) has postulated an inhibitor in mature granulocytes which would be consistent with "feedback" control system of hematopoiesis. More recently Perry and Marsh (1963) utilizing tritiated thymidine in vitro demonstrated that possibly the inhibitor of DNA synthesis was thymidine phosphorylase. Their studies showed that normal leukocytes contained more of this enzyme than leukemic leukocytes. Shen and Hoshino (1961) have postulated a stimulating substance which they referred to as neutropoietin. This substance was noted to be present in the plasma of rats following triamcionlone ingestion. The substance has a stimulatory effect on the blood neutrophils.

3. Maturation Pool

The maturation pool which includes the metamyelocytes and band forms accounts for a total of 6.3×10^9 cells per kilogram. With intravenous injection of tritiated thymidine and evaluation of the bone marrow by autoradiography, the metamyelocytes, bands, and neutrophils are not labeled initially. After 3 hours grains appeared in the metamyelocytes, after 12 hours in the bands, after 24 to 36 hours in the neutrophils. The leukocyte count in the peripheral blood has a regulatory effect on the release of cells from the bone marrow (Steinberg, 1958). Recently, experiments by Gordon and co-workers (Gordon, 1959; Gordon et al., 1959; Gordon et al., 1960), have demonstrated the existence of a circulating leukocytosis-inducing factor (LIF). The evidence for such a factor is mainly derived from leukocyte behavior in parabiosed rats when one partner is subjected to repeated leukocytophoresis plasma (LAP plasma) and on observations on the influence of LAP plasma on the leukocyte discharge from isolated perfused hind legs of rats. From these studies it appears that the action of LIF appears to be exerted directly on the bone marrow, which results in a rapid release of mature granulocytes and lymphocytes into the circulation. The reason for LIF appearing after repeated LAP plasma has been explained by the fact that the adult non-proliferative members of a cell lineage act to inhibit proliferation of stem elements of that series (Osgood, 1955; Rose, 1955; Weiss, 1954). Another explanation envisages an inherent ability of the adult leukocyte to utilize circulating LIF and on destruction of leukocytes the LIF would accumulate. The leukocytosis-inducing factor is heat-labile and resistant to freezing. Leukocytophoresis of plasma shows an accentuation of the α-globulin band on paper electrophoresis. Komiya and Katsunuma (1960) have produced samples of "neutropoietin" by injecting rabbits with typhoid vaccine. The material appears to be polypeptidic in nature (Komiya et al., 1959).

The bone marrow storage pool for leukocytes contains approximately 2.5×10^9 cells per kilogram, which are mature polymorphonuclear neutrophils. If one further utilizes the marrow leukocyte mass data of Donohue and co-workers (1958), the marrow granulocyte reserve for a 70 kg man would be 8.8×10^9 cells per kilogram, a value thirty times the circulating granulocyte mass, but only fifteen times the total intravascular mass of granulocytes. From the marrow reserve value and the 5 day lag between DNA labeling of human granulocytes in marrow and their appearance in blood, one can estimate the daily turnover of cells through the blood to be approximately (1.7×10^9 cells per kilogram per day in a 70 kg man). This storage pool can be effected by the administration of epinephrine (Gabrilove et al., 1949) or by exercise (Karvonen and Kunnas, 1953). With these measures the cells are rapidly released from the storage pool, but the total granulocyte pool is unchanged. The administration of endotoxin (Athens et al., 1959) has been shown to cause a slight rise in granulocytes in the blood after 90 minutes with a shift of many leukocytes to the marginated pool. The marginated pool includes the granulocytes that line vessel walls, and are not in active circulation. Later (after 5 hours) there is a marked increase in the total granulocytic pool due to an outpouring of cells from the storage pool of the bone marrow. Steroids also produce an increase in the size of the total granulocyte pool for the same reason.

4. Functional Pool

The functional granulocytic pool contains approximately 0.3 cells $\times 10^9$ per kilogram. By utilizing diiosopropylfluorophosphate (DFP[32]), it has been shown that two pools of granulocytes exist in blood: one, the circulating granulocytic pool, appears to be in dynamic equilibrium with the other, the marginated granulocyte pool (Athens et al., 1959). These are almost equal in size: $0.31 \pm 0.12 \times 10^9$ cells per kilogram body weight for the circulating pool and $0.35 \pm 0.16 \times 10^9$ cells per kilogram body weight for the marginated pool. By DFP[32]-labeling of leukocytes *in vitro* and returning them to their donor, it is possible to make an estimate of the blood transit time. The $T_{\frac{1}{2}}$ for this technique is 6.6 hours. From this data and other studies (Craddock *et al.*, 1960a,b) the granulocytes spend an average time of 9 hours in the circulation. Their egress from the circulation is probably one of random selection. One point which has stimulated much debate is whether cells return to the intravascular compartment after departure. Conclusive evidence to rule out some return from tissues is not available, but a number of observations cast doubt on the possibility of great numbers re-entering. The extrusion and disintegration of neutrophils at sites of infection are obvious, but the mechanism of their ultimate fate in the normal individual is not clear. The lungs, liver, and spleen have been incriminated as graveyards for granulocytes. Other tissues may also serve as a graveyard for the granulocyte. One point of argument against this, however, is the fact that pathologists have not seen the tissues infiltrated with granulocytes. Osgood (1963a) maintains that granulocytes are present in the tissue; but, due to the large bulk of tissue, their numbers appear insignificant.

5. *Eosinophil*

The eosinophil is produced in the bone marrow, travels via the blood to the tissue, performs its function, and is destroyed or extruded. Bryant and Kelly (1958) have shown in the mouse that eosinophils labeled with tritiated thymidine move through the marrow and into the circulating granulocytic pool with a similar pattern, but more rapidly than neutrophils. Administration of steroids cause the circulating eosinophils to decrease, but little change occurs in the bone marrow eosinophil count to account for this decline. Studies attempting to show redistribution of eosinophils with sequestration in organs to explain this fact have not been convincing (Gordon, 1955). Most studies seem to indicate that there is an increased destruction of eosinophils when exposed to steroids (Gordon, 1955). However, until suitable methods for measuring eosinophil turnover are developed, this interpretation remains in some doubt. Because of their greater abundance in tissue fluid than blood, an important role in detoxification has been attributed to eosinophils (Vaughan, 1953). They increase in number following injection of foreign protein and during decomposition of body protein. Also, because of the association of eosinophilia with clinical allergy and parasitic infestation, many workers postulate that the eosinophil is intimately involved in the immune responses of the body. Speirs (1955, 1958) and Litt (1960a,b, 1961) have demonstrated that eosinophils accumulate at injection sites of antigens, which is a point in favor of the above theory. Litt (1960b) has proposed that the eosinophilic response to repeated injections of antigen involves the antigen-antibody reaction, whereas the eosinophilic response to asbestos, heparin, and histamine or to a single injection of antigen may be nonspecific, resulting from tissue destruction. The eosinophilotactic material, according to Litt (1960b), is a large molecule (nondialyzable), stable to mild heating and precipitable by trichloroacetic acid. The substance is not histamine since it is dialyzable and, since antihistaminics did not block the reaction.

6. Basophil

The kinetics or proliferation of the basophilic series is largely unknown. There is general agreement that the basophil is formed in the marrow, but much disagreement as to whether the blood basophil and tissue mast cell are the same cell in different sites or are cells with similar properties but of different origin. The presence of heparin (Amann, 1961; Riley, 1954) and histamine (Valentine et al., 1955) in the two cells emphasize the similarities but do not solve the problem of relationship. The basophil stores histamine and releases this substance as well as heparin when degranulation occurs. The degranulation may be related to certain antigen-antibody interactions, both in vitro and in vivo as demonstrated by Shelley and Juhlin (Juhlin and Shelley, 1961; Shelley and Juhlin, 1962), Riley (1959), Humphrey and Mota (1959) and Archer (1960).

F. Thrombopoietic Series (Fig. 4)

1. General Considerations

In 1906, Wright (1910) reported that platelets originate from the fragmentation of megakaryocyte cytoplasm. Cytochemical studies (Storti et al., 1953; Vanquez and Lewis, 1960), phase and electron microscopy, and time-lapse photography (Yamada, 1957; Thiery and Bessis, 1956; Albrecht, 1957; Yeroshkina, 1958) have supported this concept. Humphrey (1955), utilizing the Coons fluorescent antibody technique, showed that megakaryocytes share some antigenic properties with platelets. More recently, Kinosita et al. (1957), utilizing a window technique in the femurs of rabbits, photographed in vitro platelet formation from megakaryocytes. Bessis and Burstein (1956), by means of microcinematography of bone marrow cultures in humans, showed that the nucleus of the megakaryocyte becomes pyknotic and that Wright's figures develop from the cytoplasm spreading out like the tentacles of an octopus. The pseudopodia become thinner, eventually filiform, and are broken off by contractions of the filaments and carried away as platelets by the blood stream. By utilizing cytochemistry, ultraviolet microspectrophotometry and autoradiography, information has been obtained on the chemistry and kinetics of thrombopoiesis (Whitby and Britton, 1963). Megakaryocytes may possess coarse masses which are probably composed of glycogen. These are visible at the periphery of megakaryocytes actively engaged in platelet formation. Free platelets show a strong granular posi-

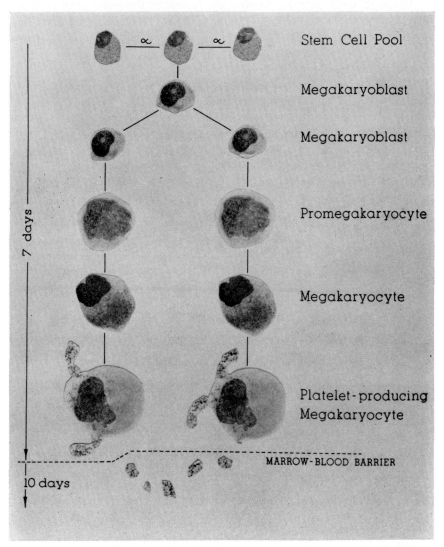

Fig. 4. Model of thrombopoiesis showing the relationship between the megakaryocyte and platelet production.

tivity for glycogen. Megakaryocytes, when examined by cytochemical techniques for lipids, show a diffuse background staining with numerous small granules dispersed throughout the cytoplasm and over the nucleus. Platelets are usually negative for lipids, but positive for phospholipids. Megakaryocytes are devoid of peroxidase and cytochrome oxidase, but contain acetyl cholinesterase, also present in other bone marrow cells.

Although most megakaryocytes are found in the bone marrow, they are also normally found in the lungs. It had been thought that lung megakaryocytes were incapable of platelet production, since Fidlar and Waters (1941) were unable to obtain satisfactory evidence of platelet formation in the lungs. Howell and Donahue (1937) have challenged this view because of the observations that the platelet count is higher in arterial blood, that fewer platelets are found in the bone marrow than in the lungs, that megakaryocytes in the lungs appear to be producing platelets and that perfusion of the bone marrow yields few platelets while lung perfusion produces many platelets. However, it is generally assumed that platelet production during adult life occurs chiefly in the bone marrow and is of megakaryocytic origin.

2. Division and Maturation Pool (Table III)

The kinetics of the megakaryocytic series have only recently received much attention and investigation into this area is still rudimentary. The megakaryoblast, arising either from the stem cell pool or from another megakaryoblast, measures about 30 μ and has a hyalin and intensely basophilic cytoplasm and a nucleus which is trapizoidal or oval. The chromatin network is quite coarse for a young cell and sometimes has a

TABLE III

MEGAKARYOCYTIC AND THROMBOPOIETIC SERIES SIZE AND TIME PARAMETERS

Pool	Cell types	Number of cells $\times 10^9$ per kilogram body weight	Generation time (days)	Turnover time (days)
Division and maturation pool	Megakaryoblast	0.00072		—
	Promegakaryocyte	0.0011		—
	Total	0.00182	7	—
Maturation pool	Megakaryocyte	0.0054		—
Functional pool	Thrombocyte	17.5	—	10

reticular appearance with particularly thick meshes. It has been shown to contain the diploid chromosome complement of the species (Kinosita *et al.*, 1961). Its nuclear division may lead to the formation of two separate megakaryoblasts or to a single promegakaryocyte. In the latter situation a diploid megakaryoblast undergoes endomitotic divisions and the nucleus may be divided into two, four, or more parts. Consequently, this cell contains an increased amount of DNA (polyploidy). The experimental evidence for this sequence is provided by the work of Feinendegen *et al.* (1962), who demonstrated that immature megakaryocytes take up more tritiated thymidine than other bone marrow cells. They also showed that nuclear lobulation was not completed by the end of DNA synthesis. The numerical dimensions of the megakaryocyte pool cannot be accurately determined at the present time, even if one assumes that the majority of these cells are in the marrow cavity. Baserga (1948) has estimated that the average man has 0.54×10^7 cells per kilogram or a total of 3.78×10^8 megakaryocytes for a 70 kg man. With this estimate and Bessis' (1956a) figures for percentage of megakaryoblasts (10%), promegakaryocytes (15%) and megakaryocytes (75%), certain approximations can be made. If the total number of cells for the entire series is 0.72×10^7 per kilogram or 5.04×10^8 cells for a 70 kg man, then megakaryoblasts and promegakaryocytes would account for 0.072×10^7 per kilogram and 0.11×10^7 per kilogram, respectively.

Information concerning the transit time of the various marrow megakaryocytic components is sparse. Feinendegen *et al.* (1962, utilizing female Sprague-Dawley rats injected with tritiated thymidine, showed that the median transit times were 6–7 hours, 8–9 hours, and 25 hours for megakaryoblasts, promegakaryocytes, and megakaryocytes, respectively. They also showed that the recognizable megakaryocytic elements originate from unrecognized precursors which continuously synthesized DNA for a period of at least 1 to 3 days prior to maturation into recognizable megakaryocytic precursors. Raccuglia and Ratterman (1962) studied the rates of incorporation of S^{35} by megakaryocytes and platelets in normal and bled rats. Labeled $Na_2S^{35}O^4$ was administered immediately and at different times after blood loss. Serial bone marrow and peripheral blood studies were obtained from each animal at 24 hour intervals. By using autoradiography on S^{35}-labeled megakaryocytes in the bled and unbled rats, they showed that activity in the megakaryocytes was maximal immediately after bleeding. The maximum activity of the platelets reached a peak in five days in the normal rats and in those bled and immediately injected, but was reduced to 24 hours in animals injected further from the time of bleeding. This would mean that a rat could reduce the turnover time for platelet production by 80%. Odell (1962) using S^{35}-sulfate labeling of rat megakaryocytes showed that the turnover time of the mature megakaryocytes does not exceed 3 days. Time sequence labeling of megakaryocytes with H^3-thymidine showed similar turnover times.

Cronkite et al. (1961) by giving intravenous tritiated thymidine to a comatose incurable patient and performing serial bone marrows showed that the megakaryocyte progressively becomes more polyploid, as demonstrated by the increasing number of nuclei and by the fact that one or more of the megakaryocytic nuclei may be labeled with tritiated thymidine. They determined the number of unlabeled megakaryocytes and the number replaced by labeled megakaryocytes and estimated a turnover time of approximately 10 days.

As early as 1932, investigators have studied factors controlling platelet production. Factors capable of producing thrombocytosis were extracted from the spleen, liver, lungs, and muscles, but large doses were reported damaging to megakaryocytes. Numerous reports (Yamamoto, 1957; Kelemen et al., 1958; Steinberg et al., 1959) have dealt with the effect of serum from bled human patients, and from thrombocythemic patients. Stefanini and co-workers (1952) reported injection of polycythemic blood brought about a long-term increase in platelets in some individuals with idiopathic thrombocytopenic purpura. Linman et al. (1959) prepared boiled plasma or ether extracts of plasma from patients with polycythemia vera, injected it into normal rats over a 2-week period and observed subsequent leukocytosis and thrombocytosis. More recently, Linman and Pierre (1963) demonstrated that phenylhydrazine-induced anemic rabbit plasma given by gastric tube to normal rats caused a 70% increase in their thrombocyte counts. They also observed thrombocytosis, leukocytosis, erythrocytosis, and reticulocytosis in rats given a thermostable fraction of plasma from a patient with essential thrombocythemia. From the data available, Linman and Pierre (1963) suggest that a single factor may exert physiological, and pathophysiological control over the proliferation of blood cell precursors. The increased activity of such a factor may contribute to the thrombocytosis and leukocytosis that accompany acute blood loss and polycythemia vera. In addition there may be a variety of humoral regulators activated in response to diverse stimuli and possessing different fundamental properties.

Odell and associates (1961) have in rats studied the effect on peripheral platelet counts of serum taken from pre-bled rat donors. Subcutaneous injections of such serum would cause a 150% rise in the platelet counts. Control donor serum was ineffective in causing a platelet rise. From the various investigations, Odell suggested that there may be two separate stimulatory factors: one factor that would bring about a rather rapid production of platelets by mature megakaryocytes, and another that acts to increase the maturation of the megakaryocytic series with eventual increased platelet release.

Matter and co-workers (1960), studying circulating platelets and marrow megakaryocytes in normal rats after acute platelet depletion by exchange transfusion, observed an immediate change in the morphology of marrow megakaryocytes, consisting of a decrease in cytoplasmic mass and the loss of cytoplasmic demarcation membranes. The number of megakaryocytes increased slightly at the time of increased thrombopoiesis, but not in proportion to the increased rate of platelet production. Marrow megakaryocytes increased slightly in number after splenectomy, but were decreased when splenomegaly was induced by methylcellulose. In general, a response to acute thrombocytopenia involved predominantly an alteration in cytoplasmic production of platelets rather than in an increase in number of megakaryocytes.

In contrast to the thrombocytosis-producing substances, agents have been described which produce thrombocytopenia. Such factors have been extracted from spleen, liver, lung, and muscle. Krevans and Jackson (1955) observed thrombocytopenia after massive transfusion of bank or fresh blood and postulated that normal blood contains a thrombocytopenogenic-factor. Harrington and co-workers (1951) have demonstrated a thrombocytopenia-producing factor in the plasma of some patients with idiopathic thrombocytopenic purpura which did not disappear after splenectomy. Stefanini (1955) has evidence which suggests that this factor is actually a platelet antibody which removes platelets from the circulation and damages megakaryocytes. However, in addition to the occasional occurrence of platelet antibodies, evidence suggests that another factor, perhaps a lipoid material, may be elaborated by the spleen and other reticuloendothelial tissues to help regulate platelet numbers (Odell and Kniseley, 1962). This agent, named thrombocytopen, seems to have only a transitory effect and may only inhibit the end stages of platelet production.

Besides the various factors mentioned above, Schulman and co-workers (1960) reported a unique case of chronic thrombopenia that did not respond to steriods or splenectomy, but to fresh blood or stored whole blood, fresh or stored plasma, or fresh frozen plasma. Close examination of this patient's bone marrow before plasma injection revealed that the megakaryocyte maturation was blocked at the level of the granular nonplatelet-producing megakaryocyte. Examination of the bone marrow after injection of the plasma suggested that the factor acted by stimulating maturation of the whole megakaryocyte line of cells culminating in platelet production. If the plasma were given during the latter part of the plasma-induced cycle, temporary refractoriness was noted. These investigators concluded that the factor acted by stimulating maturation of the entire line of megakaryocytic cells and had no effect on increasing the number of cells entering the megakaryocytic series.

3. Maturation Pool

The mature megakaryocyte is a cell 50 to 100 μ in diameter, has an irregular nucleus with large lobes of unequal size united by fine chromatin bridges. With increased granule formation, the cytoplasm becomes slightly acidophilic. These cells comprise approximately 50% of the megakaryocytic series. The next stage is the platelet-producing stage with comprises 25% of the megakaryocytic series. It is the morphologic appearance of this stage that prompted Wright to hypothesize that platelets were of megakaryocytic origin. The cytoplasm of the cell is divided into collections of azurophil granules in small groups of 10 to 12 which are separated by thin spaces of hyalin cytoplasm. This arrangement generally affects all the cytoplasm. The cell degenerates when it breaks up into platelets and the nucleus becomes pyknotic or edematous. Parts of the cytoplasm which are not platelet producing break up into small basophilic droplets and the naked nucleus is present a short time longer before it is autolysed and phagocytized. If one assumes a 7% blood volume and a normal platelet count of 2.5×10^5 per mm^3 the total number of platelets per kilogram would be 1.75×10^{10}. Since platelet life span has been determined to be 10 days by DFP[32] and Cr^{51}, then 1.75×10^9 platelets per kilogram are produced daily. Previously, Cronkite (1958) estimated platelet and megakaryocyte volumes and determined that each megakaryocyte produced approximately 7700 platelets, which gave a calculated turnover time of 25 days. If one utilizes a 10-day turnover time for the megakaryocyte as in Cronkite's more recent data, then each megakaryocyte produces approximately 3320 platelets.

4. Functional Pool

The total circulating platelets as calculated previously for an average individual were 1.75×10^{10} per kilogram. Relatively little is known about the regulation of platelet production, but some information has been obtained from the results of platelet depletion and injection of various extracts: blood, plasma and serum. This material has been presented previously under the division and maturation section on the platelet. Platelet survival can be measured with a number of different isotopes and a number of techniques (Mueller, 1953; Morgan et al., 1954, 1955; Odell and MacDonald, 1960). Sodium sulfate-S^{35} ($Na_2S^{35}O_4$), C^{14}-formate, and S^{35}-methionine apparently label platelets before their release from the megakaryocyte. The $Na_2S^{35}O_4$ labels the mucopolysaccharide fraction of the platelet (Geissinger *et al.*, 1963). Some experiments with $Na_2S^{35}O_4$ have shown that some labeling of platelets may occur in the blood stream, but that most of the labeling takes place in the megakaryocytes (Odell, 1959). Since labeling of the most mature megakaryocytes and their disintegration to form platelets occurs rapidly, the time from isotope injection to the plateau should give an estimate of the platelet life span. Activity of the platelet in rats injected daily with $Na_2S^{35}O_4$ will increase at a constant rate for approximately 5 days but after this will remain relatively stable, indicating that both platelets entering and leaving the pool were tagged. Similar experiments were carried out in a human patient (Odell, 1959).

Julliard and co-workers (1952) and later Aas and Gardner (1958) labeled platelets *in vitro*. The former group used labeled phosphate ($P^{32}O$) and found survival times ranging from 1 hour to a few days; these were shorter than those found with other isotopic methods. The latter investigators used sodium chromate-Cr^{51} ($Na_2Cr^{51}O_4$) and their estimate of survival time ranged from 9 to 11 days in humans, a time that agrees well with values obtained by other methods. Leeksma and Cohen (1956) have used diisopropylfluorophosphate (DFP^{32}), which on injection will combine immediately and irreversibly with esterase enzymes on circulating platelets. The active DFP^{32} is believed to be available only briefly after injection because of the rapid esterase binding and quick excretion. Since only a chemically inert substance which is rapidly excreted has been found after cell destruction, reutilization probably creates no difficulty. It is, of course, important to separate platelets from other blood elements since DFP^{32} attaches to esterases of all blood cells. Other investigators using DFP^{32} have reported survival times of 8 to 14 days (Pollycove *et al.*, 1958) 9 days (Van Rood *et al.*, 1958).

Although there has been some general agreement as to the platelet survival, there has been much controversy concerning the physiology of platelet destruction. Many investigators (Baldini *et al.*, 1960; Zucker *et al.*, 1961) think that platelet survival is best expressed by a linear curve and that platelets die only by aging. Others (Cohen *et al.*, 1961; Hjort and Paputchis, 1960; Heyssel, 1961) feel that platelet survival is expressed best by an exponential curve and that platelets are randomly destroyed by a process of continuous *in vivo* coagulation. One of the major problems has been the difficulty of resolving the difference between a linear and an exponential curve when there is any scatter of the points in the curve. Radioactivity in spleens and livers of normal persons injected with $Na_2Cr^{51}O_4$-labeled platelets was proportional to declining platelet activity over 6 days and consistent with the concept that the spleen removed senescent platelets from the circulation (Najean *et al.*,

1959). Control experiments with similar amounts of unbound radio-activity showed different isotope distribution than that following transfusion of labeled platelets. In a critical review of the evidence for continuous homeostasis *in vivo*, which would involve random selection of platelets, Hjort and Hasselbach (1961) were not convinced that enough evidence has accumulated to accept this concept. More recently, Mustard *et al.* (1962) showed that endothelial membranes prepared from aorta and coronary arteries of normal intact swine of all ages showed microthrombi rich in platelets. The microthrombi were most pronounced around vessel orifices and bifurcations. In addition by tagging young platelets with S^{35} and the total population (young and old platelets) with DFP^{32} in the pig and dog, these investigators obtained curves that were parallel and not divergent, which would suggest random destruction. They also observed that smoking, a diet rich in eggs, small doses of Dicumarol, or prednisone in normal subjects seems to shorten platelet survival, whereas heparin, large doses of Dicumarol in normal subjects, or prednisone in some thrombocytopenic subjects seems to prolong platelet survival. Adelson *et al.* (1963) used a new technique to recover $Na_2HP^{32}O_4$-labeled young platelets in dogs and was able to show a survival curve that was similar to the survival curve of the total platelet population. They thought that this evidence was compatible with random destruction of platelets and that aging plays a negligible role in determining life span. By giving heparin and warfarin to the dogs, they were able to show decreased platelet destruction. Since the platelet count remained unchanged, platelet production must have been decreased as well and they postulated the existence of a feedback mechanism whereby platelet homeostasis is maintained.

G. Summary

The study of bone marrow was first undertaken in the last century and with the advent of staining techniques rapidly developed along morphological lines. The release of radioactive isotopes in 1946 by the Atomic Energy Commission, greatly facilitated the study of the dynamics of bone marrow and has played a major role in our present concept of bone marrow kinetics. In this review the bone marrow was divided into a stem cell pool, and three separate cell lines—the erythrocytic, the myelocytic, and the thrombocytic. The modern concept of bone marrow kinetics seems to demand the existence of a self-perpetuating pool of undifferentiated cells (stem cells) which have homeostatic and functional obligations. Each cell line was divided into a division and maturation pool, a maturation pool, and a functional pool. The size, the speed of cellular turnover, and the homeostatic regulation of each pool were discussed.

REFERENCES

Aas, K. A., and Gardner, F. H. (1958). *J. Clin. Invest.* **37**, 1257.
Adelson, E., Kaufman, R. M., Lear, A. A., Kirby, J. C., and Rheingold, J. J. (1963). *J. Lab. Clin. Med.* **62**, 385.
Albrecht, M. (1957). *Acta Haematol.* **17**, 160.
Albritton, E. C. (1955). "Standard Values in Blood." Saunders, Philadelphia, Pennsylvania.
Allen, D. W., and Jandl, J. H. (1960). *Blood* **15**, 71.
Alpen, E. L., and Baum, S. J. (1962). *Proc. 9th Congr. Intern. Soc. Hematol., Mexico City* Vol. 3, p. 405.
Alpen, E. L., and Cranmore, D. (1959). In "Kinetics of Cellular Proliferation" (F. Stohlman, Jr., ed.), p. 290. Grune & Stratton, New York.
Amann, R., and Martin, H. (1961). *Acta Haematol.* **25**, 209.
Archer, G. T. (1960). *Australian J. Exptl. Biol. Med. Sci.* **38**, 147.
Astaldi, G. (1962). *Ciba Found. Symp. Haemopoiesis Cell Prod. Regulation*, p. 99.
Astaldi, G., Bernardelli, E., and Rondanelli, E. G. (1952). *Haematologica* **36**, 749.
Athens, J. W., Mauer, A. M., Ashenbrucker, H., Cartwright, G. E., and Wintrobe, M. M. (1959). *Blood* **14**, 303.
Baldini, M., Costea, N., and Dameshek, W. (1960). *Blood* **16**, 1669.
Baserga, A. (1948). *Haematologica Suppl.* **32**, 191.
Bernard, C. (1869). *Compt. Rend. Acad. Sci.* **19**, 68.
Bessis, M. (1956a). "Cytology of the Blood and Blood-Forming Organs," pp. 449–452. Grune & Stratton, New York.
Bessis, M. (1956b). "Cytology of the Blood and Blood-Forming Organs," pp. 566–577. Grune & Stratton, New York.
Bessis, M. (1959). In "The Kinetics of Cellular Proliferation" (F. Stohlman, Jr., ed.), p. 23. Grune & Stratton, New York.
Bessis, M., and Burstein, M. (1956). *Rev. Hematol.* **11**, 162.
Bishop, J., Leahy, J., and Schweet, R. (1960). *Proc. Natl. Acad. Sci. U. S.* **46**, 1030.
Bond, V. P., Cronkite, E. P., Fliedner, T. M., and Schork, P. K. (1958). *Science* **128**, 202.
Borsook, H. (1959). In "Kinetics of Cellular Proliferation" (F. Stohlman, Jr., ed.), p. 357. Grune & Stratton, New York.
Bothwell, T. H., and Finch, C. A. (1962). "Iron Metabolism," pp. 220–267. Little, Brown, Boston, Massachusetts.
Brooke, J. H., and Osgood, E. E. (1959). *Blood* **14**, 803.
Brown, J. R., Altschuler, N., and Cooper, J. A. (1963). *Proc. Soc. Exptl. Biol. Med.* **112**, 840.
Bryant, B. J., and Kelly, L. S. (1958). *Proc. Soc. Exptl. Biol. Med.* **99**, 681.
Burka, E. R., and Marks, P. A. (1963). *Blood* **22**, 808.
Burka, E. R., Danon, D., and Marks, P. A. (1963). *Federation Proc.* **22**, 525.
Cohen, P., Gardner, F. H., and Barnett, G. O. (1961). *New Eng. J. Med.* **264**, 1294, 1350.
Cohn, Z. A., and Hirsch, J. G. (1960a). *J. Exptl. Med.* **112**, 983.
Cohn, Z. A., and Hirsch, J. G. (1960b). *J. Exptl. Med.* **112**, 1015.
Coleman, D. H., Stevens, A. R., Jr., Dodge, H. T., and Finch, C. A. (1953). *A.M.A. Arch. Internal Med.* **92**, 341.

Comar, C. L. (1955). "Radioisotopes in Biology and Agriculture," pp. 324–359. McGraw-Hill, New York.

Craddock, C. G. (1957). *In* "The Leukemias: Etiology, Pathophysiology, and Treatment" (J. W. Rebuck, F. H. Bethell, and R. W. Monto, eds.), pp. 245–263. Academic Press, New York.

Craddock, C. G. (1963). *Blood* **22**, 834.

Craddock, C. G., Jr., Perry, S., Ventzke, L. E., and Lawrence, J. S. (1960a). *Blood* **15**, 840.

Craddock, C. G., Jr. Perry S., Ventzke, L. E., and Lawrence, J. S. (1960b). *Am. J. Med.* **28**, 711.

Cronkite, E. P. (1958). *Brookhaven Symp. Bio.* **10**, 96–109.

Cronkite, E. P., Bond, V. P., Fliedner, T. M., and Killmann, S. A. (1960a). *Ciba Found. Symp. Haemopoiesis: Cell Prod. Regulation* p. 71.

Cronkite, E. P., Bond, V. P., Fliedner, T. M., and Killmann, S. A. (1960b). *Ciba Found. Symp. Haemopoiesis: Cell Prod. Regulation* p. 79.

Cronkite, E. P., Bond, V. P., Fliedner, T. M., Paglia, D. A., and Adamik, E. R. (1961). *In* "Blood Platelets" (S. A. Johnson, R. W. Monto, J. W. Rebuck, and R. C. Horn, eds.), pp. 595–609. Little, Brown, Boston, Massachusetts.

Crosby, W. H. (1959). *J. Clin. Invest.* **38**, 997.

Dintzis, H. M., Borsook, H., and Vinograd, J. (1958). *In* "Microsomal Particles and Protein Synthesis" (R. B. Roberts, ed.), p. 95. Pergamon Press, New York.

Donohue, D. M., Reiff, R. H., Hanson, M. L., Betson, Y., and Finch, C. A. (1958). *J. Clin. Invest.* **37**, 1571.

Eigsti, O. J., and Dustin, P., Jr. (1955). "Colchicine in Agriculture, Medicine, Biology and Chemistry," pp. 378–379. Iowa State College, Ames, Iowa.

Ephrussi, B., and Temin, H. M. (1960). *Virology* **11**, 547.

Erslev, A J. (1953). *Blood* **8**, 349.

Erslev, A. J. (1955). *Blood* **10**, 616.

Erslev, A. J. (1959). *Blood* **14**, 386.

Erslev, A. J. (1960a). *Acta Haematol.* **23**, 226.

Erslev, A. J. (1960b). *Ann. Rev. Med.* **11**, 315.

Erslev, A. J. (1962b). *Proc. Soc. Exptl. Biol. Med.* **110**, 615.

Erslev, A. J. (1964a). *In* "Hemoglobin, Its Precursors and Metabolites" (F. W. Sunderman, Sr., and F. W. Sunderman, Jr., eds.), p. 273. Lippincott, Philadelphia, Pennsylvania.

Erslev, A. J. (1964b). *Blood* **24**, 331.

Erslev, A. J. (1964c). *Proc. 9th Congr. Intern. Soc. Hematol., Mexico City* Vol. 3, p. 393.

Erslev, A. J., and Gallo, R. (1963). Unpublished data.

Erslev, A. J., and Hughes, J. R. (1960). *Brit. J. Hematol.* **6**, 414.

Feinendegen, L. E., Odartchenko, N., Cottier, H., and Bond, V. P. (1962). *Proc. Soc. Exptl. Biol. Med.* **111**, 177.

Fidler, E., and Waters, E. T. (1941). *J. Exptl. Med.* **73**, 299.

Filmanowicz, E., and Gurney, C. W. (1961). *J. Lab. Clin. Med.* **57**, 65.

Finch, C. A., Hanson, M. L., and Donohue, D. M. (1959). *Am. J. Physiol.* **197**, 761.

Gabrilove, J. L., Volterra, M., Jacobs, M. D., and Soffer, L. J. (1949). *Blood* **4**, 646.

Gallagher, N. I., and Lange, R. D. (1962). *Proc. Soc. Exptl. Biol. Med.* **110**, 422.

Gardner, F. H., and Pringle, J. C. (1961). *Arch. Internal Med.* **107**, 846.

Geissinger, H. D., Mustard, J. F., Riddell, P. E., Robinson, G. A., and Rowsell, H. C. (1963). *Brit. J. Haematol.* **9**, 77.

Gesner, B., and Gowans, J. L. (1962). *Brit. J. Exptl. Pathol.* **43**, 431.

Goldfarb, B., and Tobias, L. (1963). *Proc. Soc. Exptl. Biol. Med.* **112**, 65.

Goodman, T. W., and Hodgson, G. S. (1962). *Blood* **21**, 702.

Gordon, A. S. (1954). *Recent Progr. Hormone Res.* **10**, 339.

Gordon, A. S. (1955). *Ann. N. Y. Acad. Sci.* **59**, 907.

Gordon, A. S. (1959). *In* "The Kinetics of Cellular Proliferation" (F. Stohlman, Jr., ed.), p. 259. Grune & Stratton, New York.

Gordon, A. S., Dornfest, B. S., Neri, R. O., Eisler, M., and Cursco, A. (1959). *Federation Proc.* **18**, 57.

Gordon, A. S., Neri, R. O., Siegel, C. D., Dornfest, B. S., Handler, E., LoBue, J. and Eisler, M. (1960). *Acta Haematol.* **23**, 323.

Graham, H. T., Lowry, O. H., Wheelwright, F., Lenz, M. A., and Parrish, H. H. (1955). *Blood* **10**, 467.

Green, R., and Martin, S. P. (1955). *J. Lab. Clin. Med.* **45**, 119.

Gurney, C. W., and Hofstra, D. (1963). *Radiation Res.* **19**, 599.

Gurney, C. W., Lajtha, L. G., and Oliver, R. (1962). *Brit. J. Haematol.* **8**, 461.

Harkness, R. D. (1957). *Brit. Med. Bull.* **13**, 87.

Harrington, W. J., Minnich, V., Hollingsworth, J. W., and Moore, C. V. (1951). *J. Lab. Clin. Med.* **38**, 1.

Harris, J. W. (1963a). "The Red Cell," pp. 4–6. Harvard Univ. Press, Cambridge, Massachusetts.

Harris, J. W. (1963b). "The Red Cell," p. 54. Harvard Univ. Press, Cambridge, Massachusetts.

Haurani, F. I., and Tocantins, L. M. (1961). *Am. J. Med.* **31**, 519.

Haurani, F. I., Young, K., and Tocantins, L. M. (1963). *Blood* **22**, 73.

Heyssel, R. M. (1961). *J. Clin. Invest.* **40**, 2134.

Hirsch, J. G., and Cohn, Z. A. (1960). *J. Exptl. Med.* **112**, 1005.

Hjort, P. F., and Hasselbach, R. (1961). *Thromb. Diath. Haemorrhag. Suppl.* **6**, 580.

Hjort, P. F., and Paputchis, H. (1960). *Blood* **15**, 45.

Holub, M. (1958). *Nature* **181**, 122.

Howell, W. H., and Donahue, D. D. (1937). *J. Exptl. Med.* **65**, 177.

Huennekens, F. M., Bertino, J. R., Silber, R., and Gabrio, B. W. (1963). *Exptl. Cell Res. Suppl.* **9**, 441.

Humphery, J. H. (1955). *Nature* **176**, 38.

Humphery, J. H., and Mota, I. (1959). *Immunology* **2**, 31.

Iossifides, I., Gutzait, L., Brand, M., and Tocantins, L. M. (1962). *Proc. 9th Congr. J. Soc. Blood Transf.* (*Mexico City*) p. 281.

Jacob, H. S., and Jandl, J. H. (1962). *J. Clin. Invest.* **41**, 779.

Jacobson, L. O. (1954). *Bull. N. Y. Acad. Med.* **30**, 675.

Jacobson, L. O., and Goldwasser, E. (1957). *Brookhaven Symp. Biol.* **10**, 110.

Jacobson, L. O., Goldwasser, E., Fried, W., and Plazak, L. (1957). *Nature* **179**, 633.

Jandl, J. H. (1959). *J. Clin. Invest* **38**, 161.

Jandl, J. H. (1960). *J. Lab. Clin. Med.* **55**, 663.

Jandl, J. H., and Katz, J. H. (1961). *Trans. Assoc. Am. Phys.* **74**, 72.

Jandl, J. H., Engle, L. K., and Allen, D. W. (1960). *J. Clin. Invest.* **39**, 1818.

Japa, J. (1942). *Brit. J. Exptl. Pathol.* **23**, 272.

Juhlin, L., and Shelley, W. B. (1961). *J. Am. Med. Assoc.* **177**, 371.

Julliard, J., Maupin, B., Chary, R., Theilleux, R., Nau, P., and Loverdo, A. (1952). *Compt. Rend. Soc. Biol.* **146**, 211.

Karvonen, M. J., and Kunnas, M. (1953). *Acta Physiol. Scand.* **29**, 220.

Kelemen, E., Cserhati, I., and Tanos, B. (1958). *Acta Haematol.* **20**, 350.

Killmann, S. A., Cronkite, E. P., Fliedner, T. M., and Bond, V. P. (1962). *Blood* **19**, 743.

Killmann, S. A., Cronkite, E. P., Fliedner, T. M., Bond, V. P., and Brecher, G. (1963). *Blood* **21**, 141.

Kinosita, R., Ohno, S., and Bierman, H. R. (1957). *Federation Proc.* **16**, 362.

Kinosita, R., Ohno, S., and Johnson, S. A. (1961). In "Blood Platelets" (S. A. Johnson, R. W. Monto, J. W. Rebuck, and R. C. Horn, eds.), pp. 611–617. Little, Brown, Boston, Massachusetts.

Komiya, V. E., and Katsunuma, H. (1960). *Ciba Found. Symp. Haemopoiesis: All Prod. Regulation* pp. 359, 490.

Komiya, V. E., Shibamoto, G., Noda, M., Sugimoto, T., Sato, S., Hoshi, K. and Kawashimo, N. (1959). *Folia Haematol.* **3**, 374.

Konigsberg, I. R. (1963). *Science* **140**, 1273.

Krevans, J. R., and Jackson, D. P. (1955). *J. Am. Med. Assoc.* **159**, 171.

Lajtha, L. G. (1962). *Cancro* **15**, 139.

Lajtha, L. G., and Oliver, R. (1960). *Ciba Found. Symp. Haemopoiesis: Cell Prod. Regulation*, p. 291.

Lajtha, L. G., and Oliver, R. (1962). *Ciba Found. Symp. Haemopoiesis: Cell Prod. Regulation*, p. 362.

Lajtha, L. G., Oliver, R., and Gurney, C. W. (1962). *Brit. J. Haematol.* **8**, 441.

Lamerton, L. F., Belcher, E. H., and Harris, E. B. (1959). In "The Kinetics of Cellular Proliferation" (F. J. Stohlman, ed.), p. 301. Grune & Stratton, New York.

Leblond, C. P., and Walker, B. E. (1956). *Physiol. Rev.* **36**, 255.

Leeksma, C. H. W., and Cohen, J. A. (1956). *J. Clin. Invest.* **35**, 964.

Linman, J. W., Bethell, F. H., and Long, M. J. (1959). *Ann. Internal Med.* **51**, 1003.

Linman, J. W., and Bethell, F. H. (1962). *Ciba Found. Symp. Haemopoiesis: Cell Prod. Regulation*, p. 369.

Linman, J. W., and Pierre R. V. (1963). *J. Lab. Clin. Med.* **62**, 374.

Litt, M. (1960a). *Blood* **16**, 1318.

Litt, M. (1960b). *Blood* **16**, 1330.

Litt, M. (1961). *J. Immunol.* **87**, 522.

Matter, M., Hartmann, J. R., Kautz, J., DeMarch, Q. B., and Finch, C. A. (1960). *Blood* **15**, 174.

Meislin, A. G., Lee, S. L., and Wasserman, L. R. (1959). *Cancer* **12**, 760.

Michels, N. A. (1931). *Folia Haematol.* **45**, 75.

Mollison, P. L., and Veall, N. (1955). *Brit. J. Haematol.* **1**, 62.

Morell, H., Sevore, J. C., and Loudon, J. M. (1958). *J. Biol. Chem.* **233**, 923.

Morgan, M. C., Keating, R. P., and Reisner, E. H., Jr. (1954). *Proc. Soc. Exptl. Biol. Med.* **85**, 420.

Morgan, M. C., Keating, R. P., and Reisner, E. H., Jr. (1955). *J. Lab. Clin. Med.* **46**, 521.

Mueller, J. F. (1953). *Proc. Soc. Exptl. Biol. Med.* **83**, 557.

Mustard, J. F., Robinson, G. A., Murphy, E. A., Herst, R., and Rowsell, H. C. (1962). *Blood* **20**, 799.

Nagai, K. (1962). *Proc. 9th Congr. Intern. Soc. Hematol., Mexico City* Vol. 3, p. 149.

Najean, Y., Larrieu, M. J., and Bernard, J. (1959). *Rev. Franc. Etudes. Clin. Biol.* **4**, 1071.

Nakao, K., Shirakura, T., Tanaka, H., Yaginume, H. and Azuma, M. (1962). *Proc. 9th Congr. Intern. Soc. Hematol., Mexico City* **1**, 79.

Nathan, D. G., Schupak, E., Stohlman, F., Jr., and Merill, J. P. (1964). *J. Clin. Invest.* **43**, 2158.

Neuman, E. (1868). *Lentrolbl. Fd. Med. Wiss.* **44**.

Odell, T. T., Jr. (1959). *In* "The Kinetics of Cellular Proliferation" (F. Stohlman, Jr., ed.), pp. 278–281. Grune & Stratton, New York.

Odell, T. T., Jr. (1964). *Proc. 9th Congr. Intern. Soc. Hematol., Mexico City* Vol. 3, p. 389.

Odell, T. T., Jr., and Kniseley, R. M. (1962). *In* "Progress in Hematology" (L. M. Tocantins, ed.), Vol. III, pp. 203–217. Grune & Stratton, New York.

Odell, T. T., Jr., and McDonald, T. P. (1960). *Federation Proc.* **19**, 63.

Odell, T. T., Jr., McDonald, T. P., and Detwiler, T. C. (1961). *Proc. Soc. Exptl. Biol. Med.* **108**, 428.

Osgood, E. E. (1955). *Ann. N. Y. Acad. Sci.* **59**, 806.

Osgood, E. E. (1958). *Brookhaven Symp. Biol.* **1957**, 10, 31.

Osgood, E. E. (1959). *In* "The Kinetics of Cellular Proliferation" (F. Stohlman, Jr., ed.), p. 283. Grune & Stratton, New York.

Osgood, E. E. (1963a). Personal communication.

Osgood, E. E. (1963b). Personal communication.

Patt, H. M., and Maloney, M. A. (1959). *In* "The Kinetics of Cellular Proliferation" (F. Stohlman, Jr., ed.), p. 456. Grune & Stratton, New York.

Perry, S., and Marsh, J. C. (1963). *Blood* **22**, 821.

Pollycove, M., DalSanto, G., and Lawrence, J. H. (1958). *Clin. Res. Proc.* **6**, 45.

Pollycove, M., and Mortimer, R. (1961). *J. Clin. Invest.* **40**, 753.

Powsner, F. R., and Berman, L. (1962). *In* "Erythropoiesis" (J. O. Jacobson and M. Doyle, eds.), p. 286. Grune & Stratton, New York.

Prankerd, T. A. J. (1961). "The Red Cell: An Account of Its Chemical Physiology and Pathology." Blackwell, Oxford, England.

Raccuglia, G., and Ratterman, B. (1962). *Proc. 9th Congr. Intern. Soc. Hematol., Mexico City* Vol. 3, p. 379.

Rebuck, J. W., and Crowley, J. H. (1955). *Ann. N. Y. Acad. Sci.* **59**, 757.

Reissman K. R. (1950). *Blood* **5**, 372.

Reizenstein, P. G. (1962). *Acta Med. Scand.* **172**, 685

Riley, R. F. (1954). *Lancet* **I**, 841.

Riley, R. F. (1959). "The Mast Cells," p. 182. Livingstone, Edinburgh and London.

Rose, S. M. (1955). *Ann. N. Y. Acad. Sci.* **60**, 1136.

Rosse, W. F., Berry, R. J., and Waldman, T. A. (1963). *J. Clin. Invest.* **42**, 124.

Sanchez-Medal, L., Labardini, J., and Loria, A. (1963). *Blood* **21**, 586.

Sbarra, A. M., and Karnovsky, M. L. (1959). *J. Biol. Chem.* **234**, 1355.

Schulman, I., Pierce, M., Lukens, A., and Currimbhoy, Z. (1960). *Blood* **16**, 943.

Seip, M. (1953). *Acta Med. Scand. Suppl.* **282**, 146, 1.

Shelley, W. B., and Juhlin, L. (1962). *Blood* **19**, 208.

Shen, S. C., and Hoshino, T. (1961). *Blood* **17**, 434.

Speirs, R. S. (1955). *Ann. N. Y. Acad. Sci.* **59**, 706.

Speirs, R. S. (1958). *Ann. N. Y. Acad. Sci.* **73**, 283.

Stefanini, M. (1955). *Sang* 26, 83.

Stefanini, M., Chatterjea, J. B., Dameshek, W., Zannos, L., and Santiago, E. P. (1952). *Blood* **7**, 53.

Steinberg, B. (1958). *Arch. Pathol.* **65**, 237.

Steinberg, B., Dietz, A. A., and Atomer, M. A. (1959). *A.M.A. Arch. Pathol.* **67**, 496.

Stohlman, F., Jr. (1961a). *Proc. Soc. Exptl. Biol. Med.* **107**, 884.

Stohlman, F., Jr. (1961b). *Proc. Soc. Exptl. Biol. Med.* **107**, 751.

Stohlman, F., Jr. (1962). *New Engl. J. Med.* **267**, 342.

Stohlman, F., Jr., Howard, D., and Beland, A. (1963). *Proc. Soc. Exptl. Biol. Med.* **113**, 986.

Storti, E., Perugini, S., and Soldati M. (1953). *Acta Haematol.* **10**, 144.

Suit, H. D., Lajtha, L. G., Oliver, R., and Ellis, F. (1957). *Brit. J. Haematol.* **3**, 165.

Sutherland, D. A., Eisentraut, A. M., and McCall, M. S. (1963). *Brit. J. Haematol.* **9**, 68.

Thiery, J. P., and Bessis, M. (1956). *Compt. Rend. Acad. Sci.* **242**, 290.

Thorell, B. (1947). *Acta Med. Scand. Suppl.* **200**, 1.

Valent'ne, W. N. (1960). *Am. J. Med.* **28**, 699.

Valent'ne, W. N., Lawrence, J. S., Pearce, M. L., and Beck, W. S. (1955). *Blood* **10**, 154.

Vanquez, J. J., and Lewis, J. H. (1960). *Blood* **16**, 968.

VanRood, J. J., Eernisse, J. G., and VanLeeuwen, A. (1958). *Proc. 6th Congr. Europ. Soc. Haematol., Copenhagen, 1957,* p. 821.

Vaughan, J. (1953). *Blood* **8**, 1.

Von Barta, J. (1963). *Folia Haematol.* **7**, 38.

Waldmann, T. A., Weissman, S. M., and Levin, E. H. (1962). *J. Lab. Clin. Med.* **59**, 926.

Weiss, P. (1954). *In* "The Hypophyseal Growth Hormone, Nature and Actions" (R. Smith, O. Gaebler, and C. Long, eds.), pp. 1–16. McGraw-Hill, New York.

Weiss, P. (1955). *In* "Biological Specificity and Growth" (E. G. Butler, ed.), p. 195. Princeton Univ. Press, Princeton, New Jersey.

Whitby, E. H., and Britton, C. J. C. (1963). "Disorders of the Blood." Grune & Stratton, New York.

Wintrobe, M. M., Cartwright, G. E., Palmer, J. G., Kuhns, W. J., and Samuels, L. T. (1951). *Arch. Internal Med.* **88**, 310.

Wright, J. H. (1910). *J. Morphol.* **21**, 263.

Yamada, E. (1957). *Acta Anat.* **29**, 267.

Yamamoto, S. (1957). *Acta Haematol. Japon.* **20**, 163.

Yeroshkina, A. M. (1958). *Probl. Hematol. Blood Transfusion* (USSR) (*English transl.*) 3, 296.

Yoffey, J. M., Everett, N. B., and Reinhardt, W. O. (1959). *In* "Kinet'cs of Cellular Proliferation" (F. Stohlman, Jr., ed.), p. 69. Grune & Stratton, New York.

Zucker, M. B., Ley, A. B., and Mayer, K. (1961). *J. Lab. Clin. Med.* **58**, 405.

Zucker-Franklin, D., and Hirsch, J. G. (1963). *Blood* **22**, 824.

CHAPTER 7

The Determination of Blood Volume

F. R. Paulsen

The Civic College, Ipswich, England

I. Introduction

Blood volume determination is of great clinical importance, in spite of the difficulties in defining exactly the term "blood volume." Clinical methods have, in the past, been based upon the addition of standard substances to the blood, and then determining the degree of dilution. The substances used have been (a) carbon monoxide, (b) hemoglobin, and (c) a dyestuff such as Evans Blue T-1824. Nowadays there is great interest in the use of radioactive tracers for this purpose, and what follows in this chapter is concerned solely with this method.

II. Blood Volume Determination by Application of Radioactive Elements

A. GENERAL CRITERIA

All the isotopes of a given element behave in the same way chemically. A radioactive form of an element can be used to label or "tag" the inactive form of that element, and no subsequent chemical operation will separate the isotopes. Because of the extreme sensitivity of modern radiation detecting and measuring equipment, only minute amounts of the radioactive material need be used. This is important, especially in biological work, where the organism must not be harmed by the treatment. It is generally necessary that the nonradioactive form of the element, and the radioactive form, should be in the same chemical state of combination, since otherwise chemical treatment may cause their separation. For example, if radioactive chromium-51 in the form of chromate were added to an inactive chromic salt, addition of a lead salt would precipitate only the radioactive chromium, while ammonia would precipitate only the inactive form. The choice of an isotope for a given purpose will depend on a variety of factors. For example, one must consider the availability, the cost, the energy of the emitted radiation, and so on. Toxicity is important, and the question of the rate of decay and of biological elimination may need also to be considered. Each case must be considered on its own merits. What follows will concern the use of radioactive isotopes for blood volume determination only, and the factors deciding the choice and suitability of each will receive attention.

B. LIMITATION OF DOSE

It is important to restrict the amount of radioactivity administered for blood volume determinations. The red cells or erythrocytes, unlike other cells, are not susceptible to damage, but the erythroblasts from which they originate are extremely susceptible to radiation. Radioactivity will affect both erythropoiesis, or blood formation, and assimilation of iron in the animal organism. Using radioactive iron, Hennessy and Huff (1950) showed that even after only 24 hours, with doses of 5 to 25 r there was inhibition of these processes, the sensitivity depending on the type of organism irradiated. The number of erythrocytes was reduced, there was impoverishment in hemoglobin, and eventually hemolysis of red cells. The minimum dose causing the appearance of anemia was about 500 r for rabbit, but only 200 to 300 r for rat and dog. In the rabbit, a marked reduction in lymphocyte count occurred with 50 r after 5 minutes, reaching a maximum after 24 to 48 hours. Recovery depended upon the magnitude of the dose, but usually took several weeks. There was usually also a change in the proportions of other blood constituents. At least qualitatively, the effects of neutrons and X-rays were the same.

Blood volume determination does not require the administration of doses of radioactive material large enough to damage the subject. However, in view of the suspected absence of any threshold dose for genetic damage, the possibility of affecting the offspring of a treated subject must not be overlooked.

C. THE NUCLIDES USED

Once the techniques of handling and measuring radioactive materials have been mastered, such methods prove singularly attractive, even though the capital outlay may be rather heavy for some medical facilities.

The increasing availability of isotopes, and the ease with which they may be purchased, will surely lead to a great and rapid increase in this particular medical application of radioactivity. For some 10 years, it was radiophosphorus, P^{32}, which was most frequently employed, at least for clinical blood volume determination, while for animal experiments radioiron was mainly used. Subsequently, radiopotassium, K^{42}, radiochromium Cr^{51} (as the chromates), and even thorium-B, Pb^{212}, were used. Some nuclides are trapped in the red blood cells, but K^{42} passes into the red cells and, in the circulating blood, exchanges again more slowly. Hevesy showed that P^{32} was taken up by labile organic phosphorus in the red cells. Radioiron is more firmly fixed; it is incorporated in the hemoglobin formed in the bone marrow, and retained by the red cells throughout their life, i.e., 110 days in the normal human subject. Although it is possible to label the cells even *in vitro*, blood volume determinations cannot be based upon labeled reticulocytes, and a donor is required when radioiron is used. Both Cr^{51} and Pb^{212} are fixed by red cells. Radiochromate is reduced by ascorbic acid in the blood and does not pass into the red cells. It will label the plasma proteins, however, and so the cells need to be centrifuged and washed before their activity can be measured. This is unnecessary when Pb^{212} is used since this nuclide is 99% absorbed by the red cells. Account must be taken of these peculiarities when blood determinations are made by means of radioactive species.

D. THE USE OF POTASSIUM-42

The use of erythrocytes labeled with K^{42} is described by Yalow and Berson (1951b), who found that this nuclide, by virtue of its energetic beta emission, of energy 3.6 and 2.0 Mev, and gamma emission easily detectable in liquids, was very useful, less than 2 μc being required. As the physical half-life is only 11.44 hours, tests can be repeated after short intervals and other radioactive species can be administered soon afterwards, if necessary. The authors incubated 10 ml of heparinized blood with 50 μc of carrier-free P^{32} in the form of phosphate, a similar amount of blood being treated with 100 to 200 μc of K^{42} in 50 ml of potassium carrier. The presence of serum potassium did not affect the uptake of the radiopotassium by the cells. The incubation was a modification of the method described by Reeve and Veall (1949). Between 2 and 6% of the K^{42} was taken up by the red cells. A determined amount of K^{42}-labeled cells suspended in saline solution was injected into the subject, and then heparinized blood samples were taken after 5 and 15 minutes. The procedure was repeated with the cells labeled with P^{32}. The activity of the K^{42} was determined at once, and that of the P^{32} 5 days later, when all the K^{42} had decayed. It was found that blood volumes determined by both K^{42} and P^{32} agreed well, differing from the average by 0.9 to 5.7%. The biological half-life of K^{42} *in vivo* was 28 to 35 hours.

Yalow and Berson (1951a) investigated the simultaneous determination of blood volume in humans, using red cells labeled with K^{42} and P^{32} and with albumin labeled with I^{131}. In all cases the whole blood volume as determined by means of I^{131} was greater than that from the dilution of tagged blood corpuscles. The mixing of erythrocytes and albumin was 90% within 60 to 90 seconds, and complete within 5 minutes. The loss of radioactivity from the circulating blood was 1% or less in a quarter of an hour during the first few hours, so that extrapolation to zero time was unnecessary. The ratio of the average body hematocrit value to that for the peripheral vessels ranged from 0.860 to 0.996, with a mean value of 0.934, so an accurate evaluation of whole blood requires independent determinations of the volume of the plasma and of the red cells.

Yalow and Berson felt that the half-life of K^{42} was too short for the labeling of blood cells, but its high specific activity was a valuable feature. The short life is advantageous when repeated determinations are required. The radioactivity may be easily determined by means of scintillation counters, or even by Geiger-Müller counters with solid or liquid samples. Longer-lived nuclides may be injected at the same time, and determined after the K^{42} has decayed. For example, red cells tagged with K^{42} and serum albumin labeled with I^{131} may be measured at two different times, using a scintillation counter. Red cells may be incubated at 37°C for 1 or 2 hours, the rate of exchange being about 1.5% per hour. With a hematocrit value of 50% and a potassium concentration in the red cells and in the plasma of 100 and 5 meq per liter respectively, and assuming that 100 μc of K^{42} have been used with 0.025 meq of K^{39} in a negligible volume, incubated with 10 ml of blood, the total K^{39} in the plasma will be $0.025 + 0.025 = 0.050$ meq. This means that slightly less than 15 μc of K^{42} will enter the red cells within an hour. For a greater radioactivity the plasma can be replaced by physiological saline before adding the K^{42}, when 30 μc will become incorporated in the red cells within an hour on incubation with 100 μc or more. Longer incubation periods give yet higher activities.

For nonhemolysing sterile solutions of K^{42}, a clear K^{42} stock is evaporated to dryness and reconstituted to the required concentration with physiological saline. The K^{42} solution is incubated with 10 ml of heparinized blood in a sterile rubber-capped tube, with occasional mixing, for one hour at 37°C. In place of the blood, a saline suspension of red cells may be used. The tube is centrifuged at 1000g for 5 to 10 minutes, and the plasma or saline is drawn off by means of a needle passed through the rubber cap. The cells are washed two or three times with 10 ml lots of saline, so that the unbound K^{42} is less than 1% that in the red cells. The cells are mixed well with an equal volume of saline, and injected into the subject. It is possible to use either a calibrated syringe, or weighed amounts of tagged red-cell suspensions in a syringe with needle. If the subject's blood is drawn into the syringe and reinjected three or four times, less than 0.2 to 0.3% of the activity is left in the syringe. The sample is withdrawn from another site. Normally, sampling is after 10 to 15 minutes, but after 15 to 25 minutes in cases of splenomegaly (Rothschild, 1954).

An aliquot of the injected suspension, for use as standard, is assayed from an appropriate volume dilution. Since 1 ml of 50% red blood cell suspension in saline weighs 1.025 gm, a 2.5% correction must be applied if the solution is estimated gravimetrically. The assay is best done in a 5 ml well-type scintillation counter, with average background about 200 cpm, and sensitivity 0.3×10^6 cpm per microcurie of K^{42}. With a dose of 15 μc, and blood volume of 5 liters, 5 ml of whole blood should give a count rate of 4500 above background. The same sample, in the form of a liquid, in a planchet of 1¾-inch diameter, gives only 2400 cpm above background, the latter being about 20 cpm, if the G.M. tube has a silver wall of 30 mg/cm² thickness and sensitivity of 0.16×10^6 cpm per microcurie of K^{42}.

The hematocrit is obtained by centrifuging for 30 minutes at 2000g, a correction of 2% being applied for trapped plasma. The red blood corpuscle volume is then given by the expression: counts per minute injected ÷ counts per minute per milliliter of whole blood. A correction for radioactive decay is applied, amounting to 1.4% during the first 15 minutes. A 2% correction for trapped plasma was recommended by Vasquez (1954).

E. THE USE OF PHOSPHORUS-32

Hevesy et al. (1944) described the use of P^{32} for determining the red cell content of blood. Hahn and Hevesy, in 1940, and Hevesy and Zerahn, in 1942, determined the red cell content of the blood of rabbit by using corpuscles labeled with P^{32}, a method which subsequently proved valuable for humans. In this method 25 ml of blood are withdrawn by venous puncture and heparinized, a 1 ml sample of plasma being treated with a minute amount of sodium radiophosphate (1 μc). The blood, in a paraffin-lined glass bottle, is gently rotated for two hours at 37°C, so that the radiophosphorus is evenly distributed between corpuscles and plasma. A small portion of the labeled blood is set aside as standard, the remainder being injected into the subject. If 1 gm of red cells, containing 1000 units of radioactivity, is injected into the circulation containing 1000 gm of red cells and allowed to mix, the red cells will acquire an activity of one unit. To find the amount of circulating red cells, one must know: (i) the amount of injected labeled red cells; (ii) the specific activity of these, i.e., the radioactivity of 1 gm of cells; and (iii) the activity of 1 gm of red cells taken from the circulation after mixing. The first is obtained from the volume of blood injected, the specific gravity (1.08), and the hematocrit value. The second is found from the radioactivity of 1 gm of red cells of the standard preparation. The third piece of information comes from the activity of 1 gm of cells withdrawn after allowing 5 to 10 minutes for mixing. Suppose a is the amount of corpuscles injected, and b is the activity of 1 gm of cells after mixing. Then the total amount of red cells in circulation will be $a \times b$. The blood samples are taken 5 minutes after injection, since 3 minutes will not allow good mixing, and 10 minutes will allow too much loss of activity from the cells. The authors reported the following results:

Time in minutes	1.25	2.0	3.0	4.8	6.9	9.9	15.8	18	30
Percentage of red cells injected present in 1 gm cells	0.026	0.044	0.052	0.053	0.050	0.052	0.048	0.045	0.044

There will be some errors, of course. For example, it has been assumed that the amount of plasma adherent to 1 gm of centrifuged cells of the standard is equal to that on 1 gm of cells after injection. An error arises from incomplete separation of red cells and plasma. The standard 1 gm preparation consists of 0.97 gm of red cells and 0.03 gm of plasma, say, and has an activity of 1000 units. The activity of 1 gm of red cells will be the same as that of 1 gm of plasma after two hours of rotation in the thermostat, 970 units of activity being due to corpuscles and 30 to the plasma. Assuming the activity of the 1-gm sample to be 1000 units, the contribution from adherent plasma is 8, and of the cells 992. If the activities of the two red cell samples are now compared, the red cell content in the circulation will be 2.3% too high. The activity of the plasma adherent to the sample after 10 minutes from injection will be still lower than that in the plasma after 3 minutes, and about 10% that of the injected plasma. So, the 10-minute sample will give a red cell content which is about 3% too high. This is the situation when using a centrifuge run at 5000 rpm for 10 minutes.

Again, it is not simply active corpuscles which are injected, but active whole blood, and some radiophosphorus can enter the circulating red cells. The injected blood contains active plasma, so the P^{32} can enter red cells during the course of 5 or 10 minutes of the test. However, phosphate penetrates the capillary wall much faster than the membrane of the red cells, as Hahn and Hevesy showed (Hahn, 1942). Consequently, most of the plasma P^{32} will leave the plasma within 5 minutes, thereby reducing the amount of P^{32} which would otherwise enter the red cells. Entry of P^{32} into red cells during the test results in an increase in their activity, so that the total red cell content of circulating blood appears too low. The error from this cause amounts to 5% in 10 minutes. Another error is due to loss of P^{32} from red cells, about 1.5% of the P^{32} being replaced by P^{31} from plasma in 10 minutes. This gives a higher dilution factor, and the red cell content appears too high. Plasma contains half as much inorganic phosphorus again as the same amount of red cells, which shows a larger proportion of readily exchangeable organic phosphorus in the form of adenosine triphosphate and hexosephosphate and other acid-soluble organic forms of the element. When radiophosphorus enters red cells, it interchanges with the organic phosphorus. When cells are shaken with radiophosphorus for 2 hours, much of the P^{32} from the cells is found in the organic fraction, and the inorganic fraction of P^{32} in the red cells remains lower than the inorganic plasma phosphorus. The error arising from this, in a 10-minute test, is 1.5% on the high side. So, the over-all error is $(+3) + (-5) + (+1.5) = -0.5\%$.

By a similar method, Reeve (1952) determined the whole blood volume. He incubated whole blood with a little sodium radiophosphate and found that 15 to 30% of the P^{32} entered the red cells in 30 to 60 minutes. A saline suspension of washed cells was injected intravenously into the subject, and serial samples of blood were withdrawn, the P^{32} activity being determined by means of the M 6 Geiger-Müller counter, designed especially for radioactive liquids by Veall (1948). The slow loss of P^{32} from the circulating cells was allowed for by extrapolation to zero time. About 1% of the P^{32} in the labeled cells was found in the saline of the cell suspension, and about 1% of the counts in the venous blood sample were in the venous plasma. Provided care was exercised in the preparation of the P^{32} stock and in the cell suspension, the errors were small and canceled out. With human subjects it was very necessary to avoid bacteria and dust in the samples. Chaplin (1954) and Reeve (1952) found that adsorption of P^{32} on dust or in cells caused overestimation of the cell volume. The P^{32}, as pure, sterile Na_2HPO_4 or NaH_2PO_4 or phosphoric acid neutralized with sodium hydroxide to phenol red indicator, is treated with carrier (4.6 mg Na_2HPO_4 per millicurie) and diluted with pure, distilled water to an activity of 100 to 150 μc per milliliter. This solution can be kept sterile if stored in Pyrex containers in a refrigerator, but must be discarded if it becomes cloudy. Opened ampoules must be sterilized again by boiling in a beaker of water for 30 minutes. About 15 to 30 μc are transferred to a 50-ml centrifuge tube, treated with 0.05 ml of heparin solution, of 5000 IU/ml activity, autoclaved at 15 psi for 30 minutes, and stored in the refrigerator until required. This proceedure should be followed at weekly intervals. An hour before a test 10 ml of a 20-ml blood sample from the subject is transferred to a sterile conical centrifuge tube and treated with heparin, the other 10 ml being added to the P^{32} solution in a 50-ml tube. The conical tube is centrifuged at once, the plasma being diluted to 150 ml with sterile, ice-cold 0.85% sodium chloride solution, and stored in the refrigerator. The tube with the blood and P^{32} is incubated for 30 to 60 minutes at $37°C$, with gentle mixing, until 4 to 6 μc of activity have been transferred to the cells. The following figures enable one to plot a graph from which the incubation time may be calculated:

Percentage P^{32} entering cells	8	18	28	34	38	44	48	51
Incubation time (hours) at 37–40°C	$\frac{1}{4}$	$\frac{1}{2}$	$\frac{3}{4}$	1	$1\frac{1}{4}$	$1\frac{1}{2}$	$1\frac{3}{4}$	2

After cooling in ice, any P^{32} adhering to cells, but dissolved in plasma, is washed off with three lots of prepared saline-plasma mixture, added to the labeled cells to make 45 ml, mixed by gentle inversion, and centrifuged for a short time at high speed. The supernatant fluid is sucked off by means of a glass pipette, with as many of the white cells as possible. This procedure is carried out three times. From a 15-ml sample of well mixed plasma some is withdrawn into a 10-ml pipette, cooled, and injected within 30 minutes. The patient is kept recumbent for 30 minutes, and a 7-ml blank blood sample then taken. An exactly known volume of red cells is given intravenously, using a calibrated syringe, the residual cells being washed from the syringe into a measured volume of phosphate-citrate buffer and the radioactivity measured. Three or four 7-ml samples are withdrawn, without stasis, from a vein remote from the injection site, at intervals of 12, 24, 36, and 48 minutes. From each sample 5 ml is transferred to a test tube with 7-ml of phosphate-citrate buffer. The latter contains 2.5 gm of trisodium citrate, 6.6 gm of disodium hydrogen phosphate, and 1.9 gm of potassium dihydrogen phosphate, in 1000 ml of water. If the samples are not measured at once, they must be stored in the refrigerator. A trace of saponin is added, and the tube contents shaken until lysis occurs. The hemoglobin content is measured, and also the packed cell volume, on each whole blood sample. When the labeled cell suspension is in the syringe, triplicate 1-ml samples of the remainder are transferred to 100-ml flasks, and diluted with phosphate-citrate buffer, with a trace of saponin to ensure lysis. Now 1 ml of each dilution is placed in a test tube together with 5 ml of the subject's blank blood and 6 ml of buffer are added to one sample, 11 ml to each of the others. The blank sample serves to correct for absorption of P^{32} beta emission as a result of the specific gravity of the blood being higher than that of the buffer. The count rate is determined in the saline suspending the labeled cells. The remainder of the cold suspension is centrifuged, 1 ml of the supernatant liquid being diluted with 11 ml of buffer, and the count rate determined. The diluted blood samples and standards are also "counted" in the M 6 G.M. tube.* Figure 1 shows a typical liquid counter. The time taken for 5000 to 10,000 cpm is determined. After each count, the jacket of the G.M. tube is washed with 0.9% sodium chloride, 0.1 N hydrochloric acid, and water, in turn, and then dried with filter paper. Correction is made for background (about 10 cpm) and coincidence loss.

Let a = cpm for the diluted standard, b = dilution of the standard (= 1200), c = volume of cell suspension injected, d = volume of cells in 100 ml of blood, e = cpm for whole blood, corrected for P^{32} loss from circulation and variations in cell content, and f = dilution of samples (12 : 5). Then the red cell volume, in milliliters is given by

$$\frac{a \times b \times c \times d}{e \times f \times 100}$$

* This, and the later versions, the M 6 H and M 6 M, are obtainable from 20th Century Electronics, Ltd., New Addington, Surrey, England.

The P^{32} in unit blood volume varies with cell content of the blood. As the cell content of successive samples varies, the mean cell count on three or four counts is taken as the d value. The counts from each venous sample are corrected to a standard cell content by making use of the formula $g = h \times j/k$, where g is the corrected count rate of any particular sample, h the observed count rate, j the mean cell content of

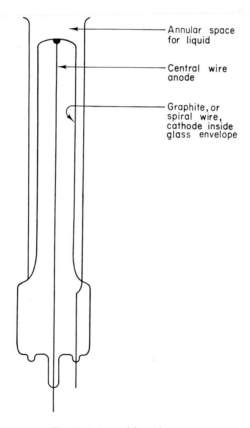

Annular space for liquid

Central wire anode

Graphite, or spiral wire, cathode inside glass envelope

Fig. 1. A typical liquid counter.

the first three venous samples, and k the cell content of the given sample. An accurate hemoglobin concentration may be used in place of the hematocrit.

To correct for the slow loss of P^{32} from the blood stream, the plot of sample count rate against time is extrapolated to zero time. The packed cell volume is corrected for the small amount of trapped plasma, which amounts to 2 to 5% of the packed cell column, but which varies with the time, speed, and arm length of the centrifuge. Reeve (1952) found it preferable to include the white cell layer. For further details, readers should consult Reeve and Veall (1949).

It has sometimes been found difficult to prepare reproducible standards, because of clumping together of the white cells. As these cells take up P^{32}, an appreciable error was encountered when the white cell content was high. Most of the white cells could be sucked off the top of the packed cells during the washing. It is recommended that the standards be made from hemolysed, centrifuged samples. In the reclining, healthy male subject, P^{32} loss from the blood-stream in labeled red cells is 6% per hour, so that two samples can be used, the average P^{32} content being corrected for this loss. By using whole blood hemolysed by saponin, instead of samples diluted with phosphate buffer, dilution errors are avoided, and an adequate count rate ensured with only small doses of P^{32}. One can use simultaneously P^{32} and Co^{60} on the same subject, as the P^{32} gives a very low count rate in the M 6 counter tube.

Reid and Orr (1950) used P^{32} for labeling red cells for injection.

Berlin et al. (1951a) determined blood volume in 16 normal females, using washed red cells labeled with P^{32}, and they found a smaller sex difference than that found when the Evans Blue method was employed.

The following are further references to the use of P^{32} in blood volume studies: Allen (1956), Berlin (1952), Berson (1954), Gregersen (1951), Ravidin et al. (1954), Schwaiger and Schmeiser (1951), and Wahlund (1954).

F. The Use of Iron Isotopes

The remarkable feature about iron, making its physiological behavior so completely different from that of other body constituents, is its utilization over and over again. Using radioisotopes of iron, it has been shown that iron remains in the hemoglobin of intact red cells, and when the latter are destroyed, the iron is not rejected by the body but is retained for reconversion into new red cells. This explains why there is normally only a small absorption of iron from the food supply. During pregnancy and rapid growth, there is an increase in the total hemoglobin, and a constant drain on the ferritin reserves, which must be replaced by absorption of iron from the food. There is normally no exchange between administered iron and stored iron.

The stability of iron in the red cells has made particularly attractive the use of radioisotopes of iron for the determination of blood volume. If a little labeled blood is injected, the iron is passed into the hemoglobin. A sample of donor's blood, equilibrated with radioiron, becomes radioactive, and when reinjected into a subject, becomes diluted so that a determination of the radioactivity of a newly drawn blood sample will give the blood volume. Blood volumes are determined using red cells labeled with short-lived Fe^{59}, while the fate of transferred blood can be followed by the behavior of the longer-lived Fe^{55}.

Early blood studies with radioiron were carried out by Hahn et al. (1939, 1942, 1943a,b). In a dog rendered anemic by blood letting and then given iron salts, the labeled iron appeared in the erythrocytes within 4 hours, and was found to be completely transferred to the red cells within 4 to 7 days. No such absorption occurred if the iron reserve in the tissues was high. A fraction of a milligram would be assimilated to the extent of 85%, but a dose of 5 mg only 12%, because iron from old, broken-down red cells is used in the formation of new ones. If red cells are destroyed by acetylphenylhydrazine, the iron is used in formation of new corpuscles.

Beinert and Maier-Leibnitz (1948) found that when young rats were fed on Fe^{55}, 0.45% of this passed into the cytochrome c, and 80% into the hemoglobin. According to Moore et al. (1944), whereas the dog can assimilate ferrous or ferric iron equally easily, man can deal readily only with ferrous salts.

Hahn et al. (1943) discovered that both mineral iron and that in hemoglobin combine with the protein apoferritin to form ferritin, a crystalline compound containing 23% iron. This combination occurs in intestinal mucosa, liver, bone marrow, and other tissues, formation of apoferritin being preceded by reduction of the ferric state; hence absorption depends on the equilibrium between the hemoglobin, ferritin, and free ferrous ions, and therefore on the redox conditions in the medium. Hahn (1942) found that in dogs the radioiron was incorporated into the newly formed erythrocytes and retained until they disintegrate again.

Determination of human blood volume with radioiron is described by Gibson (1946a) and by Peacock (1946). If radioactive Fe^{55} or Fe^{59} as ferric ammonium citrate is injected into a donor, of blood group 0, the newly formed red cells take up the iron and are in circulation within 24 hours. The radioactivity in the blood reaches a maximum after about 21 days. Now, if 70 to 100 ml of donor's blood, containing 30 or 40 ml of red cells and an activity of 2500 to 3000 cpm are injected into the subject, either intravenously or intra-arterially, the range of red cell volume from 1500 to 2500 ml is covered. After 10, 20, and 30 minutes, 15-ml samples of blood are taken. A 2-ml sample of donor's blood is diluted to 100 ml, and 10-ml aliquots are used. The recipient's blood samples are centrifuged at 3000 rpm for 30 minutes. Then donor and recipient samples are wet-washed and the iron electrodeposited on copper, and the count rate determined. If a is the number of milliliters of donor cells injected, b is the radioactivity of the donor cells, and c is that of the recipient cells, then the red cell volume of the recipient is given by ab/c. Addition of the plasma volume, determined by the dye method, gives the whole blood volume. This method gives results agreeing well with those from the carbon monoxide method, but lower than those from the dyestuff method. The method assumes no escape of radioiron from red cells, and even mixing of labeled cells with the recipient cells.

The tests should be done on the recumbent subject under basal conditions, 12–14 hours after a meal, and without loss of dye into the tissues at the injection site. Evaporation of samples must be prevented, or dye plasma will be too high. The absolute blood volume cannot be determined in a living subject.

The whole blood forms 8% and the plasma 4% of the total body weight. The whole blood represents 78 ml, the plasma 41 ml, and the red cells 37 ml, per kilogram of body weight. For the average man of 70 kg, the blood volume is 5500 ml, or 3000 ml/m² of body area. This is 7.5% higher than the value for women, the plasma volume being about the same in both sexes. In infants and young children, the blood volume is smaller per unit body weight, and per unit surface area, than in adults, the adult figures being reached at the age of 16 years.

The difficulty in getting donors and the dangers of incompatibility resulted in radioiron being largely replaced by P^{32}, Cr^{51}, and K^{42}. Radioiron is still much used in work on metabolism (Finch, 1949) and in the double tracer technique for work on the relation of total body hematocrit value to venous and arterial hematocrit values, and the distribution of plasma and red cells in the large and small blood vessels (Gibson, 1946b).

G. The Use of Iodine-131

Iodine-131 was used in blood studies by Storaasli et al. (1950), who injected labeled protein intravenously and measured the degree of dilution. An accurate estimation of the plasma volume is possible because of the retention of iodinated protein in the vascular system under normal conditions. The ready availability of human serum albumen labeled with I^{131} has made improvements possible. As I^{131} is a gamma-emitter, arterial puncture is not necessary, the radiation being measured by means of a scintillation counter external to the body (Pritchard et al. 1955).

Crispell et al. (1950) have described the determination of human serum volume by injection of human albumin (Cohn's fraction V) iodinated with I^{131}. A typical procedure for blood volume determination is

the following: Under sterile conditions, 20 μc of radioiodinated human
serum albumin are added to 10 ml of saline, mixed, and filled into a
5 ml calibrated syringe, all air-bubbles being expelled. Since radioiodine
tends to dissociate from the albumin, it is necessary to dilute just before
use. The preparation is injected into a well-cannulated vein, without infiltration of surrounding tissue. After 10 to 15 minutes, a 10-ml blood
sample is taken from the opposite arm and discharged into dry oxalate
anticoagulant. A 3-ml sample of blood is used for activity measurement in
a well-type scintillation counter.

The standard is prepared as follows: A 1-ml sample of the labeled
albumin solution is diluted with 0.9% sodium chloride solution to 500
ml and mixed by inversion. A 3-ml portion is "counted" in the well
counter, background corrections being applied to the sample and the
standard. The blood volume, in milliliters, equals

$$\frac{\text{cpm in standard} \times 500 \times 5}{\text{cpm in blood sample}} .$$

The technique for plasma volume determination is the following: After
centrifuging the blood, a 3-ml sample of plasma is examined for count-
rate in a well counter. Background corrections are applied as before.
Then the plasma volume, in milliliters, equals

$$\frac{\text{cpm in standard} \times 500 \times 5}{\text{cpm in plasma sample}} .$$

The Nuclear-Chicago Corporation (Des Plaines, Illinois) markets equipment for this work. For example, for determination of blood and plasma
volumes, using radioiodinated serum albumin, a suitable combination is
their 132B Clinical Scaler-Spectrometer, combining an automatic binary
scaler, computer, precision preset timer, and gamma-ray spectrometer in
a single compact chassis. With this could operate their DS-303 well-type
scintillation counter, fitted with 3-in. diameter crystal with 1½-in. diameter well for sample volumes up to 20 ml. This detector can also be
supplied with a 21/32-in. diameter well for 5-ml samples. The 1½-in. well
takes 25-mm. diameter test tubes or 1-in. diameter plastic or glass vials.
Where the sophistication and versatility of the 132B Scaler-Spectrometer
are not required, the DS-202 well-type scintillation detector can be used,
with the 181B Decade Scaler. Figure 2 shows the Nuclear-Chicago 132B
Clinical Scaler-Spectrometer, used with DS-303 Scintillation Counter.
Figure 3 shows the Nuclear-Chicago 181B Decade Scaler, with DS-202
Scintillation Counter. The detector has a 2-in. diameter crystal with a
well accepting ½-in. or 13-mm test tubes. A large access port in the top

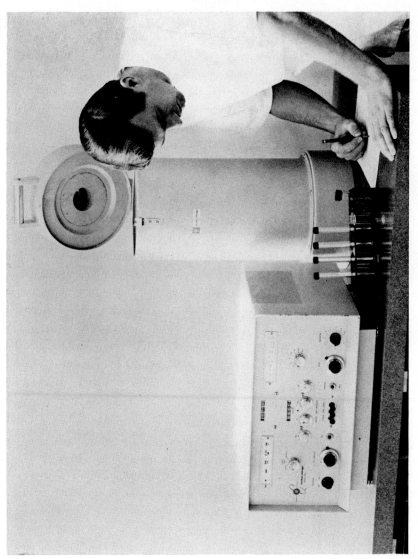

Fig. 2. Nuclear-Chicago 132B clinical scaler-spectrometer and DS-303 scintillation counter.

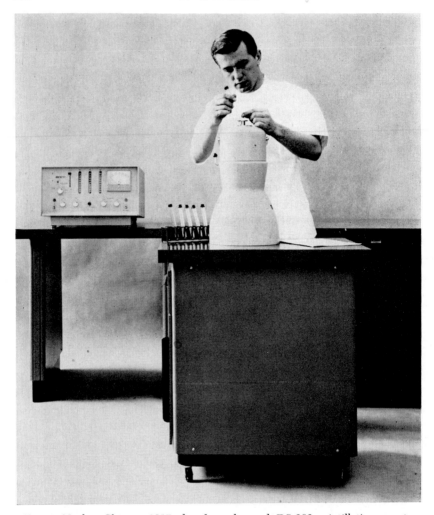

Fig. 3. Nuclear-Chicago 181B decade scaler and DS-202 scintillation counter.

of the upper shield permits larger bottles to be placed on the crystal for measurement.

H. THE USE OF CHROMIUM-51

The method employing Cr^{51} is simple, rapid, and accurate, and in many ways superior to that using radioiron. Like P^{32}, Cr^{51} will label red cells rapidly *in vitro*, so that these can be reinjected.

Wennesland (1955) reported highly reproducible results in this method. Of all the *in vitro* labeling methods, that in which Cr^{51} is used shows the least elution rate of isotope from the cells, this being less than 1.5% per day, so that no correction for such a loss is required. This advantage is lost unless the cells are washed quite free from unbound Cr^{51} as in the "open" method. Since the elution rates of P^{32} and K^{42} from tagged red cells are 3.0 and 1.5%, respectively, these two labeling nuclides involve no serious error from this cause. The long decay and biological half-lives of Cr^{51} are a disadvantage, and the energy of the gamma rays makes simultaneous work with I^{131} difficult. But Na^{24} and K^{42} can be used with it, since their emissions are more energetic. The use of Cr^{51} for blood studies was described by Sterling and Gray (1950a,b). Red cells rapidly take up Cr^{51} from radiochromate and this is held mainly in the globin moiety of the hemoglobin, uptake by the stroma being negligible. Hemoglobin, in contact with radiochromate, takes up the Cr^{51} and retains it in spite of long dialysis. Radiochromate can also label the plasma proteins. Chromium in the tervalent state, however, becomes bound by hemoglobin and plasma proteins, but not by intact red cells in whole blood. Probably the chromate enters the red cells and becomes reduced to the trivalent state, which is then coordinately bound. Red cell uptake of Cr^{51} is faster and more complete from acid solution, as from acid-citrate-dextrose (ACD or Strumia's solution). Below a pH of 6.5, the reaction

$$2H^+ + 2CrO_4{}^{2-} = Cr_2O_7{}^{2-} + H_2O$$

occurs. Unlabeled red cells do not take up activity from chromium-tagged hemoglobin or from hemolysed labeled red cells. The firm bond and the failure of destroyed red cells to cause tagging of new cells are two features which make Cr^{51} so valuable as a tagging agent for studies in red cell survival.

Frank and Gray (1953) report that administration of 100 μc of Cr^{51} to a 70 kg man gives a total body dose of only 0.1 rep. Determination of plasma volume by means of radiochromic chloride is not likely to cause damage. In the original method, whole blood (50 ml) in a sterile heparinized syringe is centrifuged, the plasma being stored in the cold. The red cells, resuspended in saline, are treated with radiochromate for an hour at room temperature, with gentle agitation. Better uptake of chromium results if the suspension is made at pH 5.0 in ACD or Strumia's solution, consisting of 2.5 gm of disodium citrate monohydrate, 0.8 gm of citric acid, and 1.2 gm of dextrose in 100 ml of water. Uptake of at least 90% then occurs in 15 to 20 minutes, or even faster at 37°C. The uptake is further improved if the red cells are separated from the plasma, because the plasma itself tends to bind some chromium. To the ACD solution in a sterile Erlenmeyer flask the appropriate amount of sodium radiochromate is added. After incubation, the red cells are washed two or three times with cold, sterile ACD solution, then gently mixed with the original plasma. Nearly all the radioactivity is now in the red cells, hardly any in the plasma. An aliquot part is set aside for count rate determination. The reconstituted whole blood is injected intravenously from a calibrated syringe, and after 10, 20, and 30 minutes blood samples are taken from the opposite arm. In cardiac failure, there is delayed mixing, so the first sample should be taken after 15 minutes.

Hematocrit values are determined on the injected and sample bloods by simultaneous centrifuging in Wintrobe tubes for 30 minutes at 2000g (or 3000 rpm in a No. 2 International Centrifuge). The hematocrit value of injected reconstituted blood is usually different from that of the samples. For the whole blood samples assay, the well-type scintillation counter is used. For extra precision, the same given volume of sample (say 5 ml) is "counted" in matched tubes or vials, so that no corrections are necessary. Sometimes one "counts" packed red cells, or even hemolysates (obtained by adding distilled water to blood or packed red cells, freezing and thawing, or by addition of saponin). The circulating red cell volume, or CRCV, is given by

$$\frac{\text{total radioactivity in CRCV}}{\text{radioactivity per ml of packed cells in samples}}.$$

The numerator is the total activity injected, derived from the volume of the reconstituted blood injected and the radioactivity per milliliter. When counts on whole blood are made, the denominator is given by the activity per milliliter of packed red cells, which is equal to

$$\frac{\text{radioactivity in whole blood sample} \times 100}{\text{volume of sample counted} \times \text{hematocrit value}}.$$

Three samples should agree to within 3 to 5%, the absolute accuracy of the method.

In the shortened "closed" method of incubation, it is no longer necessary to wash the red cells to remove unbound Cr^{51}. The following method is recommended for the determination of red cell mass: When viable red cells are incubated with Cr^{51} as chromate in Strumia's solution, a high proportion of the cells become labeled. The unbound chromate is reduced to the trivalent chromic state by ascorbic acid in the blood, and so does not become bound to red cells, but is loosely held by the plasma protein. Labeled cells are reinjected into the subject, another aliquot sample being used as standard. The plasma is removed from the latter, the cells being washed with saline, and a dilution is prepared for count rate determination. At 20 and 30 minutes after injection, blood samples are taken, cells from a measured volume of blood being separated, washed with saline, and prepared for "counting" in the same way as the standard. The actual procedure may be summarized as follows:

(1) Draw 20 ml of the subject's blood and discharge carefully into a sterile siliconed bottle containing 10 ml of Strumia's solution; mix, add 25 μc of sodium radiochromate.

(2) Incubate for 30 minutes at room temperature; add 100 mg of ascorbic acid in 1 ml of sterile solution by means of a sterile syringe; mix; allow to incubate for 5 minutes.

(3) Mix blood well in bottle; withdraw 20 ml into sterile syringe; weigh rapidly on balance to nearest 0.01 gm.

(4) Inject labeled blood through needle in vein, with another syringe; prevent any flow-back of blood into syringe.

(5) Reweigh empty syringe to find weight of injected blood.

(6) Draw 10-ml blood sample from opposite arm at 20 and 30 minutes; discharge into bottles containing anticoagulant; determine hematocrit values.

(7) Prepare standard: mix sample of labeled blood well and add about 5 ml to each of two weighed centrifuge tubes; reweigh tubes; centrifuge 10 minutes at 2000 rpm, and remove plasma; do not lose red cells; add 10 ml of 0.9% sodium chloride to tubes and gently resuspend cells; centrifuge 10 minutes at 2000 rpm. and remove supernatant; repeat sodium chloride washing and centrifuging; transfer washed cells to a 100-ml flask with water (cells are lysed); mix well; pipette 3-ml samples into glass tubes and "count" in well-type scintillation counter.

(8) Prepare timed sample: mix blood samples well and pipette 5 ml into centrifuge tube fitting into scintillation well; carry out sodium chloride washing after centrifuging; "count" red cells in counter.

(9) The calculations are as follows:

$$a. \text{ total counts administered} = \frac{(\text{weight of blood injected} \times 100)}{(\text{weight of standard} \times 3)} \times (\text{standard cpm} - \text{background});$$

$$b. \text{ red cell cpm/ml} = \frac{(\text{red cell cpm} - \text{background})}{(\text{hematocrit}) \times (\text{volume of blood washed})};$$

$$c. \text{ red cell mass} = \frac{(\text{total counts injected})}{(\text{red cell cpm/ml})}.$$

The reader may wish to consult the following references for further information on the use of Cr[51] for blood volume determinations: Reed (1954); Smolik (1956); Strumia et al. (1955).

Sterling and Gray (1950a) report that the total dosage of radio-activity in this procedure need not exceed 0.1 rep, well within the tolerance limits for humans. Bradt et al. (1945) describe the disintegration scheme. Marinelli et al. (1948) give a formula applicable to beta emitters and soft X-ray emitters:

$$\text{total dose in rep} = 88 \, ETC,$$

where E is the average energy per disintegration in Mev (i.e., 4.92×10^{-3} for Cr^{51}, T is the half-life in days (26.5 for Cr^{51}), and C is the concentration in microcuries per 1 gm of tissue. The administration of 0.4 μc of Cr^{51} per kilogram of body weight results in a dose of only 0.1 rep, assuming no excretion and that all radiation is localized in the red blood cells.

III. The Dilution Curve and Accuracy of Blood Volume Determination

George et al. (1958) have described the theory of the dilution curve of substances introduced into the circulation. They consider a volume v_1 of marker introduced into a stream of fluid entering and leaving a volume V at a constant rate equal to v_0 liters per minute. The time taken for the marker to flow into the volume V is t_1 minutes. Assuming uniform mixing and a concentration of marker in volume V equal to $c(t)$, it is possible to write

$$dc(t)/dt = (v_1/t_1 V) - [c(t)v_0/V] \tag{1}$$

over the time interval $t = 0$ to $t = t_1$, and $c(0)$ being zero. Now, if t is greater than t_1,

$$dc(t)/dt = -[-c(t)v_c]/V. \tag{2}$$

Solution of Eqs. (1) and (2) gives

$$c(t) = (v_1/t_1 v_c)(1 - e^{v_c t/V}) \tag{3}$$

when t is smaller than t_1 and

$$c(t) = (v_1/t_1 v_c)(e^{v_c t/V} - 1) e^{v_c t/V} \tag{4}$$

when t is greater than t_1.
Integration of these two expressions gives

$$\int c(t) \, dt = v_1/v_c. \tag{5}$$

Now, the circulatory system is a closed one, with exit and inlet connected, and the marker reappears after a circulation time t_2 which is normally greater than t_1. When t is greater than t_2 and the latter, in turn, greater than t_1, one can write

$$dc(t)/dt = -c(t)v_c/V + c(t - t^2)v_c/V. \tag{6}$$

Here the second term refers to the recirculation. Use of a Laplace transformation gives a power series

$$c(t) = \sum_{n=0}^{\infty} C_n(t) \tag{7}$$

where $C_n(t)$ is zero when t is less than nt_2 and C_n is equal to

$$\frac{v_1}{V}\left(\frac{v_c}{V}[t - nt_2]\right)e^n - \frac{v_c}{V}(t - nt_2).$$

The nth term expresses the effect of the nth recirculation, the nth subsidiary maximum being at time $t = nt_2 + V/v_c$, and the amplitude of these subsidiary maxima being in the ratio $1 : 0.37 : 0.27 : 0.22$. Recirculation time t_2 results in subsidiary maxima in the dilution curve, beginning at $t = t_2 + V/v_1$. Since not all the blood takes exactly t_2 minutes to circulate, the advantage of the last refinement is negligible. The $c(t)$ steadily declines from the first maximum to a steady level given by V_i/L, where L is the total blood volume in the circulatory system. Now, if t_1 can be made short compared to the mean circulation time, then sufficient of the curve corresponding to the first transit can be observed, and extrapolation gives the remainder, so that recirculation effects may be then ignored. Figure 4 shows a typical dilution curve. The shape of curves derived from the equation for $c(t)$ given above is defined by three parameters. These are t_1, the time for the marker to enter the chamber; v_c, the rate of flow through the chamber; and V, the volume of the mixing chamber. Now, since $c(t)dt = v_1/v_c$, all the curves have the same area, but they are longer and flatter as t_1 increases.

Dilution occurs in the volume V of the heart chambers, and v_c is the rate of flow or cardiac output, assumed to be constant although the flow is pulsed (negligible error occurs here, as the heart beat is brief compared to the period of complete dilution). The tracer may be Evans Blue T-1824, or sodium chloride or sugar, or erythrocytes labeled with P^{32}, or human serum albumin labeled with I^{131}.

When I^{131} is used, a collimated crystal may be placed over the base of the heart, connected to a ratemeter with strip chart recorder, the shape of the dilution curve being plotted directly, with an arbitrary vertical scale. The recorder is run for 10 minutes to get a steady level. By extrapolation of the descending portion of the curve one can obtain the area underneath, corresponding to the first transit. The area and the steady level are measured on the same arbitrary scale, and then area/steady level = blood volume/v, and the cardiac output is given by v_0 = (blood volume × steady level) ÷ (area).

The blood volume is determined by comparing the activity of a blood sample and a known fraction of the injected material. This is given by total cpm injected divided by cpm per milliliter of blood. To minimize the retention of I^{131} in the thyroid, the subject is given 1 gm of potassium iodide daily, one day before and for some days afterwards. Tests are satisfactory with 25 μc of I^{131}. The 10-ml blood samples are collected in

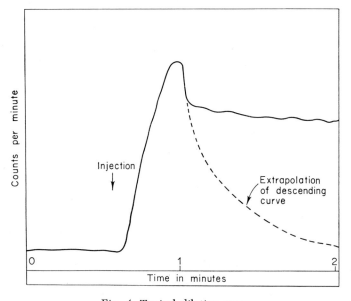

Fig. 4. Typical dilution curve.

oxalated bottles. An aliquot part of 0.001 of the injected dose is assayed in another container, diluted to the same volume with water. Results on 15 patients showed accuracy to be quite satisfactory.

The isotope technique is particularly useful in cases where the Fick method is inapplicable, e.g., in patients undergoing operations (since catheterization is not then practicable) and also in pregnancy. The isotope technique is accurate and convenient, both for the operator and the subject, and can be repeated at short intervals. In cases of congenital abnormalities, such as atrial septal defects or anomalous pulmonary veins, there are deviations from the normal dilution curve, as a result of the excessive recirculation. Spritzmetal *et al.* (1949) discussed the possibility of using isotope dilution curves as a tool for the diagnosis of such abnormalities. Unfortunately, the isotope technique is not quite reliable in its present form, because of the difficulty in siting the counter. It might be overcome by suitable modification.

IV. Plasma Volume, Hematocrit Value, and Blood Volume

The "true" blood volume is often calculated by adding the red cell volume, obtained by isotope methods, to the plasma volume, obtained by the dye method. This assumes, of course, that the latter method is an accurate one. If the blood volume is determined from the plasma volume and the hematocrit value, the result is too high. The red cell content of the total circulating blood is less than that of a blood sample used for the determination of the hematocrit value, and so the red cell volume and the total blood volume will be overestimated. Suppose the hematocrit value is 50%. Then addition of plasma volume to red cell volume gives 100. The red cell content of the circulating blood is 18% lower than that of the hematocrit sample, so to the plasma volume of 50 must be added $0.82 \times 50 = 41$, giving a total of 91 for the total blood volume. This means that the value for the blood volume obtained in this way is only 91% of that obtained by the dyestuff method. If, on the other hand, the blood volume by the red cell volume method, as determined by P^{32}, and the hematocrit value, is used, a low result is obtained. If the carbon monoxide method could give the red cell volume of circulating blood, the blood volume found by the hematocrit value and red cell volume would still be too low. The carbon monoxide method actually gives a high result, which more than compensates for the error due to underestimation of the plasma in the blood, so that the blood volume is too high.

Hahn *et al.* (1942) used radioiron for experiments on dogs, as it was more firmly bound than radiophosphorus, so that experiments could be carried out over several days, and tests done in a few minutes gave results just as reliable as those from several days' work using other techniques. It was found that when the dye method plasma figure was used in conjunction with the hematocrit value, a small red cell content was obtained, only 77% of the value deduced from other methods. Gibson and Evans (1937a) studied the relationship between plasma and total blood volume, and the venous pressure, blood velocity, physical measurements, age, and sex in ninety normal humans. They found no relation between the changes in blood volume, venous pressure, and blood velocity. The total blood volume in males exceeded that in females, differences being due to the greater red cell volume in males. The absolute red cell volume in females was smaller than in males to a much greater degree than was indicated by differences in red cell counts and the hematocrit value. As age increased, there was a decline in blood volume, comparable to decreases in basal metabolic rate and vital capacities. By comparison with the average values, absolute blood volume was high in muscular and obese persons, lower in thin ones. The volume per unit body weight was higher in muscular and thin individuals, but lower in obese persons. The blood volume of normal people varied widely. The relationship to height or surface area of the body offered a useful basis for the estimation of the normal volume in clinical investigations.

V. Expression of the Results

Blood volume results have been expressed in a variety of ways. The expression of a simple blood volume, *per se,* offers little advantage, since it makes impossible any comparison between individuals of different weights or stature. It is sometimes given as a volume per unit surface area of the body, but this involves the difficult problem of accurately measuring the surface area.

If volume is expressed on the basis of actual or ideal body weight, the normal values for total red cell volume of males and females show an undesirably wide range. The same applies when blood volume per unit weight of fat-free body tissue is used, since the degree of adiposity in humans varies widely, even in very healthy persons. Huff and Feller (1956) found it to be 20 ml of red cells per kilogram of adipose tissue, whereas Siri, using a more accurate method, obtained a figure of only 4 ml per kilogram. Measurements of body density are not widely available, so it is perhaps better to compare individuals on the basis of milliliters of red cells per kilogram of body weight.

There is considerable difference of opinion concerning the justification for calculating plasma volume from the total red blood cell volume and the venous hematocrit value. It is generally agreed that this procedure is reliable if the venous hematocrit is multiplied by about 0.9 to correct for differences between total body hematocrit value and that for the venous blood.

VI. Uses and Effects of Blood Volume Expanders

A. The Function of Expanders

Blood volume expanders, also known as plasma extenders, plasma expanders, and plasma substitutes, are fluids derived from the blood, or colloidal synthetic materials in solution, having osmotic properties virtually identical with those of blood plasma. They are used in treatment of shock, to produce an increased circulatory volume. Unfortunately, they have no oxygen-carrying properties, nor can they make up cell deficiencies. They can act as vehicles for adding red cells to the circulation. Their persistence in the circulation depends on passage across capillary walls into interstitial fluids, excretion, storage in tissues, and metabolic degradation. Plasma expanders depend, for their efficiency, on the shape, structure, molecular weight and electrical charge on their particles. The ideal molecular weight, since this is the value for plasma albumin, is 70,000. The osmotic pressure should be the same as that of normal plasma proteins. Expanders should pass out of the circulation at the same rate as the system can mobilize its normal proteins, so that the osmotic pressure of the system is maintained. The viscosity of the expander solution should not impede injections. With such exacting requirements, it is hardly surprising that the ideal expander has not yet been developed. The nearest approach must be a natural blood protein taking its part in the normal metabolism of the blood system. In 1956 Campbell said that the ideal macromolecule for use as a plasma expander would probably have properties very similar to those of serum albumin.

B. Shock and Its Treatment

Shock causes a severe decrease in the circulating volume. When histamine shock occurs, expanders are of very little use, and specific antihistamine drugs and vasoconstrictors are required. In the case of shock from bacterial toxins, the expander can reverse the symptoms, but the specific antitoxin must also be given.

During shock there follows a fall in blood pressure, with progressive concentration of constituents, decreased plasma volume, and temperature drop. Sometimes there may be decreases in plasma protein, and the rate and depth of respiration, and increases in pulse rate and coagulation time, together with darkening of the venous blood and hemolysis. For severe burns a reversible conditions exists, followed by anoxia of the tissues, leading to death, after the irreversible phase. During the reversible condition, there is a very marked sensitivity to stimuli which may easily push the organism over into the irreversible state.

Traumatic shock may involve extensive passage of blood into the affected areas. In extensive burns there may be a dangerous loss of plasma into affected areas. In nerve damage, in particular, vasodilatation occurs, with loss of protein and increased capillary permeability. Decreasing circulating volume results in anoxia and a fall in blood pressure, venous return, and cardiac output. In cases of shock other than that due to hemorrhage, it may be very difficult to determine the blood pressure and to find the amount of fluid which should be injected. Subcutaneous administration is of little use if there is depletion of protein in the plasma, as the blood will have insufficient osmotic pressure to withdraw enough fluid from tissue spaces. Infusion may result in overdilution or excessive fluid. In the former case, anemia results, with loss of oxygen-carrying capacity, only rectified by administration of whole blood. The second condition is more serious, because if an excess of expander is given, regeneration of protein is accompanied by increased volume of circulating fluid, large amounts of fluid being withdrawn from the tissues. The subject then literally "drowns," as a result of overloading the capillary bed, excretion of fluid by the lungs, and dilatation and weakening of the heart. Death ensues from pulmonary edema and heart failure.

C. Effects and Types of Plasma Expanders

As expanders, normal saline, Ringer's solution, or Ringer-Lock solution have been used, by means of intravenous drip, infusion, or subcutaneous injection. After the initial increase in blood pressure, intravenous injection may result in conversion of the reversible to the irreversible state. Intravenous saline is useful before shock sets in, but electrolytes tend to diffuse across the capillary membranes into interstitial spaces, removing plasma proteins, and prejudicing recovery. Blood sugar content may be maintained by adding 5% of glucose to the saline solution.

Gum acacia, once widely used as an expander, has now been abandoned, as it can produce allergic reactions, and interfere with protein regeneration. The same limitations apply to pectin.

Gelatin, a modified protein of molecular weight between 20,000 and 70,000, can be used in 6% concentration. It is not metabolized, and contains no useful amino acids. It attains maximum hemodilution in 3 to 4 hours, but gives a lowered hematocrit value and plasma protein concentration. Most of it is excreted in the urine within 24 hours. If shock is present, gelatin may produce adverse effects.

Dextran can be used in 6% solution, together with saline or 5% glucose, or as a 5% solution with glucose. It is a complex polysaccharide derived from the metabolism of *Leuconostoc mesenteroides* on a substrate of glucose. Its molecular weight (the British product) is up to 450,000. The volume of expansion is slightly greater than the volume injected, reaching the latter value in about an hour. After 12 hours, the volume increase is about 50% of the injected volume. The commercial material will remain effective for 48 hours, but is slowly broken down to glucose, some of which passes out with the urine. The average initial dose is 500 ml, the same volume being repeated after 30 minutes. Larger amounts may produce hemorrhage and even death.

The Germans introduced, during the Second World War, PVP, or polyvinyl pyrrolidone, of molecular weight 30,000 to 50,000. The 3 to 5% aqueous solution increases the blood volume initially by about 90% of the injected volume. About 50% of it is excreted in the urine within 3 or 4 weeks and after 12 hours the volume increase is about 30% of the injected volume.

Nowadays, the general practice is to use whole blood, since citrated blood can be stored for three weeks. For immediate use, 400 ml of blood is mixed with 100 ml of 3% sodium citrate. The cross-matching of citrated samples on slides enables one to note any agglutination, a sign of incompatibility. Blood plasma may be kept for two years, and can be used at the rate of 20 ml per pound of body weight. Blood serum obtained from naturally clotted blood can also be used as a plasma expander.

VII. Clinical Considerations

A. Blood Flow in Shock

Blood volume determinations can be of great diagnostic value, and can keep track also of therapeutic results. Nylin and Celander (1950), studying blood volume by means of isotopes, found that severe depression of circulation occurs immediately after extensive burns. The amount of blood pumped by the heart and flowing through the liver falls to a very low value several hours before there is any significant fall in blood pressure or in plasma volume. In shock due to hemorrhage the blood flow through the liver is directly proportional to the blood volume in the body. If blood is transfused in excess, the liver flow increases proportionately. The mechanism which restores the normal amount of blood following a hemorrhage is not fully understood.

B. Hematopoiesis

Using tagged red cells in the bone marrow, it is possible to find the number of erythrocyte precursors. For every 1000 mature red cells circulating in man there are 12 circulating reticulocytes, 12 marrow reticulocytes, and 12 nucleated red cell precusors. To supply 0.8 to 0.9% of the circulating cells required daily to replace destroyed cells, the marrow nucleated red cells must double their numbers each 36 hours. The turnover of radioiron in man is 3.5 days, half of which is required for nucleated red cell production, half for maturation. In anemia there may be premature delivery of marrow reticulocytes into the circulation, and in the experimental condition the entire marrow reticulocyte pool can move into the circulation. The red cell production rate in the marrow may be increased up to sixfold in cases of chronic congenital hemolytic anemia. Anemia requires the red cell destruction or blood loss to exceed the production rate, or an impaired marrow response. In Cooley's anemia and pernicious anemia, there is a disparity between the total and effective marrow activity, and it may be that red cells are then so defective that many are destroyed in the marrow before they can be delivered to the circulation.

Experimental work with the two radioactive forms of iron shows that all red cells are circulating simultaneously. It is known that administration of adrenaline results in an increased hematocrit value, once thought to be the result of reserve red cells from the spleen, but actually involving only a redistribution of cells.

Swingle and Pfiffner (1933, 1938) consider that the major role of the adrenal cortex is the regulation and maintenance of the volume of circulating fluid in the vascular system. An adrenalectomized subject dies from circulatory collapse due to deficient fluid and low blood pressure. The adrenal cortex regulates the capillary tone, ensuring normal fluid exchange between the vascular and the extravascular tissues. Suppression of cortex function causes increased capillary permeability, and hence a shift of fluid from blood to tissues. Loeb (1932), however, says that large amounts of water and salts are lost from the body via the kidneys, so that it is unnecessary to assume any shift of fluid into the tissue spaces.

C. Blood Volume in Clinical Conditions

Blood volume is important in many clinical considerations. A severe hemorrhage can cause a fall of systolic pressure to 50% of the normal value, i.e., to about 60 mm., in place of 128 mm. of mercury. After the initial large reduction in volume comes a rise to normal over a period of about 2 to 4 days, as blood from the tissues enters the blood stream. During this period there is also a fall in hemoglobin and plasma protein concentration. The dilution of the blood will result in the need for increased circulation rate, the increased pressure being maintained by vasoconstriction. Severe muscular trauma can cause a loss of even two liters of blood, or about 30 or 40% of the total body's supply. Severe burns, or abdominal injury with peritonitis, can reduce the blood volume without actual blood loss, this hemoconcentration or oligemia resulting from loss of plasma into the injured tissues, with vasoconstriction maintaining the pressure. Withdrawal of fluid from other parts to restore blood volume causes a dilution of the plasma protein. Fluid loss uncompensated by vasoconstriction will result in fall in pressure and cardiac output by as much as 50%, so that the subject suffers peripheral circulatory failure, which may also result from severe fluid loss, or loss of electrolytes, after prolonged violent vomiting or diarrhea. In the event of the shock being too long continued, treatment will probably be useless, as the irreversible state sets in.

The normal plasma volume is 49 to 59 ml per kilogram of body weight, or 1400 to 2500 ml per m² of body surface. The cells form 41 to 51% of the total blood volume. In infancy, the blood volume is only about one-third that of the adult, on the basis of surface area. The age difference is less marked on a body weight basis. There is a slight increase in blood and plasma volume in pregnancy, with higher plasma protein concentration and lower cell count. There is a comparatively huge increase in the red cells in polycythemia vera, with marked increase in total blood volume, the plasma volume being normal, or depressed, or raised. With falling blood pH, the red cells may take up water and swell, and this results in decreased plasma volume.

Bell *et al.* (1953) quote the results shown in Table I for human subjects.

TABLE I

BLOOD DIFFERENCES BETWEEN THE SEXES

	Male	Female
Blood volume (ml), average	5340	3800
Plasma volume (ml), average	2980	2280
Blood volume, ml per m² of body surface area	3100	—
Blood volume, ml per kg of body weight	78	66

The blood volume is higher in muscular, active individuals. According to Wilson,

$$\text{plasma volume (ml)} = 20W + 73H - 3250,$$

and

$$\text{blood volume (ml)} = 43W + 131H - 6250,$$

where W is the body weight in kilograms and H the height in inches. During early life the blood volume exceeds the value given by these equations.

Berlin *et al.* (1951b) studied the changes in the effects of thoracic surgery on blood volume in 27 patients. They found that about 1000 ml of blood were lost in thoracoplastics, the volume of red cell loss being relatively higher than the amount of apparent plasma loss.

Blood volume rarely increases, but this may occur in polycythemia vera, chronic leukemia before the anemic stage, and sometimes in water intoxication in diabetes insipidus or on administration of excessive amounts of water with Pituitrin. Hypertonic saline in cases of edema may cause a temporary blood volume increase, as well as an increase in plasma, but then diuresis usually ensues quite promptly, so that return to normal is fairly rapid. A slight increase in blood pressure is found in hypertension, Raynaud's disease, thromboangiitis obliterans, hyperthyroidism, the nephrotic syndrome, and congestive heart failure. Decreased blood volume may be the result of a fall in red cell volume, or in that of the plasma, or both (as in severe hemorrhage). Plasma volume will soon return to normal or even above this, but the loss of blood red cells takes longer to counteract. The restored plasma is usually deficient in proteins, but this will return to normal before the red cell count and the hemoglobin concentration are back to normal again. In chronic anemias, the total blood volume will probably be low, the plasma volume high or normal, while in pernicious anemia the total volume will probably be normal or slightly low, and the plasma volume either low or normal. Hemolytic jaundice is accompanied by a decrease in total volume, but the plasma volume is usually high. In splenic anemia and portal cirrhosis, both total blood and plasma volume will be high.

In shock, reduced plasma and blood volume result from the transudation of fluid and protein, as the capillaries are abnormally permeable. The hemoconcentration is shown by a high hematocrit value and elevated blood count. Subnormal total blood volume and plasma volume, with hemoconcentration, occur in prolonged restriction of water; excessive loss of water, as in diuresis, vomiting, diarrhea, intestinal fistula, sweating, and pancreatic and biliary fistula; in acidosis due to water loss from diuresis and passage of water from plasma to cells; in advanced diabetes mellitus, when the plasma volume is low because of diuresis and acidosis; in high external temperatures, when there is excessive sweating and loss of water through the lungs; in some cases of uremia, due to acidosis, vomiting, diuresis, and diarrhea; in ether anesthesia; and in adrenal cortical deficiency, the low plasma volume being due to excessive loss of sodium chloride and water into the urine or into the tissues. Table II shows that plasma volumes are more constant than total blood volumes.

In cases of severe vomiting, diarrhea, burns, wound shock, etc., the saline shift from body or into the tissues causes increased red cell proportions. The hemoglobin concentration, then, is a useful criterion for following rapid clinical changes, although this is not applicable when the clinical changes are slow, as the amounts of hemoglobin and red cells may change.

Swan and Wood (1953) described a method for the detection of intracardial shunts. A cardiac catheter was passed into the heart, and a
small amount of Evans Blue was passed in, the concentration curve of
the arterial blood being plotted against time, using an ear oscimeter.
Tracings were made, using the catheter tip in various chambers of the
heart. It was possible to detect intracardial shunts, and in some cases to
decide the type of shunt. Sodium radioiodide can also be used. To avoid
arterial puncture, an external counting system was used. The dilution
curve was plotted from observations made at finger tips, so that compli-

TABLE II

Blood Changes in Various Conditions

Condition	Plasma as percentage of body weight	Blood volume as percentage of body weight	Hemoglobin (%)	Red cells per mm^3 ($\times 10^6$)
Normal	5.1	8.2	16.4	4.8
Diabetes	4.8	7.3	16.3	4.6
Pernicious anemia	4.9	5.7	5.8	1.6
Polycythemia	5.1	13.7	22.4	9.1
Various conditions (average)	4.9	7.1	10.9	3.9

cations due to venous circulation were reduced. The whole area of a
scintillator crystal was employed, the collimator being removed, so that
maximum sensitivity resulted. The types of curves obtained are shown in
Fig. 5.

Similar curves were obtained by MacIntyre and Pritchard (1952) from
observations made at the ball of the foot. The shape of the curve was
determined by the diffusion of the marker into the vascular bed. The
time interval between injection of the marker through the catheter and
its appearance at the finger tips is significant. Figure 5 shows the graph of
count rate versus time for various parts of the heart. For data pertaining
the case illustrated above, see the accompanying tabulation.

Position of catheter	Appearance time (seconds)
Right auricle	6, with slow rise to 21
Right ventricle	14, with rise to 20
Left ventricle	
Right pulmonary artery	12, rising to 18

These figures indicate a shunt at a trial level, and this was confirmed at an operation.

Brown *et al.* (1951) studied the effect of congestion of the extremities on the blood volume as determined by the carbon monoxide method and the Evans Blue technique. The congestion was produced by means of pneumatic cuffs placed on three limbs of normal human subjects, so that between 20 and 25% of the total blood volume was contained in the congested limbs. It was found that the contours of the curves of concentration plotted against time were slightly different in congestion, but that

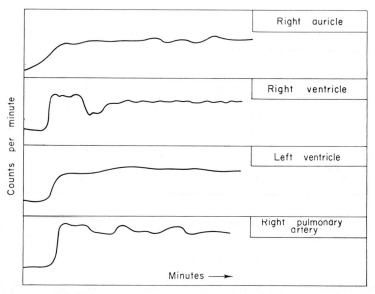

Fig. 5. Count rate versus time for various parts of heart.

these differences were insufficient to make them useful for determining the presence of, or the degree of, venous pooling. Massive congestion of limbs did not interfere with complete admixture of either carbon monoxide or dye with the entire blood supply within 20 minutes, and the carbon monoxide method gave the total, rather than the effective, blood volume.

Rowntree has classified the various combinations of whole blood volume, plasma volume, and red cell volume into nine categories. Figure 6 shows Rowntree's classification of the blood volumes.

Hoffman *et al.* (1958) used the Cr^{51} method of Gray and Sterling (1950a) on patients with disorders of the heart muscles, to test the effects of edema. They used three methods for estimating blood volumes: (i) adding the plasma volume to the red cell volume; (ii) using plasma volume and the hematocrit value; and (iii) using the red cell volume found by Cr^{51} and the hematocrit. Since both the red cell volume and the plasma volume could be determined directly, the total volume could be found in three ways. The red cell volume was found by the method of Keiderling (1956), similar to that of Necheles et al. (1953) and that of Mollison and Veall (1955) and of Ledlie and Vassar (1956). The determination of plasma volume was by the method of Huff et al. (1949,

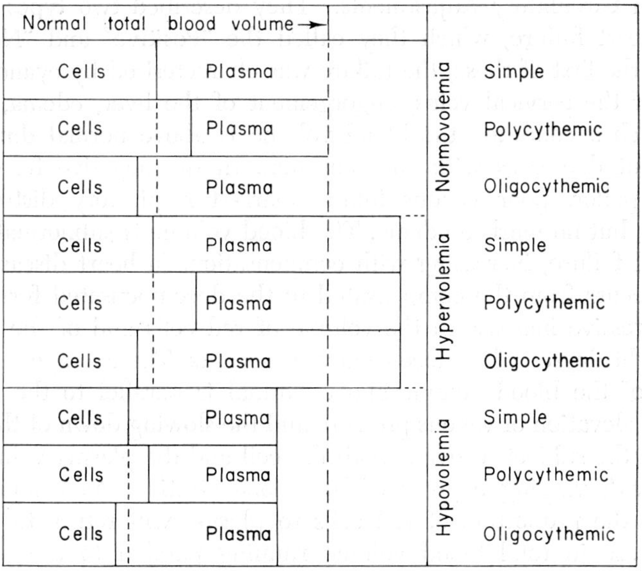

Normal total blood volume →				
Cells	Plasma		Normovolemia	Simple
Cells	Plasma			Polycythemic
Cells	Plasma			Oligocythemic
Cells	Plasma		Hypervolemia	Simple
Cells	Plasma			Polycythemic
Cells	Plasma			Oligocythemic
Cells	Plasma		Hypovolemia	Simple
Cells	Plasma			Polycythemic
Cells	Plasma			Oligocythemic

Fig. 6. Rowntree's classification of blood volumes.

1950). Observations on 46 patients, with and without edema, revealed that in very few cases did the three methods agree. In some cases there was a volume difference of 1000 ml, and differences of over 30% in more than 50% of the cases. The average, found from plasma volume, was 5.43 liters, that from red cell volume 4.47 liters, that from adding plasma volume and red cells 4.86 liters. The volumes obtained by using plasma volume and hematocrit value gave results greater than those from red cell volumes. When marked edema was present, there tended to be a greater difference between the total blood volume figures, according to whether these were found from the plasma volume or the red cell volume. These workers concluded, as did Schreiber *et al.* (1954) that plasma volumes determined on normal subjects could not be very reliably compared with those in pathological conditions. Moreover, total red cell volume could only be determined accurately by the Cr^{51} method. There were always errors introduced when a definite volume of red cells was added to a separately determined plasma volume, as the latter is always somewhat uncertain. There were even greater errors if the blood volume was deduced from the plasma volume and the hematocrit value.

Goldbloom and Libin (1935) reported on the clinical evolution of studies of the circulating blood volume, as the first part of their "Clinical Studies in Circulatory Adjustments." They described two types of congestive heart failure, which they called the "Positive" and "Negative" types. In the first of these, the failure was characterised by cyanosis, distension of the cervical veins, engorgement of the liver, edema, and so on. In such a condition the blood volume is above normal during the failure, but decreases with compensation. In the negative form, there may be pallor, poor venous filling, marked respiratory distress and weakness, but no marked edema. The blood volume is subnormal during the actual failure, increasing with compensation. In heart diseases, as a change occurs from the compensated to the decompensated form, there is a progressive increase in the volume of red cells and of the plasma, and a slight degree of hemoconcentration occurs. The average degree of increase of the blood volume above normal is parallel to the average degree of elevation of venous pressure and the slowing down of the circulation. As the subject recovers, both the cell and the plasma volumes diminish, with varying degrees of hemoconcentration. As compensation continues the proportion of red cells to plasma will return to normal, the decrease in total blood volume running parallel to the improvements in the clinical condition. There is no volume increase during recovery from chronic congestive failure. Any relapse to a more severe degree of circulatory failure is usually accompanied by further increase in the total blood volume.

Very extensive studies in compensation and decompensation were made by Wollheim (1928b, 1929, 1930, 1931). The same author's method for blood volume determination, a modification of the Keith-Rowntree technique, should also be studied (1928a). Levin (1935) has also contributed to the work on compensation and decompensation. Finally, mention must be made of the work of Gibson and Evans (1937b) on the changes in blood volume, venous pressure, and blood velocity in congestive heart failure.

VIII. A Factor Affecting the Accuracy of Blood Volume Measurements by the Radioactivity Method: the Plasma/Corpuscle Ratio

Blood volume determinations using dyestuffs such as Vital Red or Evans Blue T-1824 yield results about 15% too high. It has been found, in dogs, that red cell volumes calculated from the hematocrit value and the plasma volume do not agree with values predicted from red cells actually removed. If the erythrocyte volume before bleeding is equal to that after bleeding added to the volume of red cells removed, the hematocrit value gives the correct cell-to-plasma ratio for whole blood, but if the red cell volume before bleeding exceeds the sum of the red cell volume after bleeding and the red cell volume removed, the hematocrit value gives an incorrect cell-to-plasma ratio. In normal human subjects the red cell volume 72 hours after venesection is less than that predicted from the prehemorrhage red cell volume and the red cell volume removed, and in dogs, a great fall in the hematocrit value results from bleeding.

Total red cell volume, obtained by the use of radioactive iron, added to the total plasma volume determined by the dye method, gives the total blood volume. If this is divided into the cell volume determined by a direct method, the average hematocrit for the entire body is obtained. This is always about 20% smaller than that determined in the more conventional way. To compensate for the relatively greater number of red cells in the large vessels, the cell-to-plasma ratio in the small vessels would have to be even smaller than the average value. No significant proportion of red cells can be immobilized in the spleen, liver, and other organs, since the volume of cells in rapid circulation is almost identical with the total red cell volume. It is unlikely that rapid and complete mixing could occur if a fair proportion of the cells were immobilized, so nearly all the red cells must be in active circulation, and, to a close approximation, the circulating red cell volume is equal to the total red cell volume. Since the cell-to-plasma ratio of the fast axial stream in various vessels is fairly constant, the jugular vein hematocrit value may be taken as representative of this ratio for the rapidly circulating axial stream blood, and so the volume of rapidly circulating blood can be determined by dividing the cell volume (using the donor cell method) by the jugular hematocrit value. This proves to be considerably less than the total blood volume obtained by adding the cell volume, deduced by isotope dilution, and the plasma volume, as determined by the dye method.

References

Allen, T. H. (1956). *Metabolism* **5**, 328.

Beinert, H., and Maier-Leibnitz, H. (1948). *Science* **108**, 634.

Bell, G. H., Davidson, J. N., and Scarborough, H. (1953). *In* "Textbook of Physiology and Biochemistry," p. 333. Livingstone, Edinburgh and London.

Berlin, N. I. (1952). *New Engl. J. Med.* **247**, 675.

Berlin, N. I., Hyde, G. M., Parsons, R. J., Lawrence, J. H., and Port, S. (1951a). *Proc. Soc. Exptl. Biol. Med.* **76**, 831–832.

Berlin, N. I., Rowles, D. F., Hyde, G. M., Parsons, R. J., Samson, A. C., and Port, S. (1951b). *Surg. Gynecol. Obstet.* **92**, 712–715.

Berson, S. A. (1954). *Bull. N. Y. Acad. Med.* **30**, 750.

Berson, S. A., and Yalow, R. (1951a). *J. Clin. Invest.* **31**, 572–580.

Berson, S. A., and Yalow, R. (1951b). *Science* **114**, 14–15.

Berson, S. A., Yalow, R., Azulay, A., Schreiber, S., and Roswit, B. (1952). *J. Clin. Invest.* **31**, 581.

Bradt, H., Gugelot, P. C., Huber, O., Medicus, H., Preiswerk, P., and Scherrer, P. (1945). *Helv. Physiol. Acta* **18**, 252.

Brown, E., Hopper, J., Jr., Sampson, J. J., and Murdich, C. (1951). *J. Clin. Invest.* **30**, 1441, 1450.

Celander, H., and Nylin, G. (1950). *Circulation* **1**, 76.

Chaplin, H., Jr. (1954). *J. Physiol. (London)* **123**, 22.

Crispell, K. R., Porter, B., and Nieset, R. T. (1950). *J. Clin. Invest.* **29**, 513–516.

Evans, W. A., and Gibson, J. G. (1937b). *J. Clin. Invest.* **16**, 851–858.

Feller, D. D., and Huff, R. L. (1956). *J. Clin. Invest.* **35**, 1.

Finch, C. A. (1949). *Blood* **4**, 905.

Frank, H., and Gray, S. J. (1953). *J. Clin. Invest.* **32**, 991.

George, E. P., Hickie, J., Rocke, F. A., and Seldon, W. A. (1958). "Australian Atomic Energy Symposium," pp. 661–665. Melbourne Univ. Press (for Australian Atomic Energy Agency), Melbourne.

Gibson, J. G. (1946a). *J. Clin. Invest.* **25**, 616.

Gibson, J. G. (1946b). *J. Clin. Invest.* **25**, 848.

Gibson, J. G., and Evans, W. A. (1937b). *J. Clin. Invest.* **16**, 851–858.

Gibson, J. G., and Gregersen, M. I. (1935a). *Proc. Am. J. Physiol.* **113**, 54.

Goldbloom, A. A., and Libin, I. (1935). *Arch. Internal Med.* **55**, 454.

Gray, S. J., and Frank, H. (1953). *J. Clin. Invest.* **32**, 991.

Gray, S. J., and Sterling, K. (1950a). *J. Clin. Invest.* **29**, 1614.

Gray, S. J., and Sterling, K. (1950b). *Science* **112**, 179.

Gregersen, M. I. (1951). *Ann. Rev. Physiol.* **13**, 397.

Gregersen, M. I., and Gibson, J. G. (1935b). *Proc. Am. J. Physiol.* **113**, 54.

Hahn, P. F. (1942). *J. Exptl. Med.* **75**, 221.

Hahn, P. F., Bale, W., and Whipple, G. (1939). *J. Exptl. Med.* 1939–1944 (many).

Hahn, P. F., Bale, W., and Whipple, G. (1942). *Am. J. Physiol.* 1942–1945 (many).

Hahn, P. F., Bale, W., and Whipple, G. (1943a). *J. Biol. Chem.* 1943–1946 (many).

Hahn, P. F., Granik, S., Bale, W., and Michaelis, L. (1943b). *J. Biol. Chem.* **150**, 407.

Hennessy, T., and Huff, R. (1950). *Proc. Soc. Exptl. Biol. Med.* **73**, 436.

Hevesy, G., Köster, K. H., Sørensen, G., Warburg, E., and Zerahn, K. (1944). *Acta Med. Scand.* **96**, 561–576.

Hoffmann, G., Keiderling, W., Schmidt, H. A. E., and Schoeppe, W. (1958). *Exptl. Med.* **130**, 301–311.

Huff, R. L., and Feller, D. D. (1956). *J. Clin. Invest.* **35**, 1.

Huff, R. L., and Hennessy, T. (1950). *Proc. Soc. Exptl. Biol. Med.* **73**, 436.

Huff, R. L., Hennessy, T., and Lawrence, J. H. (1949). *J. Clin. Invest.* **28**, 790.

Huff, R. L., Hennessy, T., Austin, R., Garcia, J. F., Roberts, B. M., and Lawrence, J. H. (1950). *J. Clin. Invest.* **29**, 1041.

Keiderling, W. (1956). "Radioaktive Isotope in Klinik und Forschung," Vol. 2, p. 40. Urban & Schwarzenberg, Munich, Germany.

Ledlie, E., and Vassar, P. (1956). "Radioaktive Isotope in Klinik und Forschung," Vol. 2, p. 52. Urban & Schwarzenberg, Munich, Germany.

Levin, E. (1935). *Rev. Arg. Cardiol.* **2**, 17.

Libin, I., and Goldbloom, A. A. (1935). *Arch. Internal Med.* **55**, 454.

Loeb, R. F. (1932). *Science* **76**, 420.

MacIntyre, W. J., and Pritchard, W. H. (1952). *Radiology* **59**, 848.

Maier-Leibnitz, H., and Pritchard, W. H. (1948). *Science* **108**, 634.

Marinelli, L. D., Quimby, E. H., and Hine, G. J. (1948). *Am. J. Roentgenol.* **59**, 260.

Mollison, P. L., and Veall, R. (1955). *Brit. J. Haematol.* **1**, 62.

Moore, C., Dubach, R., Winnich, V., and Roberts, H. (1944). *J. Clin. Invest.* **23**, 755.

Necheles, T., Weinstein, I., and Leroy, G. V. (1953). *J. Lab. Med.* **42**, 358.

Nylin, G., and Celander, H. (1950). *Circulation* **1**, 76.

Nylin, G., and Hedlund, S. (1949). *Am. Heart J.* **37**, 543.

Orr, M. K., and Reid, A. F. (1950). *J. Clin. Invest.* **29**, 313.

Peacock, W. C. (1946). *J. Clin. Invest.* **25**, 605.

Pfiffner, J. J., and Swingle, W. W. (1933). *Science* **77**, 58.

Pfiffner, J. J., and Swingle, W. W. (1938). *Am. J. Physiol.* **123**, 659.

Pritchard, W. H., and MacIntyre, W. J. (1952). *Radiology* **59**, 848.

Pritchard, W. H., MacIntyre, W. J., and Moir, T. W. (1955). *J. Lab. Clin. Med.* **46**, 939.

Ravidin, I. S., Walker, J. M., and Rhoads, J. E. (1954). *Am. Rev. Physiol.* **15**, 165.

Reed, R. C. (1954). *New Engl. J. Med.* **250**, 104–107.

Reeve, E. B. (1952). *Brit. Med. Bull.* **8**, 150.

Reeve, E. B., and Veall, N. (1949). *J. Physiol. (London)* **108**, 12–23.

Reid, A. F., and Orr, M. K. (1950). *J. Clin. Invest.* **29**, 313–316.

Rothschild, M. A. (1954). *J. Appl. Physiol.* **6**, 701.

Schmeiser, K., and Schwaiger, H. (1951). *Klin. Wochschr.* **29**, 536–540.

Schreiber, S. S., Bauman, A., Yalow, R. S., and Berson, S. A. (1954). *J. Clin. Invest.* **33**, 578.

Schwaiger, H., and Schmeiser, K. (1951). *Klin. Wochschr.* **29**, 536–540.

Sjøstrand, T. (1928). *J. Biol. Chem.* **78**, 807.

Smith, L., and Haldane, J. (1900). *J. Physiol. (London)* **25**, 331.

Smolik, N. (1956). *Surg. Gynecol. Obstet.* **263**, 185.

Spritzmetal, M., Corday, E., Spritzler, R. J., and Flieg, W. (1949). *J. Am. Med. Assoc.* **139**, 617.

Sterling, R., and Gray, S. J. (1950a). *J. Clin. Invest.* **29**, 1614.

Sterling, R., and Gray, S. J. (1950b). *Science* **112**, 179.

Sterling, R., and Gray, S. J. (1950c). *J. Clin. Invest.* **29**, 1604–1613.

Storaasli, J. P., Krieger, H., Friedell, H. L., and Holden, W. D. (1950). *Surg. Gynecol. Obstet.* **91**, 458–464.

Strumia, M. M., Taylor, L., Sample, A. B., Colwell, L. S., and Dugan, A. (1955). *Blood* **10**, 429–440.

Swan, R. J. C., and Wood, E. H. (1953). *Proc. Staff Meetings Mayo Clinic* **28**, 951.

Swingle, W. W., and Pfiffner, J. J. (1933). *Science* **77**, 58.

Swingle, W. W., and Pfiffner, J. J. (1938). *Am. J. Physiol.* **123**, 659.

Vasquez, O. N. (1952). *J. Lab. Clin. Med.* **39**, 595.

Vasquez, O. N. (1954). *J. Appl. Physiol.* **6**, 437.

Vassar, P., and Ledlie, E. (1956). "Radioaktive Isotope in Klinik und Forschung," Vol. 2, p. 52. Urban & Schwarzenberg, Munich, Germany.

Veall, N. (1948). *Brit. J. Radiol.* **21**, 347.

Veall, N., and Mollison, P. L. (1955). *Brit. J. Haematol.* **1**, 62.

Veall, N., and Reeve, E. B. (1949). *J. Physiol.* (*London*) **108**, 12–23.

Wahlund, H. (1954). *Acta Med. Scand.* **150**, 199.

Wennesland, R. (1955). *Circulation* **12**, 787.

Wilson, G. M., and Miller, H. (1951). *Brit. Heart J.* **13**, 227–232.

Wollheim, E. (1928a). *Z. Klin. Med.* **108**, 463.

Wollheim, E. (1928b). *Klin. Wochschr.* **7**, 1261.

Wollheim, W. (1929). *Verhandl. Deut. Ges. Inn. Med.* **41**, 357.

Wollheim, W. (1930). *Deut. Med. Wochschr.* **56**, 556.

Wollheim, W. (1931). *Z. Klin. Med.* **116**, 269.

Wood, E. H., and Swan, H. J. C. (1953). *Proc. Staff Meetings Mayo Clinic* **28**, 951.

Yalow, R. S., and Berson, S. A. (1951a). *J. Clin. Invest.* **31**, 572–580.

Yalow, R. S., and Berson, S. A. (1951b). *Science* **114**, 14–15.

CHAPTER 8

Blood Cell Studies with Radioautography

Edoardo Storti and Umberto Torelli

Institute of Medical Pathology, University of Modena, Modena, Italy

I. Introduction

It is widely accepted today that all types of hemic cells have to be regarded as different stages of differentiation and maturation of the primitive reticulum cells. Since differentiation is characterized by the presence of specific proteins, we can assume that each type of hemic cell is characterized by a certain protein synthetic activity. Furthermore, the process of cell differentiation is allied with the mechanism of determination of protein synthesis, rather than with the ultimate appearance of protein molecules. In the study of the metabolic processes related to cell differentiation, it seems therefore advisable to examine the synthesis of nucleic acids, since their activity must occur prior to ultimate protein synthesis and differentiation.

Investigations on nucleic acid and protein metabolism in hemic cells must be carried out at the cellular level, where one may expect wide variations in the different maturation stages. Radioautography, coupling the advantages of classical morphological methods with those of radio-isotopes, appears to be the best tool.

In the present chapter, we will attempt to give an outline of the knowledge hitherto obtained on nucleic acids and protein metabolism in hemic cells with high resolution radioautography. The theory, technique, and shortcomings of radioautography are not discussed here, since they have been repeatedly reviewed. However, some technical problems related to the use of tritium-labeled compounds are briefly presented, since our exposition will be mainly concerned with the use of these compounds. No attempt will be made to cover all the rapidly expanding literature in this field, and only papers which bear directly on the problem examined will be cited.

II. General Trends in the Radioautographic Study of Nucleic Acids and Protein Metabolism in Hemic Cells

According to the opinions currently accepted about the cellular components, deoxyribonucleic acid (DNA) controls the sequence of nucleotides in ribonucleic acid (RNA), and RNA, in turn, determines amino acid sequence during protein synthesis.

The metabolic features of these substances are quite different, and involve a great number of largely unsolved problems. However, some views have today gained almost complete acceptance and form the basis for most radioautographic work.

As far as DNA is concerned, the amount synthesized in every cell before division is constant in all the maturative stages, being, as a rule, the diploid value. A crucial assumption is that of DNA metabolic stability (Hughes, 1959). Once synthesized, DNA should remain stable, without exchange or metabolization of parts of the molecule, and any reduction of the amount of label incorporated during the synthesis should be due only to cell division. From the foregoing it is evident that it is possible to utilize the radioautographic study of DNA labeling, not only in order to establish the synthetic rates in various cell types and the changes in the synthetic rate in different stages of each cell cycle, but also to follow the fate of a cell, and determine the life-span, in other words, to examine the kinetics of cellular proliferation in growing tissues.

The matters are quite different when we consider RNA and protein. Obviously, wide variations in the amount of RNA and protein synthesis must exist in different stages of maturation. These differences might also be expected from the changes in morphology commonly observed during maturation of blood cells, such as the disappearance of the nucleolus and the increase in the size of the cytoplasm. In fact, it has been shown that in the nucleolus synthesis of RNA is much more active than protein synthesis (Leblond and Amano, 1962), whereas in the cytoplasm only the synthesis of protein is observed (Prescott, 1962).

It must be further emphasized that, unlike DNA, RNA appears in many cases to be metabolically unstable, so that we need to differentiate growth synthesis from replacement synthesis, i.e., from synthesis without resultant RNA increase.

Recent advances in molecular biology have shown that several different RNA species exist in the cell and play a different role in the execution of the message contained in DNA. Ribosomal, transfer, and messenger RNA's differ in many aspects, such as base composition, molecular size, synthetic pathways, and turnover rate. Differentiation at the cellular level of synthesis of the various RNA categories should be of great interest for a better metabolic and functional characterization of hemic cells.

As far as transfer RNA is concerned, its radioautographic study would appear possible using tritiated precursors, such as pseudouridine (Sirlin et al., 1961) or 5-methylcytosine (Srinivasan, 1962), which should be specifically incorporated into transfer RNA.

As for ribosomal and messenger RNA, no method is available, at present, for the differentiation of the two RNA fractions by radioautography. However, differentiation between ribosomal and messenger RNA synthesis in hemic cells has been attempted by measuring the turnover rate of cellular RNA (Torelli et al., 1964a,b). While ribosomal RNA appears quite stable (Davern and Meselsom, 1960; Rake and Graham, 1962), messenger RNA seems to be characterized by a very high turnover rate. A rapid metabolic rate is one of the main features of microbial messenger RNA (Levinthal et al., 1962). A short-lived RNA was also repeatedly observed in mammalian cells (Scholtissek, 1962; Sibatani, 1963; Lipmann, 1963; Harris, 1964). However, the observed stability of the template in some protein-producing animal cells (Nathans et al., 1962) led some authors to postulate that the regulation of protein synthesis in animal cells is not affected by a flow of unstable RNA molecules from DNA. The demonstration of the function of polyribosomes (ergosomes) in animal cells (Goodman and Rich, 1963) and the isolation of unstable messenger RNA from purified ergosomes (Staehelin et al., 1964) and from liver cytoplasm (Munro and Korner, 1964) suggest that the mechanism by which the genetic message is translated to ribosomes is basically similar in bacterial and animal cells. Rapid renewal is one of the main metabolic features of RNA fractions to which the function of messenger has been attributed, at least up to the present time. It seems, therefore, that differentiation between ribosomal and messenger RNA synthesis may be possible by turnover studies. A criterion for distinguishing the functional meaning of an RNA fraction in a cell might be given by the position of the cell in the maturation scale. The observation that protein synthesis occurs in cells in which RNA synthesis has ceased, as shown in chicken nucleated erythrocytes (Cameron and Prescott, 1963), in reticulocytes (Pinheiro et al., 1963), and in mature plasmacytes (Mitchell and Nossal, 1963), would indicate that the information is elaborated in the early phases of the different maturation scales. The observation of the synthesis of an RNA fraction with a rapid turnover rate in cells in an early stage of differentiation might justify the identification of this RNA with a messenger fraction.

As for the relationship between unstable RNA and protein synthesis in animal cells, it must be remembered that Allfrey (1963) showed that the uptake of amino acids by ribosomes requires the prior synthesis of messenger RNA. He was able to observe that after inhibition by actinomycin of messenger RNA synthesis the protein synthetic rate remained normal for about 60 minutes. Harris (1964) recently concluded that most of the unstable RNA in animal cells may be destroyed without directly influencing the rate of protein synthesis.

III. Technical Problems

A. The Use of Tritium as a Label

The advantages of tritium as a label for radioautography are well known: substances with much higher specific activity than the C^{14} compounds are obtained, and the beta particles emitted are very soft and give a very high resolution. However, since the range of the beta particles is so short (energy of emission 0.018 Mev; average range in tissues about 1μ), the possibility of obtaining quantitative measurements of incorporation from grain counts has often been questioned. Factors affecting overall efficiency of radioautography with tritium have been repeatedly examined (Robertson et al., 1959; Kisieleski et al., 1961; Baserga and Nemeroff, 1962). As a matter of fact, if the beta particles emanating from the different cell parts pass through different thicknesses of substance before reaching the emulsion and thus undergo different amounts of self-absorption, a relevant error might be made. It must be remembered that we have no exact indication of the thickness of different blood cells on smears.

However, Wimber *et al.* (1960) observed no significant correlation between the thickness of a labeled cell and the number of grains over the nucleus. These authors think that since most of the radioautographic effect of intranuclear tritium can be due to a surface layer thickness of about $\frac{1}{2}$ μ, the fraction of the volume comprised in this layer can be considered as the fraction of the total cellular volume that is radioautographically effective. Thickness factor must be taken into consideration when comparing the incorporating activities of the various cell components, i.e., nucleus, nucleolus, and cytoplasm, and the relative correction factors have been calculated (Perry *et al.*, 1961).

A relevant problem concerning the use of tritium as label is that of radiation damage to the cell. Painter and co-workers (1958) found inhibition of HeLa cell cultures grown on a medium containing 2.5 to 5 μc/ml of H^3-thymidine, and Drew and Painter (1959) observed that few HeLa cells continued to divide after growing in a medium containing H^3-thymidine at concentrations of 0.1 μc/ml. Chromosomal damage from H^3-thymidine was repeatedly shown (Taylor, 1958; Wimber, 1959). The problem of radiation effects of tritium is complicated by the geometry, since the energy of each disintegration is dissipated in a small volume of the nucleus (Lajtha and Oliver, 1959). The problem was widely discussed at the Salt Lake Conference on the kinetics of cellular proliferation (Stohlman, 1959). Until definite conclusions are reached, it would seem highly advisable that the use of tritium-labeled compounds be limited to short-term (a few hours) experiments, in which radiation effects are unlikely to be significant.

B. TRITIATED PRECURSORS

As for the precursors used in the study of DNA, RNA, and protein synthesis in blood cells, it must be remembered that the number of labeled molecules incorporated depends on several factors, such as the dilution of the radioisotope in the medium, the concentration reached by the labeled substance in the cells under study, and the content of the unlabeled substance and its precursors in the cells. Since we have no information about the intracellular precursor pool in the different types of blood cells, it is evident that for an effective comparison of the synthetic activities in the various cells, one should employ precursors which may be incorporated easily in all the cells.

As far as DNA is concerned, it is now widely accepted that tritium-labeled thymidine is the best labeled precursor for the study of DNA synthesis. N^{15}-Thymidine was shown to be a specific precursor of DNA by Reichard and Estborn in 1951, but H^3-thymidine became available only after the work of Taylor *et al.* (1957). Lajtha (1959) has cautioned that no information is available on the intracellular pool in different cells. The problem was discussed at the *Ciba Foundation Symposium on Haemopoiesis* (Wolstenholme and O'Connor, 1960): the very existence of a significant pool of endogenous thymidine was questioned. Significant labeling was observed in human granuloblasts within one minute after injection of H^3-thymidine (Cronkite *et al.*, 1960). Likewise, significant labeling was observed in erythroblasts, as well as in lymphoblasts, within one minute after the addition of H^3-thymidine to the medium in *in vitro* experiments (Mauri and Torelli, 1960). It is evident that tritiated thymidine can cross the cytoplasm and nuclear membrane and be incorporated into the DNA of some cells in less than 60 seconds. Therefore, the influence of the intracellular pool on the uptake of H^3-thymidine does not seem great, at least as far as hemic cells are concerned.

A more complex problem at present appears to be the choice of RNA precursors. It has been questioned whether RNA labeling with tritiated nucleosides may be an index of the effective synthesis of a nucleotide chain. As a matter of fact, exchange of the uridine-containing nucleotide without synthesis of RNA has been demonstrated *in vitro* in isolated thymus nuclei (Allfrey and Mirsky, 1959), and the terminal cytidylyl-cytidylyl-adenylyl complex of the soluble RNA might also be labeled by exchange (Vincent and Baltus, 1960). However, as regards hemic cells, the observation of the effects of actinomycin on RNA labeling seems to settle the question. This substance completely inhibits the synthesis of all types of RNA (Reich *et al.*, 1962) and this action is correlated with its ability to bind DNA (Hamilton *et al.*, 1963). Actinomycin added to blood or bone marrow cultures a few minutes before the addition of tracer produces complete inhibition of RNA labeling (Torelli *et al.*, 1964a,b). This finding suggests that the radioautographically evidenced uptake of precursors is due to effective synthesis. Until recently no precursor was available which was as specific for RNA as is H^3-thymidine for DNA. Labeled orotic acid was suggested, which is the precursor of the pyrimidine groups of RNA (Hurlbert and Potter, 1952), but its use did not spread. Much more widely used in the study of RNA synthesis at present are some tritiated nucleosides, such as H^3-cytidine, H^3-uridine, and H^3-adenosine, although none of them may be regarded as the choice precursor for all types of RNA* H^3-Cytidine in tissue culture cells produces an intracellular labeling pattern different from that of H^3-adenosine (Harris, 1959; Perry *et*

---

* A step forward in the search for a more specific RNA precursor has been achieved by the introduction of uridine tritiated in the 5 position (Hayhoe and Quaglino, 1965).

al., 1961). Furthermore, H^3-uridine in peripheral blood cells exhibits a labeling pattern different from that of H^3-cytidine (Torelli *et al.*, 1964b). For the study of RNA synthesis in hemic cells, H^3-cytidine may perhaps be considered as the most useful precursor. It is widely taken up by all types of hemic cells, being perhaps less affected by the intracellular pool.

As far as amino acid uptake is concerned, although it can also represent amino acid activation or exchange, it is today generally considered as an indication that a segment of a peptide chain is being synthesized. Many tritium-labeled anino acids are available for radioautographic study. However, wide differences are observed in the uptake of different amino acids by a certain cell type. Obviously, the influence of the intracellular amino acid pool must be very high. Arginine, lysine, tyrosine, phenylalanine, and leucine labeled with tritium were tested as protein precursors in the authors' laboratory, in search of a substance which might be taken up easily by all types of blood cells. It was found that H^3-leucine give the highest labeling values in all the cells, and this substance was chosen as a protein precursor.

As to the employment of tritiated nucleosides, such as H^3-cytidine, H^3-uridine, or H^3-adenosine, a further problem is that they are incorporated not only in RNA, but also in DNA. It is evident that in all multiplying cells, such as most immature cells of hematopoietic tissue, it is necessary to distinguish between RNA synthesis and DNA synthesis. Treatment such as extraction, specific staining, or enzymatic digestion might be used. For instance, digestion with deoxyribonuclease, allowing selective elimination of DNA, may be used to determine whether the radioactive substance is of ribonucleic acid nature. However, after nuclease digestion the morphological identification of cell types is often very difficult. Furthermore, by using nuclease, cells of different functional activity are studied, since DNA-synthesizing cells are examined as well as cells which do not synthesize DNA. A way to overcome these difficulties was presented by the observation that DNA is synthesized only during a certain phase of the intermitotic cycle (Howard and Pelc, 1953; Lajtha *et al.*, 1954), so that cells which are not in phase of DNA synthesis incorporate the tritiated nucleosides only into RNA. The selection of the cells not synthesizing DNA can be achieved, as pointed out by Harris (1959), by adding H^3-thymidine to the medium containing other labeled nucleosides. Cells in the stage of DNA synthesis incorporate these compounds into both RNA and DNA, and H^3-thymidine into DNA. The nuclei of such cells are therefore much more heavily labeled than the nuclei of cells not in the phase of DNA synthesis, and the two groups of cells are easily distinguishable.

C. Study of Turnover Rate at the Cellular Level

As we have emphasized above, metabolic differentiation of RNA's by radioautography depends largely, in view of our present state of knowledge, on the measure of the rate of release of the labeled precursors. However, measurement of intracellular RNA turnover is very difficult, owing to the existence of a large intracellular precursor pool which becomes balanced with radioactive exogenous precursors very slowly. It has been shown that the products of turnover are reutilized by the cell in the resynthesis of RNA (Watts and Harris, 1959). Under this condition it seems very difficult to establish the turnover rate. In order to overcome this obstacle, Watts and Harris (1959) suggested adding to the medium some unlabeled substance which would interfere with the turnover, so that some labeled intermediate was displaced by this compound in the process of recycling.

Recently, study of the RNA turnover rate in hemic cells was attempted in the authors' laboratory by utilizing the properties of actinomycin D (Torelli et al., 1964a,b, 1965a). This antibiotic completely inhibits the synthesis of all the RNA fractions in mammalian cells (Reich et al., 1962), and its biological activity is correlated to its ability to bind DNA by complexing specifically to guanine (Hamilton et al., 1963). It must be emphasized that RNA-dependent RNA synthesis is unaffected, so that it has been suggested that all of the cellular RNA is produced in a DNA-dependent reaction (Reich et al., 1962). Furthermore, Harris (1963) was able to observe that even at a concentration of 40 μg/ml actinomycin has no effect on the polynucleotide phosphorylase-like enzyme which degrades the rapidly labeled RNA. It therefore seems possible to investigate the intracellular breakdown of labeled RNA under conditions in which concomitant synthesis of this substance is completely prevented. Of course, the possibility cannot be excluded that some artifacts may be produced by treating the cells with actinomycin. However, as pointed out by Reich (1963), it appears possible that actinomycin may be completely innocuous to all cellular processes not primarily involved in DNA metabolism.

IV. Nucleic Acids and Protein Metabolism in Bone Marrow Cells

A. DNA

In short-term incubation of bone marrow cells with labeled DNA precursors it can be observed that only a certain proportion of young dividing cells take up the DNA label, indicating that although a cell before dividing must synthesize a full diploid amount of DNA, this is synthesized only during a part of the interphase (Lajtha *et al.*, 1954). Thus it is evident that for a functionally homogeneous type of cell, the percentage of labeling indicates the length of the synthetic period in relation to the length of the over-all intermitotic time. If all the cells of the type studied are able to synthesize DNA, this percentage will increase up to 90–100% by increasing the time of contact with the label. The time of continuous labeling needed to reach the highest grain counts indicates the length of the synthetic period. Obviously, for such determinations either a prolonged *in vitro* culture or a continuous *in vivo* infusion with the label are needed, but it was observed that in prolonged experiments the maturation of young labeled cells to mature forms may cause a misleading evaluation of the proportion of mature dividing cells (Lajtha, 1959).

Detailed data on *in vivo* labeling of erythroblasts after injection of a single dose of H^3-thymidine in a human being have been presented by Bond *et al.* (1959). After intravenous introduction of 1.9 mc of H^3-thymidine, the percentages of labeled cells, as well as the mean grain counts, increased until 90 minutes after the injection. At this time, the following labeling percentages were reported: 80–100% in two different types of proerythroblasts; 74% in basophilic erythroblasts; 56% in polychromatic erythroblasts; and 0% in orthochromatic elements. Labeled orthochromatic cells began to appear only after 3 hours.

In vitro studies were carried out by Lajtha (1959), who controlled the results obtained with H^3-thymidine by repeating the experiments with formate-C^{14}, which *in vitro* is nearly as specific a DNA label as is H^3-thymidine. He reports labeling percentages of 66% in early basophilic erythroblasts and of 33% in polychromatic cells. *In vitro* studies were also performed by Gavosto *et al.* (1959) and by Mauri (1961). The results of these authors, although somewhat different, are in good agreement with the results of Lajtha (1959).

As far as granuloblasts are concerned, *in vivo* data obtained with H^3-thymidine have been reported by Cronkite *et al.* (1960). The labeling percentages were 35–93% in myeloblasts, 76% in promyelocytes, 68% in large myelocytes. Metamyelocytes were not labeled initially, and the first labeling appeared 3 hours after the injection of thymidine. Patt and Maloney (1959) observed in dogs injected with H^3-thymidine that the percentage of myeloblasts and promyelocytes labeled after 30 minutes was about three times that of myelocytes, perhaps owing to the difficulty of a sharp differentiation between myelocytes and metamyelocytes.

Labeling percentages of 60% in promyelocytes and 30% in myelocytes are given by Lajtha (1959) after *in vitro* incubation with H^3-thymidine, and similar values (40–50% in myeloblasts and promyelocytes; 10–20%

in myelocytes) are reported by Gavosto *et al.* (1959) and by Mauri (1962).

From the above-mentioned data the conclusion must be drawn that in immature cells the DNA synthetic phase(S) is long if compared to the over-all intermitotic period. This occurs although the mean length of the S period in young cells is lesser than in mature forms, owing to the higher DNA synthesis rate, as shown by the differences in the mean grain counts. Bond *et al.* (1959) report the following mean grain counts in red cell precursors: proerythroblasts, 50–80; basophilic erythroblasts, 25; polychromatic erythroblasts, 12. Lajtha (1959) obtained mean grain numbers of 74 in basophilic and 39 in polychromatic erythroblasts, while in granuloblasts the mean grain number were 60 in promyelocytes and 37 in myelocytes.

Lajtha *et al.* (1960) point out that if the synthetic rate of a substance in a cell type is constant, the radioautographic grain counts should show a Poisson distribution. However, this is not the case in myeloid cells labeled with H^3-thymidine (Lajtha *et al.*, 1960). In erythroblasts, grain count distribution studies support an exponentially changing rate of DNA synthesis, increasing from the $2n$ to the $4n$ value (Lajtha and Oliver, 1960).

The over-all intermitotic time of the young forms appears much shorter than that of the mature forms. Lajtha (1959) calculated a cell cycle time of about 18 hours in basophilic erythroblasts and 66 hours in polychromatic elements. Cronkite *et al.* (1960) report the following generation times: about 31 hours for myeloblasts; between 24 and 60 hours for promyelocytes; and about 54 hours for large myelocytes.

B. RNA and Protein

Unlike DNA synthesis, RNA, as well as protein synthesis, occur throughout the entire interphase (Lajtha *et al.*, 1954). Like DNA synthesis, RNA and protein synthesis proceed at a lower rate in the late forms than in young forms (Lajtha, 1959). However, the ratio between the uptake of RNA precursors and that of protein precursors is by no means constant in different maturation stages (Torelli *et al.*, 1964a, 1965a). Table I shows the mean grain counts after incubation *in vitro* of bone marrow cells with H^3-cytidine, H^3-uridine, and H^3-leucine. It is evident that the synthetic activity decreases as maturation of erythroblastic and granuloblastic cells proceeds, but the decrease of RNA synthetic rate is much greater than that of protein synthesis, so that the ratio between the labeling values in the young forms is several times that in the mature forms. The findings of Torelli *et al.* (1964a, 1965a) clearly demonstrate that for every molecule of leucine taken up into protein, immature myeloid cells synthesize a much greater amount of RNA than mature forms do.

In an attempt to establish the turnover rate of the RNA synthesized in myeloid cells, investigations using actinomycin D were carried out by Torelli *et al.* (1964a, 1965a). Figures 1 and 2 show the rate of release of the label in erythroblasts and in granuloblasts, respectively.

In erythroblasts, two different metabolic fractions may be clearly distinguished. The synthesis of a fraction with high turnover rate is suggested by the rapid drop in grain counts after 30 minutes of incubation with actinomycin in all types of cells, except orthochromatic ele-

TABLE I

UPTAKE OF RNA AND PROTEIN PRECURSORS IN BONE MARROW CELLS
OF A NORMAL SUBJECT[a]

Cell type	H^3-Cytidine	H^3-Uridine	H^3-Leucine	Cytidine: leucine ratio	Uridine: leucine ratio
Myeloblasts	81	83	55	1.47	1.50
Neutral promyelocytes	70	76	86	0.80	0.88
Neutral myelocytes	32	39	52	0.61	0.75
Neutral metamyelocytes	11	12	40	0.27	0.30
Proerythroblasts	90	70	85	1.05	0.82
Basophilic erythroblasts	52	50	74	0.70	0.67
Polychromic erythroblasts	21	25	30	0.70	0.67
Orthochromic erythroblasts	7	6	21	0.33	0.28

[a]The figures indicate the mean grain counts obtained after 1 hour of incubation with the labeled precursors at the concentration of 10 μc/ml.

ments. A second fraction, much more stable, is evidenced by the fact that the labeling values were almost unchanged between 60 and 120 minutes of incubation with actinomycin. This fraction appears to be the only one present in orthochromatic erythroblasts.

The rapid initial drop of radioactivity and the persistence of high labeling values at the end of the period of incubation with actinomycin suggest that a highly unstable fraction, as well as a stable one, are synthesized also in granuloblastic cells.

One of the more interesting features evidenced by the radioautographic study of RNA metabolism in myeloid cells is the synthesis, in young forms only, of an RNA fraction with high turnover rate. As for the functional meaning of this RNA fraction, we have previously pointed out (Section II) that the high turnover rate was one of the main metabolic

features of the RNA fractions to which the function of messenger has
been attributed, at least up to the present time. The hypothesis was
therefore formulated that the RNA fraction with high turnover rate synthesized in immature erythroblastic and granuloblastic cells has the functional significance of a messenger fraction (Torelli et al., 1964a, 1965a).

It seems advisable to emphasize that unstable RNA is not synthesized

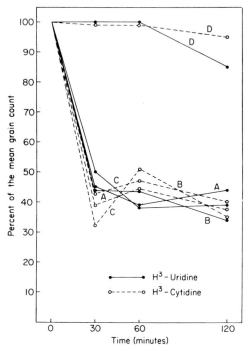

Fig. 1. Effect of actinomycin on RNA radioactivity in normal human erythroblasts
previously incubated for 1 hour with H^3-cytidine and H^3-uridine. The percentages
of the mean grain counts for each maturation stage are plotted against the interval
after the addition of actinomycin: (A) proerythroblasts; (B) basophilic erythroblasts; (C) polychromatic erythroblasts; (D) orthochromatic erythroblasts.

in orthochromatic erythroblasts and in metamyelocytes, resting cells in
which DNA synthesis is stopped. This finding must be reconnected
to the observed stability of RNA in hemoglobin-producing reticulocytes
(Nathans et al., 1962) which has been regarded as a confirmation
of the stability of messenger RNA in mammalian cells (Lipmann, 1963).
The reported synthesis of highly unstable RNA in young myeloid cells
would indicate that the information for protein synthesis is elaborated
only during the phase of active proliferation of the immature cells, so

that presumably any messenger RNA is attached to the ribosomes early in cell maturation. In this connection it must be remembered that in both chicken nucleated erythrocytes (Cameron and Prescott, 1963) and rat reticulocytes (Pinheiro et al., 1963) radioautographic study of the uptake of tritiated precursors of RNA and protein showed that RNA synthesis stops before protein synthesis.

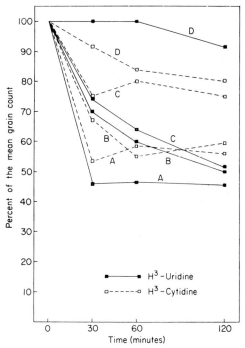

Fig. 2. Effect of actinomycin on RNA radioactivity in normal human granulo-blasts previously incubated for 1 hour with H^3-cytidine and H^3-uridine. The percentages of the mean grain counts for each maturation stage are plotted against the interval after the addition of actinomycin: (A) myeloblasts; (B) promyelocytes; (C) myelocytes; (D) metamyelocytes.

V. Nucleic Acids and Protein Metabolism in Lymphatic Cells

A. DNA

Labeling of DNA has hitherto been employed mainly in order to follow the fate of the lymphatic cells. Much less attention has been paid to the features of DNA synthesis in the different lymphatic cell types.

Schooley et al. (1959) carried out in vivo studies on lymphocytopoiesis in mice by injecting 1 μc H^3-thymidine per gram and examining at various intervals smears of blood, lymph, bone marrow, and lymph nodes. A high percentage of large cells was labeled rapidly in lymphatic tissues, whereas the starting percentage of labeled small lymphocytes was very low. This percentage however increased with time. In blood, a considerable fraction of the medium lymphocytes were labeled after a few hours, but they had completely disappeared after 9 days. On the contrary, the percentage of labeled small lymphocytes increased for the first 3 days and then declined gradually. In *in vitro* experiments, Schooley *et al.* (1959) observed that about 65–70% of lymphocytes larger than 10 μ were labeled in thymus and mesenteric nodes, whereas small lymphocytes were labeled in significant percentage (2–5%) only in the thymus.

In *vivo* studies were also performed in the guinea pig and in the rat by Everett *et al.* (1960a,b). Their results, in agreement with the findings of Schooley *et al.* (1959), were summarized as follows (Everett *et al.*, 1960b). (1) Large and medium lymphocytes are labeled early in all the tissues. (2) The proportion of labeled medium cells increases during the first few hours. (3) Small lymphocytes begin to be labeled only after a certain interval. (4) The mean intensity of labeling decreases from large to medium to small lymphocytes.

Labeling experiments with H^3-thymidine seem therefore to substantiate the opinion that maturation of lymphoid cells proceeds from large to medium to small lymphocytes.

In an attempt to obtain more detailed information on lymphocytopoiesis, the method of Algire *et al.* (1958) of *in vivo* culture in diffusion chambers, combined with radioautography, was employed by Schooley and Berman (1960) and by Everett *et al.* (1960) to study lymphocyte formation in an isolated population of labeled lymphoid cells. It was observed that the number of labeled small lymphocytes increased during the period of culture, whereas the number of labeled large and medium lymphocytes decreased. These results therefore give further support to the opinion that small lymphocytes are derived from their medium and large precursors.

Several studies were made, using tritiated thymidine, to settle the question of the life span of small lymphocytes. A long life span of most of the lymphocytes was indicated by the observations of Ottesen (1954) and Christensen and Ottesen (1955), but Hamilton (1956) suggested that reutilization by lymphocytes of large fragments of nucleic acids or nucleoproteins of their progenitors might explain the prolonged retention of radioactivity in lymphatic tissues. Little *et al.* (1962) carried out experiments in rats using continuous infusion of H^3-thymidine for 90 days. It was observed that all granulocytes were labeled by the 3rd or 4th day, all large lymphocytes by the 60th day, but 100% labeling of small lymphocytes was not achieved until after 100 days of infusion. These data therefore support a long life span for the small lymphocytes.

In agreement with these results are the observations of Caffrey et al. (1962) suggesting the existence of two populations of small lymphocytes, one having a long circulating life span (at least 8 weeks) and another with a circulating life of less than 14 days. The data of Little et al. (1962) and of Caffrey et al. (1962) seem to exclude DNA reutilization as an explanation for the prolonged life of lymphocytes.

B. RNA AND PROTEIN

Few radioautographic data are available so far on RNA and protein synthesis in lymphoid cells. Experiments aimed at studying the *in vitro* uptake of RNA and protein precursors in peripheral lymphocytes were carried out recently in the authors' laboratory (Torelli *et al.*, 1963, 1964b). Circulating human lymphocytes were subdivided into five categories. Subdivision was made on the basis of morphological characteristics, such as size of the nucleus, chromatin pattern, and amount of cytoplasm. Table II shows the mean grain counts obtained in each cell type with H^3-cytidine, H^3-uridine, and H^3-leucine.

TABLE II

UPTAKE OF RNA AND PROTEIN PRECURSORS IN NORMAL
CIRCULATING HUMAN LYMPHOCYTES[a]

Cell type	H^3- Cytidine	H^3- Uridine	H^3- Leucine	Cytidine: leucine ratio	Uridine: leucine ratio
A	92	55	18	5.11	3.00
B	66	10	19	3.40	0.52
C	33	13	10	3.30	1.30
D	36	17	27	1.33	0.62
E	45	21	51	0.88	0.41

[a]Circulating lymphocytes were grouped morphologically in 5 types, as follows. Type A: large round cells with central nucleus with nucleolus and a very fine chromatin pattern and a narrow, basophilic cytoplasm. Type B: cells of smaller size than the above-mentioned elements, with scanty basophilic cytoplasm and with a fine network of chromatin particles, mixed with areas of coarse chromatin masses. Type C: small lymphocytes, without distinct cytoplasm or with a very thin layer and large coarse chromatin masses. Type D: cells of a size larger than that of group C, with cytoplasm always evident and chromatin less dense than in small lymphocytes. Type E: large mature lymphocytes, with abundant cytoplasm and eccentrically located nucleus. The figures indicate the mean grain counts obtained after 1 hour of incubation with H^3-cytidine and H^3-uridine and 2 hours of incubation with H^3-leucine.

RNA and protein are synthesized in circulating lymphocytes, and wide differences in the synthetic rates exist between these cells. As shown in Table II, H^3-uridine gives an incorporation pattern quite different from that of H^3-cytidine. As far as these differences are concerned, one can assume that wide variations exist in size and com-

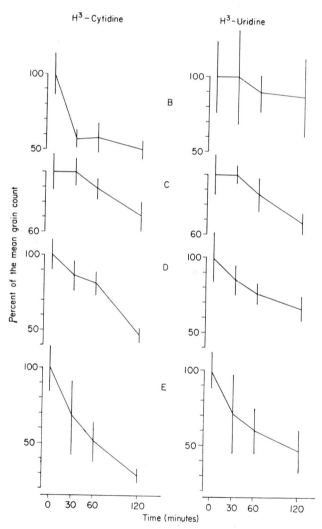

Fig. 3. Effect of actinomycin on RNA radioactivity in normal peripheral lymphocytes, previously incubated with H^3-cytidine and H^3-uridine. The percentages of the mean grain counts for each cell type are plotted against the interval after the addition of actinomycin. For the description of the cell types (A–E), see Table II.

position of pools in the different types of lymphocytes. Therefore, it is not possible to establish whether the labeling values reflect differences in metabolic pathways or differences in base composition. However, possibilities for the settlement of this question are offered by the observation of differences in the rate of release of the two labeled precursors after inhibition of the RNA synthesis with actinomycin (Torelli *et al.*, 1964b).

As shown in Fig. 3, the RNA degradation curve in lymphocytes with large cytoplasm, where H^3-uridine uptake is high, is quite different from that of immature lymphocytes, where H^3-cytidine uptake predominates. Furthermore, in the latter cells, the rate of release of H^3-uridine is much less than that of H^3-cytidine. The hypothesis was therefore formulated that H^3-cytidine labels an RNA fraction prevailing in immature lymphocytes, whereas H^3-uridine labels mainly an RNA fraction prevailing in lymphocytes with large cytoplasm.

Three different RNA metabolic fractions were identified in circulating lymphocytes (Torelli *et al.*, 1964b). A first fraction was evidenced, in immature lymphocytes, by the sharp decline in labeling in the initial period of incubation with actinomycin. Owing to the high turnover rate and to the low protein synthesis in these cells, this fraction was tentatively considered as messenger RNA. A second metabolic fraction, quite stable, is shown in the same cell type by the fact that the labeling values are unchanged between 30 and 120 minutes of incubation. Since ribosomal RNA is quite stable and since the presence of ribosomes in the nucleus has been repeatedly demonstrated (Allfrey, 1963), the synthesis of the stable RNA fraction has been attributed to the synthesis of nuclear ribosomes. A third metabolic fraction was shown in the lymphocytes having large cytoplasm. In these cells the labeling decreases gradually during the period of incubation with actinomycin, until minimal values, so that the precursor uptake cannot be related either to a stable fraction, or to a very unstable one. The difference between the RNA fraction synthesized in lymphocytes having large cytoplasm and the RNA fractions synthesized in lymphocytes of the immature type is also shown by the high uptake of H^3-uridine in the former cells.

VI. Nucleic Acids and Protein Metabolism in Plasma Cells

A. DNA

Experiments aimed at studying the H^3-thymidine uptake in plasma cells were carried out by Schooley (1961). He observed that 1 hour after the injection of H^3-thymidine in immunized mice, 80% of early plasmablasts and 45% of late plasmablasts and proplasmacytes were labeled, whereas no labeled early and late plasmacytes were found. However, a very rapid increase in the percentage of labeled plasmacytes was observed, and after 8 hours 80% of these cells were labeled. The maximum generation time for early plasmablasts, in Schooley's experiments, was 12–14 hours. Furthermore, the observation that 80% of early plasmablasts were labeled at 1 hour and that anaphase figures of cells presumed to be plasmablasts were observed at the same time suggested that DNA synthesis occurs during most of the interphase.

In the experiments of Nossal and Mäkelä (1962), immunized rats were injected with H^3-thymidine, and after the complete removal of the label from the circulatory system, a secondary response was obtained, and the animals were sacrificed at intervals. Only those cells originating from elements labeled before the secondary stimulation were labeled in these conditions. It was observed that almost all the plasma cells evoked by the secondary stimulus were labeled, which suggests that the plasma cells must have arisen from cells already capable of synthesizing DNA in the resting node. This observation should lead to exclusion of small lymphocytes, macrophages, mature plasma cells, and reticular cells from consideration as plasma cell precursors. The large lymphocytes, in agreement with data previously reported on DNA labeling in lymphoid cells, would seem to be the more probable progenitors of plasmablasts and plasmacytes. According to Nossal and Mäkelä (1962), the generation time of plasmablasts should be 12 hours or less.

Further experiments were carried out by the same authors (Mäkelä and Nossal, 1962) in order to study DNA synthesis activity of antibody-forming cells from their early stage to the completely mature form. They observed that most immature cells were incorporating H^3-thymidine, whereas mature plasmacytes did not show H^3-thymidine uptake. An inverse relationship was found between antibody-forming and DNA-synthesizing activities in the cells of the plasmacytic series.

B. RNA AND PROTEIN

Few radioautographic data are available, at present, on RNA and protein synthesis in plasma cells. What is known, however, suggests that also in this cell type no constant relationship exists between RNA and protein synthesis and that, as in myeloid and lymphatic cells, in immature forms the RNA synthetic rate is relatively much higher than that of protein, whereas in older forms protein synthesis prevails. Schooley (1961) observed that H^3-leucine uptake into proteins of both immature and mature plasmacytes was low, thus concluding that the synthesis of protein, presumably antibody protein, is minimal in mature plasma cells. This conclusion was supported by the lack of H^3-cytidine uptake in the same cells.

However, further investigations by Mitchell and Nossal (1963) led to different conclusions. These authors were able to demonstrate that mature plasma cells do not incorporate H^3-cytidine, whereas they can take up H^3-leucine when the substance is available continuously to the cells. The grain counts however do not rise further after 1 hour of incubation. It was therefore concluded that mature plasma cells do not synthesize RNA, whereas they actively synthesize antibodies, although these are quickly released. As for immature forms, on the other hand, the RNA synthesis rate appeared very high. A fraction of this RNA showed a rapid turnover rate, whereas another part was more stable.

Recent radioautographic findings (Torelli *et al.*, 1965b) indicate that in the plasma cell series the conspicuous RNA synthesis present in the more immature cells decreases as maturation progresses, while amino acid uptake is greater in mature plasmacytes. It was observed that a considerable fraction of the RNA present in plasmablasts is unstable and may possibly be identified with messenger RNA. This metabolic pattern is in sharp contrast with that found in phytohemagglutinin (PHA)—stimulated lymphocytes which, not unlike plasma cells, produce gamma globulins (Bach and Hishhorn, 1963). In PHA-transformed lymphocytes the RNA parallels closely the increase in protein synthesis (Torelli *et al.*, 1966). It was therefore suggested that this increase, which takes place in PHA cultures, is dependent on a biochemical mechanism causing an enhanced intracellular availability of transfer RNA (Torelli *et al.*, 1965b).

REFERENCES

Algire, G. H., Borders, M. L., and Evans, V. J. (1958). *J. Natl. Cancer Inst.* **20**, 1187.

Allfrey, V. G. (1963). *Exptl. Cell Res. Suppl.* **9**, 183.

Allfrey, V. G., and Mirsky, A. E. (1959). *Proc. Natl. Acad. Sci. U.S.* **45**, 1325.

Bach, F., and Hirshhorn, K. (1963). *Exptl. Cell Res.* **32**, 592.

Baserga, A., and Nemeroff, K. (1962). *Stain Technol.* **37**, 21.

Bond, V. P., Fliedner, T. M., Cronkite, E. P., Rubini, J. R., and Robertson, J. S. (1959). *In* "The Kinetics of Cellular Proliferation" (F. Stohlman, Jr., ed.), pp. 188–200. Grune & Stratton, New York.

Caffrey, R. W., Rieke, W. O., and Everett, N. B. (1962). *Acta Haematol.* **28**, 145.

Cameron, T. L., and Prescott, D. M. (1963). *Exptl. Cell Res.* **30**, 609.

Christensen, B. C., and Ottesen, J. (1955). *Acta Haematol.* **13**, 289.

Cronkite, E. P., Bond, V. P., Fliedner, T. M., and Killman, S. A. (1960). *In* "Ciba Foundation Symposium on Haemopoiesis" (G. E. W. Wolstenholme and M. O'Connor, eds.), pp. 70–92. Churchill, London.

Davern, C. I., and Meselsom, M. (1960). *J. Mol. Biol.* **2**, 153.

Drew, R. M., and Painter, R. B. (1959). *Radiation Res.* **11**, 535.

Everett, N. B., Reinhardt, W. O., and Yoffey, I. M. (1960a). *Blood* **15**, 82.

Everett, N. B., Rieke, W. O., Reinhardt, W. O., and Yoffey, Y. M. (1960b). *In*

"Ciba Foundation Symposium on Haemopoiesis" (G. E. W. Wolstenholme and M. O'Connor, eds.), pp. 43–66. Churchill, London.

Gavosto, F., Pileri, A., and Maraini, G. (1959). *Haematologica* (*Pavia*) **44**, 977.

Goodman, H. M., and Rich, A. (1963). *Nature* **199**, 318.

Hamilton, L. D. (1956). *Nature* **178**, 597.

Hamilton, L. D., Fuller, W., and Reich, E. (1963). *Nature* **198**, 538.

Harris, H. (1959). *Biochem. J.* **73**, 362.

Harris, H. (1963). *Nature* **198**, 184.

Harris, H. (1964). *Nature* **201**, 863.

Hayhoe, F. G. J., and Quaglino, D. (1965). *Nature* **205**, 151.

Howard, A., and Pelc, S. R. (1953). *Heredity* **6**, Suppl., 261.

Hughes, W. L. (1959). In "The Kinetics of Cellular Proliferation" (F. Stohlman, Jr., ed.), pp. 83–94. Grune & Stratton, New York.

Hurlbert, R. B., and Potter, V. R. (1952). *J. Biol. Chem.* **195**, 257.

Kisieleski, W. E., Baserga, R., and Vaupotic, J. (1961). *Radiation Res.* **15**, 341.

Lajtha, L. G. (1959). In "The Kinetics of Cellular Proliferation" (F. Stohlman, Jr., ed.), pp. 173–182. Grune & Stratton, New York.

Lajtha, L. G., and Oliver, R. (1959). *Lab. Invest.* **8**, 219.

Lajtha, L. G., and Oliver, R. (1960). In "Ciba Foundation Symposium on Haemopoiesis" (G. E. W. Wolstenholme and M. O'Connor, eds.), pp. 289–314. Churchill, London.

Lajtha, L. G., Oliver, R., and Ellis, F. (1954). *Brit. J. Cancer* **8**, 367.

Lajtha, L. G., Oliver, R., Berry, R. J., and Hell, E. (1960). *Nature* **187**, 919.

Leblond, C. P., and Amano, M. (1962). *J. Histochem. Cytochem.* **10**, 162.

Levinthal, C., Keynan, A., and Higa, A. (1962). *Proc. Natl. Acad. Sci. U.S.* **48**, 1631.

Lipmann, F. (1963). In "Progress in Nucleic Acid Research" (J. N. Davidson and W. E. Cohn, eds.), pp. 135–161. Academic Press, New York.

Little, J. R., Brecher, G., Bradley, T. R., and Rose, S. (1962). *Blood* **19**, 236.

Mäkelä, O., and Nossal, G. J. V. (1962). *J. Exptl. Med.* **115**, 231.

Mauri, C. (1961). *Folia Haematologica* **6**, 239.

Mauri, C. (1962). *Cancro* **15**, 145.

Mauri, C., and Torelli, U. (1960). Unpublished observations.

Mitchell, J., and Nossal, G. J. V. (1963). *Nature* **197**, 1121.

Munro, A. J., and Korner, A. (1964). *Nature* **201**, 1194.

Nathans, D., von Ehrenstein, G., Monro, R., and Lipmann, F. (1962). *Federation Proc.* **21**, 127.

Nossal, G. J. V., and Mäkelä, O. (1962). *J. Exptl. Med.* **115**, 209.

Ottesen, J. (1954). *Acta Physiol. Scand.* **32**, 75.

Painter, R. B., Drew, R. M., and Hughes, W. L. (1958). *Science* **127**, 1244.

Patt, H. M., and Maloney, M. A. (1959). In "The Kinetics of Cellular Proliferation" (F. Stohlman, Jr., ed.), pp. 201–207. Grune & Stratton, New York.

Perry, R. P., Errera, M., Hell, A., and Durwald, H. (1961). *J. Biophys. Biochem. Cytol.* **11**, 1.

Pinheiro, P., Leblond. C. P., and Droz, B. (1963). *Exptl. Cell Res.* **31**, 517.

Prescott, D. M. (1962). *J. Histochem. Cytochem.* **10**, 145.

Rake, A. V., and Graham, A. F. (1962). *Biochim. Biophys. Acta* **55**, 267.

Reich, E. (1963). *Cancer Res.* **23**, 1428.

Reich, E., Franklin, R. M., Shatkin, A. J. and Tatum, E. L. (1962). *Proc. Natl. Acad. Sci. U. S.* **48**, 1238.

Reichard, P., and Estborn, B. (1951). *J. Biol. Chem.* **188**, 839.

Robertson, J. S., Bond, V. P., and Cronkite, E. P. (1959). *Intern. J. Appl. Radiation Isotopes* **7**, 33.

Scholtissek, C. (1962). *Nature* **194**, 353.

Schooley, J. C. (1961). *J. Immunol.* **86**, 331.

Schooley, J. C., and Berman, L. (1960). *Blood* **16**, 1133.

Schooley, J. C., Bryant, B. J., and Kelly, L. S. (1959). *In* "The Kinetics of Cellular Proliferation" (F. Stohlman, Jr., ed.), pp. 208–217. Grune & Stratton, New York.

Sibatani, A. (1963). *Exptl. Cell Res. Suppl.* **9**, 289.

Sibatani, A., de Kloet, S. R., Allfrey, V. G., and Mirsky, A. E. (1962). *Proc. Natl. Acad. Sci. U. S.* **48**, 471.

Sirlin, J. L., Kato, K., and Jones, K. W. (1961). *Biochim. Biophys. Acta* **48**, 421.

Srinivasan, P. R. (1962). *Biochim. Biophys. Acta* **55**, 553.

Staehelin, T., Wettstein, F. O., Oura, H., and Noll, H. (1964). *Nature* **201**, 264.

Stohlman, F., Jr., ed. (1959). "The Kinetics of Cellular Proliferation," pp. 135–141. Grune & Stratton, New York.

Taylor, J. H. (1958). *Genetics* **43**, 515.

Taylor, J. H., Woods, P. S., and Hughes, W. L. (1957). *Proc. Natl. Acad. Sci. U. S.* **48**, 471.

Torelli, U., Grossi, G., Artusi, T., and Emilia, G. (1963). *Acta Haematol.* **30**, 129.

Torelli, U., Grossi, G., Artusi, T., Emilia, G., Attiya, I. R. and Mauri, C. (1964a). *Acta Haematol.* **32**, 271.

Torelli, U., Grossi, G., Artusi, T., Emilia, G., Attiya, I. R. and Mauri, C. (1964b). *Exptl. Cell Res.* **36**, 502.

Torelli, U., Artusi, T., Grossi, G., Emilia, G., and Mauri, C. (1965a). *Nature* in press.

Torelli, U., Quaglino, D., and Mauri, C. (1965b). *Acta Haematol.* in press.

Torelli, U., Quaglino, D., Artusi, T., Emilia, G., Ferrari, G., and Mauri, C. (1966). In preparation.

Vincent, W. S., and Baltus, E. (1960). *In* "The Cell Nucleus" (J. Mitchell, ed.), pp. 18–23. Butterworth, London and Washington, D.C.

Watts, J. W., and Harris, H. (1959). *Biochem. J.* **72**, 147.

Wimber, D. E. (1959). *Proc. Natl. Acad. Sci. U. S.* **45**, 839.

Wimber, D. E., Quastler, H., Stein, O. L., and Wimber, D. R. (1960). *J. Biophys. Biochem. Cytol.* **8**, 327.

Wolstenholme, G. E. W., and O'Connor, M., eds. (1960). "Ciba Foundation Symposium on Haemopoiesis," 490 pp. Churchill, London.

CHAPTER 9

Metabolism of Blood Cells and Their Precursors

J. Aleksandrowicz, H. Gaertner, and J. Urbańczyk*

Third Medical Clinic, Academy of Medicine, Cracow, Poland

* The authors are indebted to Dr. Edwin Paryski, Director of the Sanatorium for Pulmonary Diseases in Zakopane, for the English translation of this chapter.

† The term *lymphoreticular system* is used when referring to the system of blood cells of the active mesenchyme, which includes lymphatic as well as reticuloendothelial cells.

I. Introduction

The work of Swammerdam (1658) and Leeuwenhoek (1673) inaugurated the morphological period of blood studies. At the present time, the peak achievement on this road is electron microscopy. It has become clear, however, that morphology, being a static science, cannot satisfy the needs of the modern hematologist in his research and therapeutic activities. Starting from the premise that the appearance and shape of blood cells are a morphological manifestation of their intravital functions, it becomes understandable that morphological hematology needs supplementation by a more functional approach. The contemporary hematologist looks upon the hemogram, myelogram or lymphadenogram differently than did his predecessors, who regarded the morphology of blood cells as a static phase associated with local tissue or systemic reactions of the body. The dynamic point of view in hematology postulates the possibility of discerning from the morphological picture biochemical phenomena taking place in blood cells.

Advances in biochemistry have made possible the development of sensitive cytochemical tests which have contributed to better understanding of the cytogenesis of blood cells observed in bone marrow smears by the method of Arinkin, or in inflammatory exudates in connective tissues examined with the "skin window" method of Rebuck. With the aid of these methods of intravital observation of blood cells, we have arrived at a deeper understanding of cytogenetic mechanisms; this has enabled one of the writers (Aleksandrowicz, 1946, 1963) to formulate the neounitarian hypothesis of the genesis of blood cells.

According to this hypothesis, the cells of the circulating blood, as well as those of the active bone marrow and lymphoreticular tissue, are derived from the "reticulum cell in the resting phase." There is complete agreement between older authors (Maximow, 1923) and contemporary investigators (Yoffey and Courtice, 1956; Aleksandrowicz, 1963; Tanaka et al., 1963) that this cell exhibits the morphological characteristics of the lymphocyte. Studies carried out with modern methods of tissue culture or with the "skin window" method of Rebuck have demonstrated that lymphocyte-like reticulum cells (*schlummernde Zelle*—Rohr), under the influence of exogenous or endogenous biological stimuli, are capable of transformation into other specific morphological forms (Policard, 1963). Isotope studies have clearly demonstrated the origin of the proliferating cells from small lymphocytes (MacKinney et al., 1962). The problem, however, is not as simple as this. Tanaka et al. (1963) are undoubtedly right in stating that the stem cells in peripheral blood must travel under the guise of mononuclear cells (i.e., lymphocytes), which are not recognized morphologically as separate entities. It may be suggested that both small lymphocytes and some other "mature" mononuclear cells of the peripheral blood are potential "stem cells" capable of division under suitable conditions. Gowans (1962) found experimentally that small lymphocytes may acquire the properties of stem cells, passing through a stage of large pyroninophilic cells capable of division. The observations of Porter and Cooper (1962) furnish additional evidence that the small lymphocyte is capable of division when antigenically stimulated *in vivo*. *In vitro* phytohemagglutinins can induce this phenomenon. Clearly, the small lymphocyte is not an end cell. Lymphocyte-like mononuclear cells that possess the ability to synthesize immediately DNA have the same form. This is shown by the fact that an increased number of ribosomes correlates well with the increased basophilia noted in Giemsa-stained smears and with the isotopic evidence of increased RNA synthesis which precedes DNA synthesis and division. It appears that the blood cell traditionally called the lymphocyte may represent either typical lymphocyte with weak metabolic activity or a metabolically highly active stem cell.

These facts make understandable the evidence pointing to existence of two populations of lymphocytes—one with a brief lifespan, and the other with a long lifespan.

With the method of cytocinematography, transformation of small lymphocytes into plasmacytes, eosinocytes, basocytes, large lymphocytes, monocytes, and macrophages has been observed. A broad discussion of this problem and the pertinent literature are presented elsewhere (Aleksandrowicz, 1963; Lisiewicz, 1965, in press).

Our hypothesis brings out the fact that the active bone marrow represents a union of lymphoreticular tissue, i.e., poorly differentiated mesodermal tissue and highly differentiated myeloid tissue. When examined with anatomical methods, the bone marrow, being an intimate intermixture of these two types of tissue, appears to be homogeneous. Functional and biochemical methods, however, reveal it to be composed of two separate and different tissues united into a morphologically homogeneous whole.

Biochemical and cytoenzymatic studies demonstrate metabolic differences between cells derived from each of these two "antagonistic" tissues, i.e., active bone marrow and the lymphoreticular system. The two tissues react differently to ketosteroids, which stimulate proliferation in bone marrow but induce involution in the lymphoreticular system. Simultaneous proliferation of the myeloid and lymphoreticular systems in the form of lymphomyelocytic leukemia has never been observed, only proliferation in the marrow in the form of erythrogranulomegakaryocytic myelosis (panmyelosis), involving also the lymphoreticular system in the form of lymphoplasmacytic proliferation, and the like.

A morphological-functional scheme of cytogenesis is presented in Fig. 1.

Blood cells derived from the lymphocyte-like "resting reticulum cell" occupy a central position in the ring formed by various types of cells. The three vertical columns of blood cells below the ring represent the erythrocytic, granulocytic, and thrombocytic systems of the bone marrow proper. Experimental facts and *in vitro* and *in vivo* observations show that the blood cells of these three series have limited lifespans, i.e., after reaching maturity they undergo no further transformation into other cells. In contrast, the cells enclosed in the ring undergo such transformations.

On this basis we have proposed a nomenclature and classification of blood diseases into myelopathies and lymphoreticulopathies (Aleksandrowicz and Gaertner, 1950, 1953).

Hematopoiesis is governed by the following laws: (1) the quantitative and qualitative blood picture is an expression not only of the functions of the bone marrow, but also of the connective tissue, especially that part known as the active mesenchyme; (2) the morphology of blood cells is a reflection of their functional phase; (3) the peripheral blood picture is the resultant of processes of renewal and destruction of blood cells; (4) hematopoiesis is subject to neurohormonal influences.

Problems of metabolism of blood cells are connected with processes of maturing and aging. Maturing involves differentiation and specialization, the role of which in development and adaptation is essential. Maturation is accompanied by differences in metabolic activity between young and mature blood cells. Because of the difficulty of obtaining pure experimental material, however, this branch of hematology has not developed uniformly with regard to different blood components. Since it is easiest to isolate the red blood cells, a large body of biochemical data pertaining to the metabolism of erythrocytes has been accumulated. The metabolism of connective tissue cells, on the other hand, can be studied only by means of cytochemical and cytoenzymatic methods in individual cells. Our knowledge in this field is therefore still in an incipient stage.

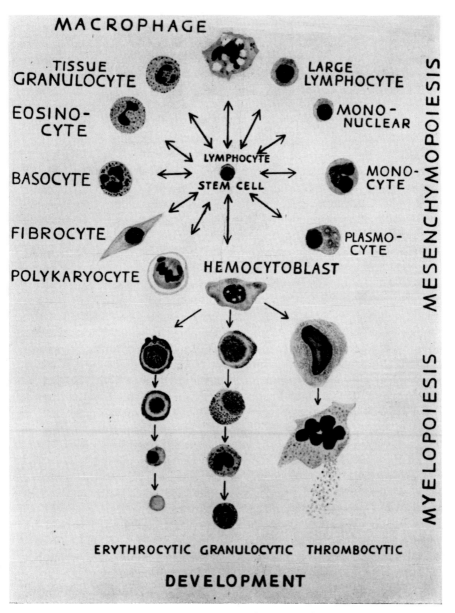

Fig. 1. A morphological-functional scheme of cytogenesis.

It is possible to review the metabolism of the blood cells from many different points of view; for instance with respect to their place of origin, life and death, cytogenesis, or morphological and functional similarities.

From the didactic standpoint, we have selected a functional classification, on the basis of which the problem will be discussed in the following order: the metabolism of the cells of the lymphoreticular system and white blood cells, of platelets, and of red blood cells.

II. Metabolism of Cells of the Lymphoreticular System

In the connective tissues there exists a network of cells known as the lymphoreticular system. Some of these cells, upon becoming detached from their substratum, pass into the blood vessels, where they become components of the circulating blood. These mesenchymal cells not only possess the ability of collecting and phagocytosing small dispersed inorganic particles of degenerated old cells and various foreign bodies, but they also react with antigens to produce antibodies.

Apart from their phagocytic and immunological properties, the lymphoreticular cells possess important, although still imperfectly understood, metabolic functions. This is shown by their esterase activity (e.g., choline esterases), as well as slight acid phosphatase activity. Alkaline phosphatases are not present. Lipid grains stained by Sudan black and PAS-positive neutral mucopolysaccharides may also be observed. Various biochemical substances after phagocytosis undergo metabolic transformations in the reticular cells. Phagocytosis of erythrocytes leads to breakdown of hemoglobin and release of iron into the plasma, from which it is added to the body stores. The role of the lymphoreticular system in this process, although undoubtedly important, is not entirely clear. Blockage of the lymphoreticular system lowers the blood plasma iron levels, while administration of nicotinic acid (which stimulates this system) elevates them. The lymphoreticular system also participates in the metabolism of lipids; its blockage diminishes the serum clearing effect and raises serum cholesterol levels. Alimentary lipemia is counteracted by heparin as "clearing factor," leading to phagocytosis of cholesterol particles by lymphoreticular cells. Nicotinic acid, by stimulating the lymphoreticular system, diminishes the blood cholesterol levels.

Besides their function in the accumulation of foreign substances, phagocytosis, and immunity, the lymphoreticular cells possess important, although not fully understood, metabolic functions. A general view of the metabolism of the connective tissues can be best presented by discussing the metabolism of its different components separately.

A. THE LYMPHOCYTIC SYSTEM

The term lymphocyte will be applied to the small mononuclear cells resembling the blood and lymph lymphocytes. The reticular cells possess the ability of ingesting nuclear fragments of degenerated lymphocytes and of utilizing their deoxyribonucleic acid (DNA). The lymph follicles, which are composed of lymphoreticular cells, are the burial grounds, as well as the birth place, of lymphocytes. According to Hill (1959), large lymphocytes are formed as the result of phagocytosis by reticulum cells of the nuclei of old, deteriorated small lymphocytes. Lymphocytopoiesis through absorption of DNA occurs not only by way of phagocytosis, but also by pinocytosis.

The nucleoproteins are the basic biochemical constituents of lymphocytes. The nuclei of blood as well as lymphatic lymphocytes have the normal, i.e., diploidal, content of DNA. Some of the lymphocytes in the lymph follicles, however, are tetraploids. Feulgen found high amounts of DNA in such cells, while lymphoblasts and medium and large lymphocytes contained more RNA than small lymphocytes. The RNA content is proportional to the degree of protein synthesis.

Isotope studies give discrepant results, indicating marked metabolic activity of small lymphocytes, which quickly incorporate S^{35}-methionine and C^{14}-glycine, among others. Conceivably, increased activity may be an effect of the radioactive emanation of the isotope upon the cells.

The small lymphocytes contain polysaccharides (demonstrated cytochemically). In small lymphocytes carbohydrate metabolism is less intensive, aerobic glycolysis is weak, and anaerobic glycolysis is seven times greater than aerobic (Policard, 1963). Suspensions of lymphocytes from the thymus break down glucose and mannose, but not fructose or xylose (Schrek, 1947). Lymphocytes contain no lipids or lipase and exhibit weak acid phosphatase, but no alkaline phosphatase activity.

The metabolism and functions of the lymphocytes remain open questions. At present it is assumed that the lymphocyte is the carrier of nucleic acids and possesses very high potential, not only as a cell, but as a carrier of nucleic acids transmitting genetic information.

B. THE PLASMACYTIC SYSTEM

Plasmacytes are associated especially with the germinative centers of lymph follicles. Biochemical changes in the microenvironment of lymphoreticular tissue may lead to "explosive" production of plasmacytes. Antigens may provoke their production, although it is known that they may be produced independently of immunologic processes, e.g., in the course of healing, or even after experimental injection of distilled water into lymph nodes. The function of the plasmacytes is not definitely known.

The cytoplasm of the plasmacytes contains large amounts of RNA. The numerous Pallade granules in their ergastoplasm are the main carriers of ribonucleoproteins.

Plasmacytes contain no glycogen, mucin, or lipids. Crystalline inclusions, histochemically resembling β-lactoglobulin crystals, have been observed, as have Russell bodies containing glyco- and mucoproteins. Alkaline phosphatase activity has not been found thus far.

The metabolism of the plasmacytes appears to be related to their insufficiently elucidated immunological function. That the plasmacytes produce immune globulins is shown by the characteristic structure of the ergastoplasm as seen electronmicroscopically. The metabolism of plasmacytes is conditioned by the biochemical character of the substances absorbed by them, such as foreign proteins, bacteria, and even dispersed inorganic particles. In contrast to earlier views, contemporary investigations indicate that bone marrow plasmacytes accumulate ferritin and Thorotrast.

C. The Basocytic System

Although the tissue and blood basocytes appear in similar body reactions and exhibit similarities in cytochemical structure, they undoubtedly represent two distinct types of cells. The differences are summarized in the accompanying tabulation according to Lennert (1961).

Knowledge of the metabolism of the tissue basocytes is of relatively recent date. It has been found that these cells produce heparin, hepa-

Differences between Blood and Tissue Basocytes in Man

	Blood basocytes	Tissue basocytes
Cell size	Smaller	Larger
Nucleus	Irregular, segmented	Round
Cytoplasm	Relatively narrow	Wide
Granulations		
Thickness	Less thick	Thicker
Size	Smaller	Larger, even
Solubility in H_2O	+	O
Sudan black B	+	±
PAS	+	+
Peroxidase	+	O
Acid phosphatase	+	+
Alkaline phosphatase	O	O
Nonspecific esterase	+	+
ATPase	+	+

rinoids, histamine, serotonin, and a number of other, unidentified substances. In 1937 Jorpes and co-workers demonstrated that basocytes play an important role in the metabolism of heparin. Their granulations contain substances which are precursors of heparin. The strict relationship between heparin levels and numbers of mast cells in connective tissue constitutes further confirmation of this hypothesis. Isolated basophilic granulations have been found to possess anticoagulant properties. Hence, there appears to be no doubt that mast cells produce and store heparin.

Basocytes also contain histamine and the numbers of basocytes are strictly correlated with histamine levels. Histamine is bound to heparin (one molecule of heparin combines with 20 molecules of histamine). Production of histamine is connected with adenosine triphosphate (ATP), and ATP and ATPase both occur in basocytes. According to Lewis and Dale (1963), histamine is liberated from basocytes during antigen-antibody reactions, leaving vacuoles as signs of its having been present.

The presence of hyaluronic acid in blood cells is a matter of discussion. It has been found that the granulations of basocytes are digested by hyaluronidase. Hyaluronic acid is probably one of the links in the chain of transformations of the mucopolysaccharides. Although this matter has not been definitely clarified, a number of authors assume that increased hyaluronidase activity is an antagonistic reaction inhibiting production of heparin (Asboe, 1957; Burkl, 1952). A specific property of basocytes is that they stimulate fibrillogenesis when added to cultures of fibroblasts.

Pathologic proliferation and hyperfunction of basocytes is accompanied by liberation of histamine, heparin, and serotonin, with typical body reactions.

D. The Eosinocytic System

Many authors are inclined to assume the existence of tissue and blood eosinocytes.

Eosinophilic granulations contain proteins, aromatic amino acids, and arginine. Lipids and phospholipids are also components, and free and bound cholesterol have been found. Vercauteren (1955) obtained different results, indicating presence of phospholipids, especially sphingomyelin, but not cholesterol. Carbohydrates are present in eosinocytes.

Eosinophilic granulations contain ribonucleic acids in the form of iron-calcium nucleoproteins. Young eosinophilic cells contain considerable amounts of RNA, which diminish with the age of the cells.

Of the cations and anions, Na, Ca, Fe, SO_4, and PO_4 have been found. The iron content of eosinocytes is especially high. Moreover, the granulations contain a considerable amount of water (Rebuck, 1952).

The enzymes in eosinocytes are represented by oxidase, peroxidase, catalase, proteinase, dehydrogenase, and especially succinic dehydrogenase. Acid phosphatase (Vercauteren, 1955) and alkaline phosphatase are also present, besides lipase, amylase, and trypsin. This, of course, is not a complete list of the enzymes associated with the functions of the eosinocytes.

The internal crystalline structure of eosinophilic granulations was discovered by electron microscopy (Aleksandrowicz et al., 1955). The crystals are anisotropic, birefringent, hexagonal, and have the shape of double pyramids. From the biochemical standpoint they represent a labile intermediate product of protein metabolism of the nucleus and cytoplasm. According to Esselier (1954), they are polypeptides and contain zinc.

E. The Monocytic System

The nuclei of monocytes contain RNA and DNA, basic proteins (histones), arginine, and free amino and sulfhydryl groups. A greater number of amino acids is found in monocytes than in the granulocytes.

Lipids occur in the form of small granules, and glycogen in variable amounts. Cytochrome oxidase is one of the enzymes in monocytes. In contrast to bone marrow granulocytes, the monocytes contain no peroxidase. Positive peroxidase activity, which has been reported occasionally, according to Undritz (1950) is due to phagocytosed granulocytes. Acid (but no alkaline) phosphatase activity has been found in monocytes. Esterases have not been reported.

The metabolism of monocytes is carried on by highly active enzymes contained in the mitochondria, such as the enzymes of the glycolytic cycle, respiratory enzymes, and enzymes of the lipid and iron metabolism (Hirsch, 1955).

Proteins, lipids, mucoproteins and other substances have been observed in the Golgi apparatus.

III. Metabolism of the White Blood Cells

Study of the metabolism and chemical composition of the leukocytes at various stages of maturity presents a comparatively unique problem because of the heterogeneity of the preparations obtained, whether from blood or from bone marrow, and the considerable differences in their metabolic abilities. Even cells which are morphologically similar may, in fact, behave in different ways and have different metabolisms. The selection of a normal pattern for comparison has presented many difficulties inasmuch as the blood is a mixture of cells of different ages, origins, and destinations, and each type of blood cell possesses more or less characteristic features, dependent upon species, strain, sex, nutritional status, and many other factors. The interpretation of the results obtained by various authors is therefore difficult, and sometimes tentative.

These difficulties make necessary the use of biochemical as well as cytochemical methods. Each of these methods has advantages as well as shortcomings. In the first method there is the difficulty in isolating a single type of cells, as a result of which mixtures of various cell types must be studied. In the cytochemical method, although the behavior of specific cell components can be studied, the observations are, in principle, only qualitative. However, since not all the substances (e.g., enzymes) contained in leukocytes have been discovered and determined with biochemical methods, the results of cytochemical studies must be included in a discussion of metabolism, despite their imperfection, with recourse to such methods as ultraviolet absorptiometry, microinterferometry, cytoenzymology, and autoradiography.

The majority of the fundamental cellular processes are represented in the white blood cells, which perform various highly specialized functions in the body. Today it is known that the leukocytes possess carbohydrates, lipids, proteins, and a very complete enzymatic apparatus. In addition, they contain substances which play very important roles in the body, such as electrolytes, heparin, histamine, vitamins, and others.

A. CARBOHYDRATES

1. *Composition*

The vital functions, development, and reproduction of leukocytes require a supply of energy, the main source of which is the breakdown of sugars. This group of compounds is represented in the leukocytes by glycogen, which presumably serves as a store of reserve energy, since it is capable of undergoing phosphorylation to glucose-6-phosphate in a reaction catalyzed by the enzyme phosphoglucomutase. In human leukocytes glycogen is present chiefly in the cytoplasm of neutrophilic granulocytes (Wagner, 1947b). The glycogen content of granulocytes increases gradually during maturation, commencing at the myelocyte stage (Lambers and Sič, 1962). In healthy persons the glycogen content of the leukocytes is constant, averaging 75.1 mg/10^{10} granulocytes, and is not altered in diabetes, during hunger, or after cortisone and adrenocorticotropic hormone (ACTH) treatment (Valentine *et al.*, 1953). It is increased in inflammatory conditions, erythremia vera with leukemic reaction, and glycogenoses (Wagner, 1947a), e.g., in Gierke-Adler disease, as a result of impairment of the function of phosphatase or phosphorylase (Larner, 1960). Significantly lower levels, reaching 37.9 mg/10^{10} granulocytes, were observed only in chronic granulocytic leukemia (Valentine *et al.*, 1952, 1953), in spite of the fact that the glycogen turnover in this disease, determined on the basis of incorporation of C^{14}, is 15 times higher than in healthy persons (Luganova and Seits, 1962).

Whether glycogen occurs in lymphocytes is disputable. Although Hertl (1960) found no glycogen in normal lymphocytes, the results of a number of other authors (Mitus *et al.*, 1958; Leikon, 1961; Luganova and Seits, 1962) show the contrary. The reason for these discrepancies probably lies in the different degrees of polymerization of glycogen or in different techniques employed. Increased content of glycogen in lymphocytes has been found in chronic lymphatic leukemias, regardless of the number of lymphocytes or of the type of therapy applied (Smetana *et al.*, 1962; Almazov *et al.*, 1963). However, this is not a specific phenomenon, since increased glycogen content of lymphocytes has been reported also in other myeloproliferative diseases (Mitus *et al.*, 1958).

Glycogen occurs also in eosinocytes (Astaldi *et al.*, 1952), monocytes (Heckner, 1956), and probably in blood basocytes (Smith, 1949), in contrast to tissue basocytes where glycogen does not occur (Avry, 1955).

The mean content of glucuronic acid in leukocytes in healthy persons, 3.7 $mg/10^{10}$ cells, is lowered in chronic granulocytic and lymphatic leukemia (Follette *et al.*, 1954). Its function in leukocytes is unknown.

2. Respiration and Glycolysis

Glucose is the principal source of energy of cells. Anaerobic and aerobic glycolysis, consisting in production of lactic acid in the presence of glucose and phosphates in an atmosphere of either nitrogen or oxygen, is a characteristic feature of mature leukocytes. Hence, the "Pasteur effect" (i.e., the inhibition of glycolysis by oxygen), which is characteristic of other cells, does not occur in leukocytes. Only Burk *et al.* (1959) and Warburg *et al.* (1958) have been able to obtain the "Pasteur effect," employing washed leukocytes suspended in homologous serum. The greatest part (55–65%) of the glucose that disappears is converted into lactic acid, and only 2.5% is oxidized to CO_2 (Luganova and Seits, 1963). The glycolysis/respiration ratio is about 30 (Beck and Valentine, 1952). Glycolysis therefore plays an important role in the production of chemical energy in the leukocyte. Far less energy is produced during glycolysis than during respiration. During glycolysis one molecule of glucose gives rise to two high energy bonds, equivalent to a gain of 22 kcal. Oxidation of two molecules of pyruvic acid gives 30 high energy bonds, i.e., 330 kcal. The reason why leukocytes utilize glucose under such low energy conditions aerobically, compared with the high energy output of oxidation, is not clear.

The highest degree of aerobic glycolysis, calculated per 10^6 cells, is shown by monocytes, followed by neutrophils and eosinocytes; the rate of glycolysis in lymphocytes is much lower (Frei et al., 1961; Vanotti, 1961). This difference is probably related to the size of the cells; when calculated in relation to protein content, the glycolysis rate is the same in all types of leukocytes (Löhr, 1961b).

In 1930 Warburg found that tumor cells are characterized by a high rate of anaerobic and aerobic glycolysis. He attributed this phenomenon to impairment of oxidative processes in the cells as a result of chronic oxygen want, leading to development of the tumor (Warburg, 1956). This assumption has been criticized by Weinhouse (1955), who showed that the high rate of aerobic glycolysis in tumor cells is not due to impairment of oxidative processes, but rather to intensified aerobic glycolysis independently of any impairment of cellular respiration. The fact that normal leukocytes exhibit aerobic glycolysis supports this standpoint.

Leukemic leukocytes have similar properties, although the results of a number of studies suggest qualitative differences. Summarizing his results in this respect, Valentine (1960) states that granulocytes in chronic granulocytic leukemia and lymphocytes in chronic lymphatic leukemia exhibit diminished aerobic glycolysis, compared with leukocytes from healthy persons, utilizing less glucose and oxygen and producing more lactic acid. Leukemic myeloblasts (Burk, 1957; Frei et al., 1961) and paramyeloblasts (Löhr, 1961a), like tumor cells, possess a higher rate of anaerobic and aerobic glycolysis than normal and leukemic granulocytes. The ratio of lactic acid to pyruvic acid produced by paramyeloblasts is 6–7 times higher than in granulocytes of chronic granulocytic leukemia (Löhr, 1961a). On the other hand, lymphoblasts, like lymphocytes of chronic lymphatic leukemia, are characterized by a low rate of aerobic glycolysis (Frei et al., 1961).

The differences in utilization of oxygen and glucose and in lactic acid production between normal and leukemic granulocytes and lymphocytes are consistent with the behavior of various glycolytic enzymes. Numerous studies (Beck, 1955, 1958a,c; Beck and Valentine, 1952; Stave and Oehme, 1961–1962; Grignani and Bunetti, 1963) showed that a number of the enzymes of the Embden-Meyerhof-Parnas pathway exhibit diminished activity in leukemic leukocytes. For instance, the activities of hexokinase, phosphofructokinase, and glycerylaldehyde phosphate dehydrogenase are diminished in leukocytes in chronic granulocytic leukemia, and lactate dehydrogenase (Vetter, 1961a) and glucose-6-phosphate dehydrogenase (Bertino et al., 1962) in chronic as well as acute granulocytic leukemia. Phosphohexoisomerase and triosephosphoisomerase activities, on the other hand, are normal or slightly increased.

Aldolase activity is reduced in paramyeloblastosis and lymphadenosis (Vetter, 1961a). Markedly lowered hexokinase activity has been observed in paramyeloblasts (Löhr, 1961b; Stave and Oehme, 1961–1962), and lowered activity of glycerol phosphate dehydrogenase in paramyeloblasts, plasmacytes of plasmatic leukemia, and eosinocytes of eosinophilic leukemia (Bock et al., 1961–1962).

Hexokinase is the enzyme which initiates glycolysis. In the presence of ATP and hexokinase, glucose is transformed into glucose-6-phosphate, initiating the phosphorylative breakdown of glucose:

$$\text{glucose} + \text{ATP} \xrightarrow{\text{hexokinase}} \text{glucose-6-phosphate} + \text{ADP}$$

Addition of purified hexokinase increases glycolysis in leukocytes from healthy persons by 50%, and in leukemic leukocytes by 300%.

Leukemic leukocytes also have a low content of nicotinamide adenine dinucleotide (NAD*) (Ehrhart et al., 1963). Whereas the NAD content of leukocytes from healthy persons is up to 2.0 $\mu g/10^6$ cells, in untreated chronic granulocytic leukemia it amounts to 0.04–0.09 $\mu g/10^6$ cells. During Myleran therapy the level drops at first, depending on the dosage of the drug. During remissions the level again rises to 0.8–1.0 $\mu g/10^6$ leukocytes. In refractory cases the initial drop in NAD level is not observed. In acute leukemias with large numbers of immature cells in the peripheral blood the NAD level drops even to 0.002 $\mu g/10^6$ cells. Silber et al. (1962) obtained diametrically opposite results: NAD content of leukocytes in chronic granulocytic leukemia was higher, and in acute granulocytic leukemia much higher than in the leukocytes of healthy persons.

Production of ADP is dependent not only on the activities of hexokinase and phosphofructokinase, but also on that of ATPase. After addition of ADP to media containing glucose as substrate, leukemic homogenates exhibit much higher per cent increase in glycolysis than homogenates of normal leukocytes. Addition of ATPase causes further increase in lactic acid production by leukemic leukocytes potentiated by addition of hexokinase, compared with the slight increase in leukocytes from healthy persons (Beck, 1955, 1958a,b,c; Grignani and Bunetti, 1963).

According to Shiro Miwa et al. (1962), the levels of pyruvate kinase, enolase, 2,3-phosphoglyceric mutase, and 3-phosphoglycerate-1-kinase are lowered in leukocytes from cases of acute and chronic lymphatic leukemia. Activity of enolase in leukocytes from acute and chronic granulocytic leukemia is higher than the mean in healthy persons; activity of

---

* NAD (formerly designated DPN); NADH₂ = reduced NAD; NADP (formerly TNP); NADPH₂ = reduced NADP.

the remaining three enzymes is unaltered. These data are not in accordance with the findings of Löhr (1961b), who observed a drop in enolase and rise in pyruvate kinase activity in paramyeloblasts as well as in leukemic lymphocytes.

The results of the studies quoted above point to disorders of carbohydrate metabolism in leukemic leukocytes, manifested mainly by the reduction in activity of almost all the glycolytic enzymes. It should be borne in mind, however, that this may be only apparent, being caused by the presence of large numbers of immature cells in leukemic blood.

An enzyme whose function in leukocytes is still obscure is glyoxalase II, which assists the transformation of methylglyoxal into lactic acid. Thus far, however, this substrate has not been found in leukocytes, notwithstanding the significant place that has been ascribed to methylglyoxal in glycolysis. Glyoxalase is present in blasts, the entire neutrophilic series, lymphocytes and probably eosinocytes (Valentine and Tanaka, 1961). Lower levels of activity of this enzyme have been reported in leukocytes of chronic granulocytic leukemia (McKinney, 1953).

3. Citric Cycle

Leukocytes contain all of the known enzymes involved in the citric cycle. Quantitatively there are fluctuations in the activity of some of these enzymes in different types of normal and pathologic leukocytes.

An equilibrium among citric, cis-aconitic, and diisocitric acids is regulated by aconitic hydratase, called aconitase. Immature leukocytes of monocytic, myelocytic, or lymphatic leukemia have significantly greater aconitase activity than mature cells of the same series. Aconitase activity is essentially similar in the neutrophil and lymphocyte; eosinocytes and basocytes have less aconitase activity (Tanaka and Valentine, 1961).

Of the oxidative enzymes, succinic dehydrogenase, which is localized exclusively in the mitochondria of lymphocytes, myelocytes, and megakaryocytes, deserves special mention. Weak activity has been observed in metamyelocytes, but not even traces in more mature forms. Hence, maturation of granulocytes is accompanied by progressive loss of this enzyme (Morrison and Kronheim, 1962).

4. Electron Transport

Oxidase and peroxidase activity increases in the course of maturation of granulocytes; it is lowest in promyelocytes, and highest in mature granulocytes (Lambers and Sič, 1962). In chronic and especially in acute granulocytic leukemia, as a result of the large numbers of young granulocytes in the peripheral blood, the total content of the oxidative enzymes diminishes. Severity of the illness and the degree of these changes have been found to be correlated (Almazov et al., 1963). Lymphoblasts and lymphocytes, like myeloblasts, contain no peroxidase (Hayhoe et al., 1960).

Activity of NADP-dependent dehydrogenase is high in neutrophils, and low in lymphocytes. Marked drop in its activity is observed only in lymphadenosis and stem cell leukemia (Ghiotto et al., 1960).

Catalase activity in normal granulocytes is higher than in lymphocytes. It is elevated in leukocytes from acute and chronic granulocytic leukemia (Tchimaru, 1959), and lowered in infectious leukocytosis (Kidson, 1962).

Cytochrome oxidase activity is similar in granulocytes and lymphocytes, and does not change in leukemias (Wachstein, 1955).

5. Phosphatases

Phosphatases perform an important function in the body, hydrolyzing phosphate esters of various organic compounds to phosphoric acid and the corresponding alcohol. Phosphomonoesterases and phosphodiesterases should be distinguished. Specificity of the phosphatases varies. Some are active against a specific type of ester linkage or specific ester, e.g., glucose-6-phosphatase (which is supposed to play an important role in the regulation of blood sugar levels), 5-nucleotidase and fructose-1,6-diphosphatase.

Phosphomonoesterases of leukocytes are present in the granulations of the cytoplasm. Increased lability of the granulations may cause a rise in phosphatase activity in spite of unchanged content of the enzyme in the cell (Hirsch and Cohn, 1960).

Alkaline phosphatase, of which the optimal pH is 9.0, shows the most characteristic changes. Its activity is enhanced by Mg^{++}, but decreased in the presence of sulfhydryl compounds such as cysteine or glutathione (Valentine et al., 1957). Alkaline phosphatase is an intracellular enzyme, unrelated to the serum alkaline phosphatase levels. It occurs in neutrophilic granulocytes, beginning at the myelocyte stage, and increases with maturity of the cells; it probably also occurs in eosinocytes (Vercauteren, 1955) and basocytes. It is not present in myeloblasts (Lambers, 1961), monocytes, plasmacytes (Kaplow, 1955; Lennert and Leder, 1963), or lymphocytes. The literature pertaining to the activity of this enzyme in leukocytes in different diseases is so extensive that it is not possible to quote all the authors. Valentine and Beck (1951), Meislin et al. (1959), Nicolau et al. (1962), and many other investigators have shown that alkaline phosphatase activity is considerably diminished in chronic granulocytic leukemia, probably as a result of the large numbers of immature cells in the blood. This is contradicted, however, by the increased activity in polycythemia vera with leukemic reaction (Valentine et al.,

1952; Nicolau et al., 1962) and in some cases of metaplastic leukemic reaction (Valentine et al., 1952) in which the numbers of immature leukocytes are also increased. It should be noted that in most patients with myeloid metaplasia, in the course of myelofibrosis high alkaline phosphatase activity was found (Maloney, 1961). Changes in the activity of this enzyme in leukemic leukocytes are so characteristic that determination of alkaline phosphatase activity has been included in routine hematologic diagnosis, since it allows differentiation of chronic granulocytic leukemia from certain syndromes which superficially resemble it. Changes in the levels of this enzyme precede morphologic alterations of the leukocytes. Low phosphatase activity has been found in the granulocytes of Japanese exposed to atomic radiation several years before leukemia developed (Maloney and Lange, 1954).

Recent research, however, raises doubt whether these changes in the level of the enzyme are primary and essential in the leukemic process, or secondary and of little or no significance (Löhr, 1961b), especially since the role of alkaline phosphatase in the metabolism of leukocytes is not clear. Similarly low activity as in chronic granulocytic leukemia has been found in paroxysmal nocturnal hemoglobinuria (Beck and Valentine, 1952; Tanaka et al., 1960a,b). Somewhat smaller and inconstant reduction in activity has been observed in primary thrombocytopenia, infectious mononucleosis, myeloid metaplasia, during relapses of Addison-Biermer disease, collagen diseases, and sometimes in other hematologic and nonhematologic diseases (Tanaka et al., 1960b). Knoblauch (1962) found low phosphatase activity in 25% of healthy persons (in one case even no activity). In 10 out of 12 patients suffering from chronic granulocytic leukemia activity was normal. In persons with low phosphorus content of the leukocytes alkaline phosphatase activity may be altogether absent (Kretschmer et al., 1958).

During treatment of chronic granulocytic leukemia phosphatase activity behaves variously; during remissions activity in granulocytes usually continues to be low, although in exceptional cases it may return to normal (Valentine et al., 1957; Mitus et al., 1959).

Alkaline phosphatase activity often increases in clinical stress conditions such as suppurative infections, myocardial infarction, diabetic coma (Valentine et al., 1954, 1957), and during pregnancy and treatment with estrogens (Borel et al., 1961). High dosage of ACTH or cortisone may produce a marked rise in activity in normal granulocytes but slight (Valentine et al., 1957), or no change in chronic granulocytic leukemia (Plenert, 1963). This phenomenon is so constant that it may prove of value in differential diagnosis. High phosphatase activity in granulocytes has been reported in various acute chemical intoxications (barbiturates,

Azotox) and in exposed X-ray technicians (Cichocki and Lyko, 1963).

Hayhoe and Quaglino (1958) reported high levels of alkaline phosphatase activity in granulocytes in acute lymphoblastic leukemia and in Hodgkin's disease, and values approaching normal in chronic lymphocytic leukemia, lymphosarcoma, and reticulum cell sarcoma.

The fact that alkaline phosphatase activity is elevated in mongolism idiocy (Trubowitz *et al.*, 1962; Alter *et al.*, 1963) together with trisomia of the 21st chromosome and proneness to acute leukemia and suppurative infections (Stewart, 1961) has aroused the interest of geneticists. This difference in activity has suggested the hypothesis that alkaline phosphatase of granulocytes is governed by a gene on the 21st chromosome because of the known deficiency of this enzyme in the granulocytes of patients with chronic granulocytic leukemia and the known partial deletion of the 21st chromosome (Ph[1] chromosome) in this disease. The increased susceptibility to infections in imbecile mongols and rise in phosphatase activity in neutrophils in the course of infections is also noteworthy.

Acid phosphatase of leukocytes is less well known; its activity is dependent on the presence of cytoplasmatic granulations. Acid phosphatase activity is present in neutrophils at every stage of development (Lambers and Sič, 1962). Increased activity occurs in granulocytes in chronic granulocytic leukemia (Tsutsumi, 1959; Bases, 1962; Löffler and Berghoff, 1962; Young and Prager, 1962), in myeloblastic leukemia (Perillie and Finch, 1961), and in polycythemia vera with leukemic reaction (Valentine and Beck, 1951). Its presence has also been demonstrated in eosinocytes (Lambers, 1961), basocytes, and monocytes (Wachstein, 1955; Lennert and Leder, 1963). It is doubtful whether lymphocytes contain acid phosphatase (Doyle, 1955). Diminished activity occurs in chronic lymphocytic leukemia (Renny and Mende, 1957).

6. *Heparin, β-Glucuronidase, and Lysozyme*

Heparin occurs almost exclusively in the granulations of mast cells and blood basocytes (Amann and Martin, 1961). After ingestion of fats, basocytes liberate heparin, initiating the well-known reaction of serum turbidity clearing [Juhlin and Shelley, (1961a); a chapter of the monograph of Gaertner (1960) is devoted to this problem].

The enzyme β-glucuronidase, which catalyzes hydrolysis of glucuronides, occurs in considerable quantities in human leukocytes. Activity of β-glucuronidase, calculated per 10^6 cells, is highest in monocytes, intermediate in neutrophils, eosinocytes, and myeloblasts, and lowest in lymphocytes and their precursors (Vanotti, 1961; Young and Prager, 1962). Low levels of activity have been observed in chronic lymphocytic and in acute leukemias, and normal or elevated values in chronic granulocytic leukemia (Valentine, 1960).

Lysozyme, contained in neutrophils (Flanagan and Lionetti, 1955), is a mucopolysaccharidase since, like hyaluronidase, it depolymerizes mucopolysaccharides, which are essential components of the bacterial cell wall. The bactericidal action of granulocytes upon bacteria consists in liberation of lysozyme into the serum. High lysozyme activity has been found in exudates and in the intestinal mucosa, especially in colitis ulcerosa, where activity more than 100 times higher than normal has been reported (Gray *et al.*, 1952). Granulocytes are regarded as the source of this high activity. Lysozyme has also been shown to be present in lymphocytes (Barnes, 1940).

B. PROTEINS AND AMINO ACIDS

1. *Metabolism of Proteins and Amino Acids*

In leukocytes from healthy persons an effective barrier which prevents serum proteins from entering the interior of the cell is believed to exist. The barrier becomes less effective in chronic granulocytic leukemia, since leukocytic extracts have been found to contain a_2-globulins (Reinek and Bednarik, 1962). Amino acids, on the other hand, are freely exchanged with the surrounding medium. Their active transport depends, in large measure, on the efficiency of the "cationic pump" (i.e., Na^+ and K^+). Yunis *et al.* (1963) studied the transport of labeled C^{14}-1-α-aminoisobutyric acid (AIB) in lymphocytes of chronic lymphatic and in granulocytes of chronic granulocytic leukemia. In the absence of Na^+ and K^+, AIB penetrated into granulocytes faster than into lymphocytes; in the presence of Na^+, transport of AIB into lymphocytes increased 300–800%, but in granulocytes only 100–200%.

According to Rouser (1957), the levels of free amino acids in plasma and in the leukocytes are related. Content of the different amino acids in leukocytes is variable, depending on the stage of maturity of the cells and on the methods of assay. Myeloblasts contain large amounts of glutamic acid, but little glutamine, taurine, glutathione, and cysteine; myelocytes have a high glutamine content; normal granulocytes possess little glutamic acid, but a considerable amount of taurine, while granulocytes of chronic granulocytic leukemia contain little glutamine. According to Iyer (1959), leukocytes of chronic granulocytic leukemia contain more alanine, aspartic and glutamic acids, glutamine, glycine, valine, leucine, isoleucine, and taurine than normal leukocytes.

Rouser (1957) observed that many leukemic patients exhibit elevated serum levels of alanine, aspartic and glutamic acids, but low levels of glutamine.

The activity of enzymes involved in the transformations of the amino acids also changes. Cells of acute and chronic leukemias at every stage of development exhibit activity of glutamic dehydrogenase fourfold higher than normal leukocytes. Neither therapy nor fluctuations of leukocytosis affect the activity of this enzyme. Similar increase in activity was observed in the leukocytes of patients with tumors (Waisman et al., 1956). Löhr (1961b) observed elevated activity only in paramyeloblasts of acute leukemia, and Renny and Mende (1957) noted markedly depressed activity in chronic and sometimes also in acute lymphatic leukemia. Leukocytes of acute and chronic leukemias also exhibit increased activity of glutamic-oxalacetic transaminase and glutamic-pyruvic transaminase (Löhr et al., 1960; Vetter, 1961a,b; Bock et al., 1961–1962).

Proteolytic activity, upon which phagocytosis depends, is highest in monocytes, intermediate in neutrophils, and slight in eosinocytes and lymphocytes (Vanotti, 1961; Frei et al., 1961).

Aminopeptidase activity can be demonstrated in granulocytes from the myelocyte stage onward, while lymphocytes and basocytes show no activity. Neutrophils in leukemia exhibit normal or increased activity (Ackerman, 1963).

Štefanovič (1963) found that rabbit neutrophils contain two proteases: cathepsin D, mainly in the nuclear fraction, and cathepsin E, distributed equally between the nuclear and cytoplasmic fractions of the cell. Cathepsin activity is elevated in neutrophils of granulocytic leukemia and lowered in lymphocytes of lymphatic leukemia (Fraenkel-Conrat and Chew, 1960). Employing C^{14}-glucose, Luganova and Seits (1963) showed that normal and pathologic human leukocytes utilize fragments of broken down glucose to regenerate intracellular compounds, including proteins, nucleic acids, and glycogen. While not pronounced in normal leukocytes, this process increases in leukemias. This is substantiated by the work of Schuler et al. (1963), who showed that protein metabolism of leukoblasts is about 15 times higher than that of mature lymphocytes.

2. Metabolism of Sulfhydryl and Other Sulfur Compounds

Sulfhydryl compounds play an important role in the metabolism of leukocytes, regulating cellular redox systems and activity of many enzymes. In addition, they participate in the formation of intermediate products of protein synthesis, particularly glutathione, L-cysteine, L-cystine, and homocysteine. Substances which oxidize or inactivate —SH groups inhibit cell division and cause leukopenia. The sulfhydryl content of leukocytes is several times greater than that of erythrocytes (Green and Martin 1955; Valentine, 1960). Normal leukocytes contain 3.3–6.3 mg of glutathione per 10^{10} cells (Hardin et al., 1954). In chronic granulocytic leukemia normal or slightly elevated sulfhydryl content was found, and in chronic lymphocytic and acute leukemias and in infectious mononucleosis it was lowered (Hardin et al., 1954; Green and Martin, 1955). Similarly, content of glutathione reductase is much lower in lymphocytes and paramyeloblasts than in neutrophils (Löhr, 1961b).

According to Notario et al. (1962a) leukemic leukocytes metabolize smaller amounts of S^{35}-cystine than normal leukocytes, but according to Weisberger and Levine (1954) larger amounts are metabolized. Leukocytes of acute and chronic granulocytic leukemias incorporate S^{35}-cystine at an especially high rate, exhibiting higher radioactivity after 20 minutes than normal leukocytes after 48 hours; this indicates more rapid metabolism in these cells. Similar results were obtained with S^{35}-L-methionine (Weisberger et al., 1954), with glycine (Winzler et al., 1959), and with C^{14}-leucine and valine (Nadler et al., 1961).

On the other hand, compared with normal leukocytes, absorption of inorganic S^{35} in the form of $Na_2S^{35}O_4$ by leukocytes is less active in acute granulocytic leukemia, moderate in chronic granulocytic leukemia, and almost nil in chronic lymphatic leukemia (Notario et al., 1962b). Urinary excretion of large amounts of S^{35} in leukemic patients may be an expression of diminished ability to incorporate inorganic sulfur by leukemic leukocytes (Weisberger and Levine, 1954), and indirectly of lower viability of leukemic leukocytes.

It has been found (Patt, 1953; Weisberger and Levine, 1954) that L-cysteine prevents induction of severe neutropenia by Au, As, benzene, nitrogen mustard, or X-rays. This protection is not effective, however, if L-cysteine is administered after injection of nitrogen mustard; moreover, D-cysteine, in contrast to glutathione and homocysteine, does not exert a similar action. This phenomenon is probably dependent both on the spatial structure of the amino acid and on the near position of the —SH, —NH₂, and —COOH groups.

Diet poor in sulfhydryl amino acids diminishes the incidence of leukemia and induces leukopenia in mice of the DBA strain receiving injections of methylcholanthrene (White et al., 1947); addition of cystine raises the morbidity rate. Granulocytes grown in vitro in synthetic medium containing no L-cysteine or L-cystine quickly degenerate (Baldini and Sacchetti, 1953). The importance of this amino acid in the metabolism of leukocytes is underlined by the fact that experimental administration of selenium cystine (an analogue of cystine in which sulfur in the amino acid molecule is replaced by selenium) causes a rapid drop in the number of granulocytes and reduction in size of the spleen in some patients with acute or chronic granulocytic leukemia (Weisberger, 1957).

Arylsulfatase, an enzyme hydrolyzing arylsulfuric acid, plays an important role in many metabolic processes. Being present in the leukocytic granulations, the enzyme exhibits highest activity in eosinocytes, followed by basocytes and neutrophils in an approximate ratio of 8:2:1 (Tanaka et al., 1962). According to Austin and Bischel (1961), eosinocytes, megakaryocytes, and neutrophils possess the highest arylsulfatase activity among blood cells. Lymphocytes and lymphoblasts have essentially no activity, and myeloblasts and monoblasts very little activity. However, if immature granulocytes and monocytes contain numerous granulations, they usually exhibit marked activity of the enzyme (Tanaka et al. 1962). High arylsulfatase activity was observed in granulocytic leukemias (Young and Prager, 1962).

3. Histamine

Almost the whole amount of histamine in the blood circulation is transported by basocytes (Graham et al., 1955), especially by the mature forms (Albanus and Winquist, 1961). Much smaller amounts are found in eosinocytes, and negligible amounts in neutrophils; lymphocytes and monocytes contain no histamine, or very little. Therefore, the total blood histamine is greatly increased (even 200 times) in chronic granulocytic leukemia. Lesser elevation is observed in polycythemia vera (Beck and Valentine, 1953), diminished levels in chronic lymphocytic leukemia and monocytic leukemia, and absence in acute granulocytic leukemia (Thiersch, 1947). As in the connective tissue mast cells, histamine is contained in the granulations of basocytes. In the presence of a specific antigen, the cell rids itself of the granulations, liberating histamine. Hence, basocytes are responsible for histamine shock in anaphylaxis (Juhlin and Shelley, 1961b).

C. Nucleic Acids and Nucleoproteins

1. Composition

The nucleic acids are built of tetranucleotides, the sequence and arrangement of which is decisive for genetic information, synthesis of specific proteins, and morphological and physiological properties of the cell and organism. Each tetranucleotide of deoxyribonucleic acid (DNA) is composed of two purine nucleotides, i.e., compounds of adenine or guanine and deoxyribose and orthophosphoric acid, and two pyrimidine nucleotides containing cytosine and thymine instead of purine bases. Ribonucleic acid (RNA) contains ribose instead of deoxyribose, and uracil instead of thymine. According to the model of Watson and Crick

(1953), the macromolecule of DNA has the form of two polynucleotide chains interwoven in the shape of a double helix around a mutual axis. The purine and pyrimidine bases are arranged within each chain and are conjugated through hydrogen bonds with the bases of the other chain, a purine always being conjugated with a pyrimidine. About 10% of the cellular protein is bound with nucleic acids forming "nucleoproteins."

Deoxyribonucleic acid, contained in the chromosomes of the cell nuclei, is concerned with cell division, heredity, and synthesis of RNA, which takes place mainly, if not exclusively, near the chromosomes. The RNA which is produced then disperses in the cytoplasm in the form of ribosomes (Zalockar, 1959). DNA is a stable substance and is more or less independent of the cell metabolism.

Ribonucleic acid is present in the nucleoli, mitochondria, microsomes, and ribosomes of cells. In contrast to DNA, RNA undergoes quantitative changes during the growth of the cell and plays an important part in protein synthesis. DNA probably produces so-called "messenger RNA," the nucleotide composition of which is similar to that of the DNA bases (Doty, 1961). It is assumed that under the influence of "messenger RNA" the ribonucleic acid of the ribosomes assumes a specific shape, producing the "matrix" on which specific protein molecules are synthesized (Berg, 1961). Each amino acid taking part in protein synthesis is transferred through mediation of soluble RNA (sRNA) to ribosome RNA and positioned on the protein molecule in linear sequence in accordance with the genetic plan transferred from DNA through "messenger RNA." Ribonucleotides possess very active metabolism, about ten times greater than that of other proteins (Valladares, 1960).

Normal but rapidly proliferating embryonic tissues, regenerating organs, some types of secretory cells, and proliferating young forms of leukocytes have much higher contents of RNA than nondividing, metabolically inert cells. Presence of nucleoli and cytoplasmic basophilia of immature leukocytes is associated with high RNA content, which diminishes as maturation proceeds.

Differences in the nucleic acid content of leukocytes are the result of the heterogeneity of the cells in the bone marrow and circulating blood, in health as well as in the course of leukemias. The work of Leuchtenberger and Leuchtenberger (1960a,b), who assayed the DNA content of cells at different stages of maturity spectrophotometrically, showed that in some immature leukocytes and tumor cells the DNA content is a multiple (2:4:8) of the content of normal leukocytes. In contrast to the diploid number of chromosomes in normal cells, myeloblasts often possess double that number of chromosomes (tetraploidia). The slightly increased DNA content in leukocytes of chronic granulocytic leukemia is therefore the consequence of increased numbers of myeloblasts in the bone marrow and circulating blood. Part of the myeloblasts have a higher DNA content as a result of multiple numbers of chromosomes (polyploidia) (Gross et al., 1961), or of internal reduplication of the chromonemal fibers of the chromosomes (polytenia) (Petrakis and Folstadt, 1955). In acute leukemia the DNA values of individual cells are mainly hyperdiploidal; only some cells have higher DNA content as a result of reduplication, indicating a low degree of proliferation, in contrast to normal granulopoiesis (Canacio and Alonzo, 1960; Müller, 1963). Following the suggestion of Leuchtenberger and Leuchtenberger (1960a,b), we have undertaken studies (Krygier and Aleksandrowicz, Czyżewska, and Ekiert, unpublished) on the cytospectrophotometric determination of DNA in mature neutrophils of normal and leukemic persons indicating existence of two different types of granulocytes in leukemias.

The RNA content of leukocytes depends on the type of cell and on its stage of maturity. Köteles et al. (1962) found the content of RNA more than fourfold higher in exudate mononuclears than in polymorphonuclear cells, and Frei et al. (1961) reported that the RNA content of lymphocytes and monocytes is 50% greater than that of polynuclear cells. Plasmacytes, in which protein synthesis is lively, possess an especially high RNA content. According to most investigators (Will et al., 1957; Carvalho et al., 1960; Canacio and Alonzo, 1960; Bielka et al., 1962), RNA levels are elevated in acute and chronic granulocytic leukemia as a result of increased numbers of immature cells in the blood circulation containing more RNA (5%) than mature cells, which contain only about 1% (Thorell, 1947). This opinion is substantiated by the fact that RNA content diminishes parallel to the decrease in number of immature cells during effective treatment of leukemias with cytostatic drugs (Müller, 1963).

2. Metabolism

The large numbers of young forms of leukocytes in leukemias may be a consequence either of high mitotic activity of the cells, or of inhibited maturation. This problem has not as yet been decisively solved. Increased assimilation of purine and pyrimidine bases by granulocytic leukemic leukocytes (Will et al., 1957), more rapid synthesis of DNA by leukocytes of chronic granulocytic leukemia than by normal leukocytes (Shapira et al., 1959), and more rapid incorporation of glycine-1-C^{14} into lymphoblasts than into maturing lymphocytes (Schuler et al., 1963) have been demonstrated. Most of the authors (Cronkite et al., 1959; Bussi et al., 1960; Gavosto et al., 1960a,b; Kozinets and Osechenskaya, 1962;

Notario *et al.*, 1962; Ruhenstroth-Bauer and Gostomzyk, 1962; Boll, 1963) employing the autoradiographic method have found markedly diminished ability of assimilating H^3-thymidine, C^{14}-glycine, and P^{32} by leukemic cells compared with normal leukocytes, pointing to an extremely low proliferative ability. Experiments on cell division inhibited in metaphase by means of colchicine ("stathmokinetic effect") (Astaldi and Cardinali, 1959) and experiments concerned with determination of mitotic indices (Salera and Tamburino, 1956; Fliedner *et al.*, 1959) with almost twofold prolongation of the time of mitosis (Boll, 1958, 1963) also point to inhibited maturation and diminished mean proliferative ability of leukemic cells compared with normal bone marrow cells. The large accumulation of granuloblasts in the bone marrow, especially in acute leukemias, seems to be dependent not on increased mitotic rate of the granuloblasts, but on their longer lifespan compared with the very short maturation time of normal granuloblasts (Boll, 1963).

Leukocytes possess the ability of synthesizing their nucleic acids from assimilated free purine and pyrimidine bases, as well as from simpler, generally available metabolites. In the course of this *de novo* synthesis purines are produced from glycine, CO_2, formate, and ammonia. Leukemic cells are thought to possess greater ability of synthesizing nucleotides *de novo* (Scott, 1962), and therefore incorporate free purines less than normal leukocytes. The phenomenon of lesser incorporation of H^3-thymine by leukemic cells (Bussi *et al.*, 1960; Gavosto *et al.*, 1960a,b; Boll, 1963) may merely be a consequence of the greater *de novo* synthesis of nucleotides at the expense of incorporation of ready exogenous precursors. This is confirmed by the results of Schuler *et al.* (1963), who found increased assimilation by leukemic cells of C^{14}-glycine, an important metabolite in the synthesis of nucleotides. This hypothesis was not confirmed by other authors (Kozinets and Osechanskaya, 1962; Notario *et al.*, 1962), who found diminished absorption of this metabolite.

Degradation of nucleic acids is the work of numerous enzymes, of which the best known are: ribonuclease (RNase) and deoxyribonuclease (DNase), nonspecific esterases, and 5'-nucleotidase. Naturally occurring inhibitors are a factor regulating the rate of degradation.

According to Maney *et al.* (1960), leukocytes contain DNase as well as RNase, but according to Herriott *et al.* (1961) only RNase. DNase inhibitor is present in large amounts in leukocytes and erythrocytes, but only in trace amounts in the blood serum. On the other hand, RNase inhibitor is found exclusively in erythrocytes and reticulocytes (Rost *et al.*, 1959; Herriott *et al.*, 1961). RNase inhibitor is a nondialyzable and thermostable substance, probably a mucoprotein. Leukemic leukocytes and tumor cells do not differ with respect to DNase activity (Greenstein, 1954). Marked deficiency of DNase inhibitor has been found in leukocytes of acute granulocytic and chronic lymphatic leukemia, and to a lesser degree in chronic granulocytic leukemia (Will *et al.*, 1957). A similar deficiency has not been observed in leukocytes of infectious leukemic reactions, infectious mononucleosis or myelofibrosis. During treatment of chronic granulocytic leukemia the concentration of the inhibitor tends to return to normal with hematological improvement; this has not been observed in chronic lymphatic leukemia. In the opinion of some writers (Will *et al.*, 1957), uninhibited activity of DNase in leukemias due to deficiency of the inhibitor may be responsible for the unrestricted ability of division supposed to characterize the cells of acute leukemia. In the light of the facts discussed previously this opinion stands alone, and such a mechanism does not seem very likely since it would necessitate the assumption that DNase can synthesize DNA. From the standpoint of leukemic mechanisms as well as of the thermodynamics of these processes (Hamilton, 1957), this is doubtful. Another inhibitor of DNase, discovered by Kurnick *et al.* (1953), is said to occur in increased amounts in leukemic leukocytes. Its existence would appear to be consistent with the generally accepted concept of depolymerizing action of DNase upon DNA.

In spite of much research, it is still difficult to define the function of the intracellular nucleases. A large body of data indicates that RNase and DNase exert a decisive influence on the metabolism of nucleic acids in cells by impairing aerobic phosphorylation (Allfrey and Mirsky, 1959; Gable and Wright, 1962). According to de Lamirande (1961), the mode of action of DNase consists in inhibition of cell division through an influence on DNA. The finding that the cell membrane is permeable to RNase, probably by way of pinocytosis, has permitted observations of the influence of exogenous RNase on the vital processes of the cell (a comprehensive review of the literature has been published by Chantrenne, 1961). The results show that RNase, acting on living cells, may damage them in various ways. It may inhibit protein synthesis without affecting the general metabolism of energy production and synthesis of various cellular components. Inhibition of protein synthesis is probably the result of breakdown of certain fractions of RNA, especially of the soluble fraction (sRNA) (Brachet and Six, 1959; Shigeura and Chargaff, 1960).

An influence of RNase on nucleic acid and protein metabolism is also supported by the results of *in vitro* and *in vivo* experiments with tumor cells. Normal tissues during cellular growth or regeneration show increased content of RNA and RNase (Brody, 1957; Brody and Balis,

1958; de Lamirande and Allard, 1959; Ledoux *et al.*, 1962). Neoplastic tissue, on the other hand, according to most authors (Brody and Balis, 1958; Ledoux and Brändli, 1958; Daoust and Amano, 1962) is characterized by disordered RNase metabolism and disturbed correlation between the content of RNA and RNase activity. This is confirmed by data showing that RNase is absorbed by tumor cells several times more rapidly than by normal cells. RNase absorbed by tumor cells inhibits protein synthesis and diminishes mitotic activity and growth of tumor cells, but does not produce any appreciable changes in normal cells (Ledoux and Pileri, 1957). Conceivably, this interesting specific action of RNase on tumor cells is a result of the relative deficiency of this enzyme in tumor tissues or of changes in the permeability of the cell membrane (Brachet, 1957).

In *in vivo* experiments injection of RNase directly into tumor tissues (Ledoux, 1955), intraperitoneally or subcutaneously (Hadjiolov and Zacharieva, 1957; Wase *et al.*, 1960) caused inhibition of tumor growth, or even disappearance of the tumor. In one strain of mice with lymphosarcoma, administration of 9-α-fluoroprednisolone caused a distinct increase in RNase activity, followed after two days by a drop in RNA level and signs of regression of the tumor (McLeod *et al.*, 1962). Wannemacher *et al.* (1962) obtained similar results with rats inoculated with Walker 256 carcinoma. A less pronounced effect was observed in mice with Ehrlich ascites carcinoma after injection of DNase (de Lamirande, 1960).

The problem of activity of RNase in leukocytes, serum and urine in leukemias is being currently studied in our department. Thus far, significant elevation of serum RNase activity (Aleksandrowicz *et al.*, 1963a), increased urinary excretion (Aleksandrowicz and Spirer, 1955; Aleksandrowicz *et al.*, 1958), and increased clearance of endogenous RNase in chronic granulocytic leukemia (Urbańczyk, 1964) have been found. At present studies in our Department are concerned with the relationship between granulocytic RNA in healthy and leukemic patients and activity of serum RNase with a view to finding a solution of the problem of the pathogenesis of chronic granulocytic leukemia. Therapeutic trials with administration of crystalline RNase in chronic granulocytic leukemia (Aleksandrowicz *et al.*, 1963b) have succeeded in most of the patients in causing a 30% reduction in the blast cells and drop of leukocytosis. These results were achieved with minimal doses of the enzyme (0.5–2 mg daily). Further studies with higher doses of RNase are planned, depending, however, on the finding of a more abundant source of the enzyme. Confirmation of an effect of RNase on RNA metabolism is also provided by the results of experiments on the inactivation of systemic

RNase by administration of heparin (de Lamirande *et al.*, 1956), resulting in accumulation of large amounts of RNA in the liver cells. Intravenous injections of heparin in patients with chronic granulocytic leukemia (Aleksandrowicz, 1959) caused transient rise in leukocytosis, which subsided after cessation of heparin administration. On the other hand, intravenous injection of antiheparin—protamine sulfate—caused a transient drop in leukocytosis. These experimental findings point to an important role of the nucleases in the metabolism of nucleic acids in leukocytes. The work of Gaertner and Lisiewicz (1962) has also provided evidence of antiheparin properties of RNase.

Monocytes have an especially high content of "nonspecific" esterase, and lymphocytes and neutrophils less (Vanotti, 1961). Maturation of the granulocytes, commencing at the promyelocyte stage, is accompanied by rising levels (Lambers and Sič, 1962). Lennert and Leder (1963), who also observed high nonspecific esterase activity in monocytes and exudate macrophages, consider that the majority of the macrophages in exudates are emigrant blood monocytes. The presence of this enzyme in monocytes has given rise to the suggestion that monocytes originate in the bone marrow from myeloblasts and promyeloblasts, and not from reticuloendothelial cells (Bakalos and Petropolous, 1963).

Presence of 5'-nucleotidase in leukocytes has been demonstrated cytochemically (Rinneberg and Lennert, 1961). In leukemias levels of the enzyme were normal.

D. LIPIDS

1. *Composition*

Almost all the protoplasmatic granulations of neutrophils, eosinocytes, basocytes and monocytes contain lipids, mainly in the form of phospholipids. In the granulocytic series lipid levels increase with maturation, beginning at the promyelocyte stage (Takikava *et al.*, 1961; Lambers and Sič, 1962). High content of lipids has been demonstrated in isolated nuclei of granulocytes, probably localized mainly in the nuclear membrane (Polli and Ratti, 1953). According to most authors (e.g., Lambers and Eggstein, 1959), lymphocytes do not contain any lipids or phospholipids. Presence of lipids in lymphocytes was reported by Polli and Ratti (1953) and by Hertl (1960). According to Polli and Ratti (1953), in chronic granulocytic leukemia the total fat and phospholipid content is elevated, and the cholesterol levels are decreased. In chronic lymphocytic leukemia total fat, total and free cholesterol, cholesterol esters, and phospholipids showed lower levels than in leukocytes of healthy persons.

2. Metabolism

High rates of total lipid synthesis have been reported in myeloblastic leukemia, and low rates in acute lymphatic leukemia (Kidson, 1961) and in chronic granulocytic leukemia (Introzzi et al., 1962).

Esterases and lipases hydrolyzing fatty acid esters are uniformly distributed in the granulocytic and agranulocytic series of leukocytes and do not show any changes in the course of leukemias (Hardin et al., 1955; Vanotti, 1961).

E. VITAMINS: FOLIC ACID, VITAMIN B_{12}, AND ASCORBIC ACID

Folic acid and its derivatives, vitamin B_{12} and ascorbic acid, which play important roles in the synthesis of nucleic acids, deserve special mention.

In the human body, in the presence of ascorbic acid, folic acid undergoes two-step reduction by reductases to the biologically active compound—tetrahydrofolic acid, a cofactor of formate activation in the presence of ATP and Mg^{++}. N^{10}-Formyltetrahydrofolic acid, the product of this reaction, serves as donor of formyl groups. It is an unstable compound and can be reversely transformed into stable N^5-formyltetrahydrofolic acid, called Citrovorum factor (CF) or folinic acid (Williams, 1962). N^{10}-Formyltetrahydrofolic acid plays an essential role in biochemical processes of transformylation through activation and transfer of one-carbon compounds to precursors of the purine nucleotides and formation of the methyl groups of thymidilic acid and methionine.

In leukemic leukocytes, especially in myeloblastic leukemia and in terminal stages of chronic granulocytic and lymphatic leukemia, the content of CF in leukocytes is increased. Hence, elevated CF activity may be the result of immaturity of leukemic cells (Svenseid et al., 1951; Ellison and Hutchison, 1957; O'Brien and Walsh, 1962).

Dihydrofolic reductase (FH_2-reductase), which catalyzes reduction of dihydrofolic to tetrahydrofolic acid, occurs only in trace quantities in normal leukocytes, but in larger amounts in immature acute and chronic granulocytic leukemic cells (Wilmanns, 1962). Amethopterin, an inhibitor of FH_2-reductase (Hakala et al., 1960), prevents reduction of dihydrofolic acid to the biologically active tetrahydrofolic acid. Its administration to leukemic patients is followed by a rise in FH_2-reductase activity of the leukocytes, achieving maximum after one week, especially in cases resistant to treatment with folic acid antagonists (Wilmanns, 1962). It has also been postulated (Bertino et al., 1963) that amethopterin absorbed by immature cells inhibits FH_2-reductase and in this way diminishes production of tetrahydrofolate, performing the role of a normal repressor of reductase activity and effecting a rise in its activity.

Leukocytes of infectious mononucleosis exhibit the same FH_2-reductase activity as leukocytes in chronic and acute granulocytic leukemia (Bertino et al., 1962).

Vitamin B_{12}, also called cyanocobalamine, takes part in the synthesis of nucleic acids and amino acids (serine and methionine), in processes of transmethylation, and probably in the synthesis of porphyrins and consequently of hemoglobin.

The normal range of total cell vitamin B_{12} is 100–800 pg/10^8 leukocytes (Kidd and Thomas, 1962). Of the leukocytes, mature neutrophils possess the greatest ability of binding $Co^{60}B_{12}$ (Meyer et al., 1962). The cell content of vitamin B_{12} is normal in chronic lymphocytic leukemia, low in chronic granulocytic leukemia (Banerjee et al., 1960; Kidd and Thomas, 1962), and high in acute leukemia and reticulum cell leukemia. Serum levels of vitamin B_{12} in chronic granulocytic leukemia, and sometimes also in acute leukemia, are markedly elevated (Beard et al., 1954; Rosanova and Mjasistcheva, 1961). Attempts have been made to explain this phenomenon as a result of increased capacity of binding vitamin B_{12} by seromucoids with the electrophoretic mobility of a-globulins (Weinstein et al., 1959), or by breakdown products of maturing granulocytes (Meyer et al., 1962). Experiments performed with $Co^{58}B_{12}$ point to the possibility of a relative shift of vitamin B_{12} from the tissues to the serum (Weinstein and Watkin, 1960) and increased binding capacity of the serum (Brody et al., 1960).

Ascorbic acid, owing to the facility with which it reduces various substances, is associated with redox processes in cells. It is reduced back to the active form by glutathione. Waldo and Zipf (1955) found lowered levels of ascorbic acid in leukemic leukocytes and in the serum. During remissions achieved with steroid hormones the levels were further lowered, while remissions after X-ray therapy or chemotherapy caused a rise in the levels of ascorbic acid. There is a difference in the uptake of ascorbic acid by leukocytes and lymphocytes. Normal as well as pathologic lymphocytes do not take up any ascorbic acid from the serum, whereas normal neutrophils and immature leukemic granulocytes take up fairly high amounts (Denson and Richards, 1962).

F. Minerals and Water Content

Human leukocytes contain 78–82% H_2O, 42–57 meq of potassium and 71–89 meq of sodium per kilogram dry weight (Roberts, 1963). Comparison of the contents of H_2O, solids, nitrogen, ash, Na, Ca and Mg per 10^{12} leukocytes in chronic granulocytic and lymphatic leukemia showed approximately twofold higher values in neutrophils than in lymphocytes

(Rigas, 1961), probably due to the smaller volume of lymphocytes. In the granulocytic series, water, K, and Na remain unaltered with the age of the cell, Mg decreases, and total solids, N, and Ca increase, in contrast to the lymphocytic series, in which there is no change in K, but marked decrease in every other constituent occurs with cell maturity (Rigas, 1961).

Zinc is present in especially high amounts in the granulations of neutrophils, eosinocytes, and basocytes, decreasing in proportion to the stage of immaturity of the cells (Amann and Wolff, 1956; Dennes et al., 1961). In some cases of granulocytic leukemia tenfold lower levels of zinc were observed during relapses, and return to normal during remissions achieved with urethane or X-rays. Intravenous administration of zinc salts has no effect on its concentration in the leukocytes or on the course of the disease (Mathies, 1958). Markedly lowered levels of zinc were observed in the leukocytes of chronic lymphocytic leukemia and monocytic leukemia (Dennes et al., 1961). Zinc activates alkaline phosphatase in leukocytes (Trubowitz et al., 1957; Valentine et al., 1960), low content of zinc in leukocytes of chronic granulocytic leukemia may be related to the low activity of this enzyme. Connective tissue mast cells and blood basocytes contain large amounts of heavy metals, mainly zinc (Amann, 1961).

Copper occurs mainly in the granulations of eosinocytes and basocytes (Amann and Wolff, 1956). Lowered content of copper has been reported in the lymphocytes of chronic lymphocytic leukemia (Gisinger, 1960).

Experimental magnesium deficiency in rats causes marked peripheral eosinophilia and infiltrations composed of eosinophilic cells in several organs (Hungerford and Karson, 1960).

G. PORPHYRINS AND VERDOPEROXIDASE

Myeloblasts, like erythroblasts, are capable of synthesizing the porphyrin ring. This ability is lost during the maturation of the cells. Myelocytes in chronic granulocytic leukemia do not produce any porphyrin. Normal mature neutrophils after incubation with δ-aminolevulinic acid are able to produce two times more porphobilinogen than lymphocytes (Vanotti and Cullity, 1960; Vanotti, 1961).

Schultz et al. (1956) while studying the pigment in transplantable chloroma (myeloblastoma) in rats found that when inspected in white light the green color is due to the presence of a green hemoprotein, known as myelo- or verdoperoxidase, and the red fluorescence in ultraviolet light is attributable to the presence of porphyrins. This enzyme oxidizes reduced diphosphopyridine, but its function in leukocytes is unknown (Schultz, 1958). According to Kelenyi et al. (1961), there is a reciprocal relationship between verdoperoxidase and porphyrins: tissues with high activity of the enzyme contain low concentrations of porphyrins, and vice versa.

IV. Metabolism of Platelets

The main biological function of blood platelets, which are richly equipped with natural biochemical substances localized at different sites, is connected with their influence on hemostatic processes. Blood platelets have been likened, with some justification, to sponges surrounded by a coating of plasma, known as the platelet atmosphere. The plasma hemostatic factors I-XII*, profibrinokinase, and antifibrinolysin are selectively taken up and concentrated in the platelet atmosphere, but no anticoagulant substances or active fibrinolysis activators have been found here. Relatively little is known about the structure, biochemical composition, and functions of the membrane of the platelets. Other specific hemostatic biochemical substances are present within the body of the platelets. Some of these substances are only transported or stored in the platelets, while others represent true structural components. Specific hemostatic substances are distributed in the granulomere as well as in the hyalomere of the platelets.

Owing to specific adsorption and concentration on the platelets, the plasma activators are conveyed together with the internal hemostatic factors of the platelets to the sites of vascular damage. In this way, functional and morphological relations between the damaged vascular wall and agglomerated blood platelets and plasmatic hemostatic factors are established.

Presently available methods are not always able to disclose the source and localization of the different platelet factors, i.e., whether they are true internal or external factors contained in the plasmatic atmosphere of the platelets, especially since the platelets display marked powers of binding and incorporating various normal and abnormal substances (proteins, fats, dextran, viruses, bacteria, etc.).

The knowledge of blood clotting has profited greatly from advances in morphology of blood platelets, especially those made possible by electron microscopy, and in the metabolism and biochemistry of hemostatic processes. In this section, however, only problems connected with the metabolism of the blood platelets will be discussed under the following headings;

* The nomenclature of the different hemostatic factors is given by MacFarlane (1961).

1. relation between structure and function of the platelets;
2. metabolism of platelets as a source of their vital energy;
3. relations between platelet metabolism and blood clotting.

A. RELATION BETWEEN STRUCTURE AND FUNCTION OF PLATELETS

The properties of blood platelets involved in their hemostatic function are adhesion, agglomeration, retractility, and specific fragility. On the one hand, the formation of the hemostatic plug is dependent on these phenomena. On the other hand, the disintegrating blood platelets release a number of specific hemostatic substances. Morphologically, manifestation of hemostatic activity by the patelets is initiated by viscous metamorphosis (VM). In this process the oval circulating form emits pseudopodia passing into the dendritic, and further into the transitional form. Coalescence of the thickening pseudopodia gives rise to the spread form. In functionally stimulated platelets the granulations of the granulomere often shift to the periphery of the platelet. The elements forming platelet agglomerates adhere closely to each other through their limiting membranes, which then gradually disappear. Both the granulomere and hyalomere participate in the formation of pseudopodia. The pseudopodia are the prehensile organs of the platelets, which establish contact with the pseudopodia of other platelets, fibrin threads, and with the vascular wall. In this way, the pseudopodia contribute to the formation of the space lattice of platelets and fibrin, platelet agglomerates, and hemostatic plug and clot, and to their subsequent retraction.

Microscopy, especially electronic, reveals that a close relationship exists between the fibrin threads and network and the platelets. The first threads formed arrange themselves radially around individual platelets and agglomerates and not infrequently exhibit relation to the granulations of the granulomere. This phenomenon is significant in view of the fact that the granulomere is the site of platelet thromboplastic factor 3, which is one of the initiators of clotting. The microscopic observations indicate that the properties and structure of the clot, in which the platelets are centers of clotting and retraction, is dependent on the behavior of the platelets. In platelet-poor plasma the fibrin threads are not distributed radially in the form of a space lattice, but often show parallel arrangement.

Thus far, it has not proved possible to localize accurately the different biochemical hemostatic factors in blood platelets. The granulomere contains lipids, especially phospholipids, and its isolated granulations exhibit thromboplastic activity in the thromboplastin generation test. The same granulations also contain glycogen as a source of stored energy. Factor 3 occurs in vacuoles in the platelet granulomere, as observed by electron microscopy. The largest amounts of this factor are thought to be present in the a granulations, and smaller amounts in β and γ granulations. The granulations of the platelets are also the seat of factor 1, as indicated by the fact that this high molecular weight protein sediments together with the granulations in the ultracentrifuge. This is noteworthy inasmuch as factor 1 in the platelets is undoubtedly identical with plasma factor V.

Most of the hemostatic activities of the platelets are not associated with activation of metabolic processes. For instance, the angiotropic (factor 5, noradrenaline and adrenaline, etc.) and coagulotropic (factors 1–4, etc.) functions and the effect on thrombofibrinolysis (profibrinokinase, antifibrinolysin) are often present for considerable periods of time in preparations in which the platelets no longer show signs of viability. On the other hand, viscous metamorphosis, agglomeration and retraction of the platelets and the accompanying clot retraction are associated with marked metabolic activity. The minimal metabolic activity of resting platelets is suddenly replaced by violent expenditure of energy in the active state, manifested by viscous metamorphosis and retraction.

Therefore, the metabolism of the blood platelets may be considered from the point of view of the vital processes of the platelets themselves, and from that of their viscous metamorphosis and retraction.

B. Metabolism of Platelets

Studies on the metabolites and metabolism of platelets have been carried out with various methods: cytochemical, cytoenzymatic, chemical, biochemical, by chromatography, electrophoresis, spectrophotometry and photometry, microinterferometry, micromanometry, and by isotope methods. As a result, much new information has been acquired, but due to the diversity of the methods, the results are often discrepant. The methods of isolating, purifying, and storing the platelets are also of importance. For instance, washing the platelets deprives them of free simple sugars, part of ATP (up to 20% of the original value), abolishes respiration and consumption of glucose and energy-rich phosphates, and paralyzes the enzymes concerned in the transfer of phosphate groups (3-phosphoglycerate-1-kinase and pyruvate kinase). After three washings the metabolism of platelets may be completely abolished.

Almost all the known metabolites occur in the blood platelets. Water constitutes 80–88% of the fresh weight of platelets. Their mean dry weight represents 12.5% of fresh weight (at 110°C). The mineral elements, which make up about 0.39% of the dry weight of human platelets, include metals as well as metalloids. Of the metals, sodium, potassium, calcium, and magnesium are present in considerable amounts, and iron, copper and manganese in trace amounts. Zinc, cobalt, and lead are not found in blood platelets. Blood platelets contain more calcium than the red or white blood cells. Nonionic platelet calcium is bound with phospholipids and cannot be exchanged experimentally with Ca^{45}. The metalloids in platelets are sulfur, nitrogen, and phosphorus. Sulfur, constituting 0.18% of the dry weight of platelets, enters into the composition of a number of organic components. Total nitrogen makes about 11% of the dry weight, and protein nitrogen 9–10%. Total phosphorus represents 1.4% of the dry weight of human platelets: more than one-half of this is acid-soluble fraction (of which a half is ATP phosphorus), and the remaining half is composed of lipid phosphorus and, to a lesser extent, protein phosphorus; only traces of nuclein phosphorus are present.

Carbohydrates make 8.47% of the dry weight of platelets. They include the simple sugars (-oses), usually contained in large molecules, and polysaccharides. Of the pentoses, no deoxyribose and only small amounts of ribose are found in the pentanucleotide, adenosine, and nucleoprotein fractions. The hexoses are represented by glucose, galactose, mannose, and fructose, and by certain hexose derivatives such as hexose phosphate, glucosamine, galactosamine, and glucuronic and sialic acid. An important polysaccharide is glycogen, which has recently been chemically extracted from blood platelets in amounts of approximately 5 mg/gm of fresh weight or 28 ± 10 mM/10^{11} platelets (10^{11} platelets correspond to 1 gm of platelet fresh weight). In cytochemical and cytoenzymatic studies glycogen occurs in the form of small, fairly regularly scattered grains, or as thick, compact grains in the protoplasm of megakaryocytes, sometimes partly covering the nucleus. Similar glycogen grains occur in the central parts of platelets in the granulomere. Human platelets contain at least one mucopolysaccharide, which has the nature of β-chondroitin sulfate or of a mixture of chondroitin sulfates B and C. Opinions differ as to the presence of hyaluronic acid in platelets. The blood group substances of the platelets are glucides.

Purine and pyrimidine bases account for about 3% of the total nitrogen of human platelets, and nucleotides for 1.8%. Adenine, cytosine, guanine, hypoxanthine, uracil, cytidylic acid, and uridylic acid have been found in the platelets. Flavin adenine nucleotide is a coenzyme of the flavoprotein type in platelets. About 90% of the free nucleotides are of the adenine type, and adenosine phosphates constitute about 1.2% of the dry weight of platelets. Adenosine triphosphate (ATP) is present in the largest amount, 21.5 mM/10^{11} platelets, i.e., approximately per one gram of fresh blood platelets. ADP and AMP (adenosine diphosphate and adenosine monophosphate) occur in small amounts, and uridine, cytidine, inosine, and guanosine triphosphates in traces only. The ATP/

ADP ratio characteristic of platelets is 3–5 : 1. Deoxyribonucleic acid, which occurs in the nuclei of megakaryocytes, is absent in blood platelets, consistently with the electron microscopic observations of absence of nuclear structures in platelets. Occurrence of ribonucleic acid has also been the subject of much discussion. While some cytochemical tests give entirely negative results, others disclose trace or minimal amounts. Biochemically, the content has been stated to be 0.1 nucleic acids per 100 total nitrogen, or 0.88 mg of nucleic acid phosphorus per one gram of dry weight of human platelets. Electron microscopy, revealing presence in platelets of fragments of endoplasmic reticulum, mitochondria, microsomes, and ribosomes, provides morphological evidence of occurrence of some ribonucleic acids in the platelets.

Lipids constitute 16–19% of the dry weight of human blood platelets. They are represented mainly by phospholipids (phosphatides), and by relatively small amounts of free and esterified cholesterol and neutral fats. Using refined chromatographic methods, the platelet lipids have been separated into lecithin (32%), cholesterol (19%), phosphatidyl ethanolamine (17%), sphingomyelin (13%), phosphatidyl serine (6%), phosphatidyl inositol (5%), and others (8%). Biochemical studies disclosed presence of neutral fats, fatty acids (palmitic—C_{16}, stearic—C_{18}, oleic—C_{18}, arachidonic—C_{20}), phosphatidic acids, phosphatidyl choline, proteo- and glycolipids, and plasmalogens (including glycerophosphoridyl ethanolamine), constituting about 23% of cephalin. Cephalin is a mixture of phosphatidyl serine (PS) and phosphatidyl ethanolamine (PE), containing traces of phosphatidyl inositol. Cephalin accounts for about 33% of the platelet lipids and 43% of the phospholipids. Factor 3 of platelets is a lipoprotein with molecular weight of over one million. A calcium-lipid complex is supposed to be formed in the patelet membrane. The results of biochemical analysis of the platelet lipids represent a marked advance beyond the information obtained by cytochemical studies.

Proteins represent 57% of the dry weight of platelets. About 20 amino acids have been discovered in platelet autolysates. Taurine (about 1.5 mg/gm dry weight of platelets) and the monoamino acids glutamic and aspartic acid and phenylalanine occur in the largest amounts. Platelets also contain glycine, alanine, valine, isoleucine, leucine, methionine, arginine, tyrosine, tryptophane, histidine, histamine, cystine, serine, cystinic acid, proline, and asparagine. Taurine is an end product of the metabolism of sulfur-containing amino acids, especially cystine and cysteine, and glycine is related to serine, which is the starting product of the synthesis of platelet phosphatides, an important factor in blood clotting.

No threonine, lysine, or ornithine, and probably no tetramethylcystine, have been found in platelets. Polypeptide nitrogen occurs in minimal amounts, less than 1% of the total nitrogen. Antiheparin factor 4 of the platelets is thought to be a high molecular weight polypeptide. Electrophoresis of platelet lysates separates their proteins into four fractions: albumin (11%) and globulins (89%), the latter including a-2- (55%), β-1- (23%) and γ-globulin (11%). Occurrence in platelet preparations of a-1-, β-2- (including β-2 M) globulins and fibrinogenoid has also been reported. Decision as to which of the above-mentioned protein fractions are true components of the platelets, and which occur in their external plasma atmosphere, is difficult. Some data indicate that these proteins belong to the platelet atmosphere. Other experiments (e.g., with I^{131}-albumin) show that proteins are very strongly adsorbed on platelets, so that washing seven times may fail to remove them. Fibrinogenoid has proved to be identical with adsorbed plasma fibrinogen. The platelet atmosphere and the platelets themselves contain still other hemostatic proteins, which are mentioned in monographs on blood clotting. A special retractile protein of the platelets, known as thrombostenin, constitutes 15% of the platelet proteins and 1% of the dry weight of platelets.

Amines: Platelets absorb adrenaline (approximately 0.002 $\mu g/10^9$ platelets) and noradrenaline (approximately 0.007 $\mu g/10^9$ platelets). The concentration of catecholamines in the platelets is about 125 times greater than in the plasma, giving evidence of the active character of absorption, transport, and storage of catecholamines in blood platelets. Human platelets contain histamine in concentrations equal to not more than 5% of its concentration in full blood. Blood platelets absorb, transport, and store serotonin (5-hydroxytryptamine, 5HT), which is also known as angiotropic factor 5 of platelets. The platelets are practically the chief source of blood serotonin, which is released from them into the blood plasma and serum. The concentration of serotonin in platelets is 0.5–1.3 $\mu g/10^9$ platelets, and the coefficient of concentration of serotonin in platelets is 200 : 1. Adenosine triphosphate is supposed to play an important role in the binding of amines by platelets. The ATP and serotonin contents of platelets have been found to be proportional. However, after reserpine and in leukemic patients, the serotonin concentration in the platelets is decreased, while ATP remains unchanged.

Blood platelets contain ascorbic acid (approximately 3 $\mu g/10^9$ platelets) and exhibit the power of absorbing it *in vivo*. Pigments found in the platelets include cytochrome and the carotenoids, lutein, lycopene, and β-carotene.

Undoubtedly, blood platelets are able to absorb, concentrate, and metabolize many biochemical substances, e.g., cortisone, which may exert an influence on the hemostatic system.

The studies of the metabolites and metabolism of the platelets have provided valuable evidence of their origin from the bone marrow megakaryocytes.

The diversity of the metabolic processes taking place in the blood platelets is due to the great variety of available metabolites as well as to enzymatic activities, which include over eighty types of enzymatic action. According to present information, enzymatic activity is connected mainly with the hyaloplasm, especially with the mitochondria.

As a result of the small number and dimensions of the mitochondria, the enzymatic activity of platelets is weaker than that of muscles, which contain numerous mitochondria, but stronger than that of erythrocytes, which possess no mitochondria. Enzymoproteins in blood platelets constitute 2%, in striated muscle 10%, and in erythrocytes only 0.3% of the total protein content. In relation to moist weight, the enzymoprotein content of platelets is 20 times greater than that of erythrocytes.

Blood platelets possess a complete set of glycolytic enzymes. Calculated per gram of protein, the glycolytic activity of the platelets is 10 times lower than that of striated muscle but 10–20 times greater than that of erythrocytes. The enzymes of the hexose-monophosphate cycle and tricarboxylic citric acid cycle (Krebs cycle), apart from relatively active malic dehydrogenase, are less active than the glycolytic enzymes. The platelets possess more enzymes of the hexose-monophosphate cycle and less glycero-1-phosphate dehydrogenase and creatine phosphate kinase than muscles. The role of the enzymes of the pentose-phosphate shunt, which occur in platelets but not in muscles, is unknown. Of the glycolytic enzymes of the platelets, hexokinase is the least active. The isocitrate, succinic and glutamic dehydrogenase activities and respiratory enzymatic chain (including oxidases) belong to the intramitochondrial enzymes. Glycero-1-phosphate dehydrogenase activity is also connected with the mitochondria. The slight activity of these enzymes in platelets is apparently related to the small number and dimensions of the mitochondria.

Blood platelets are relatively abundantly equipped with enzymes splitting and synthesizing ATP (ATPase and adenylate kinase) and acid phosphatase, but exhibit only trace alkaline phosphatase activity. The ATPase activity of platelet thrombostenin is 50–100 times weaker than muscle ATPase. Thrombostenin constitutes 1–2% of the moist weight of platelets, whereas similar contracting substances of the striated muscle account for 10–12%, those of smooth muscle about 2.5%, and in undifferentiated cells 0.1–0.2%. It should be mentioned that the movements of fibroblasts are largely the result of presence of contracting substances resembling muscle actomyosin and platelet thrombostenin, which also react to ATP. Thrombostenin accounts for 15% of the platelet proteins, muscle contracting substances for 30%, and similar substances in other tissues for 1–3% of the protein content. Thrombostenin resembles actomyosin with regard to solubility at higher ionic concentrations, insolubility in the presence of salts (even in physiological concentrations), effect of ATPase, and reaction to environmental factors (e.g., reaction to ATP, Mg, and Ca). Differences, however, also exist, e.g., concerning conditions of solubility, intensity of effect of ATPase action, contracting activity under experimental conditions, and effect on viscosity and immunological behavior.

The enzymes of amino acid metabolism (transaminases, glutamic dehydrogenase) also exhibit relatively slight activity.

Analysis of the intermediate and end products of the metabolism of platelets reveals that even under aerobic conditions glycolytic breakdown of carbohydrates predominates. Almost one-half of the glucose consumed per unit of time is converted to pyruvate and lactate, and only about one-fifth undergoes combustion to CO_2 and water. The fate of about one-fourth of the glucose consumed has not been determined, although probably not owing to inadequacy of the methods applied but to the fact that this glucose is transformed into glycogen, amino acids, and lipids. Relations between carbohydrate and amino acid metabolism are indicated by the presence in the platelets of enzymes of amino acid metabolism (transaminases; glutamic dehydrogenase) together with relatively high contents of glutamic and aspartic acids and their amides. Predominance of glycolysis over oxidative breakdown of glucose is consistent with the small numbers of mitochondria in platelets, as already mentioned. Consumption of oxygen and production of carbon dioxide, expressed by a respiratory quotient of about 1.0, also point to combustion of carbohydrates.

The blood platelets contain considerable amounts of energy-giving substances. For instance the glycogen content of the platelets is larger than in muscles. The concentration of ATP is 2 25–150 times greater in the platelets than in erythrocytes, depending on whether the calculation is referred to single platelets, large numbers, or to dry or fresh weight, respectively. The percentage content of ATP in platelets is similar to that in striated muscle, and is one-tenth of the concentration in the adrenals. The predominance of high-energy ATP over other triphosphates (uridine, inosine, cytidine, and guanosine triphosphates) is similar to that in striated muscles, but opposed to that in many other cells, e.g., in the liver. Obviously, the mechanical tasks of platelets and of muscle in both cases require a rich supply of energy-giving substances, specific enzymes and contracting proteins. Platelet thrombostenin and muscle actomyosin both react to ATP and magnesium ions by contracting. Retractility may therefore be likened, biochemically and dynamically, to muscular contraction, except that the latter, in contrast to retractility, is a reversible phenomenon.

Wealth of metabolites and enzymes enables the platelets to perform specific metabolic functions, such as gain in energy, storage of energy, liberation of energy, and transformation to mechanical work. The mechanism of gain in energy is not yet adequately known. As in other blood cells, the limiting enzymes are the hexokinases, while diphosphofructoaldolase and fructose-6-phosphate kinase play secondary roles (after addition of hexokinase). Storage of energy depends on production of ATP and glycogen. Liberation of energy is associated with violent reactions between energy-rich phosphates and phosphate transporters and splitting enzymes. This pertains especially to the reactions between ATP and ATPases, the latter including thrombostenin. These phenomena resemble those encountered in muscle tissue. Energy-rich phosphates and the enzymes attacking them are apparently separated in the circulating platelets, and come into contact and react only after viscous metamorphosis has started. Transformation of biochemical energy into mechanical work is the result of the behavior of activated thrombostenin, which has been compared to the behavior of muscle actomyosin. However, many of the reactions in which the biochemical energy of the platelets is transformed into mechanical energy, and the mechanism of the influence of the latter on the arrangement and shortening of fibrin threads, continue to be shrouded in mystery.

C. Relations between Platelet Metabolism and Blood Clotting

In the course of clotting many changes take place in the biochemistry and metabolism of the blood platelets and their physiological environment—the plasma and serum. The disintegration of platelets during blood clotting releases a number of platelet factors into the serum, such as mineral substances (e.g., potassium), organic substances (taurine, acid mucopolysaccharide), and enzymes (acid phosphatase, pyrophosphatase, ATPase, cholinesterase, glutamic-oxalacetic transaminase). Many of the liberated substances (serotonin, noradrenaline and adrenaline, histamine, mucopolysaccharide, etc.) affect the state of the capillaries and larger blood vessels. Some investigators have tried to deduce the state of the platelet membrane and degree of disintegration of the platelets on the basis of liberation of taurine, serotonin, acid phosphatase, or pyrophosphatase (phosphomonoesterase). The state of the platelet membrane is largely dependent on the influence of sulfhydryl groups. On the other hand, the biochemical changes in the plasmatic atmosphere of the platelets, especially precipitation of its fibrinogen by thrombin, activate viscous metamorphosis and disintegration of the platelets, liberating their hemostatic potential.

The thromboplastic activity of the platelets, which is determined with the thromboplastin generation test, is associated on the one hand with optimal concentration of total phosphatides, and on the other with optimal ratio between phosphatidyl serine, phosphatidyl ethanolamine, and phosphatidyl choline. These conditions are fulfilled by the phospholipids of platelets and brain, and partly of soy seeds. Polyunsaturated fatty acids are necessary for a lipid to be coagulation active. Oxidation of platelet lipids results in loss of their coagulative properties, owing to loss of double bonds. Most authors refer the thromboplastic activity of the platelet phospholipids mainly to phosphatidyl serine. Others maintain that only phosphatidyl serine is active in the thromboplastin generation test, while phosphatidyl serine and phosphatidyl ethanolamine influence the recalcification time of platelet-poor plasma. Phosphatidyl inositol (containing an admixture of phosphatidyl serine) is an activator of both hemostatic processes. Plasmalogens are probably thromboplastically inactive. According to other authors, chiefly the colamine cephalins, constituting 80–90% of cephalins, possess coagulative activity, while serine cephalins, constituting 10%, are inactive in this respect. One of the lipids is an inhibitor of thromboplastin, and one of the platelet proteins in the thromboplastin generation test inhibits production as well as activity of thromboplastin when produced. Experimental or pathological increase in the concentration of platelet lipids has an inhibitory effect on the thromboplastin generation test, giving rise to the opinion that "surplus of platelets does not favor their function." The antilipemic influence of heparin is inhibited by antiheparin factor 4 of the platelets, as may be observed in the serum clearing effect.

The most interesting changes during clotting concern ATP. Within 10–20 minutes, when the volume of exuded serum is still only 5%, the level of ATP drops to 50% of its initial value. At this time viscous metamorphosis is taking place and retraction is beginning in the recalcified platelet-rich plasma. At this time too, the most intensive energetic processes associated with breakdown of energy-rich phosphates occur. Viscous metamorphosis and retraction of the platelets are therefore endergonic processes. In experimental systems with glucose, the level of ATP depends on the glycolytic activity of the platelets; in the absence of glucose addition of thrombin increases the utilization of ATP. At the beginning of viscous metamorphosis there is a short-lasting (about 2 minutes) increase in glycolytic activity which may be due to beginning synthesis of ATP under the influence of thrombin. The further drop in ATP after 20 minutes of clotting is less pronounced. ATP and ATPase come into contact only after the disintegration of the platelets; the enzyme is presumably activated by Mg- or Ca-ATPase at that time. Frozen platelet lysates, which are rich in ATPase but poor in energy-rich phosphates (ATP), do not possess the ability to retract. After addition of plasma, thrombin, ATP and Mg, however, almost normal retraction takes place.

Factors inhibiting glycolysis (e.g., monoiodoacetate, sodium fluoride), the citric acid cycle (e.g., malonate), and the respiratory chain (e.g., cyanide), also affect the retractile efficiency of platelets and the thromboelastographic curve and lower the level of ATP. These observations are strong evidence of the dependence of the mechanical process of retraction on carbohydrate metabolism, especially glycolysis. Glucose, calcium, cysteine, and glutathione are other biochemical activators and cofactors of retraction.

During viscous metamorphosis ADP is produced, causing further aggregation of platelets, their viscous metamorphosis, and liberation of energy-rich phosphates. According to some investigators, platelet aggregation caused by ADP is reversible and occurs without viscous metamorphosis. The erythrocytic factor R of Hellem (1960) proved to be identical to ADP. According to other authors, ADP is used up during platelet aggregation; still others consider that the low level of this substance does not undergo any important change before or after clotting. Aggregation of platelets under the influence of ADP is inhibited by ATP and AMP. Trace levels of AMP are not altered during clotting, behaving similarly in plasma and serum.

The biochemistry and metabolism of the platelets vary under certain conditions, which can be only briefly mentioned here. Maturation and age of the megakaryocytes and platelets affect their biochemistry and metabolism. In megakaryocytes maturation is accompanied by gradual decrease in nucleotides, and alkaline phosphatase appears more abundantly in the protoplasm of active, but less abundantly in inactive megakaryocytes. Determination of the age of platelets has been attempted not only on morphological grounds (dimensions, shape, staining of the platelets or of their hyalomere; number, type, dimensions, shape, position and staining of granulations, and presence of vacuoles), but also on the basis of functional and biochemical criteria. Young platelets are supposed to be smaller, more bluish, and more easily agglomerated, while mature platelets show excentric distribution of the granulations of the granulomere and more numerous vacuoles. Aging platelets are supposed to show less ability of retraction concurrently with changes in glycolysis, diminished activity of glyceraldehyde-3-phosphodehydrogenase (GAPDH) and phosphoglycerate-1-kinase (PGK), and lower levels of free amino acids, nucleotides, and ATP. Phylogenesis of the platelets is also associated with biochemical and metabolic changes. Individual age in humans has no significant influence on the biochemistry and metabolism of the platelets, although lower levels of serotonin after the age of 70 years have been reported. Isolation and storage of platelets for experimental and clinical purposes also involves biochemical and metabolic problems. Fragility and vitality of platelets are largely functions of the platelet membrane, and consequently depend on metabolic processes. Diminished diastase activity leads to disorders of permeability, resulting in disintegration of the membrane and lysis of platelets and escape of enzymes (e.g., acid phosphatase and pyrophosphatase). On the other hand, the potency of dehydrogenases and phosphohexoisomerase is connected with morphological integrity of the platelets. In stored platelets activity of factors 3 and 4 persists longest, while activity of factors 1 and 2 and retractility diminish. Addition to the platelets of nucleosides, nicotinamide or reduced glutathione stabilizes the enzymes and prolongs the effect of stored platelets on retraction and normal levels of ATP sometimes up to four weeks. Ethylenediaminetetraacetate (EDTA) has an unfavorable effect on platelet peptidases, and Mg or Ca is unfavorable to glycerophosphatases, but favorable to ATPases and pyrophosphatase. Cysteine and reduced glutathione preserve activity of dehydrogenases, and sulfhydryl groups the integrity of the platelet membrane. Lyophilization and storage at $-10°C$ preserve the activity of glutamo-oxalacetic dehydrogenase, aldolase, and leucine-aminopeptidase up to 3 weeks, but diminish the activity of phosphohexoisomerase.

During menstruation, activity of ATPase, nucleotidase, and of both phosphatases is suppressed, and that of alanyl-glycine dipeptidase is increased. After the third month of pregnancy histaminase activity is increased not only in the serum, but also in the platelets.

Enzymatic and metabolic disorders in the platelets may occur after administration of certain drugs. Reserpine lowers the concentration of serotonin in platelets. During administration of the cumarol anticoagulants activity of DL-glycylleucine dipeptidase and DL-leucylglycylglycine tripeptidase is lowered at first, while that of DL-glycylalanine dipeptidase and DL-glycylglycine dipeptidase is increased. Subsequently, the activity of all these enzymes diminishes in parallel with the prothrombin level, and reacts favorably to administration of vitamin K or cessation of administration of the anticoagulant drug. Acid and alkaline phosphatase activities are diminished in thrombosis and liver diseases.

Studies on the biochemistry and metabolism of the blood platelets have helped to elucidate the pathogenesis of various hemorrhagic diatheses. A great deal of interest has been aroused by the Glanzmann-Naegeli diathesis, which has been studied by Gross and his school in Marburg. Among patients suffering from this hereditary and congenital hemorrhagic diathesis, two groups may be distinguished. In the first group platelet glycolysis and glucose consumption are diminished (to 60%) and lactate production (to 70%), while oxygen consumption and CO_2 and pyruvate production remain normal. Both hexosephosphates, i.e., glucose-6-phosphate (G-6-P) and fructose-1-6-diphosphate (FDP), accumulate. Levels of glutamic and aspartic acid and their amides are also increased (two- to fourfold), while that of taurine is diminished. Glyceraldehyde-3-phosphate-dehydrogenase (GAPDH) and pyruvate kinase (PK) show characteristic drops in enzymatic activity (to 18–30%). Changes in activity of other platelet enzymes are less significant; for instance, increased activity of acid phosphatase and lactic dehydrogenase, or diminished activity of alkaline phosphatase, phosphoglucomutase, glutamic-oxalacetic and glutamic-pyruvate transaminases and glutathione reductase. ATP levels in the platelets are lowered to about one-half of normal values, while those of ADP and AMP are unaltered. The ATP/ADP ratio is low, 1.8–2.4. All these data indicate incomplete blocking of the oxidative enzymatic reaction concerning transformation of glyceraldehyde-3-phosphate into 1,3-phosphoglycerate. The blood platelets of this group of patients when suspended in their own plasma exhibit almost normal retraction in the presence of $Mg + ATP$. The action of the tetrasodium salt of ATP is much weaker in this respect. Mg alone improves retraction; calcium has a similar, although weaker, action and in some concentrations inhibits the positive effect of Mg-ATP. In the second group of patients there are no significant enzymatic disorders, apart from moderate depression of pyruvate kinase activity, or in any of the other biochemical and metabolic processes mentioned above. On the other hand, diminished activity of Mg-ATPase is observed. In this group of patients, too, addition of Mg and ATP almost completely normalizes the pathological impairment of retraction. The levels and liberation of platelet factors 3 and 5, Na, K, Ca, and Mg (total and ionic) in the platelets and platelet-rich and -poor plasmas are normal.

The biochemical and metabolic disorders of the platelets in the Glanzmann-Naegeli diathesis are manifested by lack of adhesion, aggregation (spontaneous and under the influence of ADP), and retraction, which explains the hemorrhagic symptoms of this diathesis. In summary, the Glanzmann-Naegeli diathesis is caused by disorders of glycolysis in the platelets, involving impaired production or utilization of ATP. According to French investigators, the following possibilities must be considered: deficiency of Mg, Mg-ATPases, or thrombostenin (which was not confirmed in one case which was examined in this respect thus far) and pathological reaction of thrombostenin with ATP. It is also emphasized that in both groups of patients disorders in the ATP/ADP ratio may play a role: in the first group reduced ratio due to deficiency of ATP, and in the second group increased ratio due to deficiency of ADP as a result of impaired glycolysis. It is also thought that deficient aggregation of the platelets may be caused by an anomalous site of action of ADP upon the platelet membrane. According to Gross and his school (Gross et al., 1960; Löhr et al., 1961; Gross, 1962), in both groups of patients there is a deficiency of freely available $Mg^{++} \cdot ATP^{--}$ complex, which is needed for retraction. The pathogenesis of the Glanzmann-Naegeli diathesis, however, cannot be considered fully clarified, since there is lack of direct evidence that the enzyme deficiency is the cause of ATP deficiency.

In the pathogenesis of hereditary and congenital diathesis of Willebrand-Jürgens, disorders in the metabolism of the adenosine phosphates are also thought to play a role. The level of ATP in platelet-rich plasma and in the serum of the patients is elevated, although consumption of ATP during clotting, as well as the level and consumption of ADP, are normal. In this diathesis the aldehyde fraction of the platelet phosphatides is diminished to about one-fourth of normal values, accompanied by disorders in levels or liberation of factor 3.

In states of deficiency of factors 7, 8, 9, and 10 consumption of ATP and the ATP/ADP ratio are normal. In dystrophia thrombocytica, on the other hand, increased enzymatic activity of the platelets was accompanied by disorders of their hemostatic function. The genetic background of some enzymatic disorders consists in deficiency of glucose-6-phosphate dehydrogenase of the platelets, the specific sensitivity of which to certain pathological conditions corresponds to a similar defect of the erythrocytes in the course of hemolytic anemia caused by primaquine.

In thrombocytopenias biochemical disorders in the megakaryocytes and platelets also occur. For instance, cytochemically diminished content of glycogen has been found in patients with idiopathic hyperplasia (Werlhof's diathesis), and hypersplenic aplasia of megakaryocytes. On the other hand, secondary proliferation of megakaryocytes is accompanied by increase in their glycogen content. It may be concluded that bone marrow inhibition is accompanied by diminished glycogen content of the megakaryocytes, and stimulation by increased glycogen content of the megakaryocytes. After splenectomy in Werlhof's diathesis the content of glycogen and other glucides in the marrow megakaryocytes increases, and the disorders of the glycolytic cycle, phosphotransferases and ATP of the platelets are normalized in the patients. To a certain degree, hormonal treatment with cortisone and its derivatives exerts a similar beneficial effect. Electrophoretic studies of the platelets failed to disclose any pathologic changes in thrombocytopenia, thrombocythemia, or thrombocytopathy. Antiplatelet antibodies cause impairment of glucose consumption and diminished lactate production and deficient retraction without changes in the ATP levels in the platelets.

Biochemical and metabolic disorders of the platelets occur also in the course of erythremias and leukemias. For instance, levels of factor 5 (serotonin), acid and alkaline phosphatase and glucose-6-phosphate dehydrogenase activities are diminished, and the ratio of lactic acid production to oxygen consumption during glycolysis is increased.

It is impossible to discuss in the limits of this chapter all the biochemical and metabolic problems concerning blood platelets which interest biologists as well as clinicians. They are presented, together with the pertinent literature, in other publications. The problems concerned with morphological changes in the platelets connected with blood clotting are discussed and the literature is cited by Aleksandrowicz et al. (1954, 1957), Fonio (1957), Gaertner (1960), Lüscher and Bettex-Galland (1961), Maupin (1954), and Morita (1958). The role of platelet factors and of the platelets in hemostatic processes is discussed by Adelson et al. (1961), Ballerini (1958), Bettex-Galland and Lüscher (1961), Biggs and MacFarlane (1962), Gaertner (1960), Lüscher (1962), Lüscher and Bettex-Galland (1961), Maupin (1954), Morita (1958), Wintrobe (1962), and in the symposium "Blood Platelets" (1961). The biochemistry and metabolism of the blood platelets are the subject of publications by Bettex-Galland and Lüscher (1961), Bettex-Galland and Maupin (1961), "Blood Platelets" (1961), Gaertner (1960), Gross et al. (1960), Gross (1962), Maupin (1954, 1960, 1961), Morita (1958), Weissbach et al. (1958), Woodside and Kocholaty (1960), Zucker (1961), Zucker and Borelli (1959). The enzymology of blood platelets is presented by Bettex-Galland and Maupin (1961), Gaertner (1960), Gross (1962), Löhr et al. (1961), Maupin (1954), Morita (1958), Plat (1962), Plat et al. (1963a, b); and enzyme disorders by Bettex-Galland and Maupin (1961), Caen and Cousin (1962), Caen et al. (1963), Gross (1962), Gross et al. (1960), Inçeman et al. (1963), Larrieu et al. (1961), Löhr et al. (1961), Lüscher (1961), and Plat (1962).

V. Metabolism of Erythrocytes

The erythrocyte is a highly specialized blood cell. Its biological function consists in transport of oxygen by means of one of the catalytic substances of the body, hemoglobin, containing the iron-porphyrin compound, heme. Although hemoglobin is, in a certain sense, an integral part of the erythrocyte, the most important vital phenomena in these cells take place in the cell membrane. From the standpoint of the hematologist and biochemist, the "ghost" corpuscle deprived of its hemoglobin represents the basic blood cell. The fundamental biological processes supplying energy for the vital functions of the cells take place in the erythrocytic membrane, consisting of a thin layer of protoplasm surrounding the cell.

Limited space does not allow comprehensive discussion of all the recent advances in studies on the erythrocytes and their metabolism. While referring the interested reader to the monographs of Behrendt (1957) and Prankerd (1961), and the recent treatise by Bishop and Surgenor (1964), we will confine ourselves to the presentation of an outline of the metabolism of erythrocytes, with special reference to the following problems:

1. metabolism of the non-hemoglobin proteins of erythrocytes and of hemoglobin;
2. relations between the molecular structure and functions of the erythrocytes;
3. ion transport across the erythrocytic membrane;
4. metabolism of erythrocytes as a source of energy.

A. METABOLISM OF THE NON-HEMOGLOBIN PROTEINS OF ERYTHROCYTES AND OF HEMOGLOBIN

Large numbers of mature erythrocytes produced in the bone marrow from a relatively small number of erythroblasts pass through biochemically characteristic stages of maturation. The most characteristic metabolic changes concern the nucleic acids and hemoglobin.

Young erythroblasts contain large amounts of RNA and DNA, which are closely associated not only with the synthesis of the proteins necessary for the development of young cells, but also with the synthesis of hemoglobin. Synthesis of hemoglobin begins mainly at the stage of neutrophilic erythroblasts. At this stage the content of RNA diminishes sharply, dwindling to one-tenth of the content in basophilic erythroblasts. Traces of RNA can still be detected, however, in the eosinophilic erythroblasts and even in the reticulum of erythrocytes. In Addison-Biermer disease the erythroblasts contain more RNA, and the rate at which it vanishes is slower; nevertheless hemoglobin is produced. In posthemorrhagic anemia, on the other hand, the decline in RNA content markedly precedes the production of hemoglobin, to which the Fe deficiency is an impediment (Thorell, 1947, 1961).

Transformation of erythroblasts into erythrocytes is accompanied also by a decline in the oxygen requirement. Oxygen consumption by mature erythrocytes is about 200 times less than in the nucleated erythroblasts. In the mature erythrocyte little ability of aerobic metabolism of carbohydrates remains, owing to the loss of the electron transport system (Dajani and Orten, 1958) which ensures continuity of oxidation of reduced nicotinamide adenine dinucleotide phosphate ($NADPH_2$). ATPase activity also diminishes, contributing to the predominance of anaerobic glycolysis over respiration.

Before considering the metabolism, functions, and structure of the mature erythrocyte and its precursors, it is well to recall the biochemical structure of the mature erythrocyte. According to Behrendt (1957), water accounts for about 70% of the erythrocytic volume, 25% is occupied by hemoglobin, and only 5% by all the remaining components. The "framework" (ghost corpuscles) of the erythrocyte has its own characteristic chemical composition. The insoluble residue remaining after hemolysis of erythrocytes, known as the stroma, constitutes 2–5% of the net weight of the erythrocyte, 40–60% falls to proteins, and 10–13% to lipids. By means of electrophoresis, three lipid-containing protein fractions have been separated from the stroma. First, there is a typical protein commonly referred to as stromatin, or sometimes as fibrous or structural protein. It is very insoluble in water, forms gels easily, and is distinguished by the nature of its constituent amino acids. It differs from both keratin and collagens. Changes in the erythrocyte's shape, whether artifactual or spontaneous (spherocytes, sickle forms), are mediated by corresponding changes in the degree of stromatin gelation. Other protein substances identified in the framework include elinin, S protein, and "antispheric substance," which represent the so-called non-hemoglobin proteins of erythrocytes and also determine the shape of the erythrocyte. The non-hemoglobin proteins stand in the center of interest of contemporary biochemical hematology. Although their study has not yet emerged from its initial phase, the accompanying scheme of Moskowitz and Calvin (according to Krawczyński, 1962) may serve to illustrate the relations between the stroma fractions of the erythrocyte and its membrane.

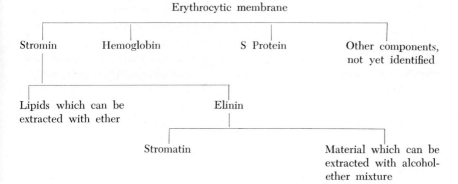

The erythrocytic membrane and stroma are built of the above-mentioned principal components of the erythrocyte. It is assumed that the membrane constitutes the external layer of the stroma, and its properties, upon which the active and passive transport of various compounds depends, are in fact also properties of the stroma.

Elinin is essentially composed of a molecule of stromin extracted with ether. Molecules of elinin bound with lipids form fibers arranged parallel to the surface of the erythrocyte. The lipid matter, on the other hand, is arranged radially, and biochemically is a protein-lipid-carbohydrate compound. Different fragments of the elinin molecule probably correspond to the A, B, Rh, M, and N group substances and to the influenza virus receptors. The Rh receptor is separated from the surface of the erythrocyte by a thin protective lipoprotein layer. The binding of antibody to receptors and agglutination of erythrocytes can therefore be enhanced by means of proteolytic enzymes such as papain or bromelin (after which the tests are named). In addition, stromin is the seat of dimerases—enzymes which play a role in the transport of glucose and monosaccharides across the cell membrane—and of amino acid carriers.

S protein, which is a hemoglobin complex, occurs in small amounts in the cell membrane and in the interior of erythrocytes. About 2% of hemoglobin incorporated in the cell stroma apparently maintains the whole remaining mass of hemoglobin in a state intermediate between solution and crystallization which is optimal for the transport of oxygen by hemoglobin.

Antispherin contained in the peripheral parts of erythrocytes is active in maintaining their constant discoid shape. According to Polonowski et al. (1961), this protein resembles myosin, the contractile protein of muscle fibers.

The different erythrocytic proteins are not homogeneous compounds, but have been obtained by using special methods. It should be borne in mind that, depending on the method of fractionation of the complete erythrocytic hemolysate, various protein fractions can be obtained and named arbitrarily. For instance, Howe (1951) obtained the protein fractions LR, LP, and LF, with differing lipid contents. The LR fraction contained lipid-rich proteins resembling elinin and the Rh, A, and B antigens and influenza virus receptors. This substance contains 16 amino acids, among which serine and threonine occur in the largest amounts, besides sialic acid, and appears to be identical with the M and N group substances.

Chromatography of the non-hemoglobin proteins on a DEAE-cellulose column yielded 13 different protein fractions, which, taken together, have been named the "non-hemoglobin profile." Hemolysates of fetal erythrocytes and of the erythrocytes of erythemia patients show changes in the nonhemoglobin profile (Markowitz et al., 1961).

Hemoglobin is a compound of heme and globin. Heme is synthesized by a combination of succinate with glycine in the presence of synthetase, pyridoxal phosphate, coenzyme A, and Mg, leading to δ-amino-β ketoadipic acid, from which through δ-aminolevulinic acid, porphobilinogen, and porphyrinogen, protoporphyrin is produced. Iron is incorporated into the protoporphyrin molecule, probably enzymatically, giving heme. Four molecules of heme combining with one molecule of globin give hemoglobin (molecular weight approximately 66,000).

Under normal conditions, hemoglobin combines loosely with oxygen in the lungs, and releases it in the tissues. In some pathological conditions hemoglobin solutions oxidize irreversibly to methemoglobin, in which iron is in the ferric state, and which is incapable of oxygenation to oxyhemoglobin. Physiologically, methemoglobin forms not more than 1% of hemoglobin. The difference between oxy- and methemoglobin is that in the former the Fe and O_2 atoms share an electron and binding is ionic; in the latter, the electron is transferred to O_2, and there is a change in the iron-protein binding (Pauling and Coryell, 1936; George and Lister, 1958).

Transformation of methemoglobin to hemoglobin is catalyzed by methemoglobin reductase. The reductase requires coenzyme activity dependent on adequate flavoprotein supply, diaphorase, and lipoamide dehydrogenase. Metabolic disorders are the cause of congenital methemoglobinemia manifested as cyanosis.

The metabolic disorders of hemoglobin refer to the precursors of heme or to globin. Disorders of porphyrin metabolism may cause various types of clinical porphyria, which are genetically conditioned enzymopathies.

Congenital porphyria is inherited as a recessive trait and is characterized by disorders in the transformation of porphobilinogen to porphyrin, a metabolic process governed by an enzymatic system. As a result, type I porphyrin is greatly increased. This type is not assimilated by erythrocytes, but is deposited in the tissues or excreted in the urine. The type III porphyrin, which is essential to the normal synthesis of hemoproteins, is produced in insufficient amounts. This enzymopathy gives rise to the known clinical syndrome of porphyria, characterized by a photodynamic effect. Other forms include acute and idiopathic porphyria and a mixed form, called *porphyria cutanea tarda*.

The metabolism of the globin moiety of hemoglobin is governed by biochemical genetic laws. The biosynthesis of the different enzymes involved is dependent on definite genes in the hereditary substance. In other words, the metabolism of the erythrocytes is dependent on genetically controlled enzymatic activities. This biological law applies also to the metabolism of hemoglobin and its disorders in the form of hemoglobinopathies.

In the healthy adult human four types of hemoglobin occur: Hb A_1, the predominating type making up 90% of the total; Hb A_2, which accounts for 2%; Hb A_3, approximately 10%; and fetal hemoglobin, Hb F, in a proportion of about 0.5%. The genetic-enzymatic errors of hemoglobin metabolism may concern each of these four types.

The most frequent are errors in the synthesis of the β chain, resulting in appearance of the abnormal hemoglobins S, C, and E. The glutamic acid is replaced in hemoglobin S by valine, and in hemoglobin C by lysine. The genetic genes of hemoglobin S and C are multiple alleles. Errors in the synthesis of the a chain concern Hb A_1, Hb A_2, and Hb F, resulting in Hb I and Hb D-a.

Perfection of the technique of studying the hemoglobins has led to the discovery or many new abnormal types, the discussion of which is impossible in the space alloted to this article.* The hemoglobinopathy in thalassemia may be mentioned, in which the level of Hb A_1 is markedly diminished, and that of Hb F is elevated. Sickle-cell anemia is another well-known hemoglobinopathy, in which hemoglobin S occurs, and which is associated with increased resistance to malaria because hemoglobin S affords poor conditions for the development of the protozoa in the erythrocytes. This anomaly occurs almost exclusively in Negroes. The genetic alteration deprives the cell of its ability of producing normal hemoglobin, and so more hemoglobin S is produced. The S characteristic is transmitted by both parents. In manifest thalassemia only a combi-

* See Laurell and Grönwall (1964).

nation of Hb S and Hb F is present. Various combinations of the genes have been described, e.g., gene Hb F with Hb S and C, SF and CF, etc.

These genetic anomalies impair the value of the erythrocytes, which break down under the influence of various stimuli which are normally without any effect, leading to life-endangering hemolytic crises. Structurally altered hemoglobin, however, retains its normal ability of reversibly combining with oxygen. The hemolytic effect is dependent on abnormal physical properties of the hemoglobin molecule, i.e., on purely structural changes without alteration of the basic functions. Most of these conditions are the consequence of alteration of protein structures by the damaged gene.

B. Structure and Functions of Erythrocytes

It is clear that the metabolism of the erythrocyte is closely connected with its cellular structure. Electron microscopic studies afford a promising line of research in this field. The data collected up to now, however, do not yet allow morphological localization of enzyme systems or of biochemical and immunological processes in erythrocytes. The reader is referred to the hematological electron microscopic studies published in our monograph (Aleksandrowicz et al., 1955), and in later monographs by Low and Freeman (1958) and Bessis (1960). It has been ascertained that the erythrocytic membrane is not homogeneous, and that it is thicker near the dell than in its peripheral parts (Bernhard, 1952). The thickness of the membrane varies from 50–5000 Å, depending on the method of measuring it. The structure of the erythrocytic membrane is fibrillar according to Bernhard, the fibrils being arranged like fish ribs, i.e., perpendicularly to the surface. Other investigators have described a cylindrical and fibrillar layer connected by lipid substances.

The work of Danon et al. (1961) based on electron microscopic observations has further advanced the morphological study of the functions of erythrocytes. These investigators were able to demonstrate that young erythrocytes possess a coarsely granular surface, whereas the surface of old erythrocytes is smooth. A highly interesting relationship was found between deficiency of glucose-6-phosphate dehydrogenase and the age and superficial texture of the erythrocyte. It remains to be seen whether the structure of the erythrocyte observed by electron microscopy is dependent on the presence of enzymes. None the less, it has been shown that in healthy individuals 70% of the surface of the erythrocytes is granular, and in patients suffering from hemolytic anemia due to deficiency of glucose-6-phosphate dehydrogenase the same proportion of the surface is smooth.

Observations of the ferritin molecule are another achievement of electron microscopy. Ferritin, as is known, supplies the erythroblast with iron needed in the synthesis of hemoglobin and represents the Fe reserve of the body. Iron released from used-up and pathological erythrocytes accumulates as ferritin. The content of 23% of iron in ferritin has made possible its visualization in erythrocytes. Because of this high concentration of high molecular weight atoms, the ferritin molecule exposed to an electron beam gives a shadow. Its identification is facilitated by the characteristic distribution of iron at six angles of an octahedron, one side of which measures 50 Å. Grains of ferritin therefore have a characteristic shape and occur in clusters, which when observed with the light microscope are known to histologists as hemosiderin.

From the examples cited above it can easily be seen that erythrocytic biochemistry and structure are closely interrelated, although the factual data are still not numerous. Advances in electron microscopy will undoubtedly be followed by further advances in this field. Nevertheless, in the present situation and in spite of the searching studies initiated by Bessis and Bernhard, who described the passage of ferritin through the erythroblastic membrane, termed "Rhopheozytose," the erythrocytic membrane must still be considered from the dynamic rather than morphological point of view.

The lack of a biomorphological formula defining the state of the erythrocytic membrane is the reason why biochemical-dynamic concepts continue to prevail. The fact that almost the whole lipid content is contained in the structure of the "ghost corpuscle" explains why fat-soluble substances readily enter the cell. The presence of proteins and lipids in the erythrocytic membrane is the basis of the lipoprotein theory of the structure of the membrane propounded by Ponder (1955); this has been supplemented by the more recent theory of Davies and Keynes (1961), based on the concept of the "conjugated pump" for sodium-potassium, hydrogen-hydroxyl, and other systems.

C. Ion Transport across the Erythrocytic Membrane

Differences between the biochemical composition of the erythrocytes and serum are dependent on factors connected with the erythrocytic membrane. The erythrocytic membrane as an extremely complex biological system guarantees homeostasis and integrity of the structure of the erythrocytes.

The process of selective transport of biochemical substances between the cell and serum may be either active or passive. Active transport involves utilization of energy accumulated in the erythrocyte in the course of intermediate metabolism and takes place in the direction of rising electrochemical potential in the system composed of the cell and extracellular fluid, or in the direction opposite to falling concentration of the substance being transported.

Passive transport, on the other hand, takes place in the direction of falling chemical potential and concentration of the transported substance, and does not require extraneous energy.

A significant characteristic of the erythrocyte, in contrast to other cells, is the high content of chlorine anions, besides potassium and phosphate. The biochemical composition of the erythrocytes and blood serum is illustrated in Table I.

TABLE I

WATER AND SOLUTES IN HUMAN SERUM AND
MATURE ERYTHROCYTES

Substance	Erythrocytes	Serum
	Millimoles per liter	
Sodium	782	5870
Potassium	81	5
Calcium	0	3
Magnesium	2	1
Inorganic phosphate	2	2
Acid-soluble organic phosphate	17	Trace
Base combined with organic phosphate	17	Trace
Chloride	52	104
Bicarbonate	19	26
Other organic neutral solutes	3	4
Glucose	3	4
Urea	5	7
Protein	5	2
Base combined with protein	44	17
Water	707	935

Transport of ions and molecules depends on the ATP content of the cell. About 12% of energy is utilized in processes of active transport [Meisels, cited according to Krawczyński (1962)] in overcoming resistance to the transfer of ions and molecules. Resistance is overcome by disruption of hydrogen bonds with water, which are formed during passage from the aqueous to the lipid phase, and by transfer of the complex thus formed across the membrane. Transfer of 3–4 equivalents of sodium ions uses up one mole of ATP; in other words, transport of one equivalent of Na ion utilizes energy corresponding to 2000 cal (Krawczyński, 1962).

The intensity of cellular metabolic processes and the phenomenon of transport across cell membranes are correlated by means of a feedback mechanism. An example of the numerous feedback mechanisms is the transport of potassium ions. As a result of utilization of a certain number of ATP molecules, potassium accumulates within the cell. Reduction in amount of ATP causes an increase in ADP and P, resulting in intensification of metabolism and oxidative phosphorylation. In the next step, the concentration of potassium ions reaches a "critical" level, above which the ionic equilibrium in the cell is disturbed, which may result in destruction of the cellular structure. Production of ATP ceases, and with it transport of potassium. The concentration of potassium diminishes until a minimal critical level is reached, at which production of ATP recommences. This phenomenon represents a self-steered inclusion and switching off of the sodium-potassium pump.

On reviewing the transport of different ions, it may be seen that the K ion passes across the erythrocytic membrane in both directions, about 4% per hour being exchanged between the erythrocytes and plasma.

The sodium ion also passes across the membrane in both directions, but penetration from the plasma to the erythrocytes is slower, not exceeding 9% in the course of 4 hours.

The ratio of plasma to erythrocytic concentration of sodium is 7.5:1. Maintenance of such high difference in the concentration of sodium on two sides of the cell membrane is connected with the existence of the above-described pump. Phosphatides and ATP play a particularly important role in this process. Under the influence of diglyceride kinase, phosphatidic acid, one of the components of the erythrocytic membrane, is produced. After combining with phosphatidic acid, the sodium ion enters the membrane. In this manner Na passes into the plasma, and the phosphate ion, which cannot leave across the membrane, remains in the interior of the cell. Transport of sodium is stimulated by aldosterone and vasopressin, and inhibited by ouabain, which is an inhibitor of phosphatase.

Transport of the chloride ion is about 600–1300 times more rapid than that of Na^+ and K^+ ions. The Cl^- anion is probably distributed on both sides of the cell membrane in accordance with Donnan's law of equilibrium. Phosphate ions pass across the erythrocytic membrane very slowly; during 95 minutes only about 30% of labeled phosphorus passes from the plasma to the erythrocytes. Transport in the reverse direction, from erythrocytes to plasma, is even slower. This phenomenon is unaffected by glycolysis, and occurs at the same rate when glycolysis is inhibited by means of monoiodoacetic acid.

Absence of calcium in the serum increases the passage of inorganic phosphorus, ATP, and phosphocreatine from the cell to the plasma. Presence of Ca^{++}, which is an integral structural element of the erythrocytic membrane, enhances its permeability. In its absence passive transport of Na into the erythrocytes is increased twentyfold.

Magnesium passes across the erythrocytic membrane similarly to Na^+ and K^+, and its transport is also associated with the action of the sodium-potassium pump.

The membrane of mature erythrocytes is impermeable to iron. Iron is taken up from the plasma by reticulocytes owing to the presence of protein carriers mediating between transferrin and the interior of the cells. In maturing erythrocytes the content of the protein carriers in the membrane diminishes, and the erythrocytes lose ability of taking up iron.

Copper passes across the cell membrane and is bound with the "S" protein, a component of the erythrocytic membrane.

Zinc permeates into erythrocytes easily, and its concentration in erythrocytes is five times as high as in the plasma. The transport of Zn^{++} across the erythrocytic membrane is active.

Sulfur is transported passively across the erythrocytic membrane and is distributed on both sides in accordance with Donnan's law of equilibrium.

Heavy metal ions such as Pb, Hg, Sn, Co, Cr, Cd, and Ni form complexes with the proteins of the cell membrane and, by changing its potential, destroy it. On penetrating into the erythrocytes they destroy enzyme systems, resulting in the death of the cell.

In pathological conditions leading to edema the Na content of erythrocytes is diminished. During diuresis and recession of edema the Na content of the erythrocytes increases. Not all investigators, however, agree with this opinion. Riecker and Bubnoff (1958) reported statistically significant elevation of the sodium content of erythrocytes and lowered potassium levels in the course of cardiovascular failure. Increased Na content is characteristic of postoperative conditions. Potassium, on the other hand, is increased in aldosteronism and cardiovascular failure. Improvement of the hemodynamic conditions by means of digitalis lowers the potassium levels. Low levels of potassium occur in microcytic hypochromic anemias and drepanocytosis; and high levels in macrocytic anemias and congenital hemolytic anemia.

Transport of saccharides into the erythrocytes is passive. Since in aqueous solutions saccharides are not electrically charged, the erythrocytes' own potential does not influence their transport. Owing to their hydroxyl groups, the saccharides exhibit hydrophilic properties which impede their transport across the lipid erythrocytic membrane. Carriers exist, however, which facilitate the transport of saccharides into erythrocytes, known as transportases, activated by permease. Permease appears to correspond to Pandle's regulating factor. Transport of saccharides into erythrocytes is impeded by various inhibitors: phlorizin and its aglucone phloretin; compounds blocking SH groups, e.g., anesthetics; and dinitro-fluorobenzene. It has not been finally decided whether the passage of saccharides across the membrane is an active process, and whether the action of permease requires the participation of ATP.

D. Metabolism of Erythrocytes as a Source of Energy

Erythrocytes exhibit lively metabolic activity. A pure suspension of erythrocytes utilizes 1.5–2.2 moles of glucose per liter per hour, corresponding to liberation of 25 calories per liter of erythrocytes per hour. Only about 7% of this energy is used in the active transport of cations; the fate of the remaining 93% is unknown, although it has been suggested that it is consumed in maintaining the shape of the cells and cytoplasmic movements.

The utilization of glucose as the main source of energy is anaerobic. Respiration values in erythrocytes are very low compared with the cells of other tissues. Oxygen consumption is 10–20 mm^3/gm/hour. The value of Q_{O_2} for washed erythrocytes suspended in Ringer solution is 0.06 (in erythroblasts 0.44).

No glycogen is found in erythrocytes, so that metabolism depends on a constant supply of glucose. The mechanism of permeation of glucose across the erythrocytic membrane is not satisfactorily known, but does not appear to consist in simple diffusion, probably involving active transport dependent on the activity of specific enzymes.

The metabolic breakdown of glucose occurs by way of the Embden-Meyerhof-Parnas cycle, i.e., anaerobically through a series of stages of phosphorylation to lactic acid. Glycolysis is associated with the action of hexokinase and triose-phosphate dehydrogenase. The cofactor of the first enzyme is ATP and of the second enzyme, NAD; ATP controls the phosphorylative processes during glycolysis leading to resynthesis of pyridine nucleotides of NAD coenzyme.

The sequence of events in glycolysis falls into two very distinct stages. In the first, glucose is degraded through a series of phosphorylated intermediates to triose phosphates and ATP is used up in a series of endergonic phosphorylative processes. In the second stage, the situation is reversed; ATP is regenerated in a series of dephosphorylating reactions involving the conversion of esters to pyruvate and ultimately lactate. The net gain by the cell is two moles of ATP, equivalent to about 20,000 calories.

Glycolysis in erythrocytes is sensitive to changes of pH. At low levels of pH glycolysis diminishes, and vice versa. Changes in potassium levels in the serum have no effect on glycolysis; a reduction in the potassium content of erythrocytes, however, retards the utilization of glucose and lowers levels of ATP.

2,3-Diphosphoglyceric acid participates actively in the process of glycolysis, as may be demonstrated by incubating erythrocytes with C^{14}-labeled glucose. At the same time, 90% of the glucose passes through the stage of this acid, whereas in other, metabolically highly active cells, 1,3-diphosphoglyceric acid predominates. Mature erythrocytes, having a low energy requirement, contain little 1,3-diphosphoglyceric acid, but large amounts, of 2,3-diphosphoglyceric acid and glucose-1,6-diphosphate ester.

Reduction in energy requirements in erythrocytes is accompanied by slowing of glycolysis, increased hydrolysis of ATP and its diminished synthesis.

Inactivation of the unused energy liberated by the erythrocyte takes place at the level of phosphotriose in the Rapoport-Luebering cycle (1950): under the influence of diphosphoglyceromutase, 1,3-diphosphoglyceric acid is transformed to 2,3-diphosphoglyceric acid. The reaction is exoergic and consists in loss of one high-energy bond (Altman, 1959).

Although remnants of tricarboxylic acid cycle enzymes appear to be present in the mature cell, the sequence of reactions is incomplete and, in addition, there is no cytochrome activity, which presumably has been lost with the last remnants of DNA at the time of nuclear extrusion. Any uptake of oxygen must therefore take place through an alternative route; this exists in the form of the hexose monophosphate shunt (Prankerd, 1961).

Two redox systems are represented in the erythrocyte; the first involves NAD $\leftrightarrows$ NADH$_2$ and appears to be supplemented by synchronization of the two dehydrogenases of triose phosphate and lactate. The other involves NADP $\leftrightarrows$ NADPH$_2$ with the glucose-6-phosphate dehydrogenase reaction and with methemoglobin (MHB) or glutathione (GSH) reductase. This is apparently a dormant reaction evoked by certain environmental conditions associated with the oxidation of hemoglobin or glutathione.

Methemoglobin is therefore reduced through an enzyme connected with NADPH$_2$ and another connected with NADH$_2$, and glutathione reductase. Reduced glutathione is present in normal erythrocytes in large amounts, preventing oxidation of hemoglobin. During normal glycolysis the concentration of MHB does not exceed 1–2%; in case of inhibited glycolysis or hemolysis, Hb is quickly oxidized to methemoglobin, the concentration of which rapidly increases. Normal erythrocytes and their hemolysates also show phosphatase activity, especially acid phosphatase. Phosphohexoisomerase (FHI) is 100 times more active in erythrocytes than in the serum; in some types of hemolytic anemia it is diminished. FHI activity interferes with the index of lactic dehydrogenase activity, which is a sign of increased activity in erythrocytes with strong glycolytic activity. This has been observed in sickle-cell anemias and in acute leukemias.

Nucleotides are also metabolized by erythrocytes, liberating ribose-5-phosphate, which may be further metabolized (Dische, 1951). Nucleoside phosphorylase has been found on the surface of erythrocytes, participating actively in this reaction. As a result of conversion of ribose nucleoside to lactate by phosphorylation, ATP is resynthesized. Nucleosides have also been found to increase the osmotic resistance of erythrocytes.

No cytochromes are present in erythrocytes. Methylene blue causes a twentyfold increase in the oxygen uptake, accompanied by increased consumption of glucose and production of CO_2. The dye increases the uptake of oxygen even in the absence of glucose, due to utilization of intracellular phosphate esters. Toluidine blue, cysteine, glutathione, and certain tissue extracts have a similar effect.

One of the most important enzymes of heme is catalase. By decomposing H_2O_2, catalase prevents oxidation of hemoglobin. The enzyme also accelerates the oxidation of some alcohols and aldehydes. Azide inhibits catalase activity, resulting in formation of methemoglobin.

Carbonic anhydrase is present in erythrocytes in large amounts. This enzyme causes rapid conversion of CO_2 and H_2O to carbonic acid. Its prosthetic group is Zn. The role of carbonic anhydrase in the transport of CO_2 from the tissues to the lungs continues to be a moot question.

Choline esterase is an enzyme of the cell membrane and stroma that is concerned with the transport of potassium. The erythrocytic potassium levels are diminished in the presence of anticholinesterase inhibitor, a phenomenon which requires further elucidation.

In erythrocytes, especially in their water-soluble components, a nonprotein substance, ergothioneine, has been found, besides substances which are cofactors of nicotinamide-ribose phosphorylase. The tripeptide glutathione (GSH), i.e., reduced glutathione, occurs in erythrocytes in large amounts in equilibrium with GS-SG (oxidized glutathione). The latter is reduced to GSH by glutathione reductase. The coenzyme of this reduction is $NADPH_2$.

Of the numerous erythrocytic enzymes concerning which the available information is insufficient, ATPase deserves attention. According to some investigators this enzyme occurs in the stroma, and according to others, in hemolysates. ATPase takes part in the transport of inorganic phosphorus, and together with triphosphoglyceraldehyde dehydrogenase plays a role in the transport of cell metabolites. Still others consider that ATPase displays activity when the cell is damaged.

Proteolytic enzymes in the erythrocytes manifest their activity in connection with the process of aging of the cells. Three types of these enzymes are distinguished according to optimum pH of activity: the first exhibits optimal activity at pH 7.4 and is activated by Zn^{++}, Fe^{++}, and SH groups; the second and third are optimally active at pH 11.

Phosphomonoesterase and diphosphoesterase are the outstanding phosphatases. The most active is acid phosphatase with optimum pH 5.0–6.0; it is activated by Ca^{++} and Mg^{++}.

Glyoxalase, fumarase, and malonic dehydrogenase have been found in erythrocytes. Their role probably consists in the reversal of the reaction of enolase (malonic dehydrogenase) and reduction of methemoglobin in the presence of fumaric acid.

Some of the enzymes of the glycolytic cycle are of particular importance in the pathogenesis of certain erythrocytopathies. It has been found (Carson, 1962) that erythrocytes with deficiency of glucose-6-phosphate ester readily undergo hemolysis under the influence of antimalaria drugs such as plasmochin, 8-aminoquinoline, furadantin, PAS, sulfonamides, etc. Lack of this dehydrogenase has been reported also in favism, i.e., in individuals sensitized to fava beans.

Aging erythrocytes exhibit diminished activity of the glycolytic enzymes. In consequence, production of lactic acid is inhibited, and pyruvic acid accumulates. Depression of the activity of these enzymes leads to diminished content of ATP and increase in ADP (Löhr et al., 1958). Penetration of O_2 into the erythrocytes and excretion of potassium are increased with age. Disordered synthesis of nucleotides leads to lowered content of NAD. As a result of the biochemical processes mentioned above, the osmotic resistance of the erythrocytes is diminished, facilitating their disintegration and phagocytosis in the reticuloendothelial system.

This outline, of course, does not cover all the aspects of the metabolism of erythrocytes. An attempt has been made to point out the advantages to hematology from advances in biochemistry and genetics, which have made possible better understanding of the pathogenesis of many genetically conditioned hemoglobin and erythro-enzymopathies, besides hemolytic mechanisms. It may be hoped that in the near future methods of treating these erythrocytopathies, which have been incurable until now, will also be developed.

VI. Concluding Remarks

The characteristics of the metabolism of white blood cells outlined above enable a biochemical inventory to be made. Analysis reveals similarities as well as differences between various groups of leukocytes.

The cytogenetic data mentioned in the beginning are based mainly on morphological criteria, which may be confronted with biochemical criteria. The comparison discloses the existence of relations among the white blood cells of the granulocytic system, and among those of the mono-, plasma-, eosino-, baso-, and fibrocytic types, mononuclears and various types of so-called virocytes, small and large lymphocytes, and some of the polysegmented granulation-poor leukocytes. According to traditional hematology, the production centers of granulocytes are located in the active bone marrow, so that these cells may be regarded as being myelogenous (or, in a broader sense, myelocytes). A second type of leukocytes is associated with the lymphoreticular system, also known as the reticuloendothelial system, i.e., with the active mesenchyme. From the point of view of their genesis, these cells are mesenchymocytes or lymphoreticulocytes.

The extent to which the genesis and metabolism of the blood cells are related, respectively discrepant, is illustrated in Fig. 1, in the upper part of which the white blood cells derived from the lymphoreticular system are represented, and in the lower part those arising in the bone marrow. From our review it may be seen that the cells enclosed in the circle have certain common cytochemical and cytoenzymatic characteristics. All these cells are digested similarly by enzymes, especially by DNase and urinary dialysate. On the other hand, the digestion of the myelogenous cells resembles the action of RNase.

The origin of the granulocytes is a controversial problem. Blood granulocytes, in contrast to those from inflammatory exudates or pus, are not digested by DNase; the latter are resistant to the action of RNase. This fact appears to support the theory of Busse-Grawitz, according to which granulocytes may be produced in the connective tissue as well as in bone marrow, and also the hypothesis of migration of Cohnheim, according to which granulocytes dominate among the morphological elements in pus even when they are absent in the blood. It may thus become necessary to revise the traditional nomenclature in which the term polysegmented "leukocyte" suggests origin of the cell exclusively in the bone marrow.

Advances in the techniques of studying the leukocytes make it difficult to resist the impression that a revision of morphological criteria is imminent. Similarly, as we have seen, the term "lymphocyte" includes cells with vigorous and with inert nucleic acid metabolism, with long or short lifespans, representing either end cells or stem cells. Traditional hematology must take into account these increasingly important problems in order to escape orthodoxy, symbolized by the belief in the incurability of many of the proliferative hemocytopathies.

Our considerations, which are based on a synthetic review of the past achievements of hematology and on new cytogenetic concepts, suggest certain reflections of a broader nature. Physical and technological advances of science have outdistanced the medicobiological and humanistic sciences. Technology today dominates the world, unrestrained by the medicobiological and humanistic disciplines. One of the results of this situation has been the widespread pollution of the biophysical and psychosocial environment by an uncountable number of mutagenic noxae. The contamination of nature by mutagenic noxae is reflected also in the molecular structure of the blood cells, e.g., in chromosomal aberrations leading to proliferative hemocytopathies. These changes can be detected with morphological methods, including electron microscopy, as well as with biochemical methods. For instance, deficiency of glucose-6-phosphate dehydrogenase in certain forms of hemolytic anemia has its counterpart in alterations in the shape of the erythrocytic membrane. Genetic disorders in the structure of hemoglobin lead to hemoglobinopathies under the clinical picture of various types of hemolytic anemia.

In the environment of the contemporary industrialized world the number of these harmful mutagenic, carcinogenic, and leukosogenic factors is continually increasing. It is alarming that this is accompanied by psychosocial perturbations manifested "clinically" by the deterioration of interpersonal relations among the members of the species *Homo sapiens*. These facts should stimulate scientists of various technological, biological, and humanistic specialties to greater efforts with the aim of genetic protection of the human population.

REFERENCES TO SECTIONS I, II, AND III

Ackerman, G. A. (1963). *Nature* 197, 189.
Albanus, L., and Winqvist, G. (1961). *Acta Haematol.* 26, 365.
Aleksandrowicz, J. (1946). "Schorzenia narządów krwiotwórczych w świetle badań bioptycznych." Friedlein, Cracow.
Aleksandrowicz, J. (1959). *Haematol. Polon.* 3, 115.
Aleksandrowicz, J. (1963). *Nucl. Hematol.* (Sept./Nov.) p. 2.
Aleksandrowicz, J., and Gaertner, H. (1950). *Szpitalnictwo Polskie* 3, 407.
Aleksandrowicz, J., and Gaertner, H. (1953). *Proc. 1st Congr. Polish Soc. Hematol.* (PZWL), Warsaw pp. 76–92; 386–410.
Aleksandrowicz, J., and Spirer, L. (1955). *Sang* 26, 212.
Aleksandrowicz, J., Blicharski, J., and Feltynowski, A. (1955). "Mikroskopia elektronowa krwi." PZWL, Warsaw.

Aleksandrowicz, J., Urbańczyk, J., Ostrowska, A., and Sierko, J. (1958). *Blood* **13**, 652.

Aleksandrowicz, J., Sznajd, J., Naskalski, J., and Schiffer, Z. (1963a). *Nucl. Hematol.* (March/May).

Aleksandrowicz, J., Sznajd, J., Urbańczyk, J., and Schiffer, Z. (1963b). *Nucl. Hematol.* (Dec. 1963/Febr. 1964).

Allfrey, V. G., Mirsky, A. E. (1959). *Proc. Natl. Acad. Sci. U. S.* **45**, 1325.

Almazov, V. A., Pavlov, B. A., and Ryabov, S. I. (1963). *Probl. Gematol. i Pereliv. Krovi* **8**(4), 15.

Alter, A. A., Lee, S. L., Pourfar, M., and Dobkin, G. (1963). *Blood* **22**(2), 165.

Amann, R. (1961). *Proc. 8th Congr. Europ. Soc. Hematol., Vienna, Abstr.* p. 7.

Amann, R., and Martin, H. (1961). *Acta Haematol.* **25**, 209.

Amann, R., and Wolff, H. P. (1956). *Z. Exptl. Med.* **127**, 281.

Asboe-Hansen, G. (1957). "Connective Tissue." Blackwell, Oxford.

Astaldi, G., and Cardinali, G. (1959). *Haematol. Latina* (*Milan*) **2**, 17.

Astaldi, G., Bernardelli, E., and Rondanelli, E. G. (1952). *Hematologica* (*Pavia*) **36**, 749.

Austin, J. H., and Bischel, M. (1961). *Blood* **17**, 216.

Avry, L. (1955). *Rev. Hematol.* **10**, 55.

Bakalos, D., and Petropolous, P. (1963). *Blut* **9**(1), 7.

Baldini, M., and Sacchetti, C. (1953). *Rev. Hematol.* **8**, 3.

Banerjee, S. K., Gandhys, G., and Chatterjea, J. B. (1960). *Indian J. Med. Res.* **48**, 571.

Barnes, J. M. (1940). *Brit. J. Exptl. Pathol.* **21**, 264).

Bases, R. (1962). *New Engl. J. Med.* **266**(11), 538.

Beard, M. F., Pitney, W. R., and Sanneman, E. H. (1954). *Blood* **9**, 789.

Beck, W. S. (1955). *J. Biol. Chem.* **216**, 333.

Beck, W. S. (1958a). *Ann. N. Y. Acad. Sci.* **75**, 4

Beck, W. S. (1958b). *J. Biol. Chem.* **232**, 251.

Beck, W. S. (1958c). *J. Biol. Chem.* **232**, 271.

Beck, W. S., and Valentine, W. N. (1952). *Cancer Res.* **12**, 818.

Beck, W. S., and Valentine, W. N. (1953). *Cancer Res.* **13**, 309.

Berg, P. (1961). *Ann. Rev. Biochem.* **30**, 314.

Berman, L. (1963). *Blood* **21**, 246.

Bertino, J. R., Simmons, B. M., and Donohue, D. M. (1962). *Blood* **19**(5), 587.

Bertino, J. R., Donohue, D. M., Simmons, B. M., Gabrio, B. W., Silber, R., and Huennekens, F. M. (1963). *J. Clin. Invest.* **42**, 466.

Bielka, H., Yenker, L., and Schneiders, I. (1962). *Z. Krebsforsch.* **64**(6), 478.

Bock, H. E., Löhr, G. W., Waller, H. D., and Wilmanns, W. (1961–1962). *Sitzungsber. Ges. Beförderung gesammt. Naturwiss. Marburg.* pp. 83–84, 429–450.

Boll, I. (1958). *Folia Haematol.* **3**, 52.

Boll, I. (1963). *Abstr. 9th Congr. Europ. Soc. Hematol., Lisbon.* p. 20.

Borel, C., Frei, J., and Vanotti, A. (1961). *Schweiz. Med. Wochschr.* **91**, 8.

Brachet, J. (1957). "Biochemical Cytology." Academic Press, New York.

Brachet, J., and Six, N. (1959). *Biochim. Biophys. Acta* **35**, 580.

Brody, E., Estren, S., and Wasserman, L. (1960). *Blood* **5**, 646.

Brody, S. (1957). *Biochim. Biophys. Acta* **24**, 502.

Brody, S., and Balis, M. (1958). *Nature* **182**, 940.

Burk, D. (1957). *Klin. Wochschr.* **35**, 1102.

Burk, D., Laszlo, J., and Wight, K. (1959). *Federation Proc.* **18**, 199.

Burkl, W. (1952). *Wien. Klin. Wochschr.* **64**, 411.

Bussi, L., Taglioretti, D., Pizzi, F., and Carrara, P. M. (1960). *Radiobiol. Latina* **5**, 209.

Canacio, P., and Alonzo, M. (1960). *Riforma Med.* **74**(18), 497.

Chantrenne, H. (1961). "The Biosynthesis of Proteins." Pergamon Press, New York.

Christopherson, W. M., Broghamer, J. L., Jr., and Swartz, F. J. (1963). *Am. J. Pathol.* **42**(3), 337.

Cichocki, T., and Lyko, J. (1963). *Zjazd Pol. Tow. Lek., Bialystok.*

Cronkite, E. P., Bond, V. P., Fliedner, T. M., Rubini, J. R., and Kilman, S. A. (1959). *Proc. 9th Intern. Congr. Radiol., Munich.*

Dameshek, W. (1963). *Blood* **21**, 243.

Daoust, R., and Amano, H. (1962). *Proc. Am. Assoc. Cancer Res.* **3**(4), 313.

Dennes, E., Tupper, R., and Wormall, A. (1961). *Biochem. J.* **78**, 578.

de Carvalho, S., Rand, H. J., and Meyer, D. P. (1960). *J. Lab. Clin. Med.* **55**, 706.

de Lamirande, G. (1960). *Proc. Am. Assoc. Cancer Res.* **3**(2), 105.

de Lamirande, G. (1961). *Nature* **192**, 52.

de Lamirande, G., Weber, G., and Cantero, A. (1956). *Am. J. Physiol.* **184**, 415.

de Lamirande, G., and Allard, C. (1959). *Ann. N. Y. Acad. Sci.* **81**, 570.

Denson, K. W., and Richards, J. D. M. (1962). *Nature* **196**, 1218.

Doty, P. (1961). *Biochem. J.* **79**, 15P.

Doyle, W. L. (1955). *J. Biophys. Biochem. Cytol.* **1**, 221.

Ehrhart, H., Tsirimbas, A., and Terzani, S. (1963). *Proc. 9th Congr. Europ. Soc. Hematol., Lisbon* p. 22.

Ellison, R. R., and Hutchison, D. J. (1957). *In* "The Leukemias" (J. W. Rebuck, F. H. Bethell and R. W. Monto, eds.). Academic Press, New York.

Esselier, A. F. (1954). *Acta Haematol.* **11**, 21.

Flanagan, P., and Lionetti, F. (1955). *Blood* **10**, 497.

Fliedner, T. M., Cronkite, E. P., Bond, V. P., Rubini, J. R., and Andrews, G. (1959). *Acta Haematol.* **22**, 449.

Follette, J. H., Valentine, W. N., Hardin, E. B., and Lawrence, J. S. (1954). *J. Lab. Clin. Med.* **43**, 134.

Fraenkel-Conrat, J., and Chew, W. B. (1960). *Blood* **16**, 1447.

Frei, J., Borel, C., Horvath, G., Cullity, B., and Vanotti, A. (1961). *Blood* **18**(3), 317.

Gable, W., and Wright, L. D. (1962). *Proc. Soc. Exptl. Biol. Med.* **109**(2), 403.

Gaertner, H. (1960). "Blood Coagulation." (In Polish.) Cracow.

Gaertner, H. (1962). *Med. Lab.* **12**(106), 179.

Gaertner, H., and Lisiewicz, J. (1962). *Folia Haematol.* **79**, 258.

Gavosto, F., Maraini, G., and Pileri, A. (1960a). *Blood* **16**(5), 1555.

Gavosto, F., Maraini, G., and Pileri, A. (1960b). *Nature* **187**, 611.

Ghiotto, G., de Sandre, G., and Perona, G. (1960). *Acta Med. Patavina* **20**(2), 173.

Gisinger, E. (1960). *Wien. Z. Inn. Med. Grenzg.* **41**, 1.

Gowans, J. L. (1962). *Ann. N. Y. Acad. Sci.* **99**, 432.

Graham, H. T., Lowry, O. H., Wheelright, F., Lenz, M., and Parish, H. H., Jr. (1955). *Blood* **10**, 467.

Gray, S. J., Reifensteis, R. W., and Beson, J. A. (1952). *J. Am. Med. Assoc.* **148**, 1489.

Green, R., and Martin, S. P. (1955). *J. Lab. Clin. Med.* **45**, 119.

Greenstein, J. P. (1954). "Biochemistry of Cancer," 2nd ed. Academic Press, New York.

Grignani, F., and Bunetti, P. (1963). *Proc. 9th Congr. Europ. Soc. Haematol.*, Lisbon p. 195.

Gross, R., Grundmann, E., and Brehmke, H. (1961). *Folia Haematol.* **6**, 357.

Hadjiolov, A. A., and Zacharieva, L. (1957). *Naturwissenschaften* **44**, 45.

Hakala, M. T., Zakrzewski, S. F., and Nichol, C. A. (1960). *Proc. Am. Assoc. Cancer Res.* **3**, 115.

Hamilton, L. D. (1957). *In* "The Leukemias" (J. W. Rebuck, F. H. Bethell, and R. W. Monto, eds.). Academic Press, New York.

Hardin, E. B., Valentine, W. N., Follette, J. H., and Lawrence, J. S. (1954). *Am. J. Med. Sci.* **228**, 73.

Hardin, E. B., Valentine, W. N., Follette, J. H., and Lawrence, J. S. (1955). *Am. J. Med. Sci.* **229**, 395.

Hayhoe, F. G., and Quaglino, D. (1958). *Brit. J. Haematol.* **4**, 375.

Hayhoe, F. G., Quaglino, D., and Flemans, R. J. (1960). *Brit. J. Haematol.* **6**, 23.

Heckner, F. (1956). *Acta Haematol.* **16**, 1.

Herriott, R. M., Connolly, J. H., and Gupta, S. (1961). *Nature* **189**, 817.

Hertl, M. (1960). *Aerztl. Forsch.* **14**, 3.

Hill, M. (1959). *Nature* **183**, 1060.

Hirsch, G. C. (1955). "Allgemeine Stoffwechselmorphologie des Cytoplasmas." Berlin.

Hirsch, J. G., and Cohn, Z. A. (1960). *J. Exptl. Med.* **112**, 1005.

Hungerford, G. F., and Karson, E. F. (1960). *Blood* **16**(5), 1642.

Introzzi, P., Notario, A., and Ricotti, V. (1962). *Haematol. Arch.* **47**(1), 1.

Iyer, G. Y. N. (1959). *J. Lab. Clin. Med.* **54**, 229.

Jorpes, J. E., Holmgren, H., and Wilander, O. (1937). *Z. Mikroskop. Anat. Forsch.* **42**, 279.

Juhlin, L., and Shelley, W. B. (1961a). *Am. J. Med. Sci.* **242**, 211.

Juhlin, L., and Shelley, W. B. (1961b). *J. Am. Med. Assoc.* **177**, 371.

Kaplow, L. S. (1955). *Blood* **10**, 1023.

Kelényi, S., Pongratz, J., Orban, S., and Deck, G. (1961). *Blood* **18**(4), 417.

Kidd, H. M., and Thomas, J. W. (1962). *Brit. J. Haematol.* **8**(1), 611.

Kidson, Chew (1961). *Australasian Ann. Med.* **10**(4), 282.

Kidson, Chew (1962). *Blood* **19**(1), 82.

Knoblauch, M. (1962). *Helv. Med. Acta* **29**(2), 143.

Köteles, G. J., Antoni, F., and Szabó, L. D. (1962). *Acta Physiol. Acad. Sci. Hung.* **22**, 1.

Koprowski, H., and Fernandes, M. V. (1962). *J. Exptl. Med.* **116**, 467.

Kozinets, G. I., and Osechenskaya, G. V. (1962). *Med. Radiol.* **7**(11), 53.

Kretschmer, N., Stone, M., and Bauer, C. (1958). *Ann. N. Y. Acad. Sci.* **75**, 279.

Kurnick, N. B., Schwartz, L. J., Pariser, S., and Lee, S. L. (1953). *J. Clin. Invest.* **32**, 193.

Lambers, K. (1961). *Proc. 8th Congr. Europ. Soc. Haematol.*, Vienna p. 139.

Lambers, K., and Bauer Sič, P. (1962). *Deut. Med. Wochsch.* **87**(38), 1913.

Lambers, K., and Eggstein, M. (1959). *Verhandl. Deut. Ges. Inn. Med.* **65**, 191.

Larner, J. (1960). *Federation Proc.* **19**, 971.

Laves, W., and Falzi, G. (1963). "Untersuchungen zur zytochemischen Identifizierung menschlicher und tierischen Leukozyten." Breitenecker, Vienna.

Ledoux, L. (1955). *Nature* **176**, 36.

Ledoux, L., and Brändli, S. (1958). *Nature* **181** (4613).

Ledoux, L., and Pileri, A. (1957). *Biochem J.* **66**, 22P.

258   J. ALEKSANDROWICZ, H. GAERTNER, AND J. URBAŃCZYK

Ledoux, L., Galand, P., and Huart, R. (1962). *Biochim. Biophys. Acta* **55**, 97.
Leikon, S. L. (1961). *Proc. Soc. Exptl. Biol. Med.* **106**, 286.
Lennert, K. (1961). *Arch. Klin. Exptl. Dermatol.* **213**, 606.
Lennert, K., and Leder, H. D. (1963). *Proc. 9th Congr. Europ. Soc. Haematol.*, Lisbon p. 18.
Leuchtenberger, C., and Leuchtenberger, S. (1960a). *Biochem. Pharmacol.* **4**, 128.
Leuchtenberger, C., and Leuchtenberger, S. (1960b). *In* "Cell Physiology of Neoplasia," p. 295. Univ. of Texas Press, Austin, Texas.
Lewis, S. M., and Dale, J. H., according to Niebauer, G. (1963). *Wien. Klin. Wochschr.* **10**, 174.
Löffler, H., and Berghoff, W. (1962). *Klin. Wochschr.* **40**(7), 363.
Löhr, G. W., (1961a). *Proc. 8th Congr. Europ. Soc. Haematol.*, Vienna, p. 149.
Löhr, G. W. (1961b). *Folia Haematol.* **6**, 49.
Löhr, G. W., Waller, H. D., and Bock, H. E. (1960). *Verhandl. Deut. Ges. Inn. Med.* **66**, 1045.
Luganova, I. S., and Seits, I. F. (1962). *Vopr. Med. Khim.* **8**(4), 354.
Luganova, I. S., and Seits, I. F. (1963). *Probl. Gematol. i Pereliv. Krovi* **8**(4), 9.
McKinney, G. R. (1953). *Arch. Biochem.* **46**, 246.
MacKinney, A. S., Stohlman, F., Jr., and Brecher, G. (1962). *Blood* **19**, 349.
McLeod, R. M., King, C. E., and Hollander, V. P. (1962). *Proc. Am. Assoc. Cancer Res.* **3**, 340.
Maloney, W. C. (1961). *Proc. 8th Congr. Europ. Soc. Haematol.*, Vienna, p. 169.
Maloney, W. C., and Lange, R. D. (1954). *Blood* **9**, 663.
Maney, B. E., Maloney, W. C., and Taylor, F. H. L. (1960). *Lab. Invest.* **9**, 466.
Mathies, J. C. (1958). *J. Biol. Chem.* **233**, 1121.
Maximow, A. (1923). *Arch. Mikroskop. Anat.* **97**, 314.
Meislin, A. G., Lee, S. L., and Wasserman, L. R. (1959). *Cancer* **12**, 760.
Meyer, L. M., Cronkite, E. P., Miller, I. F., Mulzac, C. W., and Jones, I. (1962). *Blood* **19**(2), 229.
Mitus, W. J., Bergna, L. J., Mednicoff, I. B., and Dameshek, W. (1958). *Blood* **13**, 748.
Mitus, W. J., Bergna, L. J., Mednicoff, I. B., and Dameshek, W. (1959). *New Engl. J. Med.* **260**, 1131.
Morrison, J. H., and Kronheim, J. (1962). *J. Histochem. Cytochem.* **10**, 402.
Müller, D. (1963). *Proc. 9th Congr. Europ. Soc. Haematol.*, Lisbon p. 22.
Nädler, S. B., Hanson, H. J., Spraque, C. C., and Sherman, H. (1961). *Blood* **18**, 336.
Nicolau, C. T., Nicoara, S. T., Vermont, I., Giorgiu, T., and Eugeniu, E. (1962). *Med. Interna* **14**, 1173.
Notario, A., Ricotti, V., and Zanetti, A. (1962), *Haematologica (Pavia)* **47**(8), 591.
Notario, A., Ricotti, V., and Doneda, G. (1962a). *Haematologica (Pavia)* **47**(8), 603.
Notario, A., Ricotti, V., and Di Marco, N. (1962b). *Haematologica (Pavia)* **47**(8), 665.
O'Brien, J. S., and Walsh, J. R. (1962). *Proc. Soc. Exptl. Biol. Med.* **109**, 843.
Patt, H. M. (1953). *Physiol. Rev.* **33**, 35.
Perillie, P. E., and Finch, S. C. (1961). *Blood* **18**(5), 572.
Petrakis, N. L., and Folstadt, L. J. (1955). *Blood* **10**, 1204.
Plenert, W. (1963). *Folia Haematol.* **80**(1), 52.

Policard, A. (1963). "Physiologie et pathologie du systeme lymphoide." Masson, Paris.

Polli, E., and Ratti, G. (1953). *Biochem. Z.* **323**, 546.

Porter, K. A., and Cooper, E. H. (1962). *Lancet II*, 317.

Rebuck, J. W. (1952). *Proc. Eosinophil. Conf., Pearl Harbor.*

Reinek, J., and Bednarik, T. (1962). *Časopis Lekaru Českych* **101**(44), 1305.

Renny, D., and Mende, H. J. (1957). *Aerztl. Forsch.* **11**, 389.

Rigas, D. A. (1961). *J. Lab. Clin. Med.* **58**(2), 234.

Riley, J. F., according to Niebauer, G. (1963). *Wien. Klin. Wochschr.* **10**, 174.

Rinneberg H., and Lennert, K. (1961). *Klin Wochschr.* **39**, 971.

Roberts, B. M. (1963). *Proc. 9th Congr. Europ. Soc. Haematol., Lisbon,* p. 26.

Rosanova, M. L., and Mjasistcheva, N. V. (1961). *Proc. 8th Congr. Europ. Soc. Haematol., Vienna, Abstr.* p. 212.

Rost, G., Hahn, Ch., and Viereck, G. (1959). *Acta Biol. Med. Ger.* **3**, 276.

Rouser, G. (1957). In "The Leukemias" (J. W. Rebuck, F. H. Bethell, and R. W. Monto, eds.), p. 361. Academic Press, New York.

Ruhenstroth-Bauer, G., and Gostomzyk, J. G. (1962). *Z. Krebsforsch.* **65**(2), 108.

Salera, U., and Tamburino, G. (1956). *Sci. Med. Ital.* **4**, 425.

Schrek, R. (1947). *J. Cellular Comp. Physiol.* **30**, 203.

Schuler, D., Siegler, J., and Kiss, S. (1963). *Proc. 9th Congr. Europ. Soc. Haematol., Lisbon,* p. 21.

Schultz, J., (1958). *Ann. N. Y. Acad. Sci.* **75**, 22.

Schultz, J., Turtle, A., Greenstein, M., and Shay, H. (1956). *Proc. Am. Assoc. Cancer Res.* **2**, 145.

Scott, J. L. (1962). *J. Clin. Invest.* **41**, 67.

Shapira, J., Bornstein, I., Wells, W., and Winzler, R. J. (1959). *Cancer Res.* **21**, 265.

Shigeura, H. T., and Chargaff, E. (1960). *Biochim. Biophys. Acta* **37**, 347.

Shiro, Miwa, Tanaka, K. R., and Valentine, W. N. (1962). *Acta Haematol. Japan.* **25**(1), 12.

Silber, R., Gabrio, B. W., and Huennekens, F. M. (1962). *J. Clin. Invest.* **41**(2), 203.

Smetana, K., Heřmansky, F. and Pösnerová, V. (1962). *Neoplasma* **9**(6), 549.

Smith, C. (1949). *Proc. Soc. Exptl. Biol. Med.* **72**, 209.

Stave, U., and Oehme, J. (1961–1962). *Enzymol. Biol. Clin.* **1**(2), 75.

Štefanovič, J. (1963). *Bratislav. Lekarske Listy* **43**, 456.

Stewart, A. (1961). *Brit. Med. J.* p. 452.

Svenseid, M. E., Bethell, F. H., and Monto, R. W. (1951). *Cancer Res.* **11**, 864.

Takikava, K., Takahashi, H., Kawabata, S., and Ohta, H. (1961). *Proc. 8th Congr. Europ. Soc. Haematol., Vienna* p. 248.

Tanaka, K. R., and Valentine, W. N. (1961). *Acta Haematol.* **26**, 12.

Tanaka, K. R., Valentine, W. N., and Fredrick, R. E. (1960a). *Clin. Res.* **8**, 132.

Tanaka, K. R., Valentine, W. N., Fredrick, R. E. (1960b). *New Engl. J. Med.* **261**(18), 912.

Tanaka, K. R., Valentine, W N., and Fredrick, R. E. (1962). *Brit. J. Haematol.* **8**, 86.

Tanaka, Y., Epstein, L. B., Brecher, G., and Stohlman, F., Jr. (1963). *Blood* **22**(5), 614.

Tchimaru, M. J. (1959). *Kyushu Haematol. Soc.* **9**, 722.

Thiersch, J. B. (1947). *Australian J. Exptl. Biol. Med. Sci.* **25**, 75.

260   J. ALEKSANDROWICZ, H. GAERTNER, AND J. URBAŃCZYK

Thorell, B. (1947). Acta Med. Scand. Suppl. p. 200.
Trubowitz, S., Feldman, D., Benante, C., and Kirman, D. (1957). Proc. Soc. Exptl. Biol. Med. 95, 35.
Trubowitz, S., Kirman, D., and Masek, B. (1962). Lancet, II, 486.
Tsutsumi, F. (1959). Japan. Arch. Internal Med. 6, 833.
Undritz, E. (1950). Rev. Haematol. 5, 644.
Urbańczyk, J. (1964). Clearance of endogenous RNase in chronic granulocytic leukemia. Dissertation for the M.D. degree, Academy of Medicine, Cracow.
Valentine, W. N. (1960). Am. J. Med. 28(5), 699.
Valentine, W. N., and Beck, W. S. (1951). J. Lab. Clin. Med. 38, 39, 245.
Valentine, W. N., and Tanaka, K. R. (1961). Acta Haematol. 26, 303.
Valentine, W. N., Beck, W. S., Follette, J. H., Mills, H., and Lawrence, J. S. (1952). Blood 7, 959.
Valentine, W. N., Follette, J. H., and Lawrence, J. S. (1953). J. Clin. Invest. 32, 251.
Valentine, W. N., Follette, J. H., Hardin, E. B., Beck, W. S., and Lawrence, J. S. (1954). J. Lab. Clin. Med. 44, 219.
Valentine, W. N., Follette, J. H., Solomon, D. H., and Reynolds, J. (1957). In "The Leukemias" (J. W. Rebuck, F. H. Bethell, and R. W. Monto, eds.), p. 457. Academic Press, New York.
Valentine, W. N., Tanaka, K. R., and Fredrick, R. E. (1960). J. Lab. Clin. Med. 55, 303.
Valladares, Y. (1960). Arch. Med. Exptl. (Madrid) 23, 185.
Vanotti, A. (1961). In "Biological Activity of the Leukocyte" (Ciba Foundation Study Group No. 10), p. 79. Churchill, London.
Vanotti, A., and Cullity, B. (1960). Schweiz. Med. Wochschr. 90, 955.
Vercauteren, R. (1955). Verhandl. Kon. Vlaamse Acad. Geneesk. (Belg.) 17, 263.
Vetter, K. (1961a). Acta Haematol. 26, 344.
Vetter, K. (1961b), Folia Haematol. 6, 80.
Wachstein, M. (1955). Ann. N. Y. Acad. Sci. 59, 1052.
Wagner, R. (1947a). Am. J. Diseases Children 73, 559.
Wagner, R. (1947b). Blood 2, 235.
Waisman, H. A., Monder, C., and Williams, J. N. (1956). Cancer Res. 16, 344.
Waldo, A. L., and Zipf, R. E. (1955). Cancer 8, 187.
Wannemacher, R. W., Jr., Allison, J. B., Chu, D., and Crossley, M. L. (1962). Proc. Soc. Exptl. Biol. Med. 111(3), 708.
Warburg, O. (1956). Science 123, 309.
Warburg, O., Gawehn, K., and Geisler, A. (1958). Z. Naturforsch. 13b, 515.
Wase, A., Cardenas, J., and Podolsky, S. (1960). Proc. Am. Assoc. Cancer Res. 3(2), 160.
Watson, J. D., and Crick, F. H. C. (1953). Nature 171, 737.
Weinhouse, S. (1955). Advan. Cancer Res. 3, 269.
Weinstein, B. I., and Watkin, D. N. (1960). J. Clin. Invest. 39, 1667.
Weinstein, B. I., Weissman, S. M., and Watkin, D. N. (1959). J. Clin. Invest. 38, 1904.
Weisberger, A. S. (1957). In "The Leukemias" p. 423. New York.
Weisberger, A. S., and Levine, B. (1954). Blood 9, 1082.
Weisberger, A. S., Suhrland, L. G., and Griggs, R. C. (1954). Blood 9, 1095.
White, J., White, F. R., and Mider, G. B. (1947). J. Natl. Cancer Inst. 7, 199.
Will, J. J., Glaser, H. S. and Vilter, R. W. (1957). In "The Leukemias" (J. W. Rebuck, F. H. Bethell, and R. W. Monto, eds.) p. 417. Academic Press, New York.
Williams, W. (1962). Proc. 9th Congr. Intern. Soc. Haematol., Mexico.

Wilmanns, W. (1962). *Klin. Wochschr.* **40**(10), 533.

Winzler, R. J., Wells, W., Shapira, J., Williams, A. D., Bornstein, I., Burr, M. J., and Best, W. R. (1959). *Cancer Res.* **19**, 377.

Yoffey, J. M. (1962). *Lancet* I, 206.

Yoffey, J. M., and Courtice, F. G. (1956). "Lymphatics, Lymph and Lymphoid Tissue." Arnold, London.

Young, J. E., and Prager, M. D. (1962). *J. Lab. Clin. Med.* **60**(3), 385.

Yunis, A. A., Arimura, G. K., and Kipnis, D. M. (1963). *Proc. 9th Congr. Europ. Soc. Haematol., Lisbon.*

Zalockar, M. (1959). *Nature* **183**, 1330.

REFERENCES TO SECTION IV

Adelson, E., Rheingold, J. J., and Crosby, W. H. (1961). *Blood* **17**, 767.

Aleksandrowicz, J., Blicharski, J., and Feltynowski, A. (1954). "Electron Microscopy of Blood Cells" (in Polish). P. W. N., Warsaw.

Aleksandrowicz, J., Blicharski, J., and Feltynowski, A. (1957). *Folia Morphol.* **2**, 161.

Ballerini, G. (1958). *Attualita Emato.* **2**, 67.

Bettex-Galland, M., and Lüscher, E. F. (1961). *Biochim. Biophys. Acta* **49**, 536.

Bettex-Galland, M., and Maupin, B. (1961). *Hemostase* **1**, 375.

Biggs, R., and MacFarlane, R. G. (1962). "Human Blood Coagulation and Its Disorders." Blackwell, Oxford.

"Blood Platelets," *Proc. 10th Intern. Symp. on the Blood Platelets, Henry Ford Hospital, Detroit, 1960.* Little, Brown, Boston, Massachusetts, 1961.

Caen, J., and Cousin, C. (1962). *Nouvelle Rev. Franc. Hematol.* **2**, 685.

Caen, J., Lasneret, J., and Michel, H. (1963). *Nouvelle Rev. Franc. Hematol.* **3**, 251.

Fonio, A. (1957). *In* "Handbuch der gesamten Hämatologie," Vol. 1, p. 313. Urban & Schwarzenberg, Munich.

Gaertner, H. (1960). "Blood Coagulation—Physiopathology of the Hemostatic System." (in Polish). Publ. by the author, Cracow.

Gross, R. (1962). *Proc. 22nd Congr. Intern. Union Physiol. Sci., Leiden,* p. 253.

Gross, R., Gerok, W., Löhr, G. W., Vogell, W., Waller, H. D., and Theopold, W. (1960). *Klin. Wochschr.* **38**, 194.

Inçeman, S., Caen, J., and Bernard, J. (1963). *Nouvelle Rev. Franc. Hematol.* **3**, 575.

Larrieu, M. J., Caen, J., Lelong, J. C., and Bernard, J. (1961). *Nouvelle Rev. Franc. Hematol.* **1**, 662.

Löhr, G. W., Waller, H. D., and Gross, R. (1961). *Deut. Med. Wochschr.* **86**, 897, 946.

Lüscher, E. F. (1961). *Folia Haematol.* **6**, 84.

Lüscher, E. F. (1962). "Erbliche Stoffwechselkrankheiten," p. 480.

Lüscher, E. F., and Bettex-Galland, M. (1961). *J. Physiol.* (*Paris*), **53**, 145.

MacFarlane, R. G. (1961). *In* "Functions of the Blood" (R. G. MacFarlane and A. H. T. Robb-Smith, eds.), pp. 225-326. Academic Press, New York.

Maupin, B. (1954). "Les plaquettes sanguines de l'homme." Masson, Paris.

Maupin, B. (1960). *Biol. Med.* **49**, 75.

Maupin, B. (1961). *Hémostase* **1**, 29 and 375.

Morita, H. (1958). "Blood Platelets in Clinical Medicine." Publ. by author, Tokyo.

Plat, P. M. (1962). "Activités enzymatiques des plaquettes sanguines chez l'homme normal." Grande Imprimerie Nouvelle, Montluçon.

Plat, P. M., Bastide, P., and Dastugue, G. (1963a). *Nouvelle Rev. Franc. Hematol.* **3**, 393.

Plat, P. M., Bastide, P., and Dastugue, G. (1963b). *Pathol. Biol. Semaine Hop.* **11**, 352.

Weissbach, H., Bogdanski, D. F., and Udenfriend, S. (1958). *Arch. Biochem. Biophys.* **73**, 492.

Wintrobe, M. M. (1962). *In* "Clinical Hematology," p. 276 Lea & Febiger, Philadelphia, Pennsylvania.

Woodside, E. E., and Kocholaty, W. (1960). *Blood* **16**, 1173.

Zucker, M. B. (1961). *In* "Fortschritte der Hämatologie" (L. M. Tocantins, ed.), Vol. 2, p. 203. Thieme, Stuttgart.

Zucker, M. B., and Borelli, J. (1959). *J. Appl. Physiol.* **14**, 575.

REFERENCES TO SECTION V

Aleksandrowicz, J., Blicharski, J., and Feltynowski, A. (1955). "Mikroskopia elektronowa krwinek." PZWL, Warsaw.

Altman K. J. (1959). *Am. J. Med.* **27**, 936.

Behrendt, H. (1957). *In* "Chemistry of Erythrocytes: Clinical Aspects." Thomas, Springfield, Illinois.

Bernhard, W. (1952). *Nature* **170**, 359.

Bessis, M. (1960). *In* "Die Zelle im Elektronenmikroskop" Sandoz, Monographien.

Bishop, C., and Surgenor, D. M. (1964). "The Red Blood Cell." Academic Press, New York.

Carson, R. (1962). "Silent Spring." Houghton Mifflin, Boston, Massachusetts.

Dajani, R. M., and Orten, J. M. (1958). *J. Biol. Chem.* **231**, 913.

Danon, D., Sheba, Ch., and Ramot, B. (1961). *Blood* **17**, 229.

Davies, R., and Keynes, R. (1961). "Membrane Transport and Metabolism," p. 336. Prague.

Dische, Z. (1951). "Phosphorus Metabolism," p. 71. Johns Hopkins Press, Baltimore, Maryland.

George, P., and Lister, R. S. J. (1958). *In* "Conference on Haemoglobin." *Publ. Natl. Acad. Sci. U. S.* **557**, 33.

Howe, C. (1951). *J. Immunol.* **66**, 9.

Krawczyński, J. (1962). *Postępy Biochem.* **8**,(4), 523.

Krawczyński, J. (1963). *Postępy Biochem.* **9**,(4), 451.

Laurell, C.-B., and Grönwall, C. (1964). *Adv. Clin. Chem.* **8**, 135.

Löhr, G. W., Waller, H. D., Karges, O., Schlegel, B., and Müller, A. (1958). *Klin. Wochschr.* **36**, 1008.

Low, F. N., and Freeman, J. A. (1958). "Electron Microscopy Atlas of Normal and Leukemic Human Blood." McGraw-Hill, New York.

Markowitz, H., Hill, A., Cartwright, G., and Wintrobe, M. (1961). *Federation Proc.* **20**, 63.

Moskowitz, M., and Calvin, M. (1952). *Exptl. Cell. Res.* **3**, 33.

Pandle, P. (1961). "Membrane Transport and Metabolism," p. 431. Kleinzeller & Kotyk, Prague.

Pauling, I., and Coryell, C. D. (1936). *Proc. Natl. Acad. Sci. U. S.* **22**, 210.

Polonovski, M., Boulanger, P., Macheboeuf, M., and Roche, J. (1961). "Biochimie medical." Paris.

Ponder, E. (1955). "Red Cell Structure and Its Breakdown: Protoplasmatologia," p. 10.

Prankerd, T. A. J. (1961). "The Red Cell." Blackwell, Oxford.

Rapoport, S., and Luebering, J. (1950). *J. Biol. Chem.* **183**, 507.
Riecker, G., and Bubnoff, M. (1958). *Klin. Wochschr.* **36**, 556.
Szczeklik, E. (1963). "Enzymologia kliniczna." PZWL, Warsaw.
Thorell, B. (1947). *Acta Med. Scand.* Suppl. p. 200.
Thorell, B. (1961). *In* "Clinical Hematology" (M. M. Wintrobe, ed.), p. 43. Lea & Febiger, Philadelphia, Pennsylvania.
Wintrobe, M. M. (1961). "Clinical Hematology." Lea & Febiger, Philadelphia, Pennsylvania.

CHAPTER 10

Acute Radiation Effects: Damage of Hematopoiesis

Thomas J. Haley*

Laboratory of Nuclear Medicine and Radiation Biology of the Department of Biophysics and Nuclear Medicine, School of Medicine, University of California, Los Angeles, California

I. Introduction

The great radiosensitivity of the hematopoietic organs—spleen, lymph nodes, thymus, and bone marrow—was first observed over 60 years ago by Heineke (1903). Subsequent investigations have served to elucidate more fully the changes that occurred after acute whole-body exposure to ionizing radiations and to point out the varying sensitivity in various animal species from mice to burros.

* This study was supported by Contract AT(04-1)Gen-12 between the Atomic Energy Commission and the University of California.

II. Pathogenic Factors and the Possibilities of Regeneration

Changes in the peripheral blood cellular content depend upon the radiosensitivity of the precursor cells for any one cellular group, upon their ability to recover from the initial injury, and upon their life span or rate of utilization as mature cells. Alterations in the bone marrow, spleen, and lymph nodes are reflected in the number and type of cells in the peripheral blood (Lawrence *et al.*, 1948; Jacobson *et al.*, 1949a). Many indirect factors probably play a part in the utilization, destruction, and production of all types of blood cells. Acute whole-body irradiation causes a derangement of all body systems, and the resultant enteric organism infection as well as internal bleeding results in a decrease in the effective blood cell mass and circulating fluid volume. Barnes and Furth (1943) have shown that localized irradiation gives rise to lymphoid tissue damage that is remote from the site of irradiation. Thus, there is also an indirect effect of irradiation on the hematopoietic system.

A. GENERAL EFFECTS ON THE LEUKOCYTES

In 1905, Aubertin and Beaujard first described a leukocytosis prior to the appearance of a leukopenia. During the first 24 hours post-irradiation, the total leukocyte mass, as reflected in the peripheral blood count, was in a state of flux. There was a reduction in circulating leukocytes which could be correlated with the continuing reduction of the lymphocytes, because the granulocyte count remained constant. Jacobson *et al.* (1947) reported that the leukocytosis was biphasic, appearing at both 8 and 24 hours postirradiation. Moreover, it occurred in the presence of a depletion of the lymphocytes, and an increase in the circulating granulocytes. Jacobson *et al.* (1949a) suggested that the first peak might be associated with increased maturation of cells in the bone marrow and the second one with a mobilization phenomenon in response to widespread tissue injury.

With these introductory remarks, it now becomes necessary to discuss the individual cells of the leukocyte series separately because their radiation sensitivity differs as does their rate of recovery from radiation injury.

B. EFFECTS ON LYMPHOCYTES

The lymphocyte is among the most radiosensitive of all body cells, and the degree of its depression in the peripheral blood is dose dependent (Table I). With doses above 50 r, the depression begins in 15 minutes. Above 300 r, the time for recovery of the peripheral blood lymphocyte values is dose dependent even though Bloom (1947), using histological methods, reported that lymphatic tissue and lymphocyte production was essentially normal at 20 to 30 days after radiation doses of 300 r and above. The response of circulating lymphocytes in burros, dogs, mice, monkeys, rats, and guinea pigs is essentially the same as in the rabbit, but Valentine *et al.* (1947) reported that for a dose of 200 r the lymphopenia in the cat was less severe. However, in all species studied, the lymphocyte is the last cell in the peripheral blood to return to normal values.

TABLE I

LEUKOCYTE DEPRESSION AND RECOVERY IN RABBITS AFTER
ACUTE WHOLE-BODY X-IRRADIATION[a]

Dose (r)	Per cent depression		Maximum depression (Hours)		Recovery to normal (Days)	
	Lympho-cytes	Granulo-cytes	Lympho-cytes	Granulo-cytes	Lympho-cytes	Granulo-cytes
24	25	—	24	—	2	—
50	25	—	48	—	16	—
100	50	—	48	—	36	—
300	74	—	24	—	50	—
500	90	50	48	72	50	9
600	90	75	48	96	50	9
800	90	90	72	96	50	23

[a] Adapted from Jacobson *et al.* (1950).

C. EFFECTS ON MONOCYTES

The monocytes of the peripheral blood have an initial pattern similar to the lymphocytes but return to normal values by the sixth day after 100 r or more. Plasma cells show no significant change in peripheral blood values.

D. EFFECT ON GRANULOCYTES

In general, the response of the granulocyte to ionizing radiation is the same for all species studied, from mice to burros. Aubertin and Beaujard (1908) observed an initial increase in granulocytes in peripheral blood with a return to normal in 24 hours followed by a maximum depression in 48 to 96 hours. Similar results were reported by Jacobson *et al.* (1947) who observed two elevations in granulocyte levels within 24 hours. Wuensche (1938) suggested that the preliminary granulocytosis was the result of increased maturation of these elements in the bone marrow and their release into the peripheral blood. Jacobson *et al.*

(1949a) attributed the second rise to mobilization of these cells from the tissues in response to injury. Lymphoid tissue has been shown to be invaded by granulocytes at times corresponding to the peripheral blood peaks (Bloom, 1947). It is evident (Table I) that the granulocyte is more radioresistant than the lymphocyte, and, for a given dose of radiation, the peripheral blood levels of the former return to normal more rapidly than the latter. Both cells show a dose-dependent response, although the granulocyte appears to respond more slowly, then very abruptly for a given dose above 500 r in the rabbit, but other species show similar responses depending upon the particular species' over-all radiosensitivity.

E. EFFECTS ON ERYTHROCYTES

After a histological comparison of the various cell types in the bone marrow, Bloom and Bloom (1947) reached the conclusion that the erythroblast was equally as radiosensitive as the lymphocyte. However, the peripheral blood values of the erythrocytes do not reflect this great sensitivity at doses below 300 r. On the other hand, Hennesey and Huff's (1950) Fe^{59} uptake studies indicate profound inhibition of the erythrocyte precursors in the bone marrow. Moreover, decreased Fe^{59} uptake can be produced with radiation doses as low as 5 r. Larger doses have an even greater effect as Haley et al. (1958) showed in their studies of radiation-induced hyperferremia. These observations indicate a deficient production of erythrocytes and not a lack of iron with its decreased incorporation into hemoglobin. Extravasation of erythrocytes into the tissues in which they are hemolyzed also contributes to the reduction in the total number of these cells in the circulation. Valentine and Pearse (1952) have tabulated the response of the erythrocytes of several species to ionizing radiation (Table II), and it can be seen that the time for maximum reduction depends more on the species than the radiation dose within the ranges listed. Furthermore, as with other blood cells, the rate of recovery is delayed as the radiation dose increases.

At doses below 100 r, the immediate precursors of the erythrocyte are not significantly reduced, but, above that dose, the reticulocyte values are progressively reduced. Recovery proceeds in the reverse manner until a physiological overshoot is observed. In germ-free animals, however, such results are not observed, and the animals die with an anemia resulting from the suppression of erythropoiesis (Reyniers et al. 1956). Thus, it becomes apparent that under more specialized conditions, it is possible to observe profound changes in the one circulating cell, the erythrocyte, which, because of its long life (up to 120 days), does not show the abrupt changes seen in the leukocyte series.

F. EFFECT ON THROMBOCYTES

Radiation effects on the thrombocytes are more complicated than on other blood cells because of the blood coagulation process. Whole-body irradiation produces a thrombocytopenia coupled with prolonged bleeding time, prolonged whole blood clotting time, increased capillary fragility, and impaired clot retraction. The function of the thrombocyte has been summarized by Allen (1952) as follows: thrombocyte agglutination at the site of injury forms a plug to decrease blood loss, to preserve

TABLE II

EFFECT OF TOTAL-BODY X-IRRADIATION ON PERIPHERAL
BLOOD ERYTHROCYTE VALUES[a]

Species	Dosage (r)	Maximum reduction (Days)	Per cent reduction	Per cent recovery at 26 days
Guinea Pigs	220	14	60.0	77.7
	210	14	71.1	56.6
	420	14	62.2	82.3
Rats	300	12	18.0	95.0
	500	18	45.0	70.0
	550	10.5	81.8	100 (41 days)
	600	14	32.2	67.7
	700	18	72.0	60.0
Rabbits	500	17	19.3	85.5
	800	15	27.5	86.2
Dogs	200	20	42.5	71.3 (24–35 days)
	300	23	50.0	55.6 (24–35 days)
	350	21	32.25	79.04

[a] Modified from Valentine and Pearse (1952).

thromboplastin sources, to activate prothrombin accelerator, to enhance antiheparin action, and to contribute to vascular wall integrity. The other factors, calcium and fibrinogen, are normal in irradiated animals. However, the length of the fibrin strands appears to be shortened by the irradiation. Such an effect would tend to produce a defective clot which would not adhere strongly to the vessel walls, and the bleeding would again occur when the clot retracted. Thrombocytopenia following whole-body irradiation becomes severe in rats above 300 r (Cohen, 1952); after 200 r in guinea pigs (Lorenz, 1951); above 300 r in mice (Jacobson et al, 1950); and at 200 r in dogs (Prosser et al, 1947) and swine (Cronkite, 1950). Rabbits require 500 r (Jacobson et al, 1949b). The nadir of the thrombocytopenia is reached in 5 to 9 days, with recovery to normal levels requiring 14 to 21 days. The increased clotting time observed in X-irradiated guinea pigs (Haley and Harris, 1950) has also been seen in all other species studied. Cronkite *et al.* (1950) showed that the administration of platelet-rich plasma would counteract the hemorrhagic tendency in irradiated animals. Even if clotting time does return to normal under such treatment, there is a tendency for capillary leakage of the cellular mass (Furth *et al.*, 1951). Perhaps, this effect is related to circulating ferritin which decreases the sensitivity of the precapillary sphincters to adrenergic stimulation, thus preventing their closure and contributing to blood loss (Haley *et al.*, 1952).

G. Effect on the Immune Mechanism

It was recognized early in radiobiology that inhibition of antibody formation was a major contributor to acute hematopoietic death (Benjamin and Sluka, 1908). Hektoen (1915) demonstrated a correlation between the degree of inhibition of antibody formation and the extent of hematopoietic system damage. Such damage is also reflected in a fulminating bacteremia (Warren and Whipple, 1923; Miller *et al.*, 1951). After reviewing the available evidence of the effects of radiation on the immune mechanism, Taliaferro and Taliaferro (1951) concluded that the reduction in immunity could best be explained by the pronounced radiosensitivity of the lymphocyte. However, there is as yet no explanation of whether this antibody production inhibition is a direct or indirect effect of radiation (Smith and Cheever, 1959), but it is certain that radiation-induced leukopenia coupled with inhibition of antibody formation and enteric organism bacteremia is not conducive to survival (see also Chapter 11). The total sequence of events involved in acute hematopoietic radiation death is given in Table III.

H. Regeneration of the Hematopoietic System

When the radiation dose is small, the possibility of regeneration is great, but, as the radiation dose increases, it becomes more and more difficult for those cells that remain to act as seed beds for regeneration, and the organism dies. However, even larger radiation doses have been counteracted by the administration of bone marrow. When recovery does occur it is essentially complete in 6 to 12 weeks.

III. Laboratory Diagnosis of Acute Radiation Damage

The usual clinical hematological examination of the peripheral blood leukocyte series will indicate bone marrow depression arising from radiation exposure. The most pronounced effect will be on the lymphocytes, which will not only decrease in number but will tend to disappear al-together within the first 48 hours postexposure. However, because of a granulocytosis, the total leukocyte count may remain within normal limits until the granulocytopenia develops between 48 and 96 hours. The use of a sternal puncture to obtain a sample of bone marrow will add con-firmatory evidence and indicate the degree of acellularity that is develop-ing during the postirradiation period. This, in turn, may be confirmed by use of the Fe^{59} uptake in red cells. Thrombocyte counts would only be

TABLE III

SEQUENCE OF EVENTS IN ACUTE HEMATOPOIETIC RADIATION DEATH

Cell or system	Lowest effective dose (r)	Disappearance time (Days)	Duration of effect (Days)	Effect of increased dose
Lymphocyte	25	1	2	Prolonged inhibi-tion of recovery
Granulocyte	500 to 800	3	9 to 23	Prolonged inhibi-tion of recovery
Erythrocyte	200 to 800	15	26	Decreased num-bers masked by death
Thrombocyte	500 to 800	5 to 9	14 to 21	Prolonged inhibi-tion of recovery
Fe^{59} Uptake	5 to 25	1	3 to 5	Prolonged de-crease
Immune mechanism	500	1	28	Lack of function masked by death

confirmatory, because their wide range in normal subjects would require a greater depression to indicate acute radiation damage. Moreover, the granulocytopenia would already be evident by the time the thrombocytes reached their greatest depression in peripheral blood. Furthermore, petechial hemorrhages would appear and add more confirmatory evi-dence. Acute radiation damage depends upon total dose at the time of exposure; other physiological changes may be more prominent prior to the time that an acute hematological deficit becomes apparent (*Table IV*). The data in Table IV indicate a great need for more simplified diagnostic tests in the lower radiation dosage levels.

It is far better to depend upon film badge or ionization chamber dosimetry in a diagnosis of the degree of radiation exposure than upon hematological changes because many drugs can produce the same type of hematopoietic injury as that associated with the radiation syndrome (Erslev and Wintrobe, 1962).

TABLE IV

INTERDEPENDENCE OF RESPONSE ON RADIATION DOSE

Dose	Physiological response
0.001 r/day	Natural background radiation. No detectable effect
0.01 r/day	Permissible dose, 1957. No detectable effect
1 to 10 r/day	Debilitation within 6 weeks; death in 3 to 6 months
10 r	Few or no detectable effects
100 r	Hematopoietic system depression; decreased Fe^{59} uptake; mild radiation illness
1000 r	Progenitive tissue necrosis; 100% lethal in 1 to 2 months
10,000 r	Death in minutes or hours by profuse diarrhea and nervous system dysfunction often before hematopoietic system damage is evident

REFERENCES

Allen, J. G. (1952). "Conference on Blood Clotting and Allied Problems." Trans. 5th Josiah Macy, Jr. Foundation, pp. 213–246.

Aubertin, C., and Beaujard, E. (1905). *Compt. Rend. Soc. Biol.* **58**, 177.

Aubertin, C., and Beaujard, E. (1908). *Arch. Med. Exptl. Anat. Pathol.* **20**, 273–288.

Barnes, W. A., and Furth, O. B. (1943). *Am. J. Roentgenol. Radiation Therapy Nucl. Med.* **49**, 662–681.

Benjamin, E., and Sluka, E. (1908). *Wien. Klin. Wochschr.* **21**, 311.

Bloom, W. (1947). *Radiology* **49**, 344–347.

Bloom, M. A., and Bloom, W. (1947). *J. Lab. Clin. Med.* **32**, 654–659.

Cohen, S. H. (1952). *Blood* **7**, 225–234.

Cronkite, E. P. (1950). *Blood* **5**, 32–45.

Cronkite, E. P., Halpern, B., Jackson, D. P., and LeRoy, G. V. (1950). *J. Lab. Clin. Med.* **36**, 814.

Erslev, A. J., and Wintrobe, M. M. (1962). *J. Am. Med. Assoc.* **181**, 114–119.

Furth, J., Andrews, G. A., Storey, R. H., and Wish, L. (1951). *Southern Med. J.* **44**, 85–92.

Haley, T. J., and Harris, D. H. (1950). *Science* **111**, 88.

Haley, T. J., Riley, R. F., Williams, I., and Andem, M. R. (1952). *Am. J. Physiol.* **168**, 628.

Haley, T. J., Flesher, A. M., and Komesu, N. (1958). *Am. J. Physiol.* **192**, 560.

Heineke, H. (1903). *Muench. Med. Wochschr.* **50**, 2090–2092.

Hektoen, L. (1915). *J. Infectious Diseases* **17**, 415.

Hennessy, T. G., and Huff, R. L. (1950). *Proc. Soc. Exptl. Biol. Med.* **73**, 436.

Jacobson, L. O., Marks, E. K., Gaston, E. O., Hagen, C. W., and Zirkle, R. E. (1947). USAEC Rept. MDDC-1174.

Jacobson, L. O., Marks, E. K., and Lorenz, E. (1949a). *Radiology* **52**, 371–395.

Jacobson, L. O., Marks, E. K., and Lorenz, E. (1949b). *Radiology* **52**, 371–395.

Jacobson, L. O., Simmons, E. L., Bethard, W. F., Marks, E. K., and Robson, M. J. (1950). *Proc. Soc. Exptl. Biol. Med.* **73**, 455–459.

Lawrence, J. S., Dowdy, A. H., and Valentine, W. N. (1948). *Radiology* **51**, 400–413.

Lorenz, E. (1951). *J. Chim. Phys.* **48**, 264–274.

Miller, C. P., Hammond, C. W., and Tompkins, M. (1951). *J. Lab. Clin. Med.* **38**, 331.

Prosser, C. L., Painter, E. E., Lisco, H., Brues, A. M., Jacobson, L. O., and Swift, M. N. (1947). *Radiology* **49**, 269–365.

Reyniers, J. A., Trexler, P. C., Scruggs, W., Wagner, M., and Gordon, H. (1956). *Radiation Res.* **5**, 591.

Smith, L. W., and Cheever, F. S. (1959). *Proc. Soc. Exptl. Biol. Med.* **100**, 817.

Taliaferro, W. H., and Taliaferro, L. G. (1951). *J. Immunol.* **66**, 181.

Valentine, W. N., and Pearce, M. L. (1952). *Blood* **7**, 1–13.

Valentine, W. N., Adams, W. D., and Lawrence, J. S. (1947). *Blood* **2**, 40–49.

Warren, S. L., and Whipple, G. H. (1923). *J. Exptl. Med.* **38**, 713.

Wuensche, H. W. (1938). *Arch. Exptl. Pathol. Pharmakol.* **189**, 581.

CHAPTER 11

Total Body Irradiation Injury: A Review of the Disorders of the Blood and Hematopoietic Tissues and their Therapy

Georges Mathé

Institut de Cancérologie et d'Immunogénétique,
*Hôpital Paul Brousse, Villejuif (Seine), France**

I. Introduction

The very marked radiosensitivity of blood cells and of hematopoietic tissues has been known since the beginning of this century from the classical work of Heineke (1903, 1904a,b), and has been the subject of a great deal of investigation, reports on which we can find in many journals (Bauer, 1940; Bloom, 1948; Clemedson and Nelson, 1960; Dunlap, 1942;

---

* The author is also associated with the Faculty of Medicine, University of Paris, and the Hematological Service of the Institut Gustave-Roussy.

Furth and Upton, 1953; Jacobson, 1954; Mathé and Bernard, 1960; Minot and Spurling, 1924; Selling and Osgood, 1938; Warren and Whipple, 1922) and in various books (Cronkite and Bond, 1960; Ellinger, 1957).

The present study is concerned only with the effects of total body irradiation, regardless of whether the source of irradiation is outside (external irradiation) or inside the body (internal irradiation). Also, this investigation is limited to the rapidly demonstrable effects, and the leukemogenic action of ionizing radiations has intentionally been left out of consideration.

II. Acute External Irradiation

Most studies have been concerned with the effects of external irradiation, with which homogeneity can more easily be obtained than with internal irradiation by introduction of isotopes. For this reason we shall take the lesions brought about by this method of irradiation as typical for purposes of description.

A. MORPHOLOGICALLY OBSERVED EFFECTS

External total body irradiation causes pronounced disorders of the blood and hematopoietic cells which can be analyzed by cytological studies of the blood and of the hematopoietic organs and by histological examination of these organs.

1. *Blood*

Although total, homogeneous external irradiation with X-rays or with gamma-rays causes cellular disorders in the peripheral blood which for a given dose are not precisely identical from one species to another, from one strain to another, or from one individual to another, on the whole these disorders run a course that is more or less the same for most species, races, strains or individuals, in any case among mammals (Bond and Cronkite, 1957; Brecher *et al.*, 1948; De Bruyn, 1948a,b; Cronkite, 1949; Cronkite and Bond, 1960; Dobson and Chupp, 1957; Hartweg, 1956; George *et al.*, 1957; Henshaw, 1944a,b; Jacobson *et al.*, 1949; Küss *et al.*, 1962; Langendorff, 1936, 1937, 1938; Lawrence *et al.*, 1948; Mardersteig, 1938; Mathé and Bernard, 1960; Pape and Kollert, 1952; Riopelle *et al.*, 1957; Stearner *et al.*, 1947; Stodtmeister and Fliedner, 1954; Tullis *et al.*, 1955; Warren, 1954).

Figure 1 to 5 (Mathé and Bernard, 1960) show the disorders of the counts of the various blood cells brought about by different doses of X-rays in the mouse.

The mononuclear cell count shows the most rapid decrease. The lowest count is as a rule seen from the 24th hour after the irradiation.

The maximal fall of the granulocyte and reticulocyte counts is only seen towards the 3rd day (the count of the neutrophil granulocytes shows a mild, transient increase during the first 2 hours). The thrombocyte count does not reach its minimum before the 10th day. The decrease of the hemoglobin level and of the erythrocyte count occurs even later than that of the thrombocyte count. These disorders vary to a considerable extent with the dose. As can be seen, it is only the mononuclear elements that are rapidly sensitive to 50 r (in the mouse it is difficult to distinguish between the lymphocytes and the monocytes). When the animals survive, the phase of cytopenia is followed by a restoration, which occurs the more quickly the smaller the dose has been.

In man, the development of disorders of the blood runs a more or less identical course. Figures 6 and 7 present our personal findings (Table I) (Mathé et al., 1964). For the same dose, cytopenia lasts longer and is more pronounced then in the mouse. However, the curves have the same shape, there is a similar tendency toward restoration, and the relative sensitivities are also similar; in man also the lymphocytes are the first group of cells to decrease with a given dose and they are the only group that are rapidly affected by doses as small as 50 r. Since in man the distinction between lymphocytes and monocytes can easily be made, it can be shown that only the former group shows this extreme sensitivity; the sensitivity of the monocytes is of the same order as that of the granulocytes.

TABLE I

ACUTE TOTAL BODY IRRADIATION IN MAN
(γ-RAYS FROM A Co[60] SOURCE)

Dose (rads)	Number of Patients	Lesion	Reason
50	1[a]	Glomerular nephropathy	Anti-immune treatment
100	1[a]	Glomerular nephropathy	Anti-immune treatment
250	2[b]	Chronic renal insufficiency	Kidney transplantation
400	2[b]	Chronic renal insufficiency	Kidney transplantation
600	1[b]	Chronic renal insufficiency	Kidney transplantation
750	1[c]	Leukemia	Bone marrow transplantation[c]
800	3[c]	Leukemia	Bone marrow transplantation[c]
850	6[d]	Leukemia	Bone marrow transplantation[c]

[a]Observations by Mathé, Tubiana, Lalanne, Milliez, and Lagrue.

[b]Observations by Küss, Legrain, Mathé, Nedey, Tubiana, Lalanne, Schwarzenberg et al.

[c]Observations by Mathé, Amiel, Cattan, Schwarzenberg, Schneider, Tubiana, Lalanne et al.

[d]Observations by Mathé, Bernard, Schwarzenberg, Lalanne, Amiel, Tubiana et al.

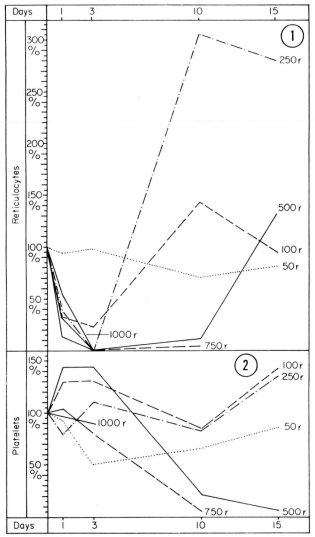

Figs. 1 and 2. Effect of different doses of total body irradiation by X-rays (with 200 kv) on the counts of various blood cells in the mouse (from Mathé and Bernard, 1960).

2. Medullary Tissue

Since the first studies by Heineke (1903, 1904a,b), many reports have been published concerning the effect of radiations on bone marrow in various species (Aubertin and Beaujard, 1908; Bloom, 1948; Bloom and Bloom, 1947; Brecher *et al.*, 1948; De Bruyn, 1948a,b; Denstad, 1943; Dunlap, 1942; Helber and Linser, 1905; Henshaw, 1944a,b; Jacobson

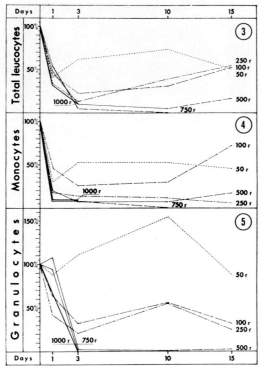

Figs. 3–5. Effect of different doses of total body irradiation by X-rays (with 200 kv) on the counts of various blood cells in the mouse (from Mathé and Bernard, 1960).

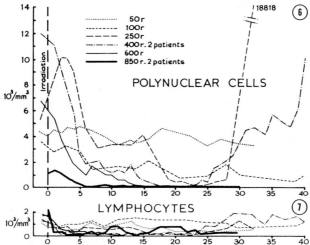

Figs. 6 and 7. Alterations in the counts of various leukocytes in man caused by total body irradiations with different doses of γ-rays (from Mathé *et al.,* 1964).

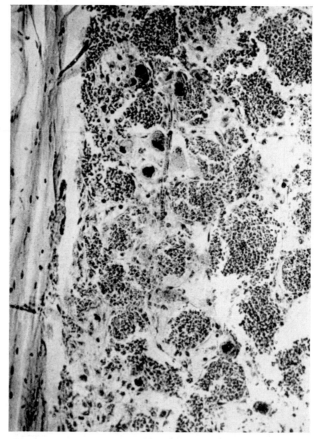

Fig. 8. Histological aspects of bone marrow after total body irradiation. Mouse irradiated with 800 rads.

et al., 1949; Jacobson, 1954; Krause and Ziegler, 1906; Küss *et al.*, 1962; Lamson and Tullis, 1951; Lawrence *et al.*, 1948; Lindell and Zajicek, 1957; Mathé and Bernard, 1960; Mathé *et al.*, 1963a,b; Milchner and Mosse, 1904; Pape and Kollert, 1952; Selling and Osgood, 1938; Stearner *et al.*, 1947; Stodtmeister and Fliedner, 1954; Töppner, 1941; Tullis, 1951; Tullis *et al.*, 1955; Warthin, 1906).

After a large dose of total body irradiation, bone marrow, studied histologically in sections or cytologically in smears, shows lesions that can be discerned after some 30 minutes, in particular arrest of mitoses, and the degeneration of certain cells (Bloom, 1948). The bone marrow shows rapid depletion during the days that follow. The most important lesions that can be observed are summed up in Table II and shown in Figs.

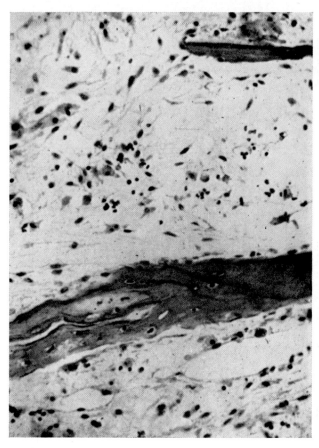

Fig. 9. Histological aspects of bone marrow after total body irradiation. Man irradiated with 400 rads.

8 and 9. A striking element is the morphological intactness of the reticular and pseudo-endothelial cells and other interesting findings are the persistence of a few histiocytes, the disappearance of the lymphocytes and of immature myeloid elements, whereas the mature cells complete their normal life span (which leads to an apparent initial increase of the polynuclear elements). All the myeloid series are affected; their relative sensitivities will be discussed below. It can be seen that the megakaryocytes disappear more slowly (Fig. 8). The hyperbasophil cells [plasmocytes, and others; for the significance of these cells, see Mathé et al. (1963b)] persist and even appear to increase in number. The sinuses are dilated; the bone marrow is edematous and hemorrhagic.

TABLE II

MORPHOLOGICAL LESIONS OF THE BONE MARROW AFTER TOTAL BODY X-RAY IRRADIATION WITH A LETHAL DOSE IN THE MOUSE[a]

Time	Modifications of the structure and disseminated lesions	Cellular lesions					
		Mitoses	Erythroblasts	Granulocytes	Megakaryocytes	Reticular cells	Plasmacytes
From the moment of irradiation to the 10th hour	Congestion of the sinuses	Cellular debris of erythroblasts	Decrease then disappear	Decrease in number after the first hour	—	—	Persistence	Persistence
From the 10th to the 30th hour	Same as above	Debris of erythroblasts and granulocytes	Reappearance; become numerous with anomalies	Disappeared	Decrease in number; morphological anomalies	—	Same as above	Same as above
From the 30th to the 60th hour	Same as above	Same as above	Again decrease in number	Same as above	Disappeared	Morphological anomalies; decrease in number	Erythrophagocytosis and erythrophagia	Slight increase in number
From the 60th to the 90th hour	Same as above	Same as above	Disappeared	Same as above	Same as above	Decrease in number	Same as above	Same as above

[a]Based on findings of Bloom (1948), of Barrow and Tullis (1952) and on personal observations.

If the animals survive in spite of the cytopenia, a restoration can then be observed. When an LD_{50} is administered, this restoration begins on the 10th day in the mouse and on about the 25th day in man. When repeated medullary punctures are carried out in human subjects, one sees first of all a few rare myeloblasts and proerythroblasts, then a few promyelocytes and basophil erythroblasts, and finally, myelocytes and erythroblasts of different ages and megakaryocytes. Two phases can be distinguished: a phase in which the number of cells is very small, and another phase during which the number increases rapidly.

On the whole, the changes of the bone marrow occur more slowly than those of the lymphoid tissues (Tullis, 1951).

3. The Spleen

London (1903) was the first to study the effects of irradiation on this organ in the mouse; it was he who suggested to Heineke (1903, 1904a,b) that a study of the effects of irradiation on the hematopoietic system would be interesting. The latter has given a description of atrophy of the organ, of aplasia of the Malpighian corpuscles, and of cellular destruction, with stress on the early affection of the lymphocytes. These observations have been confirmed by a great many authors who have carried out their studies in many different species, e.g. the mouse (Ellinger, 1945; Henshaw, 1944a,b; Lamson and Tullis, 1951), the rat (Lawrence et al., 1948; Pape and Kollert, 1952; Pohle and Bunting, 1936; Pape and Jellinek, 1948), the chicken (Stearner, 1951), the large mammals such as the hog (Tullis, 1951) and man (Küss et al., 1962, Mathé et al., 1959a,b, 1960). Murray (1948) has given a very good review of the lesions of the spleen.

In the small mammals (Table III), the spleen is a mixed lymphoid and myeloid organ and its study enables us to compare the two systems (cf. Table II). It can clearly be seen that the myeloid cells, which are affected just as in the bone marrow, are less sensitive than the lymphocytes. Pyknoses can be seen in these cells within 3 hours, as has been described by Heineke (1903, 1904a,b). This author has also pointed out that the first pyknoses appear in the Malpighian corpuscles.

After an X-ray dose of 400 to 800 r, mitoses are inhibited practically immediately and a few lymphocytes die (Murray, 1948). During the next few hours, most of the lymphocytes disappear. The dividing lines between the two pulps become effaced. A dose of 50 r causes histologically demonstrable lesions in the lymphoid tissue of the spleen (Nettelship, 1944).

In contrast to what can be seen for the lymphocytes and for the myeloid cells, the reticular cells do not undergo any morphological change

TABLE III

MORPHOLOGICAL LESIONS OF THE SPLEEN[a] AFTER A TOTAL BODY X-RAY IRRADIATION WITH A LETHAL DOSE IN THE MOUSE[b]

Time	Modifications of the structure and disseminated lesions	Cellular lesions					
		Lymphocytes	Myeloid elements — Erythroblasts	Myeloid elements — Granulocytes	Megakaryocytes	Reticular and histiocytic cells	Plasmacytes
From the moment of irradiation to the 4th–5th hour	—	—	Cellular lesions[c]	—			
From the 5th to the 10th hour	Structure of the white pulp disintegrated; Much cellular debris	Disappearance of mitoses — Decrease in number — Disappearance	Disappearance	Decrease in number	Persistence	Persistence	Persistence
From the 10th to the 36th hour	Much cellular debris; presence of polynuclear cells in the pulp	Reappearance of some cells in mitosis (lymphoblasts ?)	Disappearance	Disappearance of elements younger than the metamyelocytes	Same as above	Persistence; formation of syncytia; phagocytosis of cellular debris	Persistence and slight increase in number
From the 36th to the 50th hour	Same as above; congestion of the sinuses	Increase of the mitoses; abnormal mitoses[d]	Same as above	Same as above	Same as above	Same as above; erythrophagocytosis and erythrophagia	Considerable increase in their number; accumulation in groups
From the 50th to the 80th hour	Same as above	Same as above; appearance of lymphocytes in the sinusoids and the regions of the central arterioles	Same as above	Disappearance of the immature granulocytes	Nuclear lesions, decrease of the surface of the cytoplasm then decrease in number and disappearance	Same as above	Same as above

[a] In the lymph nodes the cellular lesions are the same as in the spleen.

[b] On the basis of findings of Bloom (1948), of Barrow and Tullis (1952) and of personal findings.

[c] Nuclear vacuoles, pyknosis, karyorrhexis, karyolysis, etc.

[d] Tripolar, multipolar; chromosomal anomalies, etc.

(Scherer, 1956). It seems that they even undergo hyperplasia (Fig. 10). Another effect of total body irradiation on the spleen is the increase of macrophagia and the accumulation of pigments, the latter phenomenon having its maximal manifestation between the 5th and 7th day (Heineke, 1904a,b; Scherer and Stolle, 1954). Just as in the bone marrow, the

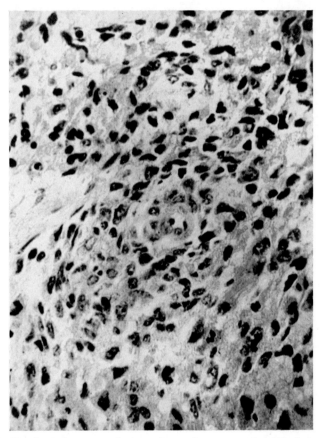

Fig. 10. Histological aspect of the spleen of a mouse irradiated *in toto* with 800 rads.

various hyperbasophil cells appear to be affected only little. Repopulation of the spleen begins in the subcapsular region where foci of lymphocytes are formed which appear to infiltrate the pulp progressively (Van Albertini, 1932); this restoration begins even while the depopulation is still in progress. The length of the regeneration is inversely proportional to the dose (Ellinger, 1945).

4. Lymph Nodes, Peyer's Patches, and Tonsils

It was also Heineke (1903, 1904a,b) who described the effect of ir-radiation on the lymph nodes and on Peyer's patches. His findings have been confirmed by many authors studying various species of animals: the rabbit (De Bruyn, 1948); the rat (Lawrence et al., 1948; Stearner et al., 1947); the mouse (Lamson and Tullis, 1951); the hog (Tullis, 1951; Tullis et al., 1955); and man (Küss et al., 1962; Mathé et al., 1959a,b, 1960). Like the spleen, the lymph nodes and Peyer's patches undergo atrophy in the germinal centers (Van Albertini, 1932). Histo-logically visible lesions are caused in the mouse (Nettelship, 1944), the guinea pig, the rat, and the rabbit (De Bruyn, 1948a,b) by a total body irradiation minimal dose of 50 r. For complete destruction of the lymph nodes, very large doses are required (Hughes and Job, 1937), because of their great regenerative ability (Taussig, 1940). Signs of regeneration may actually be observed while pyknosis still continues (Van Albertini, 1932). Many nodules form again after 3 weeks. Regeneration in the lymph nodes occurs throughout the organism (Van Albertini, 1932; Taussig, 1940). The tonsils are atrophic and often ulcerated after large doses (Draeger and Warren, 1947).

5. The Thymus

The first descriptions of the effect of irradiation on the thymus were given by Heineke (1903, 1904a,b) and Rudberg (1907). These authors already noted that pyknotic lesions of the thymocytes could be observed during the first few hours after irradiation. All further studies have con-firmed the marked radiosensitivity of thymocytes.

The effects of irradiation on the thymus has been studied in the rat, the mouse, the rabbit, the guinea pig, and the chicken (Murray, 1948). These effects are: first, a destructive phase can be seen during which the thymocytes die; then a phase of epuration follows, which is characterized by phagocytosis of the damaged cells by the macrophages (Dustin and Grégoire, 1931); the next phase is marked by aplasia and a certain proliferation of the connective tissue; the last phase is that of regenera-tion. There is a good correlation between the degree of cellular destruc-tion, the decrease of the cortical layer, and the weight of the organ. The reticular cells and the corpuscles of Hassal are highly resistant: they are not affected by 800 r. An increase of the number of mast cells has been described.

In a comparative study of the effect of different doses on the weight of the spleen and of the thymus, it was shown that the latter is more sensi-tive than the former (Kallman and Kohn, 1954).

B. BIOCHEMICAL EFFECTS

A total body irradiation decreases the DNA and RNA content of the bone marrow (Kirpichnikova *et al.*, 1956; Mandel *et al.*, 1951; Rodesch *et al.*, 1955). The quantity of DNA of the spleen decreases very markedly (Cole and Ellis, 1954a,b, 1955, 1956; Dubois and Petersen, 1954; Petersen *et al.*, 1955). A decrease of RNA of the cytoplasm of medullary cells that do not appear to be in lysis is generally observed at an early stage (Kirpichnikova *et al.*, 1956). Later on, an absence of RNA can be observed while DNA can still be found. In the thymus, on the other hand, the level of RNA increases for 1 to 4 days after irradiation, which suggests a change of cellular population (Weymouth *et al.*, 1955). After a total body irradiation, an increase of DNase and RNase has been found in the thymus of the mouse (Weymouth *et al.*, 1955). A number of enzymatic activities have been studied in the spleen after irradiation. Normally, an increase of the phosphatase activity can be seen, but this is not of great importance and probably only relative, due solely to a decrease of the weight (Eichel, 1955; Feinstein, 1956). The acid phosphatase activity increases in the spleen and in the thymus (Rahman, 1962). An increase of ATP activity and of 5-nucleotidase in the irradiated rat's spleen has also been described (Cole and Ellis, 1954a,b; Fellas *et al.*, 1954).

The β-glycuronidase activity of the lymph nodes is increased during the period of weight loss (Pelegrino and Villani, 1956). It is also increased in the spleen (Rahman, 1962).

The —SH groups are also decreased in the spleen, during the 3 days that follow the irradiation (Scherer and Gebhardt, 1954). Incorporation of C^{14}-formate into serine, cysteine, the nucleoproteins, and the lipids of the spleen is decreased after large doses (Seibert and Collins, 1956). Synthesis of saturated and nonsaturated fatty acids into the bone marrow increases to a high degree immediately after the irradiation (Altmann *et al.*, 1951).

C. FUNCTIONAL CONSEQUENCES

1. *Anemia*

The effect of irradiation on cells of the red series is the development of anemia, which appears only after a certain interval, but which undergoes a sudden intensification. Hemorrhages essentially due to thrombocytopenia certainly contribute to the erythrocyte disorder from which the anemia originates.

The blood and plasma volumes decrease towards the 5th day in the dog (Varteresz et al., 1958). The serum iron shows an increase (Melville et al., 1957).

2. Alteration in the Defenses of the Organism and Immunological Disorders

One of the principal causes of death after total body irradiation is the occurrence of superinfections. A large number of studies have been published on these conditions in the animal and, in particular, on their mechanism. Granulopenia is the major cause; a decrease in production of antibodies and failure of the protective barriers (the skin and the intestinal, buccopharyngeal, and respiratory barriers) are additional causes. These factors are analyzed in Chapter 12 of this volume (by Mathé and da Costa). In man, also, these infections constitute the major danger. Table IV lists the frequencies and types of infections that we have encountered in our material. Note the importance of staphylococcal

TABLE IV

HEMORRHAGES AND INFECTIONS IN OUR PATIENTS

Dose (r)	Case	Hemorrhage	Infection
50	Nephropathy[a]	—	—
100	Nephropathy[a]	—	—
250	Transplant of kidney[b]	—	Staphylococcal septicemia
250	Transplant of kidney[b]	—	—
400	Transplant of kidney[b]	—	—
400	Transplant of kidney[b]	—	—
600	Transplant of kidney[b]	—	—
750	Leukemia[c]	—	—
800	Leukemia[c]	Collapse	—
800	Leukemia[c]	—	—
800	Leukemia[c]	—	—
850	Leukemia[c]	—	Candida albicans; infection on the 25th day
850	Leukemia[c]	—	Staphylococcal infection of the lungs on the 25th day
850	Leukemia[c]	—	—
850	Leukemia[c]	—	—
850	Leukemia[c]	—	—
850	Leukemia[c]	—	—

[a]Observations by Mathé, Tubiana, Lalanne, Milliez, and Lagrue.

[b]Observations by Küss, Legrain, Mathé, Nedey, Tubiana, Lalanne, and Schwarzenberg.

[c]Observations by Mathé, Bernard, Schwarzenberg, Lalanne et al.

and *Candida albicans* infections. In our opinion, neutropenia, in man as well as in the animals, plays a much more important part in the pathogenesis of these infections than any other mechanism: in most of the patients who have high fever during the phase of agranulocytosis, we have seen this fever drop 1–3 days after the beginning of the return of the neutrophils (Mathé *et al.*, 1959a, 1960, 1963b, 1964).

It does not appear that a disorder of the reticuloendothelial system plays a part in the etiology of these infections: the phagocytic capacity of this system is not affected by either LD_{50} or LD_{100} (Stiffel *et al.*, 1959) (see Chapter 12). The decrease in production of antibodies, on the other hand, may play a certain part. In the mouse, a marked hypogammaglobulinemia can be seen which is in proportion to the lymphoid hypoplasia and to the dose (Mathé *et al.*, 1959c) (see Chapter 12); in man, this disorder is absent or very mild (Mathé *et al.*, 1959a, 1960).

3. Disorders of Hemostasis

Hemorrhages are the second most important cause of death; they are almost as dangerous as infections in irradiated subjects.

a. Disorders Connected with Thrombocytopenia. Thrombocytopenia is by far the most severe disorder of hemostasis, as proved in particular, in our material, by the excellent preventive effect of transfusions of thrombocytes in these hemorrhagic disorders. Actually, thrombocytopenia causes several abnormalities, as illustrated in Fig. 11: lengthening of the bleeding time, the tourniquet or cupping glass sign, absence of clot retraction, decrease of prothrombin consumption, and decrease of the thrombocytic activity of the serum. Clinically, it may, when the thrombocyte count falls below 50,000 per cubic millimeter, cause petechiae, ecchymoses, and mucous or visceral hemorrhages. We have lost only one patient out of 17 by hemorrhage (Table IV).

In the dog, the marked decrease of the thrombocytes as a rule precedes death by 2 to 4 days (Jackson *et al.*, 1952a,b; Shouse *et al.*, 1931).

b. Other Disorders. Hypercoagulability of the blood has been seen after administration of small doses (of approximately 100 r), particularly when the spleen and the liver (Tichy, 1920) are included in the irradiated volume; it ought to have been possible also to observe this effect in blood irradiated *in vitro* (Feisley, 1921; Herzfeld and Skinz, 1923; cf. Velden, 1912). Large doses of radiation, on the other hand, have long been known to prolong the coagulation time (Zunz and La Barre, 1927). Stender and Elbert (1953) have observed in rabbits exposed to 500 rad a shortening of the thrombin time in an early stage, followed by its lengthening after the 3rd day. Jackson *et al.* (1952a,b) have observed

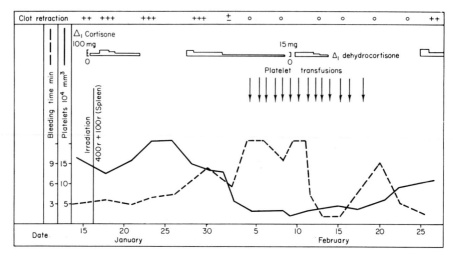

Fig. 11. Development of the platelet factors after total body irradiation with 400 rads in man (from Küss *et al.,* 1962).

incoagulability of the blood 48 to 24 hours prior to the death of dogs exposed to a dose of 600 r (which occurred on approximately the 12th day). Similar disorders have been seen in human subjects who had been exposed to a lethal dose (Hempelmann *et al.,* 1952; Le Roy, 1950).

A number of attempts have been made to analyze the effect of irradiation on the various factors involved in blood clotting. No involvement of fibrin and prothrombin has been observed (Barnes, 1941; Levy-Dorn and Schulhof, 1923; Verhagen and Suren, 1953). Anomalies of proaccelerin have been observed by some authors (mentioned by Ellinger, 1957), and not by others (Jackson *et al.,* 1952a,b). Finally, some authors have observed the increase of an anticoagulant of the heparin type (Allen *et al.,* 1948), an abnormality which has never been observed by other authors (Holden *et al.,* 1949; Monkhouse *et al.,* 1952; Rosenthal and Benedek, 1950).

We have made an analysis of the plasma disorders in patients irradiated with doses varying from 150 to 850 rad (Küss *et al.,* 1962; Mathé *et al.,* 1959a, 1960, 1965a). These are in general not very significant and may be summed up as a slight increase of the accelerin which follows irradiation and a moderate increase in fibrinemia (Fig. 12). The cofactors other than accelerin that determine the Quick time remain normal. No circulating anticoagulant of the type of antithromboplastin or anti-thrombin has been observed. No fibrinolytic activity has been detected.

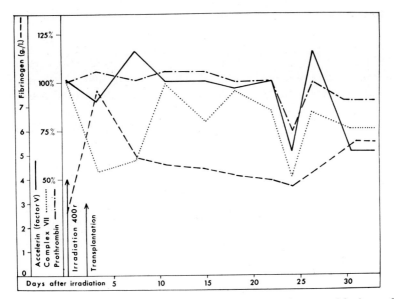

Fig. 12. Development of plasmatic factors of hemostasis after a total body irradiation with 400 rads in man (from Küss *et al.*, 1962).

4. *Correlations between These Disorders*

These three types of disorders—anemia, infections, and hemorrhages—are far from being independent of each other. We have already said that thrombocytopenia enhances anemia. Clinically, we have found that anemia aggravates an infectious condition. We also had the impression that infections are more difficult to prevent and to cure in a patient who bleeds. Also, general infections and local necroses due to neutropenia increase the chance of hemorrhages in a patient whose hemostasis is deficient.

5. *Mortality and Its Correlation with Hematological Disorders*

It is a classical concept that below the dose which irreversibly affects the intestine, and which amounts to approximately 1000 rad or more in many species of mammals [e.g., mouse, rat (the most sensitive of all mammals), and man] (Quastler, 1956; Williams *et al.*, 1958), death is due directly to the hematological effects: anemia, infections and infestations, and hemorrhages.

Anemia is not a great danger in itself unless its sudden aggravation is caused by hemorrhages.

There is no doubt that hemorrhages account for a good number of all deaths; in animal studies, this has been clearly proven by the considerable decrease in the death rate resulting from transfusions of thrombocytes (Cronkite and Brecher, 1952a,b; Fliedner *et al.*, 1958; Woods *et al.*, 1953) and it also emerges from the absence of hemorrhagic complications in human patients irradiated with doses of 400 to 800 rad and treated systematically with transfusions of thrombocytes (Küss *et al.*, 1962, Mathé *et al.*, 1959a, 1960, 1965a).

Infections, however, are the most important cause of death. Also it seems that when an infection and a hemorrhagic syndrome are present together, the dangers of death from either factor are greatly multiplied.

D. Causes of the Hematological Disturbances

The hematological disturbances observed are the result of the accumulation of effects of the various lesions induced by irradiation and of the reactions by which the organism tries to compensate for the insufficiency of certain tissues or organs.

1. General Effects of Irradiation on the Cells

The effects of ionizing radiations on the cells of the blood and on hematopoietic tissues are not specific: they are due to the different actions exerted by the radiations on any sort of cell; however, the blood cells have a short life span and since the hematopoietic cells divide often in order to ensure the numerical constancy of the cell population of the blood, these elements have a particularly marked radiosensitivity as is shown in Table V (Cronkite and Bond, 1960); furthermore, since these cells are present throughout the organism, the effect of radiation on them will be clearly visible only when their whole population is exposed, i.e., if a homogeneous total body irradiation is administered.

An irradiation may bring about immediate death of the cells, inhibition of their mobility, cessation of their division or induction of anomalies of mitosis, and finally mutations.

Cells that are killed immediately or rapidly by the irradiation do not show any markedly characteristic behavior after irradiation *in vitro:* after a latency period of several hours (Schrek, 1945), one observes pyknosis, vacuolization (Wernicke, 1938), fragmentation, and decrease in motility (Wallgren, 1933), and subsequently cytolysis which manifests itself with necrosis. *In vivo*, the cellular fragments undergo phagocytosis by macrophages. The lymphocytes are an excellent example of cells which die in this way after being exposed to an irradiation *in vivo* (Trowell, 1952). In the irradiated thymus, a direct correlation has been observed between the degree of pyknosis and changes in cellular respiration, particularly in glycolytic processes (Chèvremont, 1935).

It may nevertheless be considered that with the exception of the lymphocytes, cells will rarely be killed directly by exposure *in vivo* at the doses used; as a matter of fact, studies of irradiation *in vitro* have revealed the great resistance of the leukocytes (Knott and Watt, 1929; Lacassagne and Grigouroff, 1927; Neumann, 1924; Spurling and Lawrence, 1925; Wallgren, 1933): a dose of 1600 r in air is necessary to produce pyknosis in 5 hours in 50% of the leukocytes cultured *in vitro*.

Irradiation kills the cells much more often after some delay rather than immediately, and this gradual death occurs through inhibition of cell division.

TABLE V

LIST OF THE VARIOUS CELLS AND TISSUES AC-
CORDING TO DECREASING ORDER OF RADIO-
SENSITIVITY[a]

Spermatogonia
Lymphocytes
Erythroblasts
Other hematopoietic cells
Cells of the small intestine
Stomach
Colon
Skin
Central nervous system
Muscle
Bone
Collagenous tissue

---

[a]Based on data of Cronkite and Bond (1960).

Let us first consider the preparations for cellular division under normal conditions and how it takes place. After mitosis, the daughter cells begin a period of rest during which no biochemical phenomenon connected with the reproduction can be demonstrated; the duration of this period varies with the turnover of the cellular system in question. This period is followed by the stage of DNA synthesis, during which the quantity of this substance is doubled, a fact that can be demonstrated by cytochemical methods (quantitative determination of the material stained by Feulgen reagent) or by autoradiographic methods (counting of the granules visible in cells that have been brought into contact with a labeled DNA precursor, such as H^3-thymidine). Then follows another period of rest which precedes mitosis, the stages of which are well known. The precise biochemical causes that precipitate the synthesis of DNA and mitosis itself are not yet known. The duration of the various periods mentioned is variable. In the cells of mammals, the period of DNA synthesis lasts approximately 7 to 14 hours. The premitotic rest period may be as short as one hour.

After irradiation, certain cells, whose mitoses are inhibited, nevertheless continue to synthesize DNA: they increase in size to a considerable degree and show nuclear anomalies and polyploidism (Lacassagne and Monod, 1922). In other cells, the divisions are not inhibited but they are abnormal: tripolar mitoses, unequal distribution of the chromosomes among the daughter cells, abnormal chromosomes of the type of those shown in Figs. 13 and 14 which we have observed in a human subject irradiated *in toto*. In still other cells, no abnormalities can be observed.

On the whole, the most distinct effect of radiation on the radiosensitive tissues is the decrease of the number of cellular divisions (see Fliedner *et al.*, 1959; Knowlton and Hempelman, 1949).

2. *Direct Effect of Irradiation on the Life Span of Blood Cells*

Except for lymphocytes, cytopenia develops at a speed that depends on the life span of the specific type of cell; this fact suggests that it is essentially connected with the inhibition of hematopoiesis. For the lymphocytes, on the other hand, the cellular death appears to be independent of mitosis and the question arises as to what degree this phenomenon plays a part in the case of other cells.

a. Lymphocytes and Thymocytes. Although we know little about the life span of these cells, certain authors (see Gowans and McGregor, 1963) have concluded that there exist two varieties of lymphocytes, viz., a variety with a short life span (Ottesen, 1954; Hamilton, 1959) and those with a long life span. As Heineke (1914) has already pointed out, the sudden and pronounced decrease of the numbers of these cells in the peripheral blood and in the tissues is not satisfactorily explained just by the cessation of their production from the stem cells. Pyknotic lesions and disintegration are observed during the first 24 hours after the irradiation (Trowell, 1952). The same is true of the thymocytes (Weymouth *et al.*, 1955). It is known that although for a given radiation the lethal dose varies from one species to another, lymphopenia of the blood and involution of lymphoid tissues brought about by an irradiation are almost completely independent of genetic factors and are closely correlated with the dose (Bloom, 1948; Brues and Rietz, 1948; De Bruyn, 1948a,b). Brues and Rietz (1951) believe that an important factor in the radiosensitivity of cells may be the ratio of nucleic acids in the nuclei to nucleic acids in the cytoplasm. Schrek and Ott (1952) have suggested that the nuclei may have certain features in common with those of the stem cells which divide frequently, features that might be responsible for

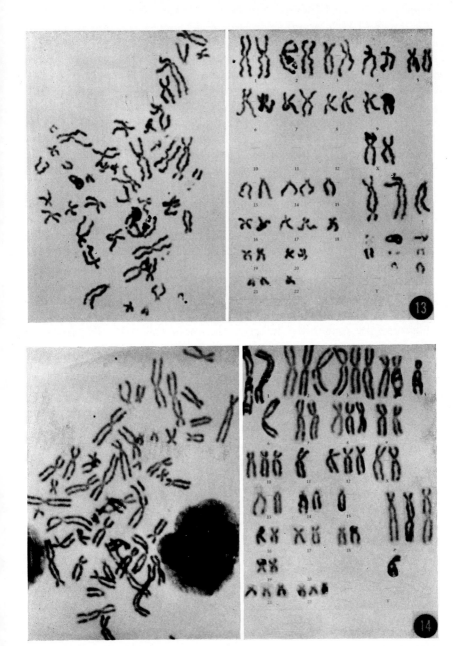

Figs. 13 and 14. Chromosomal abnormalities observed in a man after total body irradiation with 800 rads. From Papiernik *et al.* (1963).

the radiosensitivity. The recent studies of Gowans (1962) and of Porter and Cooper (1962) according to which the lymphocytes are precursors, reserves of immunologically competent cells, ready to divide in case of antigenic stimulation, and the works of Cudkowicz et al. (1964), according to which the lymphocytes might even be precursors and reserves of various hematopoietic stem cells, may constitute ways to obtain confirmation of this view.

b. Erythrocytes. There have been many studies on the effect of radiations on mature red cells. Irradiations in vitro have shown that in order to bring about hemolysis, it is necessary to administer fairly large doses, on the order of 10,000 to 100,000 r (Davis et al., 1950). Following irradiation in vitro with large doses, the electron microscope reveals signs of denaturation of the membrane (Lindemann, 1951; Zacek and Rosenberg, 1950).

In the case of irradiations in vivo, many authors have attempted to determine a fragility of the red cells by various tests; the results have varied from one investigation to another and, it seems, from one test to another (Goldschmidt et al., 1950; Krömeke, 1926; Smith and Grenman, 1951; Ten Doornkaat Koolman, 1926); the interval between the irradiation and the moment the blood sample is taken seems to be particularly important (the longer the interval, the more the red cell population studied will consist of aged cells, which are more sensitive than the young cells). It should be noted that the life span of the red blood cells in the irradiated rabbit is normal (Kahn and Furth, 1952). Still, although the red cells decrease relatively slowly after an irradiation, it can nevertheless be observed that they decrease more quickly than was to be expected on the basis of their presumed life span (Mathé et al., 1959a, 1960, 1965a).

In particular, it has been suggested that irradiation may damage the capillary vessels and bring about the escape of red cells into the interstitial tissues and lymph, where they are altered (Kahn and Furth, 1952).

In red cells, a decrease in activity of carbonic anhydrase has been observed (Finardzhyan et al., 1956) and also an increase in cholinesterase activity (Sabine, 1956); acetylcholinesterase activity, on the other hand, remains unchanged (Lundin et al., 1957).

Finally, a description has been given of premature maturation, consisting in particular of an early loss of the nucleus by the erythroblast (mentioned by Ellinger, 1957).

c. Granulocytes. The neutrophil granulocyte count after irradiation decreases in a time more or less identical with the life span of the mature granulocyte, which suggests that the life span is not shortened by irradiation. The appearance of granulocytes with many nuclear lobes (Jacobson et al., 1949) even raises the question as to whether the cells do not survive longer than normally. The myelocytes present a premature maturation (Casati, 1929).

d. *Thrombocytes*. In irradiated animals, examples of granular degeneration and giant thrombocytes have been seen (Jacobson et al., 1949).

The thrombocyte count only approaches zero after a period longer than the normal life span of these elements; this fact suggests that their life span is not greatly shortened by irradiation and that even under the influence of the latter the megakaryocytes continue to mature and to liberate these elements through scission of their protoplasm.

To conclude, the three types of myeloid cells do not disappear from the blood after whole-body irradiation because of a shortening of their life span, and their absence from the blood is therefore to be attributed essentially to a lack of renewal.

e. *Reticular and Pseudo-endothelial Cells; Histiocytes and Monocytes*. The reticular and pseudo-endothelial cell frequencies are not affected.

The monocyte level of the blood, on the other hand, decreases in a manner similar to that of the neutrophils and parallel with the latter (Küss et al., 1962; Mathé et al., 1959a, 1960, 1965a). As the life span of the monocytes is not known, we cannot venture a guess concerning a possible effect of irradiation on the life span.

f. *Plasmacytes*. The life span of the plasmacytes is not known. After irradiation the plasmacyte frequency in tissues does not decrease except when the tissue lesions are considerable, in which case their destruction is probably not specific. It appears therefore that irradiation does not significantly decrease the life span of the plasmacytes.

3. *Direct Effect of Irradiation on Hematopoiesis*

It can be concluded from the previous section that with the exception of the lymphocytes, it is not a pronounced shortening of the life span of the cells that causes cytopenia. The essential cause is therefore, as Heineke has already pointed out (1903, 1904a,b), the inhibition of cell production, and this inhibition affects myelopoiesis as well as lymphopoiesis.

Regardless of what procedure is used in studying the effect of an irradiation on hematopoiesis—histological examination of sections of bone marrow or of lymphoid organs, cytological analysis of smears or prints from these tissues, histo- or cytoradiographic study after administration of labeled DNA precursors such as H^3-thymidine, quantitative determination of DNA, etc.—a clear conclusion derived from all these methods is that ionizing radiations decrease production of blood cells by inhibiting mitoses. And this process, which can be easily observed in the two types of tissue, myeloid and lymphoid, affects all cells of the series.

In the particular case of erythropoiesis, Belcher *et al.* (1954) and Baxter *et al.* (1955) have studied the phenomenon with the aid of Fe^{59}. Even a dose as small as 50 r causes a considerable transient decrease; minimal values are observed after 2 days; after 2 more days, incorporation of iron returns to normal. Richmond *et al.* (1951) have studied synthesis of hemoglobin in the rat after total body irradiation: 24 hours after exposure to 600 r, inhibition of synthesis of the globin is three times as pronounced as that of the heme; after a week, on the other hand, the synthesis of heme is nil, whereas there is a small production of globin. Other authors have confirmed these anomalies of synthesis of hemoglobin after irradiation (Baum *et al.*, 1957, 1958).

One reservation must be made: when immunologically competent cells have been stimulated by an antigen prior to irradiation, the latter has little or no effect on the production of antibodies which is conditioned by a proliferation of cells with hyperbasophil cytoplasm; it is therefore probable that irradiation only slightly inhibits mitoses of immunologically competent cells stimulated by the antigen prior to exposure (see Chapter 12).

4. Various Indirect Effects

The opinion has been advanced that various additional mechanisms may also play a part in hematological disturbances.

Zwerg (1932) supposed that the liberation of toxic substances might play a part. He observed that the irradiation of an isolated skin patch had no effect on leukocytosis when the circulation of that zone was arrested for a period of 4 hours, and that leukopenia appeared shortly after the circulation had been restored. Furthermore, Dougherty and White (1946) have shown that adrenalectomy suppresses the leukopenia that is brought about by small doses of irradiation.

Irradiation of the abdomen of the rat causes hypoplasia of the thymus that can be prevented by adrenalectomy (Segal and Leblond, 1938). Adrenalectomy even decreases the frequency of the pyknoses after direct irradiation of the organ (Halberstaedter and Ickowicz, 1947), decreases its aplasia (White and Dougherty, 1945), and accelerates its restoration (Grégoire, 1943).

Finally it has been suggested that leukopenia might be in part connected with the migration of the cells into certain organs (Trowell, 1952). On the other hand, a movement of granulocytes of the visceral organs to the blood is held responsible for the polynucleosis observed during the first few hours after irradiation (Ellinger, 1957).

E. RADIOSENSITIVITY OF THE VARIOUS STRAINS OF CELLS

Classification of blood cells according to their radiosensitivity is a widely accepted practice, but not all authors are in agreement concerning the order of this list.

(a) Lymphoid tissue is more sensitive than myeloid tissue. The decrease in lymphocytes in the circulating blood is regarded as the most sensitive index of irradiation (Warren, 1954). In the bone marrow, lymphocytes are the first to be affected by a given dose, and they are affected even by very small doses that do not appear to alter myeloid cells. Lymphoid tissue is also affected more rapidly than the bone marrow. It has been suggested that the radiosensitivity of the "lymphocytes" is more marked in the lymph nodes than in the blood (Trowell, 1952).

The very marked radiosensitivity of thymocytes that has been pointed out by Heineke (1903, 1904a,b) has been confirmed by all authors. The thymus of the young animal, the hyperplastic thymus, and the thymus in involution are said to be particularly sensitive (Ellinger, 1957). The thymus of the male appears to be more sensitive than that of the female (Hughes and Job, 1937). The main causes of this very high degree of sensitivity of lymphocytes and/or thymocytes is that they are affected twice: the developed cell undergoes lysis and mitoses of the strain cells are inhibited.

(b) Myeloid tissue appears to be relatively less sensitive because it is practically only affected in its stem cells. Since Heineke (1903, 1904a,b), it has been the accepted custom to attribute different sensitivities to the different myeloid series; however, whereas Heineke classified myelocytes with erythroblasts, most authors agree with Bloom (Bauer, 1940; Bloom and Bloom, 1947; Tullis, 1951) that erythroblasts are slightly more sensitive than immature granulocytes. These differences in radiosensitivity between the erythroblastic and granulocytic series can be demonstrated in the chicken after fractionated irradiation: erythropoiesis is localized in the vessels of the bone marrow, and granulopoiesis outside these vessels (as stated by Clemedson and Nelson, 1960).

All authors agree that the thrombocytic series is relatively radio-resistant. It has been observed that the minimal dose required to block mitoses in the bone marrow is approximately 200 r as a skin dose for the erythroblasts and the myelocytes, and 300 r for the megakaryocytes (Denstad, 1943). As regards the "hemocytoblasts," these are said to show the same sensitivity as the erythroblasts (Bauer, 1940).

(c) The reticuloendothelial cells are classically the most resistant elements (Pappenheim and Plesch, 1912; Brecher et al., 1948). Nevertheless, they also undergo morphological changes (Scherer, 1956). A distinction should perhaps be made between the fixed elements (reticular cells and pseudo-endothelial cells), which appear not to be affected by doses of LD_{100} or less *in vivo*, and the mobile, free elements which constitute the histiocytes and the monocytes: the counts of the latter groups decrease in the blood in the same way as those of the granulocytes.

As regards the physiological disorders provoked by radiations in the RES, certain authors have reported a decrease of these functions (Chrom, 1935; Taplin *et al.*, 1954), whereas others have reported an increased or a normal phagocytosis (Barrow *et al.*, 1951; Brecher *et al.*, 1948; Di Luzio, 1955; Gabrieli and Auskaps, 1953; Stiffel *et al.*, 1959).

F. HEMATOPOIETIC RESTORATION

One of the most remarkable characteristics of hematopoietic tissues that have been exposed to radiation, even to total irradiation, is their tendency to restoration through compensatory proliferation.

As a result the bone marrow has a strong regenerative capability: even after a dose of the order of LD_{50}, restoration is evident some 10 days after irradiation in the mouse. In the rat and the rabbit, erythroblastic regeneration begins before granulocytic regeneration (Bloom, 1948; Furth and Upton, 1953). In the mouse (Bloom, 1948; Mathé and Bernard, 1960) and in man (Jammet *et al.*, 1959; Küss *et al.*, 1962; Mathé *et al.*, 1959b), they are simultaneous. In the lymph nodes, many nodules are formed again after 3 weeks in the rabbit (De Bruyn, 1948a, b). Regeneration takes place in the whole organ (Van Albertini, 1932; Taussig, 1940).

In the spleen of rodents, lymphoid restoration reconstitutes the Malpighian glomeruli and myeloid proliferation takes place in the red pulp. It has been alleged that in animals irradiated with a large dose, restoration may always occur as long as the Malpighian corpuscles are still present in the spleen (Ellinger, 1945). This repopulation of the spleen begins in the subcapsular region, where foci of lymphocytes are formed which appear to infiltrate progressively into the pulp (Van Albertini, 1932); this restoration begins while the depopulation is still in progress.

The amount of time before restoration begins depends on the dose, although there is no close correlation between the dose and the degree of depletion (Ellinger, 1957). The correlation is, however, indirect: the moment of onset of restoration depends on the moment of development of cytopenia, which will be sooner if the dose is larger, and it further depends on the number of stem cells capable of multiplication, which is inversely proportional to the dose.

This restoration depends on the presence of humoral factors such as erythropoietin for the red cells, the secretion of which is evoked by cytopenia. We have shown that bleeding the animals prior to the irradiation stimulates the erythropoietic reaction (Mathé and Bernard, 1957).

The curve of regeneration of granulocytes is often undulating (Jammet et al., 1959), as if there occurred some abortive compensation waves.

The possibilities of restoration after total body irradiation constitute a separate problem. It is probable that these possibilities are better than they seem. In surviving subjects restoration may be observed. The apparent possibilities of restoration after total body irradiation are the possibilities of this restoration in the period of survival given by conservative treatment. On the other hand, we cannot deduce the possibilities of actual restoration from the data obtained after local irradiation, because the irradiated lesions may be repopulated by the circulating stem cells. In this connection there are several interesting facts to be observed: we may mention for instance that after a fractionated skin dose of 7500 r, the bone marrow situated in the field may show partial regeneration, whereas after 12,000 r it appears to remain permanently aplastic (Denstad, 1943); it is possible that the cause of this difference between the effect of the two doses is to be sought not in the hematopoietic cells but in the connective tissue and the vessels.

Interesting findings have also been observed during studies of cultures of bone marrow in vitro: Rachmilewitz et al. (1945) have shown that, whereas doses of 250 and 1000 r cause a decrease of the number of mitoses followed by a normalization of the divisions, a dose of 2500 r causes a complete and lasting aplasia.

Is the restoration, once achieved, a normal one? Studies carried out in the cat with repeated irradiations with precisely determined doses suggest that even when the bone marrow has returned to a morphologically normal appearance and the blood to physiological values, a pronounced functional sequela persists (Valentine et al., 1952). We have made the same observation in man. A second irradiation of 100 r of a human subject irradiated 6 weeks previously with a dose of 400 r, and whose blood and bone marrow had become repopulated to an apparently normal degree, presented a longer and more severe cytopenia than after the first irradiation (Fig. 15) (Küss et al., 1962).

G. THE INFLUENCE OF VARIOUS FACTORS

1. The Dose

There is a close correlation between the dose and the effect of irradiation on the blood and on hematopoietic tissues, which makes it possible

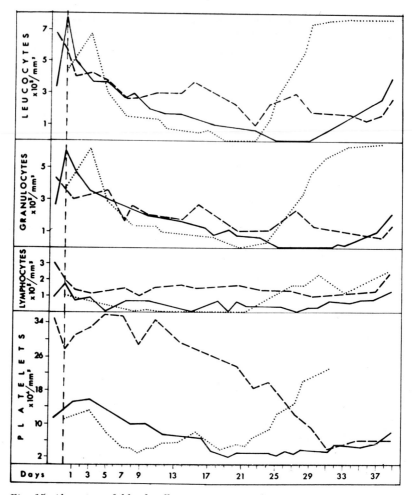

Fig. 15. Alteration of blood cell counts in man after an irradiation of 100 rads (- - -), an irradation of 400 rads (• • • •), and an irradiation of 100 rads (−) after the first irradiation of 400 rads. From Küss *et al.* (1962).

to use this effect as the best means of biological dosimetry. In the assessment of this correlation it must always be kept in mind that the disorders observed result from the total accumulation of aplastic effects and compensatory reactions of the organism; the earlier and more pronounced the aplasia, the sooner and more intense are these reactions.

Figures 1 to 7, which show the effects on the blood of various doses of irradiation in the mouse and in man, give a perfect illustration of this correlation. This view is illustrated by Figs. 16–18, which show in man the correlations between dose and intensity of aplasia (Fig. 16), length of the period of development of aplasia (Fig. 17), and the mortality (Fig. 18) (Mathé et al., 1962).

Hematological lesions are particularly suitable for dosimetry where the sublethal doses (from 100 to 400 r) are concerned; beyond a certain dose, the damage reaches its maximum and the differences for doses that differ from one another by 100 rad are very slight. For small doses, disorders of the lymphocytes can be used. The degree and duration of lymphocytopenia are closely correlated with the dose: doses as small as 250 millirem of X-rays in man cause a temporary decrease (Report of the United Nations, 1958), and a considerable decrease is brought about by a dose of 100 r. After an exposure to 300 r, the return to normal may take 2 months. After repeated doses of a few r, morphological alterations of the lymphocytes may appear, particularly binuclear (Dobson and Chupp, 1957) or bilobular forms (Report of the United Nations, 1958).

There has also been observed a very good correlation between the dose of X-rays, the effect on the volume of the spleen (Carter, 1950; Kallman and Kohn, 1954) and the Malpighian corpuscles (Ellinger, 1945), and the effect on the weight of the lymph nodes (De Bruyn, 1948a,b).

The minimal weight of the thymus after irradiation is a curvilinear function of the dose. The duration of the different periods described by Murray (1948) is closely correlated with it. After very small doses, very few cells die. Below 175 r practically no depletion of the cortex is seen.

Duration of regeneration of the spleen is inversely proportional to the dose: in the mouse, restoration is not complete on the 28th day after exposure to LD_{75}, but it is complete for a minimal lethal dose (Ellinger, 1945).

Hypogammaglobulinemia, which is the consequence of lymphoid aplasia, is also proportional to the dose, as we have demonstrated for the mouse (Mathé et al., 1959c) (see Chapter 12).

2. Fractionation

Radiotherapists have been aware for a long time that for a given total dose, fractionation decreases the effect on the leukocyte count. The influence of fractionation has been confirmed for the effects of total body irradiation in the mouse (Langendorff, 1936, 1937, 1938) and in the monkey (Paterson et al., 1956). Tubiana and Lalanne (1963) have compared the effects in man of a total body irradiation of 400 rad with cobalt-60, administered in one and in two sessions: they found no appreciable differences in the effects on granulocytes and thrombocytes,

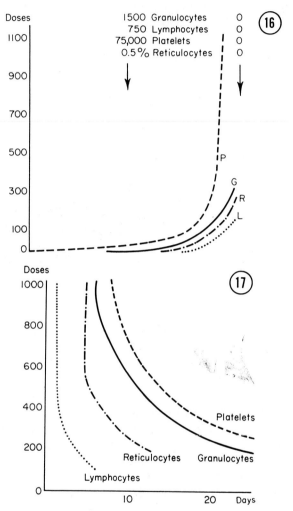

but they observed that the effect on lymphocytes after fractionated irradiation was of shorter duration.

The effect on the spleen of a given dose administered in fractions is also less pronounced than the effect of the same dose given all at once (Langendorff and Sauerborn, 1943).

3. The Time-Intensity Factor

No histological lesions of the spleen could be observed after an X-ray dose of 300 r distributed over a period of 20 hours, whereas the same dose administered rapidly brought about severe karyorrhexis in 6 hours (Pape and Jellinek, 1950).

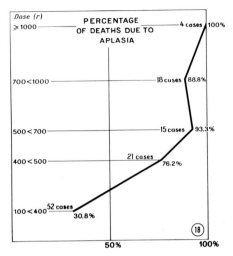

Figs. 16–18. Study in man of the correlation between the dose of total body irradiation and the intensity of blood cytopenia (Fig. 16), the development of that cytopenia (Fig. 17), and the mortality (Fig. 18) (from Mathé, 1962).

4. The Various Radiations

A study that has been made with bone marrow cultured *in vitro* showed that X-rays of 200 r produce the same effect whether they are emitted at 200 or 1000 kv; accordingly, the wavelength does not appear to be of importance (Osgood *et al.*, 1942). *In vivo*, it is only of importance insofar as it determines the penetration, i.e., the homogeneity of irradiation in those animals of considerable volume. The effect of neutrons on such a system *in vitro* proved to be 4 times as strong as the effect of X-rays (Osgood *et al.*, 1942). Neutrons have qualitatively the same effects as X-rays on the spleen (McDonald, 1947) or the thymus (Murray, 1948), and the same can be said of deuterons (Rosahn *et al.*, 1952). Quantitatively, on the other hand, the effects are different. Whereas a dose of X-rays of 35 r (Pape and Jellinek, 1948) to 50 r (Nettelship, 1944) is the minimal dose that brings about histological lesions in the spleen of the rat and of the mouse, a dose of 11.3 n of neutrons appears to be the minimal dose that can decrease the volume of this organ (McDonald, 1947).

Quantitatively, the RBE (relative biological effectiveness ratio) of X-rays to fast neutrons is approximately 5 and that of X-rays to slow neutrons is approximately unity (Murray, 1948).

Only few data are known about man in this respect. However, in the persons who were accidentally exposed to radiation in Vinca (Yugoslavia) we were able to compare the data obtained by physical dosimetry carried out after the accident by the team of Hurst *et al.* (1961) (Table VI) with the results of biological dosimetry which was carried out by comparing the hematological, histological, and clinical symptoms shown by these patients with those presented by subjects whom we had ir-

TABLE VI

DOSES RECEIVED BY THE VICTIMS OF VINCA (YUGO-
SLAVIA) ACCORDING TO THE DETERMINATIONS OF HURST,
et al. (1961)

Patient	Charges Particle Dose	$H(n, \gamma)D$ γ-dose	External γ-dose	Total
V	89	133	214	436
M	87	130	209	426
G	90	135	189	414
D	91	136	192	419
H	66	99	158	323
B	45	67	95	207

radiated intentionally, in precise doses and in a homogeneous manner, with the gamma rays of cobalt-60. The results of this comparison (Table VII) indicate that the doses received, which on the basis of the physical and hematological data were estimated at approximately 400 rad, corresponded to doses of more than 850 rad estimated on the basis of histo-

TABLE VII

BIOLOGICAL DOSIMETRY OF PERSONS IRRADIATED ACCI-
DENTALLY IN VINCA, CARRIED OUT BY COMPARISON OF
THEIR LESIONS WITH THOSE IN SUBJECTS IRRADIATED
DELIBERATELY WITH GAMMA RAYS OF COBALT-60[a]

Doses of the 5 most exposed subjects from Vinca	Corresponding dose in gamma rays (rads)
"Hematological" dose	≈ 400
"Histological" dose	> 600 > 800 > 850
"Clinical" dose	> 600 > 800 > 850

[a]From Mathé *et al.* (1964).

logical lesions and clinical symptoms, and this suggests that the RBE is higher than 1 (Mathé *et al.*, 1964).

An *external* total body irradiation with beta rays emitted by P-32 in a dose of 5000 rep, which kills 20% of the animals, has no effect on the thymus.

5. Genetic Factors

a. The Species. There are differences of radiosensitivity of blood cells or at least of their population between one species and another, although essentially the lesions are qualitatively similar. It is these differences that explain the different LD_{50} and LD_{100} values of the various species that are listed in Table VIII.

TABLE VIII

$LD_{50/30}$ OF DIFFERENT MAMMALS

Species	Dose (r)	References
Hamster	800	Gerber, 1957
Rabbit	800	Hagen and Sacher (1946)
Rat	650	Hagen and Simmons (1947)
Mouse	550	Gerber (1957)
Monkey (Macaca mulatta)	438	Allen *et al.* (1960)
Man	400	Mathé (1962)
Guinea pig	326	Newton and Ter-Pogossian (1960)
Dog	335	Shively *et al.* (1958)
Swine	275	Tullis *et al.* (1952)

This is not an absolute rule, however. For instance, although the $LD_{50/30}$ of the guinea pig is lower than that of the rat, the bone marrow of the rat appears to be more radiosensitive than that of the guinea pig. A singular fact is that the bone marrow localized in the epiphyseal regions reacts more quickly and intensely than that of the metaphyses and the diaphyses; this phenomenon may be due to certain physiological properties which we do not yet know (Bloom, 1948). After treating rats with radium, Thomas and Bruner (1933) found an aplastic bone marrow in two-thirds of the diaphyses. Classically it is considered that the radiosensitivity of the lymphocytes does not differ from one species to another (De Bruyn, 1948a,b). Nevertheless, a dose of 175 r causes the same lesions in the lymph nodes of the guinea pig as a dose of 400 r in the rat and rabbit.

b. The Race, the Strain, and the Individual. Less distinct, but nevertheless appreciable differences in radiosensitivity appear also to exist between the various races, strains, and individuals (Table VIII).

6. Various Physiological and Pharmacological Factors

Anoxia at high altitudes (Schack and McDuffee, 1949) increases the resistance of the bone marrow to irradiation. Anemia caused by blood letting (Mathé and Bernard, 1957) or by administration of phenyl-hydrazine (Jacobson et al., 1948) seemingly increases the resistance of the erythrocytic series; actually, it only favors restoration, probably by causing its earlier start through the intermediary of erythropoietin. Deoxycorticosterone (Betz, 1951; Ellinger, 1948) is said to activate restoration of the bone marrow. Adrenalectomy is alleged to stimulate restoration of the bone marrow after small, but not after large doses (Betz, 1953).

The various chemical protecting agents, administered prior to irradiation, render the hematological effects less marked; this is the case, for instance, with potassium cyanide (Betz, 1952). It has been shown that these various products, which are only efficacious when they are administered prior to irradiation, act as if they decreased the dose (see Pihl and Eldjarn, 1958).

7. Pathological Factors

There is no doubt that a previous infection renders the subject more sensitive to total body irradiation. With the exception of this condition, pathological factors have only a moderate influence, and then primarily with doses of approximately LD_{50} as is shown in Table IX, which lists

TABLE IX

Data on Mortality and Spontaneous Restoration of 110 Patients Who Received More than 100 r of Total Body Irradiation without a Bone-Marrow Transplantation[a]

	Dose (r)[b]									
	100–400		400–500		500–700		700–1000		1000	
	(1)	(2)	(1)	(2)	(1)	(2)	(1)	(1)	(1)	(2)
Cancer	10	22	3	0	1	0	—	—	—	—
Leukemia	6	12	5	0	10	1	15	2	3	0
Nethropathies (Renal transplants)	1	1	8	5	3	0	1	0	1	0
Total	17	35	16	5	14	1	16	2	4	0

[a]From Mathé (1962).
[b]Groups: (1) = death due to aplasia; (2) = spontaneous restoration.

the results of an examination carried out by us among those human subjects who had been most exposed to radiation (Mathé, 1962).

H. Various Forms of Treatment

1. Conservative or Symptomatic Treatment

The very extensive possibilities of spontaneous restoration justify the hope that, for those doses the lethality of which is due to hematological disorders, a simple symptomatic treatment may be found by which these complications can be avoided so that the exposed subject may benefit from this restoration and mortality may be very considerably reduced.

In our personal experiments, we have attempted to work out such a treatment, with a maximum of efficacy. The therapeutic means and their indications are listed in Table X. Emphasis may be laid on the value of ϵ-aminocaproic acid, which apparently can decrease the frequency and the severity of hemorrhages not only in cases of fibrinolytic syndrome but also in cases of thrombocytopenia alone (Cattan et al., 1963); another valuable procedure is transfusions of thrombocytes which, al-

TABLE X

VARIOUS SYMPTOMATIC TREATMENTS AND THEIR INDICATIONS

Indication	Treatment
Anemia ($< 2 \times 10^6$)	Blood transfusions
Thrombocytopenia ($< 10^5$)	(a) Aminocaproic acid (b) Platelet transfusions (c) Δ_1 Cortisone (?)
Leukopenia (a) Routine	(a) Keep the patient in sterile room with ultraviolet light and filtered air under a positive pressure; every article and all food should be sterile (b) γ-Globulin (c) Mycostatin, paromomycin (?)
(b) With fever (1) Positive blood or swab culture from a focus of infection	Antibiotic to which the organism has been found to be sensitive in vitro
(2) Negative blood culture and no visible focus of infection	Broad-spectrum antibiotic (avoid Chloramphenicol); Mycostatin; γ-globulin; symptomatic treatment for the fever

though they do not restore the blood level of these cells to its normal value, as a rule correct the bleeding time, the prothrombin consumption, and the clot retraction and which, particularly when they are administered systematically from the beginning of thrombocytopenia, decrease the hemorrhagic manifestations, including the petechiae, (Mathé et al., 1964). Figure 19 shows the evolution of various elements of the hemo-

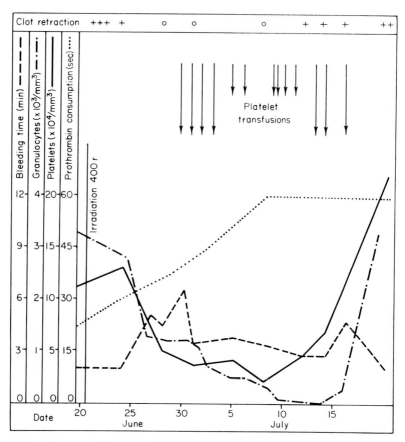

Fig. 19. Effect of platelet transfusion on the factors of hemostasis.

stasis in a subject irradiated with a dose of 400 rad and treated systematically with thrombocyte transfusions (Küss et al., 1962). Adrenocortical steroids certainly decrease this bleeding tendency of subjects with thrombocytopenia, but we do not favor their administration because they enhance the danger of infections, in particular of mycotic infections.

The prevention of infections of exogenic origin is based essentially on keeping the patients in conditions of maximal asepsis: in principle this is done by keeping the patients in aseptic rooms or apartments (Table X). The number of microorganisms is decreased in these rooms by the following means: supply of filtered air under pressure, ultraviolet irradiation, cleaning to the best possible degree of sterility and bacteriological control of the staff and objects going in. Figure 20 (Mathé and Forestier, 1964) shows a plan of the aseptic apartment created in the Institute of Cancerology and Immunogenetics (Villejuif).

Antibiotics are only used when necessary (Table X) and, if at all possible, only after determination of the sensitivity of the microorganism in question. With regard to paromomycin (a nonabsorbed antiobiotic) we have not yet had sufficient experience to judge the value of its systematic administration. Systematic administration of Mycostatin, on the other hand, seems advisable.

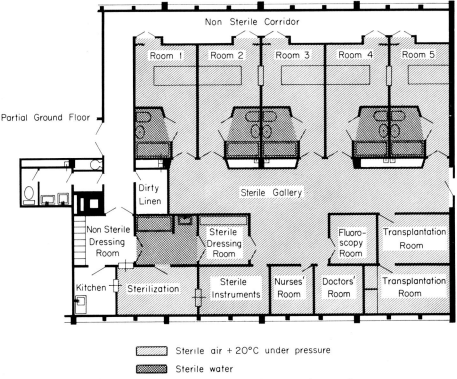

Fig. 20. Aseptic apartment in the Institute of Cancerology and Immunogenetics (Villejuif).

2. Transfusion or Transplantation of Bone Marrow

Transfusion of bone marrow is a more difficult method of treatment, but it may be efficacious when the symptomatic treatment has failed.

Since the subject is discussed by Szirmai in Chapter 16 of this volume, we shall restrict ourselves here to summing up the results of our personal experiments in man and to considering the indications of this method of treatment of subjects exposed accidentally to radiation; for the experimental data we refer the reader to Chapter 16 and to a study which we have previously published on the subject of bone-marrow grafting (Mathé and Amiel, 1962).

a. Transfusion of Compatible, Autologous, or Isogenic Bone Marrow. Various authors have treated subjects irradiated with a lethal or sublethal dose, with transfusion of compatible bone marrow, i.e., their own bone marrow removed prior to the irradiation (Kurnick *et al.*, 1958, 1959; MacGowern *et al.*, 1959), or with bone marrow of a monozygotic twin (Atkinson *et al.*, 1959; Thomas *et al.*, 1959; Mathé *et al.*, 1965). As a rule, after a transfusion one can see a rapid restoration. The statistical study which we have carried out (Mathé, 1962) with comparison of the mortality of subjects irradiated with different doses and not treated, as against the mortality of subjects irradiated with the same doses but treated with transfusions of isogenic bone marrow, proved that this treatment is efficacious (Table XI). There is some doubt, however, concerning the permanent character of the taking of the transfused cells: we have demonstrated (Papiernik *et al.*, 1963) in a child irradiated with 800 rad and treated with transfusion of the bone marrow from its monozygotic twin, followed by rapid restoration, that there were nu-

TABLE XI

Total Body Irradiation: Comparison of the Mortality Rates in Those Treated by an Isogenic Marrow Transplantation with Those Not
Treated by This Method

Dose(r)	Deaths due to aplasia[b]		Hematopoietic restoration[a]	
200–400	0	(17)	2	(35)
700–1000	0	(16)	3	(2)
1000	1	(3)	2	(0)
Total	1		7	

[a]From Mathé *et al.* (1962).

[b]The figures in parentheses represent the total number of irradiated patients at different doses who died or who showed hematopoietic restoration. It may be seen that for all the radiation doses, isologous marrow transplantation seems to decrease the mortality.

merous chromosomal anomalies, which were clearly due to the irradiation. Whether the grafting effect is transient or the bone marrow has only a symptomatic effect, it is clear that there is rapid resumption of spontaneous restoration, in contradistinction to the results in subjects transfused with allogenic bone marrow.

b. Transfusion of Allogenic Bone Marrow. Therapeutic trials have been carried out in human subjects under the conditions that permit grafting of bone marrow in animals, and the findings suggest that grafting such tissue is also possible in man, and that the conditions are scarcely different from those observed in other species of animals. Our personal experience now includes a total of 23 trials with 3 groups.

The first trial was carried out in 8 subjects with leukemia in the terminal phase who were subjected to total body irradiation with a conventional radiotherapy apparatus or with a betatron (from 200 to 400 rad). The transfused allogenic bone marrow did not take in any of these subjects and the patients died after some 10 days. The irradiation had in no way aggravated their already very severe condition, particularly since the leukemia was already manifesting itself with a maximal myeloid insufficiency (Mathé, 1959).

The second group (Mathé et al., 1959b) consisted of 5 subjects who were irradiated accidentally in the nuclear center of Vinca (Yugoslavia) with a mixture of gamma rays and neutrons, in doses that have been the subject of discussion, but which, after comparison of physical, clinical, hematological, and histological data, we estimated as higher than LD_{75} for 4 of them and higher than LD_{30} for one of them (Mathé et al., 1964).

These patients were treated with a transfusion of bone marrow; the interval between the irradiation and the transfusion was different for each of them, because the indication of this treatment and the time at which it was given were determined by the presumed failure of the symptomatic treatment. These transfusions were followed by myeloid restoration, which we were able to attribute to taking of the transfused cells for two reasons. (a) An indirect reason: although these subjects were irradiated at the same instant and 4 of them were given the same dose, they received their transfusions of bone marrow at different times and also showed myeloid restoration at different times that were closely correlated with the dates of bone-marrow transfusion (Fig. 21). (b) A direct reason: owing to the differences in the erythrocytic phenotypes between donors and recipients, it was possible to calculate the quantity of red cells produced by the grafts and this quantity represented, over a period of 3 weeks, the whole amount of blood produced. Moreover, this quantity of blood due to the grafts did not increase after these

3 weeks; it then decreased and this marked the return of autologous myeloid production. We concluded that a transient grafting had taken place, the therapeutic importance of which was demonstrated by the fact that only one of these patients has died, while 4 of them had received a dose of more than LD_{75}. The patient who died, furthermore, showed excellent myeloid restoration but succumbed to an intestinal

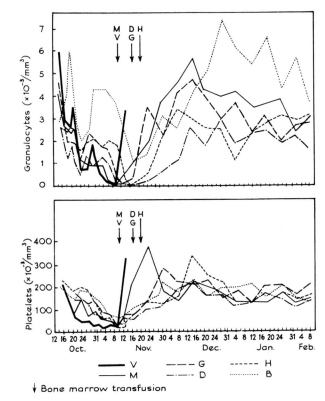

Fig. 21. Treatment of accidentally irradiated subjects by allogenic bone marrow transfusion. Myeloid restoration occurred at different times that were closely correlated with the dates of the bone-marrow transfusions.

complication. None of the patients developed a secondary syndrome, which was probably due to the transient character of the taking of the graft.

The third group consisted of 10 patients with leukemia who were deliberately subjected to a total body irradiation with cobalt-60 at a dose of approximately 800 rad and who were treated with transfusions of allogenic bone marrow under the conditions listed in Table XII (Mathé

TABLE XII

PRINCIPAL DATA CONCERNING HOMOLOGOUS BONE MARROW TRANSFUSIONS TO IRRADIATED LEUKEMIC SUBJECTS

Recipient	Donor	Date according to irradiation	Volume (cc)	Number of Nucleic cells	Difference in the phenotype of erythrocytic groups	Markers
D.V. Female	1st female	3rd and 4th day	450	1.4×10^{10}	N Ee Kell + MN ee MN kk	M M
V.L. Female	Male	7th and 11th day	400	1.1×10^{10}	M CC MN Cc	c
F.B. Female	Male	7th and 13th day	538	1.3×10^{10}	M ee MN Ee S	E
P.F. Male	1st female 2nd female 3rd female 4th–7th male	7th and 15th day 11th day 21st and 23rd day 32nd day	578 272 658 534	1.16×10^{10} 6.2×10^{9} 1.36×10^{10} 1.18×10^{10}	ee Fy (a+) Jk (a+) Fy (a−) Jk (a−) ss Ee	Appendices of granulocytes E
E.D. Male	Mother	11th and 14th day	578	1.45×10^{10}	Same phenotype	Appendices of granulocytes
M.V. Female	Male	11th day	401	1.13×10^{10}	S P + CC eeLe (a−b−) ssP − Cc EeLe(a−b+)	E et c
P.M. Male	Female	2nd and 9th day	650	2×10^{9}	$A_1(A_2)$ N Le(b+)Fy(a+)Jk(a−)	Appendices of granulocytes
N.P. Female	5 males	6th day	1350	2.7×10^{10}	C Le(a+)S C C Fy(a−) C	Appendices of granulocytes
	1 monozygote twin sister	21st day	283	1.417×10^{10}	C Jk(a−)S Same phenotype	C
B.F. Female	Dizygote twin sister	8th day	476	1.09×10^{10}	M Fy(a−)	M
B.B. Male	4 males, 2 females (father, mother, 3 brothers, 1 sister)	6th day	1985	5.8×10^{10}	Same phenotype Jk(a−) Le(a + b−)Jk(a−) ss CC Le(a + b−) CC Fy(a−) P_2 CC	Appendices of granulocytes and monocytes; cells with XX chromosome

et al., 1959a, 1960, 1963a, 1965a,b). The results can be summed up as follows. (*a*) In 3 patients, the attempt was a failure; it was not followed by restoration; 2 of the patients died from the consequences of aplasia due to irradiation; in the third, restoration was obtained after a transfusion of isogenic bone marrow. (*b*) All the other patients after the bone-marrow transfusion showed myeloid restoration (Fig. 22) but their subsequent clinical courses were variable because of the diversity of the aspects of the secondary syndrome which complicated the grafting. (1) In two of these patients, the secondary syndrome was very severe and occurred in a very early stage, viz., simultaneously with the beginning of myeloid restoration (before the restoration, which was pronounced in the bone marrow, had brought about a repopulation of the blood). (2)

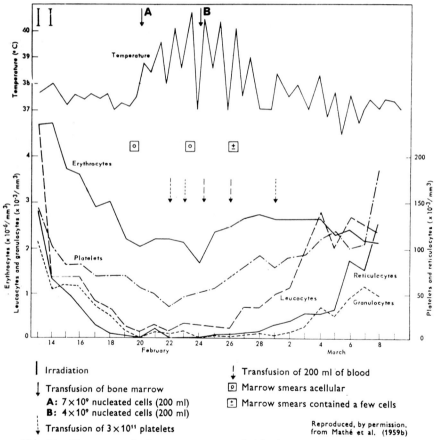

| | Irradiation
| ↓ | Transfusion of bone marrow
| | A: 7×10⁹ nucleated cells (200 ml)
| | B: 4×10⁹ nucleated cells (200 ml)
| ↓ | Transfusion of 3 × 10¹¹ platelets

| ↓ | Transfusion of 200 ml of blood
| ⊡ | Marrow smears acellular
| ⊡ | Marrow smears contained a few cells

Reproduced, by permission, from Mathé et al. (1959b)

Fig. 22. Changes in body temperature and blood cell count of patient V.L. during bone marrow aplasia and subsequent recovery (from Mathé *et al.,* 1960).

In three of these patients, the secondary syndrome appeared while the myeloid restoration was in progress and the blood was being repopulated: two of these have died in spite of the correction of neutropenia and of thrombocytopenia (Fig. 23); in the third, on the other hand, although the secondary syndrome was very severe and of long duration (2 months), it could be controlled. (3) In two patients, finally, the secondary syndrome occurred one month after myeloid restoration. This syndrome itself lasted approximately one month and could easily be suppressed (Fig. 24).

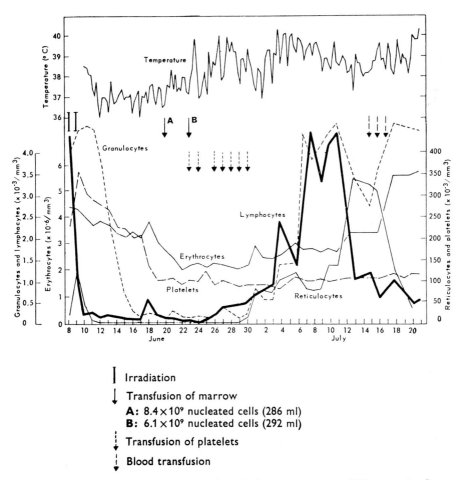

Fig. 23. Clinical events and hematological changes in patient E.D. after irradiation showing development of an acute secondary syndrome (from Mathé *et al.*, 1960).

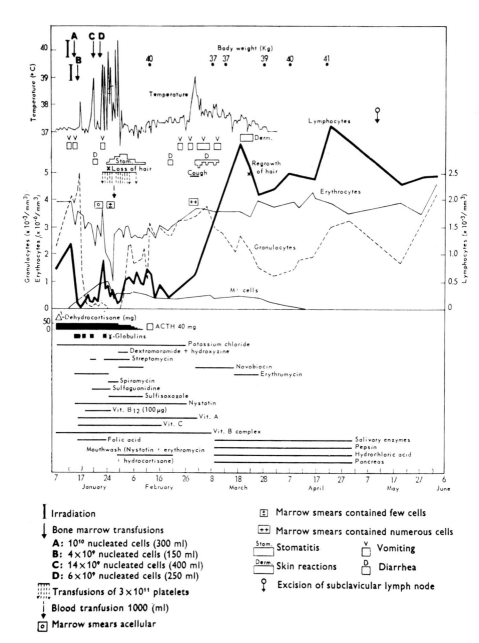

Fig. 24. Clinical events and hematological changes in patient D.V. after irradiation to development of the secondary syndrome (from Mathé *et al.*, 1959a).

In the various subjects whose bone marrow showed restoration, the taking of the graft could be proved in different ways: (*a*) production of erythrocytes which showed the antigenic characteristics of the donors; (*b*) the production by a male receptor, transfused with bone marrow from female donors, of polynuclear cells with drumsticks and with a female-type percentage of mononuclear cells with heterochromatic lobules, (*c*) the production by a receptor of a given sex of cells with chromosomes of the other sex; (*d*) the production of γ-globulin of the type of the donor; (*e*) specific tolerance due to chimerism (Fig. 25).

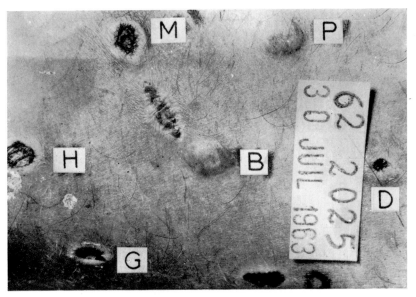

Fig. 25. Specific tolerance due to chimerism. Aspects of 6 skin grafts in a human chimera: tolerance of the autologous (B) graft and of the graft of the donor (P) whose bone marrow has repopulated the recipient's bone marrow (from Mathé *et al.*, 1963b).

In the case of patients who have survived the secondary syndrome, taking has been of variable duration: this duration was 3 months in the two patients whose secondary syndrome occurred at a late stage and was of less intensity; it was 7 months at the time of writing in the patient whose secondary syndrome, severe and of early appearance, could be controlled.

The symptomatology of the secondary syndrome in man is very similar to that observed in other species, particularly in the monkey. It consists of clinical signs [anorrhexia, nausea, vomiting, diarrhea, loss of weight, hepatomegaly, erythrodermia (Fig. 26), desquamation, various infections]; hematological signs (lymphopenia, eosinophilia); histological signs [lymphoid aplasia (Fig. 27), necrosis, aplasia of the intestinal crypts (Fig. 28), particular skin lesions consisting of hyperkeratosis, dyskeratosis, acanthosis, and dermal infiltrates (Fig. 29)]; and biochemical abnormalities (disorders of the serum levels of the γ-globulins and of various enzymes, in particular of hepatic enzymes).

This syndrome is particularly severe in man and it therefore constitutes the principal obstacle to large-scale therapeutic use of transplantations of allogenic hematopoietic cells.

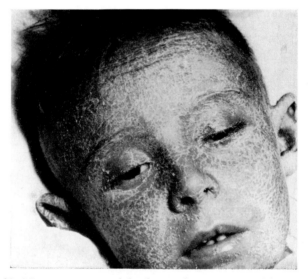

Fig. 26. Macroscopic view of skin lesions due to the secondary syndrome.

The efficacy of bone-marrow grafting in the treatment of irradiation effects is clearly demonstrated in the cases of the 5 subjects accidentally exposed in Vinca (Yugoslavia), if we compare (Table XIII) the mortality that might be expected after the doses received, which we estimated at LD_{75} for 4 of these patients and at LD_{30} for the last one, with the actual mortality, which was only one in five; moreover the deceased patient had already shown excellent myeloid restoration and died from an intestinal radiolesion (Jammet *et al.*, 1959; Mathé *et al.*, 1959b, 1964).

The indications for transfusion of allogenic bone marrow in subjects accidentally exposed to radiation have been the object of a great deal of discussion. The relevant data and our personal conclusions are laid down in Tables XIV and XV.

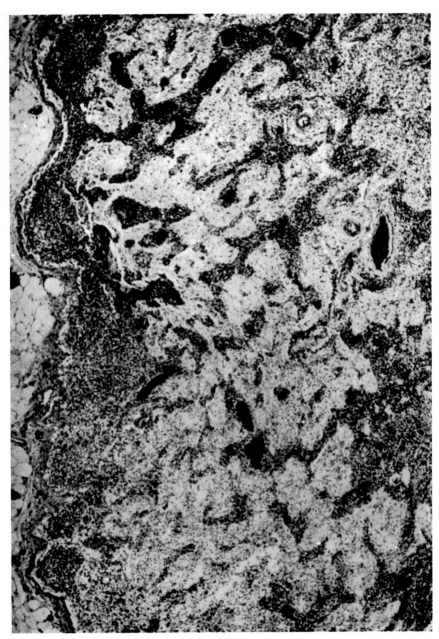

Fig. 27. Microscopic view of lymphoid aplasia due to the secondary syndrome.

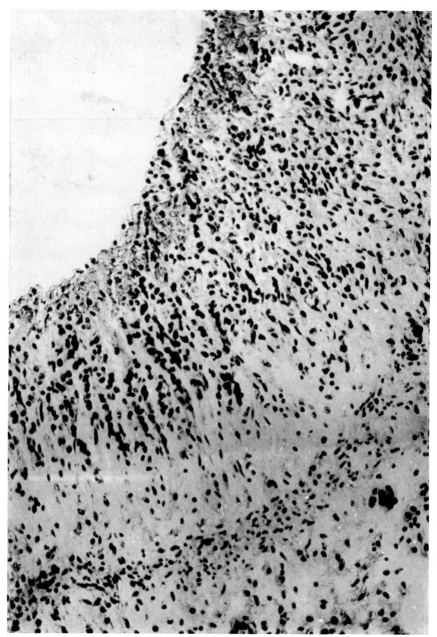

Fig. 28. Microscopic view of aplasia of intestinal crypts due to the secondary syndrome.

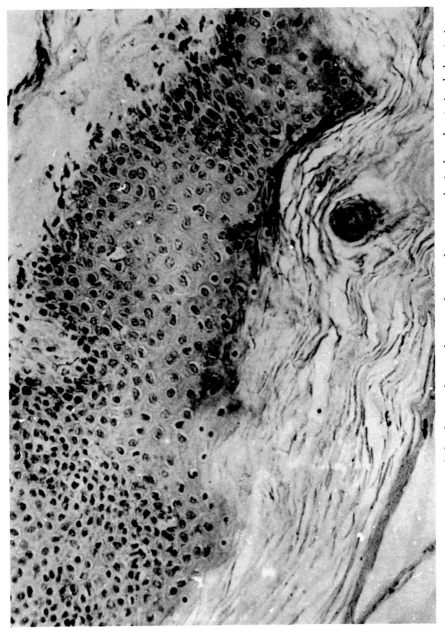

Fig. 29. Microscopic view of skin lesions due to the secondary syndrome: acanthosis, hyperkeratosis, dyskeratosis.

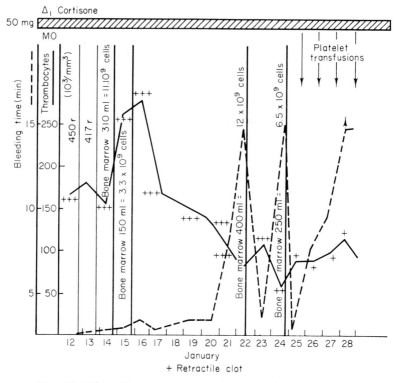

Fig. 30. Effect of bone-marrow transfusions on the bleeding time.

TABLE XIII

HAS BONE-MARROW TRANSFUSION BEEN VALUABLE IN THE VINCA CASUALTIES?

(1) *Physical dosimetry*		*Mortality rate with these doses (with aplasia)*
Various estimates:		
Jammet *et al.* (1959) (rem)	: 600–1000	90%
Savic (1959) (rem)	: 683 ± 15%	90%
Hurst *et al.* (1961) (rad)	: 436, 414, 426	
	419	75%
	323	30%

(2) *Biological dosimetry and the neutron problem*	
Hematological disorders	$\leq$ 400 rad in gamma rays (non-homogeneity)
Histological lesions	$>$ 850–900 rad in gamma rays (digestive tract)
General condition and failure of the symptomatic treatment	$\approx$ 600 rad and 850–900 rad

TABLE XIV

INDICATIONS FOR ALLOGENIC BONE MARROW TRANS-
PLANTATION AFTER LETHAL IRRADIATION (100%)

(a) *Unfavorable factors:*
    Immediate risk—pulmonary embolism
    Secondary syndrome

(b) *Favorable factors:*
    Absence of any other treatment
    The secondary syndrome is not always fatal—
       there is hope of controlling it
    Symptomatic effect

(c) *Conclusion:*
    Bone marrow transplantations as soon as it is
    known that the dose is lethal

TABLE XV

INDICATIONS FOR ALLOGENIC BONE MARROW TRANSPLANTATION AFTER
SUBLETHAL DOSE OF RADIATION
($< 100\%$)

(a) *Reasons against bone marrow transplantation*
    Small chance of it taking
    Allogenic bone marrow transplants in sublethally irradiated mice can increase
       their mortality rate (Trentin, 1956)
    Immediate risk: pulmonary embolism
    Risk of secondary syndrome
    Symptomatic therapy can diminish the mortality

(b) *Reasons in favor of bone-marrow transplantation*
    Symptomatic effect
    Allogenic marrow transplants in sublethally irradiated mice has diminished the
       mortality rate in the majority of genetic combinations (Uphoff, 1963)
    Possibility of taking in:
        Mice (Uphoff, 1963)
        Man (Mathé *et al.*, 1959b)
    Absence of secondary syndrome
    A sublethal dose is not a "dose inferior to a dose 100% fatal" but merely one
       which kills less than 100% of subjects

(c) *Conclusion*
    Bone-marrow transplantation as soon as there is failure of symptomatic therapy

All authors agree that this treatment is indicated in case of a 100% lethal dose. In case of irradiation with a smaller dose, a so-called sublethal dose, it was believed for a time on the basis of experimental findings that transfusion of bone marrow was useless on the one hand, because it is not followed by taking, and dangerous on the other, because it increases mortality (Trentin, 1956). Recent studies have shown, however, that even in the mouse, the transfusion of bone marrow increases mortality only under exceptional conditions of histoincompatibility, and that it decreases mortality in most cases and may very well be followed by taking (Uphoff, 1963). This applies definitely to man as well, as has been proved by the cases from Vinca, and furthermore we have shown that not only is the transfusion of bone marrow not dangerous, but it may even be of benefit when taking does not occur, because of the symptomatic effects, especially on hemostasis (Fig. 21).

From the practical point of view we may conclude that a transfusion of allogenic bone marrow may reasonably be regarded as indicated whether the irradiation has been 100% lethal or sublethal; as our experience has shown that this treatment is not an urgent matter, symptomatic treatment may be administered during the early period, and the decision as to administration of bone marrow should be taken when it is felt that the symptomatic treatment has not been successful (Mathé, 1960; Mathé et al., 1959b, 1964).

III. Chronic External Irradiation

There have been numerous investigations on the effects of chronic irradiation in animals of various species, such as the mouse, the rat, the guinea pig, and the rabbit (Lorenz et al., 1947; Langendorff and Sauerborn, 1943; Spargo et al., 1951), and the dog and the monkey (Ingram and Masan, 1950). From the results of these studies it may be concluded that a sufficient dose is required to produce a leukopenic effect: a dose of 8.8 r per day, provided it is repeated often enough, may induce leukopenia in a late stage; with doses of 2.5 r per day in the rat, on the other hand, even a full year of treatment caused no demonstrable hematological disorders, although there was a subsequent increase in the frequency of leukemia.

A dose of 7.7 r per day during 8 months in the rat decreases lymphocytosis after the first month; the granulocytes are apparently not affected (Stearner et al., 1947).

A dose of 33.5 r per day for 3 months in the rat causes a decrease in lymphocytes after the first week, and thereafter, the granulocytes decrease; anemia appears only after the 50th day (Stearner et al., 1947).

A chronic irradiation of 1.1 r per day during 3 years in the guinea pig causes a decrease in lymphocytes after the first year. A similar effect could not be observed in the mouse and the rabbit. Beginning with a dose of 2.2 r per day, all three species are affected (Jacobson *et al.*, 1949).

When mice are irradiated with a dose of 4.4 r per day, only the lymphocytes are affected but not very significantly; from a dose of 8.8 r per day, the granulocytes are affected.

Severe aplastic anemia has been observed in animals exposed to chronic irradiation with small doses (Aubertin and Beaujard, 1905; Jacobson *et al.*, 1949). When rats are exposed for 3 months to a daily dose of 33.5 r anemia appears only after 50 days (Stearner *et al.*, 1947). When mice are exposed to a daily dose of 8.8 r, anemia appears only after one year.

When a fractionated irradiation is administered to a large total dose, the animals may ultimately develop severe thrombocytopenia (Jacobson *et al.*, 1949).

Chronic exposure of the whole body to small doses causes a depletion of the thymus; the effect depends on the dose. Modifications are distinctly visible after 6 months of treatment with 8.8 r per day and after 8 months of treatment with 4.4 r per day (Spargo *et al.*, 1951). A dose of 1.1 r per day had an effect after 10 months; the thymus showed a pronounced increase of mast cells.

A dose of 0.25 r per day administered for a year to the rat, on the other hand, causes a slight increase in the number of lymphocytes and some increase in the weight of the thymus (Pape and Kollert, 1952).

The consequences of subacute and chronic irradiation in man may be quite as dramatic as those of acute irradiation. Let us consider for example the case of five Mexicans who in 1962 were accidentally exposed to the radiation of a capsule of 5 curies (Gonzalez *et al.*, 1962, 1963), which a child had got hold of and which it had left in the kitchen of an apartment. For 3 months and 22 days, a family was exposed to subacute irradiation in this way. The doses received were 4700, 3500, 2870, and 1200 r. All the subjects developed progressive aplasia (the larger the exposure dose, the more rapidly it developed), and the 4 subjects who had received the largest doses died within 2 to 3 months.

The problems created by chronic exposure to very small doses are of even greater importance in industrial medicine. Hematologists are frequently consulted by persons who work in places that are more or less exposed to ionizing radiations—radiologists, X-ray assistants, and physicians and chemists who handle radioisotopes—in whom a mild cytopenia, usually a leukopenia, has been discovered. It is only in exceptional cases

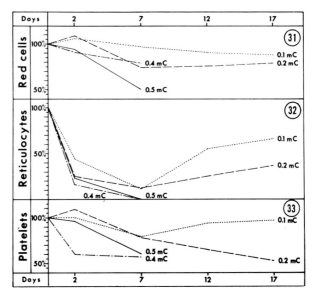

Figs. 31–33. Effect of different doses of Au[198] on the counts of various blood cells in the mouse.

that the doses to which these persons have been exposed are actually responsible for the cytopenia, and as we know that idiopathic minor leukopenia is not infrequent (Bousser and Mathé, 1953), it is clear that most of these cases are merely coincidental.

Cases of thrombocytopenia without leukopenia have been reported in persons whose work was connected with radiological diagnostic examinations (Mossberg, 1958).

IV. Internal Irradiation by the Principal Isotopes

Aplasia of the bone marrow brought about by internal irradiation as a rule occurs more gradually than in cases of external exposure; less cellular debris is observed because there is time for it to be removed by phagocytosis (Bloom, 1948). The effect of internal irradiation on the thymus is also generally more protracted and gradual than that of external irradiation (Bloom and Bloom, 1954).

Phosphorus-32: An administration of 20 μc per gram in the mouse brings about aplasia of the bone marrow in which proliferation of the reticular cells can be seen (Burstone, 1952; Hankins et al., 1953). A dose of 2.5 μc per gram has only a very slight effect on the spleen and on the thymus (Murray, 1948).

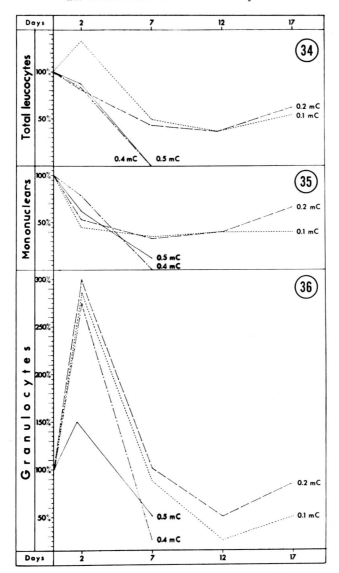

Figs. 34–36. Effect of different does of Au[198] on the counts of various blood cells cells in the mouse.

In man, P[32] is used in the treatment of the various forms of chronic leukemia and of Vaquez's polyglobulia (Friedel and Storaasli, 1949); the danger of myeloid aplasia is well known.

It may be mentioned that Osgood *et al.* (1942), who examined the effect of irradiation on bone marrow, cultured *in vitro*, found that 1 mc of P^{32} had the same effect in 24 hours as a 35-r X-ray dose.

Strontium-89: 0.015 μc per gram has no effect at all in the mouse, the rat, and the rabbit; 0.068 μc per gram causes a moderate decrease of the granulocytes; 2 μc per gram brings about a mild anemia (Jacobson *et al.*, 1949). In the dog, 0.10 μc per gram causes a 60% decrease in leukocytes (Jacobson *et al.*, 1949). In the rat 4.5 μc per gram provokes cytopenia in 15 days (Latta and Waggener, 1954). Administration of Sr^{89} in a dose of 3.6 μc per gram had only a very slight effect on the spleen (Murray, 1948). Occasionally, it enhances myeloid metoplasia of this organ.

Strontium-90: 0.5 μc per gram in the rabbit brings about leukopenia, anemia, and thrombocytopenia after 6 to 8 weeks. After one year, certain sectors of the bone marrow are aplastic, while other sectors show hyperplasia (Owen *et al.*, 1957). Doses of 0.1 to 0.5 μc per gram in the rat brought about similar disorders of the bone marrow (Anderson *et al.*, 1956). Doses larger than 2.5 μc per gram caused more pronounced aplastic lesions of the bone marrow.

Gold-198: 4 μc in the rat brings about bone-marrow aplasia (Fliedner and Stodtmeister, 1956). In the mouse (Figs. 31–36), doses of 0.1 and 0.2 μc lead to reversible cytopenia, and doses of 0.4 and 0.5 μc to fatal cytopenia (Mathé *et al.*, 1959); intravenous injection of 0.4 μc causes marked aplasia of the lymphoid tissue and a considerable decrease of the level of the serum γ-globulins (Mathé and Bernard, 1960).

Barium-140 and Lanthanum-140: 0.2 μc per gram injected intraperitoneally causes leukopenia due to lymphopenia and neutropenia in the mouse, which lasts approximately 100 days. After a dose of 17 μc per gram, the animals die in a state of cytopenia within 15 days (Jacobson *et al.*, 1949). The administration of Ba^{140}–La^{140} (5.6 μc per gram) causes a rapid, moderate depletion of the white pulp of the spleen with hyperplasia of myelopoiesis of the red pulp; it also brings about atrophy of the thymus.

Yttrium-91: An oral dose of less than 10 μc per gram causes no hematological disorders. A dose of 10 μc per gram causes a transient lymphopenia, a dose of 20 μc per gram brings about a fairly intensive lymphopenia which begins on the 3rd day, with maximal anemia on the 20th day (Jacobson *et al.*, 1949). Internal administration of Y^{91} (2 μc per gram) causes a very pronounced depletion of the spleen.

Iodine-131: 10 to 90 μc per gram causes atrophy of lymphoid tissue in the rat (Clemedson and Nelson, 1960).

Plutonium-239: A dose of less than 0.006 μc per gram causes no hematological lesions. A dose of 0.0025 μc per gram (Jacobson *et al.*,

1949) causes a significant decrease of the lymphocytes in the dog (Dougherty *et al.*, 1955). A dose of 0.003 to 0.006 μc per gram brings about leukopenia in all species, with anemia and thrombocytopenia in the rat and the mouse (Jacobson *et al.*, 1949; Burstone, 1952). The administration of small doses of Pu^{239} (0.08 μc per gram) has a moderate effect on the spleen of the mouse, but a more marked effect on the spleen of the rat.

Polonium-210: The biological effects of this alpha particle emitter are extensively described in a recent supplement (No. 5) of Radiation Research. The hematological aspects are discussed by Casarett (1964).

Radium: A dose of 0.01 μc per gram causes no hematological disorders. A dose of 0.03 μc per gram causes anemia with leukopenia in the rat and the mouse, whereas 0.1 μc per gram causes only leukopenia without anemia in the rabbit (Jacobson *et al.*, 1949). A dose of 1.1 μc per gram bodyweight in the mouse brings about atrophy of the thymus (Murray, 1948).

Sodium-24: A dose of 12 μc per gram administered to the mouse remains without effect; 23 μc per gram causes a marked leukopenia; and a dose of 48 μc per gram is followed by death in 8 days (Jacobson *et al.*, 1949).

References

Allen, R. G., Brown, F. A., Logie, L. C., Rovner, D. R., Wilson, S. G., Jr., and Zellmer, R. W. (1960). *Radiation Res.* **12**, 532.

Allen, R. M., Sanderson, M. D., Milham, M. D., Kirschon, A., and Jacobson, L. O. (1948). *J. Exptl. Med.* **87**, 71.

Altman, K. J., Richmond, J. E., and Salomon, K. (1951). *Biochim. Biophys. Acta* **7**, 460.

Anderson, W. A. D., Zander, F. E., and Kuzma, J. F. (1956). *A. M. A. Arch. Pathol.* **62**, 433.

Atkinson, J. B., Mahoney, J. F., Schwartz, I. R., and Hesch, J. A. (1959). *Blood* **14**, 228.

Aubertin, C., and Beaujard, E. (1905). *Compt. Rend. Soc. Biol.* **58**, 217.

Aubertin, C., and Beaujard, E. (1908). *Arch. Med. Anat. Pathol.* **20**, 273.

Barnes, W. A. (1941). *Am. J. Roentgenol.* **46**, 356.

Barrow, J., and Tullis, J. L. (1952). *A. M. A. Arch. Pathol.* **53**, 391.

Barrow, J., Tullis, J. L., and Chambers, F. W. (1951). *Am. J. Physiol.* **64**, 822.

Bauer, R. (1940). *Strahlentherapie* **67**, 424.

Baum, S. J., and Alpen, E. L. (1958). *Federation Proc.* **17**, 12.

Baum, S. J., and Kimeldorf, D. J. (1957). *Am. J. Physiol.* **190**, 13.

Baxter, C. F., Belcher, E. H., Harris, E. B., and Lamerton, L. F. (1955). *Brit. J. Haematol.* **1**, 58.

Belcher, E. H., Gilbert, J. G. F., and Lamerton, L. F. (1954). *Brit. J. Radiol.* **27**, 387.

Betz, H. (1951). *Compt. Rend. Soc. Biol.* **145**, 465.

Betz, H. (1952). *Acta Unio Intern. Contra Cancrum* **7**, 814.

Betz, H. (1953). *Compt Rend. Soc. Biol.* **147**, 168.

Bloom, M. A. (1948). *In* "Histopathology of Irradiation from External and Internal Sources" (W. Bloom, ed.), Chapter VI. McGraw-Hill, New York.

Bloom, M. A., and Bloom, W. (1947). *J. Lab. Clin. Med.* **32**, 654.

Bloom, W., and Bloom, M. A. (1954). *In* "Radiation Biology" (A. Hollaender, ed.), Vol. I, Chapter 17. McGraw-Hill, New York.

Bond, V. P. and Cronkite, E. P. (1957). *Ann. Rev. Physiol.* **19**, 299.

Bousser, J., and Mathé, G. (1953). "L'interprétation des leucopénies mineures isolées durables." Entr. Bichat.

Brecher, G., Endicott, K. M., Gump, H., and Brawner, H. P. (1948). *Blood* **3**, 1259.

Brues, A. M., and Rietz, L. (1948). Argonne Natl. Lab. Rept. 4227, p. 183.

Brues, A. M., and Rietz, L. (1951). *Ann. N. Y. Acad. Sci.* **51**, 1497.

Burnet, F. M. (1959). "The Clonal Selection Theory of Acquired Immunity." Cambridge Univ. Press, London and New York.

Burstone, M. S. (1952). *Am. J. Pathol.* **28**, 1183.

Carter, R. E. (1950). U. S. At. Energy Comm. Doc. AECU, 709.

Casarett, G. W. (1964). *Radiation Res. Suppl.* No. 5., pp. 246; 322; 347; 361.

Casati, A. (1929). *Strahlentherapie,* **32**, 721.

Cattan, A., Schwarzenberg, L., Schneider, M., Amiel, J. L., and Mathé, G. (1963). In press.

Chèvremont, M. (1935). *Arch. Biol.* (*Paris*) **46**, 507.

Chrom, S. A. (1935). *Acta Radiol.* **16**, 641.

Clemedson, C. J., and Nelson, A. (1960). *In* "Mechanisms in Radiobiology" (M. Errera and A. Forssberg, eds.), Vol. 2. Academic Press, New York.

Cole, L. J., and Ellis, M. E. (1954a). *Cancer Res.* **14**, 738.

Cole, L. J., and Ellis, M. E. (1954b). *Radiation Res.* **1**, 347.

Cole, L. J., and Ellis, M. E. (1955). *In* "Symposium de radiobiologie." Butterworth, London and Washington.

Cole, L. J., and Ellis, M. E. (1956). *Federation Proc.* **15**, 411.

Cronkite, E. P. (1949). *J. Am. Med. Assoc.* **139**, 366.

Cronkite, E. P., and Bond, V. P. (1960). "Radiation Injury in Man." Thomas, Springfield, Illinois.

Cronkite, E. P., and Brecher, G. (1952a). *Ann. Rev. Med.* **3**, 193.

Cronkite, E. P., and Brecher, G. (1952b). *In* "Transaction of the 5th Conference on Blood Coagulation." Josiah Macy, Jr. Foundation, New York.

Cudkowicz, G., Upton, A. C., Smith, L. H., Gosslee, D. G., and Hughes, W. L. (1964). *Ann. N. Y. Acad. Sci.* **114**, 571.

Davis, R. W., Dole, N., Izzo, M. J., and Young, L. E. (1950). *J. Lab. Clin. Med.* **35**, 528.

DeBruyn, P. P. H. (1948a). *Anat. Record* **101**, 373.

DeBruyn, P. P. H. (1948b). *In* "Histopathology of Irradiation from External and Internal Sources" (W. Bloom, ed.) McGraw-Hill, New York.

Denstad, T. (1943). *Acta Radiol. Suppl.* **52**.

DiLuzio, N. R. (1955). *Am. J. Physiol.* **181**, 595.

Dobson, B. I., and Chupp, M. M. (1957). *Proc. Soc. Exptl. Biol. Med.* **95**, 360.

Dougherty, T. F., and White, A. (1946). *Endocrinology* **39**, 370.

Dougherty, T. F., Bowers, J. Z., Bay, R. C., and Keyanonaa, P. (1955). *Radiology* **65**, 253.

Draeger, R. H., and Warren, S. (1947). *U. S. Naval Med. Bull.* 47.
Dubois, K. P., and Petersen, D. F. (1954). *Am. J. Physiol.* 176, 282.
Dunlap, C. E. (1942). *A. M. A. Arch. Pathol.* 34, 562.
Dustin, A. P., and Grégoire, C. (1931). *Compt. Rend. Soc. Biol.* 107, 1565.
Eichel, H. J. (1955). *Proc. Soc. Exptl. Biol. Med.* 88, 155.
Ellinger, F. (1945). *Radiology* 44, 125.
Ellinger, F. (1948). *Radiology* 51, 394.
Ellinger, F. (1957). "Medical Radiation Biology." Thomas, Springfield, Illinois.
Feinstein, R. N. (1956). *Radiation Res.* 4, 217.
Feissley, R. (1921). *Muench. Med. Wochschr.* 68, 1418.
Fellas, V. M., Meschan, I., Day, P. L., and Douglass, C. D. (1954). *Proc. Soc. Exptl. Biol. Med.* 87, 231.
Finardzhyan, V. A., Papoyan, S. A., Kyandaryan, C. A., Demirchoglyan, I. G., and Sherkuryan, S. G. (1956). *Tr. Perovi Zatravk. Konf. Med. Radiol.* p. 151.
Fliedner, T. M., and Stodtmeister, R. (1956). *Strahlentherapie* 101, 289.
Fliedner, T. M., Sorensen, D. K., Bond, V. P., Cronkite, E. P., Jakson, D. M., and Adamik, E. (1958). *Proc. Soc. Exptl. Biol. Med.* 99, 731.
Fliedner, T. M., Cronkite, E. P., Bond, V. P., Rubini, J. R., and Andrews, G. (1959). Cited in Cronkite and Bond, 1960.
Freidell, H. L., and Storaasli, J. P. (1949). *J. Lab. Clin. Invest.* 28, 1308.
Furth, J., and Upton, A. C. (1953). *Ann. Rev. Nucl. Sci.* 3, 303.
Gabrieli, E. R., and Auskaps, A. A. (1953). *Yale J. Biol. Med.* 26, 159.
George, L. A., Kackett, P. L., and Bustad, L. K. (1957). *Am. J. Vet. Res.* 18, 631.
Gerber, G. (1957). "Wissenschaftliche Grundlagen des Strahlenschutzes." Braun, Karlsruhe, Germany.
Goldschmidt, L., Rosenthal, R. L., Bond, V. P., and Fishler, M. C. (1950). *Am. J. Physiol.* 154, 202.
Gonzalez-Constandse, R., Halvas-Guerrers, J., Telich, J., and Berumen, L. (1962). "Primer reports on accidente por irradiacion." Com. Nacional de Energia Nuclear, Mexico City.
Gonzalez, R., and Berumen, L. (1963). *Rev. Franc. Etudes Clin. Biol.* in press.
Gowans, J. L. (1962). *Ann. N. Y. Acad. Sci.* 99, 432.
Gowans, J. L., and McGregor, D. D. (1963). *In* "Cell Proliferation" (L. F. Lamerton and R. J. M. Fry, eds.). Blackwell, Oxford.
Grégoire, C. (1943). *J. Morphol.* 72, 239.
Hagen, C. W., and Sacher, R. G. (1946). *Chem. & Ind. (London)* p. 3754.
Hagen, C. W., and Simmons, E. L. (1947). *Chem. & Ind. (London)* p. 3815.
Halberstaedter, L., and Ickowicz, M. (1947). *Radiol. Clin.* 16, 340.
Hamilton, L. D. (1959). *In* "Kinetics of Cellular Proliferation" (F. Stohlman, ed.), p. 151. Grune & Stratton, New York.
Hankins, R. M., Leonard, A. B., and Leone, C. A. (1953). *U. S. Atomic Energy Comm. Rept.* 2642.
Hartweg, H. (1956). *Strahlentherapie* 100, 121.
Heineke, H. (1903). *Muench. Med. Wochschr.* 50, 2090.
Heineke, H. (1904a). *Mitt. Grenzgeb. Med. Chir.* 14, 21.
Heineke, H. (1904b). *Muench. Med. Wochschr.* 51, 1382.
Heineke, H. (1914). *Muench. Med. Wochschr.* 61, 807.
Helber, E., and Linser, P. (1905). *Muench. Med. Wochschr.* 52, 689.
Hempelmann, L. H., Lisco, H., and Hoffman, S. G. (1952). *Ann. Internal Med.* 36, 279.

334   GEORGES MATHÉ

Henshaw, F. S. (1944a). *J. Natl. Cancer Inst.* 4, 474.
Henshaw, F. S. (1944b). *J. Natl. Cancer Inst.* 4, 485.
Herzfeld, E., and Skinz, H. R. (1923). *Strahlentherapie* 62, 301.
Holden, W. D., Cole, J. W., Portmann, A. F., and Storaasli, J. P. (1949). *Proc. Soc. Exptl. Biol. Med.* 70, 553.
Hughes, C. W., and Job, T. T. (1937). *Radiology* 29, 194.
Hurst, G. S., Ritchie, R. H., Sanders, S. W., Reinhardt, T. W., Auxier, J. A., Wagner, E. B., Callihan, A., Morgan, K. Z., and Smith, J. W. (1961). *Health Phys.* 1, 179.
Ingram, M., and Masan, W. B. (1950). U.S. Atomic Energy Comm. Doc., U. R. 121.
Jackson, D. P., Cronkite, E. P., Jacobs, G. J., and Behrens, C. F. (1952a). *Am. J. Physiol.* 169, 208.
Jackson, D. P., Cronkite, E. P., LeRoy, G. V., and Halpern, B. (1952b). *J. Lab. Clin. Med.* 39, 449.
Jacobson, L. O. (1954). *In* "Radiation Biology" Vol. I, Part II, Chapter XVI. McGraw-Hill, New York.
Jacobson, L. O., Marks, E. K., Gaston, E. O., Simmons, E. L., and Block, M. H. (1948). *Science* 107, 248.
Jacobson, L. O., Marks, E. K., and Lorenz, E. (1949). *Radiology* 52, 371.
Jammet, H., Mathé, H. G., Pendic, B., Schwarzenberg, L., Duplan, J. F., Maupin, B., Latarjet, R., Larrieu, M. J., Kalic, D., and Djukic, Z. (1959). *Rev. Franc. Etudes Clin. Biol.* 4, 226.
Kahn, J. B., and Furth, J. (1952). *Blood* 7, 404.
Kallman, R. F., and Kohn, H. J. (1954). *Federation Proc.* 13, 76.
Kirpichnikova, E., Shapiro, N. I., Belitsina, N. V., and Ol'Shevskaya, L. V. (1956). *Obschsci. Biol.* 17, 340.
Knott, F. A., and Watt, W. L. (1929). *Brit. Med. J.* 542, 1929.
Knowlton, N. P., and Hempelmann, L. H. (1949). *J. Cellular Physiol.* 33, 73.
Krause, P., and Ziegler, K. (1906). *Fortschr. Gebiete Röntgenstrahlen Nuklearmed.* 10, 126.
Krömeke, F. (1926). *Strahlentherapie* 22, 608.
Küss, R., Legrain, M., Mathé, G., Nedey, R., Camey, M., Tubiana, M., Lalanne, C., Schwarzenberg, L., Larrieu, M. J., Maisonnet, M., Basset, F., and Delaveau, P. (1962). *Rev. Franc. Etudes Clin. Biol.* 7, 1028.
Kurnick, N. B., Montano, A., Gerdes, J. C., and Feder, B. H. (1958). *Ann. Internal Med.* 49, 973.
Kurnick, N. B., Feder, B. H., Montano, A., Gerdes, J. C., and Nakamura, R. (1959). *Ann. Internal Med.* 51, 1204.
Lacassagne, A., and Grigouroff, G. (1927). *J. Radiol. Electrol. Med. Nucl.* 11, 573.
Lacassagne, A., and Monod, O. (1922). *Arch. Franc. Pathol. Gén. Exptl.* 1.
Lamson, B. G., and Tullis, J. L. (1951). *Military Surg.* 109, 281.
Langendorff, H. (1936). *Strahlentherapie* 55, 308.
Langendorff, H. (1937). *Strahlentherapie* 59, 652.
Langendorff, H. (1938). *Strahlentherapie* 62, 304.
Langendorff, H., and Sauerborn, G. (1943). *Strahlentherapie* 73, 91.
Latta, J. S., and Waggener, R. E. (1954). *Anat. Record* 119, 357.
Lawrence, J. S., Dowdy, A. H., and Valentine, W. N. (1948). *Radiology* 51, 400.
Le Roy, G. V. (1950). *Arch. Internal Med.* 86, 691.

Levy-Dorn, M., and Schulhof, E. (1923). *Fortschr. Gebiete Röntgenstrahlen Nuklearmed* **30**, 152.

Lindell, B., and Zajicek, J. (1957). *Experientia* **13**, 27.

Lindemann, R. (1951). *Fortschr. Gebiete Röntgenstrahlen Nuklearmed.* **75**, 523.

London, E. S. (1903). *Berliner Klin. Wochschr.* **40**, 523.

Lorenz, E., Heston, W. E., Eschenbrenner, A., and Deringer, M. K. (1947). *Radiology* **49**, 274.

Lundin, J., Clemedson, C. J., and Nelson, A. (1957). *Acta Radiol.* **48**, 54.

MacDonald, E. (1947). "Neutron Effects on Animals." Williams & Wilkins, Baltimore, Maryland.

MacGowern. J. J., Russel, P. S., Atkine, L., and Webster, E. W. (1959). *New Engl. J. Med.* **260**, 675.

Mandel, P., Metais, P., Gros, C. M., and Voegelin, R. (1951). *Compt. Rend. Acad. Sci.* **233**, 1685.

Mardersteig, K. (1938). *Strahlentherapie* **61**, 107.

Mathé, G. (1959). *In* "Biological Problems of Grafting," p. 314. Blackwell, Oxford, England.

Mathé, G. (1960). *Rev. Hematol.* **15**, 3.

Mathé, G. (1962). *In* "Cancer, leucémie et radiobiologie," p. 85. Gauthier-Villars, Paris.

Mathé, G., and Amiel, J. L. (1962). "La greffe, aspects biologiques et cliniques." Masson, Paris.

Mathé, G., and Bernard, J. (1957). *Rev. Hematol.* **12**, 507.

Mathé, G., and Bernard, J. (1960). *In* "Lésions provoquées par les radiations ionisantes" (J. Delarue and L. Frühling, éds.), p. 28. Masson, Paris.

Mathé, G., and Forestier, P. (1965). Techniques hospitalières (to be published).

Mathé, G., Hartmann, L., Loverdo, A., Bourdon, R., and Bernard, J. (1958). *Rev. Franc. Etudes Clin. Biol.* **3**, 1088.

Mathé, G., Bernard, J., Schwarzenberg, L., Larrieu, M. J., Lalanne, C., Dutreix, A., Denoix, P., Schwarzmann, V., and Ceoara, B. (1959a). *Rev. Franc. Etudes Clin. Biol.* **4**, 679.

Mathé, G., Jammet, H., Pendic, B., Schwarzenberg, L., Duplan, J. F., Maupin, B., Latarjet, R., Larrieu, M. J., Kalic, D., and Djukic, Z. (1959b). *Rev. Franc. Etudes Clin. Biol.* **4**, 226.

Mathé, G., Pays, P., Bourdon, R., and Maroteaux, P. (1959c). *Rev. Franc. Etudes Clin. Biol.* **4**, 272.

Mathé, G., Bernard, J., de Vries, M. J., Schwarzenberg, L., Larrieu, M. J., Lalanne, C., Dutreix, A., Amiel, J. L., and Surmont, J. (1960). *Rev. Hematol.* **15**, 115.

Mathé, G., Jammet, H., Playfair, J., and Amiel, J. L. (1962). *Compt. Rend. 8° Congr. Soc. Europ. Hematol.* p. 67. Karger, Basel.

Mathé, G., Amiel, J. L., Schwarzenberg, L., Cattan, A., and Schneider, M. (1963a). *Compt. Rend. Acad. Sci.* **257**, 3527.

Mathé, G., Binet, J. L., Seman, G., Amiel, J. L., and Daughet, G. (1963b). *In* "Tolérance," p. 359. C. N. R. S., Paris.

Mathé, G., Amiel, J. L., and Schwarzenberg, L. (1964). *Ann. N. Y. Acad. Sci.* **114**, 368.

Mathé, G., Amiel, J. L., Schwarzenberg, L., Cattan, A., Schneider, M., de Vries, M. J., Tubiana, M., Lalanne, C., Binet, J. L., Papiernik, M., Seman, G., Matsukura, M., Mery, A. M., Schwarzmann, V., and Flaiser, A. (1965a). *Blood* **25**, 179.

Mathé, G., de Vries, M. J., Schwarzenberg, L., Amiel, J. L., Cattan, A., and Schneider, M. (1965b). *Rev. Europ. Cancer* (in press).

Melville, G. S., Jr., Conte, E. P., and Upton, A. C. (1957). *Am. J. Physiol.* **190**, 17.

Milchner, E., and Mosse, W. (1904). *Berliner Klin. Wochschr.* **41**, 1267.

Minot, G. R., and Spurling, R. (1924). *Am. J. Med. Sci.* **168**, 215.

Monkhouse, F. C., Fidler, E., and Barlon, J. C. D. (1952). *Am. J. Physiol.* **169**, 712.

Mossberg, H. (1958). *Acta Radiol.* **24**, 419.

Murray, R. G. (1948). In "Histopathology of Irradiation from External and Internal Sources" Vol. I., Chapter 7, Nat. Nuclear Energy Ser. McGraw-Hill, New York.

Nettelship, A. (1944). *Radiology* **42**, 64.

Neumann, A. (1924). *Strahlentherapie* **18**, 74.

Newton, W. T., and Ter-Pogossian, M. (1960). *Radiation Res.* **13**, 298.

Osgood, E., Aebersold, P. C., Erf, L. A., and Packham, E. A. (1942). *Am. J. Med. Sci.* **204**, 372.

Ottesen, J. (1954). *Acta Physiol. Scand.* **32**, 75.

Owen, M., Sissons, H. A., and Vaughan, J. (1957). *J. Brit. Cancer* **11**, 229.

Pape, R., and Jellinek, N. (1948). *Radiol. Austriaca* **1**, 59.

Pape, R., and Jellinek, N. (1950). *Radiol. Austriaca* **3**, 44.

Pape, R., and Kollert, G. (1952). *Strahlentherapie* **87**, 382.

Papiernik, M., Amiel, J. L., and Mathé, G. (1963). *Compt. Rend. Acad. Sci.* **256**, 5232.

Pappenheim, A., and Plesch, J. (1912). *Folia Haematol.* **14**, 1.

Paterson, E., Gilbert, C. Q., and Haigh, M. V. (1956). *Brit. J. Radiol.* **29**, 218.

Pelegrino, C., and Villani, G. (1956). *Biochem. J.* **65**, 509.

Petersen, D. F., Fitch, F. W., and Dubois, K. P. (1955). *Proc. Soc. Exptl. Biol. Med.* **88**, 399.

Pihl, A., and Eldjarn, L. (1958). *Pharmacol. Rev.* **10**, 437.

Pohle, E. A., and Bunting, C. H. (1936). *Strahlentherapie* **57**, 121.

Porter, K. A., and Cooper, E. H. (1962). *J. Exptl. Med.* **115**, 997.

Quastler, H. (1956). *Radiation Res.* **4**, 303.

Rachmilewitz, M., Rosin, A., Goldhaber, G., and Doljanski, L. (1945). *Proc. Soc. Exptl. Biol. Med.* **59**, 129.

Rahman, Y. E. (1962). *Proc. Soc. Exptl. Biol. Med.* **109**, 378.

Report of the United Nations (1958). Scientific Committee on the Effects of Atomic Radiation, U. N., New York.

Richmond, J. E., Altmann, K. J., and Salomon, K. (1951). *Science* **113**, 404.

Riopelle, A. J., Ades, H. W., and Morgan, F. E., Jr. (1957). *Radiation* **7**, 581.

Rodesch, J., Javdel, L., Chirpaz, B., and Mandel, P. (1955). *Experientia* **11**, 437.

Rosahn, P. D., Tobias, L. A., and Lawrence, J. H. (1952). *Am. J. Pathol.* **28**, 37.

Rosenthal, R. L., and Benedek, A. L. (1950). *Am. J. Physiol.* **161**, 505.

Rudberg, H. (1907). *Arch. Anat. Entwickl. Suppl.* **23**(1), 1.

Sabine, J. C. (1956). *Am. J. Physiol.* **187**, 275.

Savic, P. P. (1959). *Bull. Inst. Nucl. Sci. "Boris Kidrich"* (*Belgrade*) **9**, 1.

Schack, J. A., and MacDuffee, R. C. (1949). *Science* **110**, 259.

Scherer, E. (1956). *Strahlentherapie* **100**, 211.

Scherer, E., and Gebhardt, W. (1954). *Klin. Wochschr.* **32**, 601.

Scherer, E., and Stolle, F. (1954). *Strahlentherapie* **93**, 317.

Schrek, R. (1945). *Proc. Soc. Exptl. Biol. Med.* **58**, 285.

Schrek, R., and Ott, J. N. (1952). *Arch. Pathol.* **53**, 363.

Segal, G., and Leblond, C. P. (1938). *Compt. Rend. Soc. Biol.* **129**, 279.

Seibert, R. A., and Collins, V. P. (1956). *Federation Proc.* **15**, 471.

Selling, L., and Osgood, E. E. (1938). *In* "Handbook of Hematology" Vol. IV, p. 2716. Harper (Hoeber), New York.

Shively, J. M., Michaelson, S. M., and Howland, J. W. (1958). *Radiation Res.* **9**, 445.

Shouse, S. S., Warren, S. L., and Whipple, G. H. (1931). *J. Exptl. Med.* **53**, 421.

Smith, F., and Grenman, M. M. (1951). *Federation Proc.* **10**, 128.

Spargo, B., Bloomfield, J. R., Glotzer, D., Gordon, E., and Nichols, O. (1951). *J. Natl. Cancer Inst.* **12**, 615.

Spurling, R. G., and Lawrence, J. S. (1925). *Am. J. Med. Sci.* **169**, 157.

Stearner, S. P. (1951). *Am. J. Roentgenol.* **65**, 265.

Stearner, S. P., Simmons, E. L., and Jacobson, L. O. (1947). *U. S. At. Energy Comm. Rept.* 4001.

Stender, H. S., and Elbert, O. (1953). *Strahlentherapie* **89**, 568.

Stiffel, C., Halpern, B., Mouton, B., Biozzi, G., and Mathé, G. (1959). *Rev. Franc. Etudes Clin. Biol.* **4**, 164.

Stodtmeister, R., and Fliedner, M. T. (1954). *Schweiz. Med. Wochschr.* **84**, 1113.

Taplin, G. J., Finnegan, C., Noyes, P., and Sprague, G. (1954). *Am. J. Roentgenol.* **71**, 294.

Taussig, F. J. (1940). *Am. J. Roentgenol.* **43**, 539.

Ten Doornkaat Koolman, M. (1926). *Strahlentherapie* **1**, 668.

Thomas, E. D., Lochte, H. L., Jr., Cannon, J. M., Sahler, O. D., and Ferrebee, J. W. (1959). *J. Clin. Invest.* **38**, 1709.

Thomas, H. E., and Bruner, F. H. (1933). *Am. J. Roentgenol.* **29**, 641.

Tichy, H. (1920). *Zentr. Chir.* **47**, 1389.

Töppner, R. (1941). *J. Exptl. Med.* **109**, 369.

Trentin, J. J. (1956). *Proc. Soc. Exptl. Biol. Med.* **92**, 688.

Trowell, O. A. (1952). *J. Pathol. Bacteriol.* **64**, 687.

Tubiana, M., and Lalanne, C. M. (1963). *Ann. Radiol.* **6**, 561.

Tullis, J. L. (1951). *Military Surg.* **109**, 271.

Tullis, J. L., Chambers, F. W., Morgan, J. E., and Zeller, J. H. (1952). *Am. J. Roentgenol., Radium Therapy* **67**, 620.

Tullis, J. L., Lamson, B. G., and Madden, S. C. (1955). *Am. J. Pathol.* **31**, 41.

Uphoff, D. E. (1963). *J. Natl. Cancer Inst.* **30**, 1115.

Valentine, W. N., Pearce, M. L., and Lawrence, J. L. (1952). *Blood* **7**, 14.

Van Albertini, A. (1932). *Pathol. Anat. Allgem.* **89**, 183.

Varteresz, V., Frater, I., Kalman, E., and Wald, B. (1958). *Strahlentherapie* **105**, 467.

Velden, R. (1912). *Deutsch. Arch. Klin. Med.* **108**, 377.

Verhagen, A., and Suren, H. (1953). *Strahlentherapie* **91**, 263.

Wallgren, A. (1933). *Acta Radiol.* **14**, III.

Warren, S. (1954). *Physiol. Rev.* **24**, 225.

Warren, S. L., and Whipple, G. H. (1922). *J. Exptl. Med.* **35**, 203.

Warthin, A. S. (1906). *Intern. Clinics (Philadelphia)* **4**, 243.

Wernicke, E. (1938). Thesis, University of Kiel, Germany.

Weymouth, P. P., Delpel, N. E., Doell, R. J., Steinbock, H. L., and Kaplan, H. S. (1955). *J. Natl. Cancer Inst.* **15**, 981.

White, A., and Dougherty, T. F. (1945). *Federation Proc.* **4**, 109.

Williams, R. B., Toal, I. N., White, J., and Charpenter, H. M. (1958). *J. Natl. Cancer Inst.* **21**, 17.

Woods, M. C., Gamble, F. N., Furth, J., and Bigelow, R. R. (1953). *Blood* **8**, 545.

Zacek, J., and Rosenberg, R. (1950). *Compt. Rend. Soc. Biol.* **144**, 462.

Zunz, E., and LaBarre, J. (1927). *Compt. Rend. Soc. Biol.* **96**, 712.

Zwerg, H. G. (1932). *Strahlentherapie* **43**, 201.

CHAPTER 12

Effect of Irradiation on Immunity

G. Mathé

Institut de Cancérologie et d'Immunogénétique,
Hôpital Paul Brousse, Villejuif (Seine), France*

and

H. Da Costa

Atomic Energy Establishment, Medical Division, Bombay, India

* The senior author is also associated with the Faculty of Medicine, University of Paris, and the Hematological Service of the Institut Gustave-Roussy.

I. Introduction

Immunity is a state of resistance developed by an organism to substances foreign to itself, which it has encountered previously.

The effect of radiation on the acquisition and maintenance of this state of immunity has been the subject of many investigations (Taliaferro and Taliaferro, 1951; Hale and Stoner, 1953; Hašek and Lengerová, 1960; Makinodan and Gengozian, 1960; Leone, 1962). These results have served a double purpose by contributing towards the comprehension of the immunological mechanism per se and by their practical implications in the increased incidence of infections complicating the recovery of human beings irradiated either accidentally or therapeutically. Moreover, these authors have also explored the possibility of preconditioning the body with irradiation for the acceptance of a homograft, which is one of the most ambitious endeavors of medical therapeutics of our day.

II. Review of Fundamental Concepts of Immunity

The development of immunity to a foreign substance or organism (the antigen) is determined by various events which form the basic sequence underlying the process—entry of the antigen into the organism, its contact with the antibody producing cells, the state of activity of these cells leading to the formation of the specific antibodies and the properties of these antibodies.

We shall review briefly these different factors [see also the works of Rosenau and Anderson (1908), Arthus (1921), Richet (1923), Wells (1925), Marrack (1938), Bordet (1939), Pauling (1940), Landsteiner (1945), Haurowitz (1952, 1953), Nakamura (1954), Jerne (1955), Heidelberger (1956), Boyd (1956), Talmage (1957,) Dixon (1957, 1958), Monod (1958), Burnet (1959), Medawar (1961), Mathé et al. (1963a,b,c), Mackay and Burnet (1963)].

A. Antigens

Antigens are most often macromolecular substances, proteinic or polysaccharide in nature; the antigenic determinant, however, may be only a small organic molecule as has been shown by studies conducted with artificial antigens.

B. Antibodies

Antibodies, composed principally of γ_2-, γ_1M-, and γ_1A-globulins, are produced by cells which are called "immunologically competent" and which are found in lymphoid tissue, the bone marrow, and the circulatory blood (Miller, 1963b).

According to Gowans (1962) it is the small lymphocyte which is the immunologically competent but noncommitted cell; antigenic stimulation transforms it into a large hyperbasophilic cell which then proliferates.

Various theories have been postulated regarding the mechanism of the production of antibodies and especially on the specificity of the immunologically competent cells (Jerne, 1955; Burnet, 1959; CIBA Found. Symp., 1960; Mackay and Burnet, 1963).

Antibodies are specific for the antigens which have induced their formation; this specificity is, however, limited in that an antibody caused by an antigen can give a reaction with certain other antigens (cross reaction). The majority of antibodies can only be demonstrated in an organism after it has been exposed to the antigen ("immune antibodies"). The "natural antibodies," however, are demonstrable without the organism being apparently stimulated by the corresponding antigen.

The administration of an antigen, even in repeated doses, may give rise to a state of tolerance instead of one of immunity. Such an "immunological tolerance" has been observed in those cases where the antigen has come into contact with the host during fetal life or, in some species, even on the day of birth or a few days after. Also, the administration of a large quantity of antigen to children and adults has been known to cause "immunological paralysis."

Finally, a state of nonspecific tolerance can be induced by thymectomy at birth which reduces the absolute lymphocyte population of the animal (Miller, 1963a).

C. ANTIGEN–ANTIBODY REACTIONS

Antigen-antibody reactions are manifested in various ways; by the neutralization of toxins as in infections, by the precipitation of proteins, by the agglutination or lysis of cells, by the lethal effect on bacteria, by the swelling of bacterial capsules, or by the rejection of incompatible grafts. Sometimes, however, they are manifested by the liberation of histamine, 5-hydroxytryptamine, proteases, and other substances toxic to the host, giving rise to anaphylaxis.

D. PARA-IMMUNOLOGICAL DEFENSES

1. Mechanical Barriers

Whatever the nature of the antigen, its entrance is impeded by barriers such as the skin, the mucous membranes, the pulmonary tissues and the mucosa of the alimentary tract. These form barriers not only as mechanical obstructions but also by producing lysozyme which splits muramic acid of the bacterial cell wall.

2. Direct Cellular Defenses

The polymorphonuclear neutrophils migrate to the inflamed zone, phagocytose the invading organism, and lyse it *in situ* or take it to the lymphatic tissue for further destruction; they contribute to the immunological mechanism by carrying the antigen to the immunologically competent cells.

The role of eosinophils in immunological reactions still remains unknown but Speirs (1957) believes that they may be concerned with the enzymic status of the immunologically competent cells.

The macrophages in the form of monocytes, histiocytes, reticulum cells, and pseudoendothelial cells play an important role at the time of the antigenic invasion, when their phagocytic functions are stimulated; their migration to the site of invasion is more rapid if the victim has been previously exposed to the same antigen and has developed a state of immunity with respect to it.

3. Lytic Properties of Blood

Serum contains alexine, which has lytic properties, and the properdine system, which has nonspecific bactericidal and viral-inhibiting properties. Moreover, certain leukocytes secrete lysozyme which kills, without lysis, gram-negative microorganisms.

III. Effect of Irradiation on Immunity

It was at the beginning of the century that Benjamin and Sluka (1908) gave radiation immunology an impetus by showing that rabbits irradiated with X-rays formed fewer antibodies to a foreign protein than did the controls.

This was followed by the observation of Amoss (1919) that irradiated animals were more sensitive to viruses, and that of Warren and Whipple (1923) and Chrom (1935) that such animals succumbed frequently to infections, especially to those of the gastrointestinal tract.

Corroborating these findings with the earlier ones of Heineke (1903, 1904a,b) who had described lymphatic aplasia following irradiation, many research workers have dealt with the role of the lymphatic system in radiation immunology and the subject now includes observations on human beings irradiated either accidentally (Jammet *et al.*, 1959) or therapeutically (Küss *et al.*, 1962a,b; Mathé *et al.*, 1959a,b,c, 1960, 1963b).

Analyses of available data indicates that ionizing radiations effect both the direct and the para-immunological mechanisms.

A. γ-GLOBULINS

The relationship of gamma globulins to antibodies has been established (Cohen, 1963) and their diminution in irradiated animals (Mathé *et al.*, 1959b) (Fig. 1) has been demonstrated. Maurer *et al.* (1953) have shown that this change is quantitative and not qualitative in rabbits, the γ-globulins not differing immunochemically from those of the non-irradiated controls.

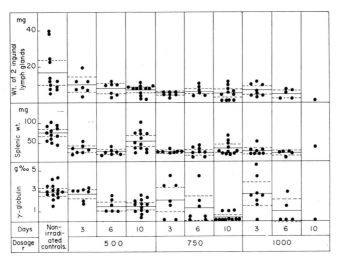

Fig. 1. Effect of 500, 750, and 1000 r on γ-globulin level of blood in mice (from Mathé *et al.*, 1959b).

B. ANTIBODY FORMATION

The effect of total body irradiation on the production of antibodies against a great variety of antigens has been studied and it has been shown that the results depend primarily on whether or not the animal has received a prior injection of the antigen in question.

1. *Primary Antibody Response*

Benjamin and Sluka (1908) showed that total body irradiation generally inhibits antibody formation if the antigen is administered after the irradiation and Hektoen (1915) demonstrated that this inhibition was directly proportional to the dose of the ionizing radiation.

Taliaferro (1952, 1954) conducted a more detailed study in rabbits with 500 r of total body irradiation, examining their hemolysin production ability against Forssman-type sheep antigen. They observed a diminution of antibody titers when the antigen was administered 12–24 hours after the ionizing radiation; however, when the antigen was administered immediately after irradiation, antibody production was almost normal, though somewhat retarded. When antigen was administered shortly before irradiation, production was retarded, but the final titer obtained was higher; administration of the antigen 4 days prior to the acute irradiation resulted in normal titers though there was some delay in the appearance of antibodies.

Gengozian *et al.* (1957) irradiated mice with 710 r and observed a poor antibody response to sheep red cells injected later until the 28th day (Fig. 2); Dixon *et al.* (1952) corroborated the fact that antibody

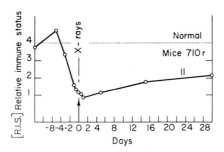

Fig. 2. Antibody production in total body irradiated animals when antigen is given before X-rays. Relative immune status (R.I.S.) of mice. Sheep red cells administered −10 to +30 days with respect to time of irradiation (from Gengozian and Makinodan, 1958).

production is not diminished if the antigen is administered before irradiation.

The importance of the dose of radiation should be stressed. Hale and Stoner (1952) demonstrated the absence of an inhibiting effect of 300 r of X-rays on the antibody-producing ability of mice injected with tetanus antitoxin, whereas 475–875 r gave a result similar to that of Taliaferro and Taliaferro (1952).

The "transitoriness of the depression of antibody production" was shown by Craddock and Lawrence (1948), who obtained a negative and a positive response to antigens administered on the 8th and 30th–40th post-irradiation days, respectively.

Clemmesen and Anderson (1948), Hale and Stoner (1956), Taliaferro and Taliaferro (1957), and Smith *et al.* (1958a,b) have all demonstrated the reduction in efficacy of a total radiation dose when this is "staggered" over two or more administrations. Stoner and Hale (1958) studying the "rate" of administration of ionizing radiations concluded that 4 rem/hour (96 rem/day) and even 1 rem/hour (672 rem in 28 days) were sufficient to suppress an antibody response to a subsequently administered antigen.

2. Secondary Antibody Response

The majority of authors agree that the secondary antibody response is relatively radioresistant. Stoner and Hale (1962) have stated that the primary response was 3 times more radiosensitive than the secondary response.

Talmage *et al.* (1956) showed that relative radioresistance was obtained by the administration of larger quantities of the antigen, and Taliaferro and Taliaferro (1957) showed that the antigens having a longer life span gave a response which appeared to be more radiosensitive than the antigens enjoying shorter lives since the former were destroyed to a greater degree than the latter.

3. Mechanism of the Effects of Irradiation on Antibody Response

The work of Taliaferro and Taliaferro (1952, 1954) lead us to conclude that the antibodies formed prior to the administration of ionizing radiations are not affected and that it is only their production immediately following irradiation that is influenced; this explains the variability of response with respect to the time of administration of the antigen and the irradiation.

It was stated by Taliaferro and Taliaferro (1957) that antibody production occurs in 3 stages. The first of these is the "preinduction phase" of 1–4 hours essential for the initiation of the process of antibody synthesis; this phase, extremely radiosensitive, is dose-dependent. It does not appear that this period corresponds to a phase of antigen fixation (Fitch *et al.*, 1956). The effect of irradiation on it seems related to the inhibition of cellular proliferation which is concerned with antibody synthesis. This is suggested by the observation of Stevens *et al.* (1953), who have studied the correlation between the effect of irradiation, the formation of antibodies, and the synthesis of DNA. Taliaferro and Taliaferro (1954) showed that the relationship between the production of antibodies and the radiation dose is sigmoid; seemingly characterizing the lethal effect of irradiation on cells. These authors as well as Stevens *et al.* (1953) have concluded that this phase corresponds to the multiplication of the radiosensitive parent antibody-producing cell.

Speirs (1957) has observed a good correlation between the radio-sensitivity of this "preinduction period" and the fall in the eosinophil count following irradiation; his opinion regarding the role of these cells in immunology has already been stated.

The second phase of Taliaferro and Taliaferro (1951) is that of "induction." During this stage ionizing radiations do not effect quantitatively the antibody peak but merely delay its appearance.

The third phase is that of "production," when synthesis of the antibody actually takes place.

Numerous theories have been forwarded to explain the detailed mechanism of action of irradiation on the cellular production of antibodies. The first of these is the inhibition of phagocytosis of the antigen. Dixon et al. (1951) and Donaldson et al. (1956) and Stiffel et al. (1959) found, however, that the phagocytic process was radioresistant per se and could be said to be only relatively inefficient in view of the large amount of debris that had to be removed after radiation injury. A second possibility, that of inhibition of the proteinic secretions by cells with hyperbasophilic cytoplasm, was therefore expounded. Against this hypothesis, Dickson et al. (1958) found that if irradiated cells are incapable of dividing, they are capable of synthesizing deoxyribonucleic acid (DNA), ribonucleic acid RNA, and proteins. Van Bekkum (1956), however, showed that the oxidative phosphorylation in the mitochondria of splenic cells of rats is markedly effected 2 hours after an irradiation of 700 r L. Creasey and Stocken (1959) have observed a reduction of this process in the nuclei of splenic, thymic, medullary, and lymph nodes cells of rats irradiated with only 25 r. These findings are in accordance with those of Pauly (1959) and of Novelli (1961) that although the destruction of enzymes requires large doses of ionizing radiations, the process of the formation of adaptative enzymes is radiosensitive.

Another theory explaining the mechanism of action of ionizing radiations on antibody formation is the reduction in number and inhibition of mitosis of the parent immunologically competent cells.

The recent work of Gowans (1962) and of Porter and Cooper (1962) introduce the possibility of the small lymphocyte being the immunologically competent cell. According to these authors, the administration of an antigen transforms this cell into a large cell with a hyperbasophilic cytoplasm, the proliferation of which gives hyperbasophilic, pyroninophilic cells and results in hypertrophy of the organs containing lymphoid tissue; these cells also infiltrate the zone of administration of the antigen and secrete antibodies. Irradiation could, then, act via the small lymphocytes; the marked radiosensitivity of these cells both *in vivo* and *in vitro* is well known (Trowell, 1952). This action of ionizing radiations on the lymphocytes is independent of mitoses and remains inexplicable.

C. CIRCULATING ANTIBODIES

Hollingsworth (1950) showed that a 300 r total body irradiation in rabbits did not alter the destruction rate of administered antibodies and the results of Perkins and Marcus (1957) with LD_{100} lead us to conclude that circulating antibodies are radioresistant in doses administered *in vivo*.

D. LOCAL IRRADIATION

Local irradiation is, as a general rule, insufficient to cause the inhibition of the antibody response. This is due to the dissemination throughout the body of hematopoietic tissue containing immunologically competent cells; thus, if one of these zones is in the irradiated area, the remaining sites will undergo compensatory hyperplasia, liberate parent cells into the blood stream, and repopulate the aplastic site.

Jacobson and Robson (1952) showed that rabbits irradiated with 500–800 r total body irradiation form hemolysins against sheep red cells if their spleens are protected during irradiation. Süssdorf and Draper (1956) observed a similar effect with appendicular shielding.

E. TOLERANCE

The essential action of ionizing radiation on the production of antibodies consists of a reduction in the number of immunologically competent cells, thus producing a state of tolerance. The duration of this state can be prolonged by the administration of certain chemical substances (Da Costa *et al.*, 1964). Moreover, it has been shown that this non-specific tolerance and the specific tolerance induced by the administration of an antigen at birth or a large quantity of it later on in life, have a common character, both giving an elevated ratio:

$$\frac{\text{quantity of Antigen}}{\text{number of immunologically competent cells}}$$

In 1918 Murphy and Taylor showed that irradiation facilitates the taking of an incompatible tumor graft and explained that this was made possible by the lymphatic aplasia which follows irradiation. Clemmesen (1939, 1940) confirmed this observation and specified that only the primary grafts were thus facilitated, irradiation being incapable of permitting such a graft in animals which had been previously immunized by a graft from the same donor. Toolan (1957) succeeded in grafting a number of human tumors into sublethally irradiated hamsters and rats and even succeeded in maintaining pure tumor strains by a large number of passages in this manner.

Dempster *et al.* (1950) studied the effect of irradiation on the tolerance of allogenic skin grafts in rabbits; with 250 r he could double the survival time of the primary graft. Piomelli *et al.* (1961), however, obtained a prolonged graft survival only with mice whose genetic constitution did not differ markedly.

The allogenic hematopoietic graft is possible only in hosts irradiated with near-lethal doses of ionizing radiation. We will deal with this important question in Section V of this chapter.

F. Facilitation of the Immune State

Irradiation does not always inhibit the immune response. It sometimes causes a reversal of this effect in favor of the immune state, as shown by Taliaferro and Taliaferro (1951). This action, however, is generally encountered in low doses range. Taliaferro and Taliaferro (1951) suggested this to be the result either of vascular changes allied to hyperemia or to the stimulation of the reticuloendothelial system. Bloom (1948) believed that it was caused by compensatory hyperplasia leading to a temporary increase in the cell population.

IV. Effect of Irradiation on Para-Immune Defenses

Attenuation of specific antibody formation is not the only alteration initiated by ionizing radiations with respect to the maintenance of the normal immune status of the organism and we will now consider its effect on the para-immune defenses of the body.

A. Mechanical Barrier

The skin and the lungs are affected by relatively high doses of ionizing radiations but the buccal, the upper respiratory, and the intestinal mucosae are very radiosensitive and lesions of crypts and Peyer's patches, even ulcers with perforations, are known to add to the gravity of the patient's condition.

B. Direct Cellular Defenses

Polymorphonuclear neutrophils undoubtedly play an important role in the capture and ingestion of the antigen, irrespective of whether it is a chemical substance or a living organism. These cells being radiosensitive, irradiation reduces the absolute number available for attack on the invader; however, no diminution in their migration ability follows irradiation (Schechmeister and Fishman, 1955).

Eosinophils are also sensitive to irradiation *in vivo* and their destruction may interfere with the enzyme status of the immunologically competent cells (Speirs, 1957). Basophils (Marcus and Donaldson, 1954) and platelets (Donaldson, 1954) are also believed to effect the immunological status of an irradiated subject.

The effect of irradiation on the reticuloendothelial system has been the subject of numerous studies (Fig. 3). Although the clearance of non-

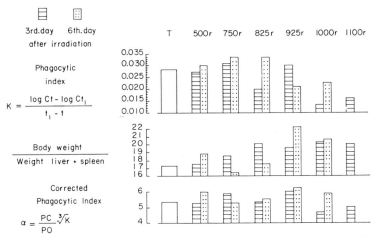

Fig. 3. Effect of 500–1100 r total body X-irradiation on phagocytic ability of reticuloendothelial system of mice (from Stiffel *et al.*, 1959).

cellular antigens by this system does not seem affected (Dixon *et al.*, 1951; Stieffel *et al.*, 1959), erythrocytic phagocytosis was found to be reduced (Donaldson *et al.*, 1954).

C. Lytic Properties of Blood

The properdin titer in dogs (Michaelson *et al.*, 1957) and man (Jammet *et al.*, 1959) is diminished following a whole body irradiation and Pillemer *et al.* (1954) have demonstrated the beneficial effect of the administration of properdin to rats irradiated with LD_{90}.

V. Practical Applications of the Effect of Irradiation on Immunity

A. Infections in Irradiated Subjects

1. Experimental Work

Since Lawen's (1909) emphasis on the sensitivity of irradiated animals to infections, a considerable amount of experimental work has been done on this subject (Murphy and Ellis, 1914; Morton, 1916; Corper and

Chovey, 1920; Waters *et al.*, 1922; Schwienhorst, 1928; Spinelli and Talia, 1931; Zinzzer and Casteneda, 1932; Clemmesen, 1939; Roberts *et al.*, 1939; Angevine and Toggle, 1941; Liu *et al.*, 1941; Gear and Davis, 1942; De Gara and Furth, 1945; Gowen and Zelle, 1945; Clemmesen and Anderson, 1948; Burrows *et al.*, 1950).

Spontaneous infections in mice commence on the 3rd or 4th post-irradiation day and normal resistance reappears after 3 weeks. The most frequent invaders were found by Miller *et al.* (1950) to be paracolon and coliform organisms, *Proteus, Pseudomonas,* alpha-*Streptococcus,* and some anaerobic organisms. In 91% of these, infection was due to a single invader, only 9% of the animals manifesting a double infection.

In the initial stages of radiation research the alimentary tract was considered to be the portal of entry for these bacteria. But the intestinal lesions are maximal a few hours after irradiation and repair is almost complete within 60 hours (Metcalf *et al.*, 1954) to 5 days (Pierce, 1948); furthermore, Congdon *et al.* (1955) could find no histological evidence of a bacterial invasion via this tract during the first three post-irradiation days; however, as Osborne *et al.* (1952) discovered bacteremia with intestinal organisms following irradiation only of the head and face, the nasopharynx was believed to be the site of entry; the findings of Wensinck and Renaud (1957), of Wensinck (1961a,b) and of Vos *et al.* (1959) seem to corroborate this view.

A correlation was described between neutropenia and thrombocytopenia, and the time of occurrence of infections (Donaldson, 1954; Smith *et al.*, 1954, 1958; Donaldson and Miller, 1959; Hammond *et al.*, 1959; Hirsch, 1960). Callaway and Kerby (1951), Gordon *et al.* (1955), Hollingsworth (1955), and Fitch *et al.* (1953) had already cast suspicion on the role of polymorphonuclear cells in this respect and Nelson and Becker (1959) and Nelson and Berk (1960) demonstrated the ability of bacteria to survive and proliferate in the phagocytosing cell after an irradiation of 500 r or more. Furthermore, Donaldson *et al.* (1954) demonstrated the inability of the macrophages to digest the phagocytosed organism at these doses.

Donaldson and Marcus (1953), Marcus and Donaldson (1953), Kornfeld *et al.* (1960), Muschel (1960) considered the diminished bactericidal ability of blood between the 3rd and 21st post-irradiation days to be an important contributing factor to the acquisition of infections by these animals.

2. *Clinical Observations*

Infections pose a grave problem to the clinician in charge of a subject who has received a large dose of total body irradiation; they played an important role in the death of victims of reactor accidents (Warren, 1946; Le Roy, 1947; Howland and Warren, 1948; Liebow et al., 1949; Warren and Bowers, 1950; Bowers, 1951) other than that of the Zero-Energy Reactor at Vinča, Yugoslavia (Jammet et al., 1959; Mathé et al., 1959a). Even in spite of strict asepsis being maintained, several patients deliberately irradiated for tissue transplantation (Mathé 1959a,b,c, 1960, 1963b; Hamburger et al., 1962; Küss et al., 1962a,b) had an infectious episode. Of our group of patients, one had staphylococcal septicemia, another pulmonary staphylococcal infection, and the third septicemia with Candida albicans. The authors noticed that these infections occurred during the phase of neutropenia.

B. ALLOGENIC TRANSPLANTS

1. Kidney Transplantation

a. In Animals. Working on animals, Dempster (1953), Hume et al. (1960), and Calne (1963) could not obtain permanent allogenic "taking" of a renal transplant with radiation doses varying from 200–1000 r. Hume et al. (1960) eventually determined a dose of 1200–1500 r to be sufficient for the suppression of cellular infiltration at the transplantation site; however, the animals died of radiation injury.

b. In Humans. The results in human beings are only a little more encouraging (International Congress of Nephrology, Prague, 1963) than those in dogs, although vigorous efforts have been made to efficiently suppress the immune state of the recipients (Küss et al., 1961; Hamburger et al., 1962; Küss et al., 1962a,b; Lambert, 1962; Mowbray, 1962; Murray et al., 1962; Traeger, 1962; Woodruff et al., 1962).

The initial radiation dose to the recipient has been varied between 200 and 600 r and Hamburger et al. (1962) did not hesitate to submit the patient to a second radiation of 110 r when rejection phenomenon appeared 6 months after the operation; however, the patient succumbed to hematopoietic failure. Küss et al. (1962a,b) also administered a repeat dose of 100 r, combining it with corticosteroids and 6-mercaptopurine, but eventually death resulted from renal insufficiency, presumably due to inadequate suppression of the immune mechanism.

Prolongation of the depressed immune status was attempted by Küss et al. (1962) by the administration of only 6-mercaptopurine when the hematological picture returned to normal. It should be stressed here that cellular infiltration (Hamburger et al., 1959; Merrill et al., 1960) is not always followed by an immediate rejection of the graft (Dossetor, 1962).

2. Bone Marrow Transplants

This subject has been treated in Chapter 16 of this volume.

REFERENCES

Amoss, H. L., Taylor, H. D., and Witherbee, W. D. (1919). *J. Exptl. Med.* **29**, 115.

Angevine, D. M., and Toggle, A. (1941). *Am. J. Roentgenol.* **46**, 96.

Arthus, H. (1921). "De l'anaphylaxie à l'immunité." Masson, Paris.

Benjamin, E., and Sluka, E. (1908). *Wien. Klin. Wochschr.* **21**, 311.

Bloom, M. A. (1948). *In* "Histopathology of Irradiation from Internal and External Sources" (W. Bloom, ed.), Vol. II, Chapter VI. McGraw-Hill, New York.

Bordet, J. (1939). "Traité de l'immunité dans les maladies infectieuses." Masson, Paris.

Boyd, W. C. (1956). "Fundamentals of Immunology." Wiley (Interscience), New York.

Burnet, F. M. (1959). "The Clonal Selection Theory of Acquired Immunity." Cambridge Univ. Press, London and New York.

Burrows, W., Deupree, N. G., and Moore, D. E. (1950). *J. Infect. Diseases* **87**, 158.

Callaway, J. W., and Kerby, G. P. (1951). *Arch. Dermatol. Syph.* **63**, 200.

Calne, R. Y. (1963). "Renal Transplantation." Arnold, London.

Chrom, S. A. (1935). *Acta Radiol.* **16**, 641.

CIBA Foundation Symposium (1960). "Cellular Aspects of Immunity." Churchill, London.

Clemmesen, J. (1939). *Am. J. Cancer* **35**, 378.

Clemmesen, J. (1940). *Am. J. Cancer* **29**, 313.

Clemmesen, J., and Anderson, E. K. (1948). *Acta Pathol. Microbiol. Scand.* **35**, 615.

Cohen, C. (1963). *Brit. Med. Bull.* September, p. 202.

Congdon, C. C., William, F. P., Rabermann, R. T., and Lorenz, E. (1955). *J. Natl. Cancer Inst.* **15**, 855.

Corper, H. J., and Chovey, P. (1920). *J. Infect. Diseases* **27**, 491.

Craddock, C. G., Jr., and Lawrence, J. S. (1948). *J. Immunol.* **60**, 241.

Creasey, W. A., and Stocken, L. A. (1959). *Biochem. J.* **72**, 519.

Da Costa, H., Mery, A., and Tenenbaum, R. (1964). *Rev. Franc. Etudes Clin. Biol.* **9**, 90.

De Gara, P. F., and Furth, J. (1945). *J. Immunol.* **50**, 255.

Dempster, W. J. (1953). *Brit. J. Surg.* **40**, 477.

Dempster, W. J., Lennox, B., and Borg, J. W. (1950). *Brit. J. Exptl. Pathol.* **31**, 620.

Dickson, M., Paul, J., and Davidson, J. N. (1958). *Biochem. J.* **70**, 189.

Dixon, F. J. (1957). *J. Cellular Comp. Physiol.* **50**, Suppl. 1, 27.

Dixon, F. J. (1958). *In* "Rapport du III° congrès international d'allergologie." Flammarion, Paris.

Dixon, F. J., Bukantz, S. C., and Dammin, G. J. (1951). *Science* **113**, 274.

Dixon, F. J., Talmage, D. W., and Maurer, P. H. (1952). *J. Immunol.* **68**, 693.

Donaldson, D. M. (1954). Thesis, University of Utah, Salt Lake City.

Donaldson, D. M., and Marcus, S. (1953). *J. Immunol.* **72**, 203.

Donaldson, D. M., and Miller, M. L. (1959). *J. Immunol.* **82**, 69.

Donaldson, D. M., Marcus, S., and Gyi, K. K. (1954). *Federation Proc.* **13**, 490.

Donaldson, D. M., Marcus, S., Gyi, K. K., and Perkins, E. H. (1956). *J. Immunol.* **76**, 192.

Dossetor, J. B. (1962). Cited by Calne, R. Y., 1963.

Fitch, F. W., Parker, P., Soules, K. H., and Eissler, R. W. (1953). *J. Lab. Clin. Med.* **42**, 598.

Fitch, F. W., Wissler, R. W., Lavia, M. F., and Barker, P. (1956). *J. Immunol.* **76**, 151.

Gear, J., and Davis, D. W. H. (1942). *Trans. Roy. Soc. Trop. Med. Hyg.* **36**, 1.

Gengozian, N., and Makinodan, T. (1958). *J. Immunol.* **80**, 189.

Gengozian, N., Urso, I. S., Congdon, C. C., Conger, A. D., and Makinodan, T. (1957). *Proc. Soc. Exptl. Biol. Med.* **96**, 714.

Gordon, L. E., Cooper, D. B., and Miller, C. P. (1955). *Proc. Soc. Exptl. Biol. Med.* **89**, 577.

Gowans, J. L. (1962). *Ann. N. Y. Acad. Sci.* **99**, 432.

Gowen, J. W., and Zelle, M. R. (1945). *J. Infect. Diseases* **77**, 85.

Hale, W. M., and Stoner, R. D. (1952). *Intern. Record Med.* **165**, 358.

Hale, W. M., and Stoner, R. D. (1953). *Yale J. Biol. Med.* **25**, 236.

Hale, W. M., and Stoner, R. D. (1956). *J. Immunol.* **77**, 410.

Hamburger, J., Vaysse, J., Crosnier, J., Tubiana, M., Lalanne, C., Antoine, B., Auvert, J., Soulier, J. P., Dormont, J., Salmon, Ch., Maisonnet, M., and Amiel, J. L. (1959). *Presse Med.* **67**, 1771.

Hamburger, J., Vaysse, J., Crosnier, J., Auvert, J., Lalanne, C., and Dormont, J. (1962). *Rev. Franc. Etudes Clin. Biol.* **7**, 20.

Hammond, C. W., Anderle, S. K., and Miller, C. P. (1959). *Radiation Res.* **11**, 242.

Hašek, M., and Lengerová, A. (1960). *In* "Mechanisms in Radiobiology" (M. Errerra and A. Forssberg, eds.), Vol. II, p. 207. Academic Press, New York.

Haurowitz, F. (1952). *Biol. Rev.* **27**, 247.

Haurowitz, F. (1953). *In* "Nature and Significance of the Antibody Response." Columbia Univ. Press, New York.

Heidelberger, M. (1956). *Ann. Rev. Biochem.* **25**, 641.

Heineke, H. (1903). *Muench. Med. Wochschr.* **50**, 2090.

Heineke, H. (1904a). *Mitt. Grenzg. Med. Chir.* **14**, 21.

Heineke, H. (1904b). *Muench. Med. Wochschr.* **51**, 1382.

Hektoen, L. (1915). *J. Infect. Diseases* **22**, 28–33.

Hirsch, J. G. (1960). *J. Exptl. Med.* **112**, 15.

Hollingsworth, J. W. (1950). *Proc. Soc. Exptl. Biol. Med.* **75**, 477.

Hollingsworth, J. W. (1955). *Yale J. Biol. Med.* **28**, 56.

Howland, J. W., and Warren, S. L. (1948). *Advan. Biol. Med. Phys.* **1**, 387.

Hume, D. M., Jackson, B. T., Zukoski, C. F., Lee, H. M., Kauffman, H. M., and Egdahl, R. H. (1960). *Ann. Surg.* **152**, 354.

Jacobson, L. O., and Robson, M. J. (1952). *J. Lab. Clin. Med.* **39**, 169.

Jammet, H., Mathé, G., Pendic, B., Duplan, J. F., Maupin, B., Latarjet, R., Kalic, D., Schwarzenberg, L., Djukic, Z., and Vigne, J. (1959). *Rev. Franc. Etudes Clin. Biol.* **4**, 210.

Jerne, N. K. (1955). *Proc. Natl. Acad. Sci. U. S.* **41**, 849.

Kornfeld, L., Hammond, C. W., and Miller, C. P. (1960). *J. Immunol.* **84**, 77.

Küss, R., Legrain, M., Camey, M., Desarmenien, J., Mathé, G., Nedey, R., and Vourc'h, C. (1961). *Mem. Acad. Chir.* **87**, 183.

Küss, R., Legrain, M., Mathé, G., Nedey, R., and Camey, M. (1962a). *Postgrad. Med. J.* **38**, 528.

Küss, R., Legrain, M., Mathé, G., Nedey, R., Camey, M., Tubiana, M., Lalanne, C., Schwarzenberg, L., Larrieu, M. J., Maisonnet, M., Basset, F., and Delaveau, P. (1962b). *Rev. Franc. Etudes Clin. Biol.* **7**, 1028.

Lambert, P. P. (1962). Cited by Calne (1963).

Landsteiner, K. (1945). "The Specificity of Serological Reactions," 2nd ed. Harvard Univ. Press, Cambridge, Massachusetts.

Lawen, A. (1909). *Mitt. Grenzg. Med. Chir.* **19**, 141.

Leone, C. A. (1962). "Ionizing Radiations and Immune Processes." Gordon & Breach, New York.

Le Roy, G. V. (1947). *J. Am. Med. Assoc.* **134**, 1143.

Liebow, A. A., Warren, S., and Delovrsey, E. (1949). *Am. J. Pathol.* **25**, 853.

Liu, P. Y., Snyder, J. C., and Enders, J. F. (1941). *J. Exptl. Med.* **73**, 669.

Mackay, I., and Burnet, F. (1963). In "Autoimmune Diseases." Thomas, Springfield, Illinois.

Makinodan, T., and Gengozian, N. (1960). In "Radiation Protection and Recovery" (A. Hollaender, ed.), p. 316. Pergamon Press, New York.

Marcus, J., and Donaldson, D. M. (1953). *Proc. Soc. Exptl. Biol. Med.* **83**, 184.

Marcus, J., and Donaldson, D. M. (1954). *Federation Proc.* **13**, 504.

Marrack, J. R. (1938). "The Chemistry of Antigens and Antibodies," Spec. Rept. Ser. Med. Council No. 230. H. M. Stationary Office, London.

Mathé, G., and Amiel, J. L. (1960). *Rev. Franc. Etudes Clin. Biol.* **5**, 20.

Mathé, G., Bernard, J., Schwarzenberg, L., Larrieu, M. J., Lalanne, C., Dutreix, A., Denoix, P., Schwarzmann, V., and Ceoara, B. (1959a). *Rev. Franc. Etudes Clin. Biol.* **4**, 675.

Mathé, G., Pays, P., Bourdon, R., and Maroteaux, P. (1959b). *Rev. Franc. Etudes Clin. Biol.* **4**, 272.

Mathé, G., Amiel, J. L., and Tran Ba Loc (1959c). *Rev. Franc. Etudes Clin. Biol.* **4**, 475.

Mathé, G., Amiel, J. L., and Bernard, J. (1960). *Bull. Cancer* **47**, 333.

Mathé, G., Amiel, J. L., and Friend, Ch. (1963a). *Bull. Cancer* **19**, 416.

Mathé, G., Amiel, J. L., Schwarzenberg, L., Cattan, A., and Schneider, M. (1963b). *Compt. Rend. Acad. Sci.* **257**, 3527.

Mathé, G., Binet, J. L., Seman, G., Amiel, J. L., and Daguet, G. (1963c). In "La tolérance," p. 359. CNRS, Paris.

Maurer, P. H., Dixon, F. J., and Talmage, D. W. (1953). *Proc. Soc. Exptl. Biol. Med.* **83**, 163.

Medawar, P. R. (1961). *Science* **133**, 303.

Merrill, J. P., Murray, J. E., Harrison, J. H., Friedman, F. A., Dealy, J. B., and Dammin, G. J. (1960). *New Engl. J. Med.* **262**, 1251.

Metcalf, R. G., Blandan, R. J., and Barnett, T. B. (1954). In "Biological Effects of External Radiations" (H. A. Blair, ed.), p. 11. McGraw-Hill, New York.

Michaelson, S. M., Shively, J. N., Nowland, J. W., and Pillemer, L. (1957). *Radiation Res.* **7**, 438.

Miller, C. P., Hammond, C. W., and Tomkins, M. (1950). *Science* **111**, 540.

Miller, J. (1963b). *Brit. Med. Bull.* **19**(3), 214.

Miller, J. F. A. P. (1963a). *Brit. Med. J.* p. 459.

Monod, J. (1958). "Cellular and Humoral Aspects of the Hypersensitive States." Harper (Hoeber), New York.

Morton, J. J. (1916). *J. Exptl. Med.* **24**, 419.

Mowbray, J. F. (1962). Cited by Calne, R. Y., 1963.

Murphy, J. B., and Ellis, A. M. (1914). *J. Exptl. Med.* **20**, 397.

Murphy, J. B., and Taylor, H. D. (1918). *J. Exptl. Med.* **28**, 1.

Murray, J. E. (1962). Cited by Calne (1963).

Murray, J. E., Merrill, J. P., Dammin, G. J., Dealy, J. B., Alexandre, G. W., and Harrison, J. H. (1962). *Ann. Surg.* **156**, 337.

Muschel, L. H. (1960). *Ann. N. Y. Acad. Sci.* **88**, 1265.

Nakamura, K. (1954). "Allergy and Anaphylaxis." Nippon Med. School, Tokyo.

Nelson, E. L., and Becker, J. R. (1959). J. Infect. Diseases 104, 13.

Nelson, E. L., and Berk, R. S. (1960). Radiology 42, 64.

Novelli, G. D. (1961). Proc. 15th Ann. Symp. on Fundamental Cancer Res. in press.

Nygaard, O. F. (1962). In "Effects of Ionizing Radiations on Immune Processes," Vol. I, p. 47. Gordon & Breach, New York.

Osborne, J. W., Bryan, H. S., Quastler, H., and Rhoades, H. F. (1952). Am. J. Physiol. 170, 414.

Pauling, L. (1940). J. Am. Chem. Soc. 62, 2643.

Pauly, H. (1959). Nature 184, 1570.

Perkins, E. H., and Marcus, S. (1957). Immunology 79, 136.

Pierce, M. (1948). In "Histopathology of Irradiation from External and Internal Sources" (W. Bloom, ed.), p. 502. McGraw-Hill, New York.

Pillemer, L., Blum, L., Lepow, I. H., Ross, O. A., Todd, E. W., and Wardlaw, A. C. (1954). Science 120, 279.

Piomelli, S., Behrendt, D. M., O'Connor, J. F., and Murray, J. E. (1961). Transplant. Bull. 27, 431.

Porter, K. A., and Cooper, E. H. (1962). J. Exptl. Med. 115, 997.

Richet, Ch. (1923). "L'anaphylaxie." Alcan, Paris.

Roberts, E., Severens, J. M., and Card, L. E. (1939). In "World's Poultry" Congr. Expos. Proc. 7, 52.

Rosenau, K. J., and Anderson, J. F. (1908). J. Infect. Diseases 5, 85.

Schechmeister, I. L., and Fishman, M. (1955). J. Exptl. Med. 101, 259, 401.

Schwienhorst, M. (1928). Beitr. Pathol. Anat. Allgem. Pathol. 81, 375.

Smith, F., Smith, W. W., Gonshery, L., and Grenman, M. M. (1954). Proc. Soc. Exptl. Biol. Med. 87, 23.

Smith, F., Ruth, J., and Grenman, M. M. (1958a). Proc. Soc. Exptl. Biol. Med. 97, 451.

Smith, W. W., Alderman, I. M., and Gillespie, R. E. (1958b). Am. J. Physiol. 192, 263.

Speirs, R. S. (1957). J. Immunol. 77, 437.

Spinelli, A., and Talia, F. (1931). Arch. Radiol. 7, 877.

Stevens, K. M., Gray, I., and Schwartz, M. S. (1953). Am. J. Physiol. 175, 141.

Stiffel, C., Halpern, B., Biozzi, G., and Mathé, G. (1959). Rev. Franc. Etudes Clin. Biol. 4, 164.

Stoner, R. D., and Hale, W. M. (1958). Radiation Res. 8, 438.

Stoner, R. D., and Hale, W. M. (1962). In "Effects of Ionizing Radiation on Immune Processes," p. 183. Gordon & Breach, New York.

Süssdorf, D. H., and Draper, L. R. (1956). J. Infect. Diseases 99, 129.

Taliaferro, W. H., and Taliaferro, L. G. (1951). J. Immunol. 6, 181.

Taliaferro, W. H., and Taliaferro, L. G. (1952). J. Immunol. 66, 201.

Taliaferro, W. H., and Taliaferro, L. G. (1954). J. Infect. Diseases 95, 117, 134.

Taliaferro, W. H., and Taliaferro, L. G. (1957). J. Infect. Diseases 101, 85.

Taliaferro, W. H., Taliaferro, L. G., and Jansens, E. F. (1952). J. Infect. Diseases 91, 105.

Talmage, D. W. (1957). J. Cellular Comp. Physiol. 50, Suppl. 1, 229.

Talmage, D. W., Freyer, G. G., and Thompson, A. (1956). J. Infect. Diseases 99, 246.

Toolan, H. W. (1957). Cancer Res. 17, 418.

Traeger, J. (1962). Cited by Calne, R. Y., 1963.

Trowell, O. A. (1952). J. Pathol. Bacteriol. 64, 687.

van Bekkum, D. W. (1956). "Ionizing Radiations and Cell Metabolism," p. 77. Churchill, London.

Vos, O., Wensinck, F., and van Bekkum, D. W. (1959). *Radiation Res.* **10.**

Warren, S. (1946). *Cancer Res.* **6,** 449.

Warren, S., and Bowers, J. Z. (1950). *Ann. Internal Med.* **32,** 207.

Warren, S., and Whipple, G. H. (1923). *J. Exptl. Med.* **38,** 713.

Waters, C. A., McCready, P. B., and Hitchcock, C. H. (1922). *Am. J. Roentgenol.* **9,** 469.

Wells, H. C. (1925). "The Chemical Aspects of Immunity." Chem. Catalog Co., New York.

Wensinck, F. (1961a). *J. Pathol. Bacteriol.* **81,** 395.

Wensinck, F. (1961b). *J. Pathol. Bacteriol.* **81,** 401.

Wensinck, F., and Renaud, E. (1957). *J. Exptl. Pathol.* **38,** 483.

Woodruff, M. F. A., Robson, J. S., McWhirter, R., Nolan, B., Wilson, T. I., Lambre, A. T., McWilliam, J. M., and McDonald, M. K. (1962). *Brit. J. Urol.* **34,** 3.

Zinzzer, H., and Casteneda, M. R. (1932). *Proc. Soc. Exptl. Biol. Med.* **29,** 840.

CHAPTER 13

Chronic Radiation Effects: Damage of Hematopoiesis

E. H. Betz

Institute of Pathology, University of Liège, Liège, Belgium

Since Heineke (1903) recognized that the hematopoietic tissues are highly sensitive to ionizing radiations, a large amount of research has been devoted to this question. The injuries of the blood-forming tissues and their manifestations in the peripheral blood have been studied mainly during the acute phase following irradiation. Animals belonging to various species have been exposed to X-rays, gamma-rays, or neutrons. It seems that the hematopoietic lesions produced by these radiations are qualitatively the same and that there is no need to discuss separately the effects of the various types of penetrating radiations.

Much more important are the conditions in which the irradiation is performed. In the present review, we shall distinguish between a single dose irradiation, a fractionated irradiation in which several exposures are performed at given intervals, each dose being delivered in a short period of time, and a chronic irradiation in which daily exposures are spread over at least 8 hours per day.

I. Single Dose Irradiation

A. EXPERIMENTAL RESULTS

1. Hematological Modifications

Studies on the acute effects of an irradiation on the hematopoietic tissues have shown that the sensitivity of these tissues varies according to species: rabbit, rat, mouse, chicken, man, goat, guinea pig, and dog, in order of increasing sensitivity. It appears also that in all species the lymphocytes are the most sensitive blood cells and that the lymphocyte values are generally the last to return to normal levels after a whole-body irradiation. Monocytes of the circulating blood initially follow a pattern of response similar to that of the lymphocytes but return much more rapidly to normal values. The granulocytes, after a possible initial rise, decrease in the blood; the recovery occurs earlier than in the case of lymphocytes. Various investigators have demonstrated that erythro-blasts are very sensitive to ionizing radiation. The occurrence of anemia depends upon the destruction of these cells in the lymphatic tissues and tissue spaces. The relative importance of these two components varies greatly according to the species and the dose of radiation.

Although an impressive number of papers has been published on the acute effects of a single dose of radiation, there are only a few dealing with the late effects. The most extensive studies in this field have been made by Cottier (1961) who exposed Swiss Albino mice to 600 r X-rays. Two to 24 months after irradiation, this author observed a slight granulocytopenia in the animals which were still in good health when killed. Granulocytopenia was often more marked when the animals were examined in the prelethal stage. Eosinophilia was not found as a late effect of irradiation; it was present only during the two months following exposure.

The histological examinations of the bone marrow were not conclusive; in some animals, its cellularity seemed to be decreased. The examination of smears indicated a shift in the cell population of the granulocyte series with a decrease in immature forms and an increase in differentiated ones. It appears therefore that irradiation does not merely interfere with dif-ferentiation of the cells but rather with their production.

Ludwig (1961) counted the total number of nucleated cells in the bone marrow of RF mice exposed to 300 r X-rays 18 months prior to sacrifice. He observed a decrease of the cell population in the marrow of irradiated animals as compared to controls.

According to Cottier (1961), the absolute number of lymphocytes in blood was little modified and, owing to the granulocytopenia, a relative lymphocytosis may be observed. Nevertheless, he found some cases of lymphopenia which occurred from 2 to 18 months after exposure. In C57 Black mice irradiated with 250–450 r, Metcalf (1959) observed an absolute lymphocytosis 3 to 15 months after exposure. This event, which is apparently an unusual late effect of a whole-body irradiation, is possibly related to the strain of mice and the conditions of irradiation.

Histological examination of lymphoid tissues (Cottier, 1961) did not reveal any late effect on the structure of the lymph follicles. The most conspicuous alteration in spleen and lymph nodes was an infiltration by plasma cells. The increase of these cells in hematopoietic tissues is well known as an acute effect of whole-body irradiation (De Bruyn, 1948; Murray, 1948; Wohlwill and Jetter, 1953; Betz, 1956). Cottier (1961) has noticed that this early infiltration decreases gradually during the first year following a single exposure of 600 r. Later on, the number of plasma cells increases again until death. Similar infiltrations occur also in unirradiated controls, but irradiation seems to hasten development of plasma cell infiltrates. There is probably a relationship between the occurrence of these cells and the occurrence of amyloidosis, which is frequently found in previously irradiated animals.

Thrombocytopenia was described by various investigators as a late effect of a single exposure to X-rays in mouse (Cottier, 1961), rat (Bennett et al., 1953; Dowdy and Bennett, 1955), and dog (Michaelson et al., 1960). In the bone marrow of mice irradiated with 600 r, the number of megakaryocytes was not significantly decreased and there were some cases with an increased number of these cells (Cottier, 1961). It must be pointed out that in many animals, as a late effect of irradiation, hemorrhagic foci are found scattered in various organs. Such hemorrhages are difficult to explain by a moderate thrombocytopenia; they are more probably related to permanent damage of the capillary bed.

The erythrocytes are also chronically affected by a single whole-body irradiation. A long-lasting anemia has been described in mice (Cottier, 1961), rats (Bennett et al., 1953; Stearner et al., 1947), and rabbits (Jacobson et al., 1947). The occurrence of anemia depends upon the dose administered: 600 r produce a chronic anemia in Swiss Albino mice (Cottier, 1961), whereas 400 r produce only a temporary decrease of red cells in A mice (Hollcroft et al., 1955). In dogs irradiated with doses in the range of $LD_{50-80/30\ days}$ the anemia lasted for 4 months with a later return of the erythrocytes to normal values (Michaelson et al., 1960). In the goat, 300 r did not significantly alter the level of red cells (O'Brien et al., 1963).

Various types of anemia have been reported. In the mouse, Cottier (1961) found normochromic anemia with a significant increase in blood reticulocytes. Reticulocytosis was also found in the rat by Bennett *et al.* (1953). In the rabbit, Jacobson *et al.* (1949) described macrocytic anemia without megaloblasts in the bone marrow. In *Macacca mulatta* exposed to neutrons (583 or 834 rep), Leffingwell *et al.* (1963) observed macrocytic anemia with a permanent increase of reticulocytes.

The mechanism of anemia is poorly understood. The increased number of reticulocytes in the peripheral blood as well as the accumulation of iron pigment in the reticulohistiocytic system and in the liver suggest the possibility of a hemolytic component. Hemorrhages into tissues may also contribute to development of the anemia. Anyway, these two factors are not sufficient to explain the changes observed in the red cell count. It seems indeed that in most cases, the total amount of erythropoietic tissue is not increased; in the marrow there is a shift of the erythropoietic cells towards the more differentiated forms. The disturbance appears to be a rather complex one in which the response of the bone marrow to the stimulus produced by increased erythrocyte destruction is impaired.

It must be kept in mind that many factors control the activity of the hematopoietic bone marrow. As far as the production of red blood cells is concerned, we know the influence of Erythropoietin, of various hormones, and possibly of inhibiting factors (Erythropenin). Nothing is known about the late effects of irradiation on the Erythropoietin-producing system. Such a study would be interesting because the kidney plays a role in the elaboration of this factor and we know that a whole-body irradiation causes chronic renal lesions.

An exposure to ionizing radiation produces acute disturbances in the secretion of various hormones (Betz, 1956). On the contrary, the late effects of endocrine glands have seldom been investigated. Hormonal disturbances may influence the activity of the bone marrow in different ways, some of which may be quite indirect. In this regard, an interesting observation has been made by Cottier (1961). In female mice given 600 r, he discovered frequently an enlargement of the internal bone trabeculae with a narrowing of the spaces occupied by the marrow. This generalized bone lesion which reduced markedly the amount of marrow was only found in animals that showed signs of hyperestrogenism due to the development of ovarian tumors. The induction of hyperostosis by estrogens has been well known since the work of Gardner and Pfeiffer (1943). In this particular case, irradiation impaired the hematopoietic activity by a very indirect mechanism involving the ovary and bone tissue.

2. Tumor Induction

It is well known that a single dose of ionizing radiations may induce leukoses in animals (Krebs *et al.*, 1930; Furth and Furth, 1936; Henshaw, 1944a). A large number of experiments have been devoted to this problem. It must first be emphasized that susceptibility to radiation-induced leukoses depends largely upon species, strain, sex, age, and physiological status. The present survey will be restricted to experimental radiation leukoses in the mouse, this species being by far the most susceptible to this disease. In the rat, a whole-body irradiation enhances the development of various kinds of tumors, but the incidence of leukoses is apparently little affected.

Among the group of murine leukoses a distinction must be made between thymic lymphomas, nonthymic lymphomas, and myeloid leukemias. Besides these three main types of leukoses, there are some others, the differential diagnosis of which is often difficult.

a. Thymic Lymphoma. In most strains of mice, the thymic lymphomas induced by a whole-body irradiation are more frequent in females than in males. The highest incidence of tumors is obtained when young animals are irradiated (around one month old). The sensitivity to the leukemogenic effect varies with the strain used, the physiological conditions, and the mode of irradiation. After a single dose of X-rays, the relation between the incidence of lymphomas and the radiation dose is nonlinear, a break in the dose-response curve occurring between 100 and 400 r, depending on the strain of mice.

It is well established that periodic total body irradiations elicit a much higher incidence of thymic lymphomas than an equal dose given as a single exposure. Therefore, the problem will be studied in further detail in the paragraph devoted to the effect of a fractionated irradiation.

b. Nonthymic Lymphoma. These tumors are much rarer than the thymic type. As has been stressed by Mole (1958) and Upton (1961), the nonthymic lymphomas form a nonhomogeneous group of diseases rather than a single disease entity. Their behavior varies according to the strain of mice used. In LAF$_1$ (Furth *et al.*, 1959) and RF mice (Upton, 1959), the incidence of extrathymic lymphomas is unaffected by irradiation. One even has the impression that the incidence of these tumors is rather decreased by the increasing amount of radiation (Furth *et al.*, 1959). However Upton *et al.* (1958) drew attention to the fact that the incidence of nonthymic lymphomas was not significantly lowered by irradiation if an adjustment was made for reduced survival, since these lymphomas occurred relatively late in life. Cole *et al.* (1960)

observed also a decreased incidence of nonthymic lymphomas in (C57Bl X A) F_1 mice exposed to a single dose of 690 r as compared with the control group. In some strains, however, the incidence of this type of tumor may be increased by irradiation (Furth and Furth, 1936).

It is interesting to note that in experiments by Upton *et al.* (1958) the removal of the thymus before irradiation, which eliminated the induction of thymic lymphomas, shifted the site of tumor formation to other lymphoid tissues. However, Kaplan (1950) did not observe any increase of extrathymic leukoses in thymectomized C57Bl mice subjected to a fractionated irradiation.

c. Myeloid Leukemia. The frequency of this tumor also depends upon the strain of mice used. In general, the incidence is increased by irradiation and is higher when young animals are irradiated. However, newborns are less susceptible than mice a few weeks old (Upton and Furth, 1958).

It seems that the amount of radiation needed to increase the incidence of myeloid leukemia is smaller than the one needed to increase the frequency of thymic lymphomas (Upton *et al.*, 1958). In RF mice, the incidence is increased many times by a single exposure of 150 r, the dose-response curve leveling off and declining between 300 and 450 r. When the incidence was adjusted to correct for mortality from other causes, the curve did not decrease above 300 r. The lowering of the slope of the myeloid leukemia induction curve above 150 r suggests that the rate was approaching "saturation" at higher dose levels. For the dose range below 150 r, the dose-response curve seems not to be linear (Upton *et al.*, 1958; Upton, 1961).

The shielding of a body part containing bone marrow (Upton *et al.*, 1958) as well as a splenectomy performed before the irradiation (Upton *et al.*, 1958) have a protective effect. The influence of sex on the susceptibility to myeloid leukemia seems to vary with the strain of mice.

B. OBSERVATIONS IN MAN

1. Hematological Modifications

The late effects of a whole-body irradiation in human beings have been extensively studied in survivors of the atomic bombing in Japan (see also Chapter 17 by Watanabe in this volume). These persons received in a very brief period of time varying amounts of radiations according to their distance from the hypocenter of the explosion and the amount of protective shielding. This last factor is usually difficult to appreciate accurately. It seems that the more reliable sign of the absorption of large amounts of radiation is the epilation of the scalp; the epilation dose of gamma-radiation of this type is estimated to be about 400 r.

In such patients, hematological modifications were prominent during the first weeks following irradiation. The leukocytes which were at the lowest level after 4 weeks began to increase after the 6th week and return to normal values around the 10th week. The lymphocytes recovered later than the granulocytes and reached normal values only after 15 to 18 weeks. The eosinophils frequently showed a rise above normal levels during the 9th and 10th weeks. The decrease of platelets appeared a little later than that of leukocytes; platelet recovery also seemed to be delayed as compared with that of leukocytes. Erythrocytes decreased until the 8th week; thereafter, they increased gradually although they were still under normal values after 15 to 18 weeks.

Recovery of the peripheral blood was markedly delayed in some patients who showed persistent leukopenia. Examining survivors of Hiroshima, one year after the bombing, Kikuchi and Wakisaka (1952) found more cases with leukopenia, thrombocytopenia, or anemia in the exposed group than in the control subjects. They observed also that both phagocytic activity and migrating function of the neutrophils were impaired in some atomic bomb sufferers. Two years after the explosion, the same authors still found patients presenting these changes. Nevertheless, they were less frequent than after one year. Snell et al., (1949) have performed careful hematological studies with similar people 20 to 33 months after the bombing. They reported that the erythrocyte count, the hemoglobin concentration, and the hematocrit reading were slightly but significantly decreased in irradiated subjects. Although the total leukocyte count was the same as in the controls, there was a slight relative depression of lymphocytes and a slight elevation of eosinophils. Similar results were published by Yamasowa (1953) who conducted his survey 33 to 44 months after the detonation of the bomb in Hiroshima. Studying the sternal bone marrow blood, Takeshima (1953) concluded that in patients who had conspicuous epilation, the erythropoietic function had not completely recovered after two years. These authors agree with Snell et al. (1949) on the fact that caution must be exercised in attributing the slight recorded differences to the irradiation. It is indeed difficult to appreciate adequately the possible effect of parasitism and malnutrition on the hematological picture observed in these people.

Seven and eleven years after the bombing, there was still a tendency towards leukopenia with neutropenia (Kono, 1957; Watanabe, 1958). Kono noticed that some survivors with a normal peripheral blood picture nevertheless showed abnormalities of the bone marrow. He found disturbances in the maturation of the erythroblastic and granulocytic series and in the production of the platelets. Lange *et al.* (1955) have reported 6 cases of "refractory" anemia (anemia, leukopenia, and thrombocytopenia) among survivors of the Nagasaki explosion. Four of these patients were exposed at distances of less than 1500 meters and developed definite radiation symptoms. The authors believe that "the occurrence of 4 cases of refractory anemia in a population of 5075 individuals representing the survivors under 1500 meters in Nagasaki, is suggestive of a probable cause and effect relationship between the exposure to the atomic bomb and the subsequent development of refractory anemia." Five similar cases were found among the survivors of Hiroshima.

A careful survey of Marshallese people exposed to fall-out radiation during the experiments at Bikini has been regularly performed every year since 1954. Sixty-four inhabitants of the island of Rongelap received the largest exposure: an estimated dose of 175 r of whole-body gamma irradiation, contamination of the skin sufficient to result in beta burns, and slight irradiation by ingested or inhaled radioactive materials. Eight years after the accident, the exposed group showed mean neutrophil and lymphocyte levels lower than a control group. The platelet levels were also slightly lower, whereas no difference was noticed in the erythrocyte levels. In some cases, bone-marrow examination revealed abnormalities in the erythroid and myeloid precursors (Cronkite *et al.*, 1955; Conard *et al.*, 1963).

2. Tumor Induction

Many reports have established the increased incidence of leukemia in survivors of Hiroshima and Nagasaki (Valentine, 1951; Folley *et al.*, 1952; Lange *et al.*, 1954; Moloney and Lange, 1954; Moloney and Kastenbaum, 1955; Wald, 1958; Heyssel *et al.*, 1960). No case of leukemia could be ascertained in the survivors in the years prior to 1947. It seems therefore that the minimum delay between irradiation and appearance of leukemia was about 3 years. The incidence of the disease was maximal between 1950 and 1952, 4 to 7 years after the explosion. Since 1952, there has been a steady decline in the number of cases reported. Nevertheless, the risk apparently continues to exist as late as 13 years after the irradiation.

Although it is difficult to estimate the dose of radiation received by these patients, it appears that the dose response curve is linear for air doses in excess of approximately 50 rads.

The leukemogenic effects of radiation are manifested equally in both sexes. All age groups seem to have been affected, however the youngest groups manifested the greatest susceptibility. It is quite clear that the irradiation did not simply accelerate the onset of the tumors but did really cause new occurrences of the disease. Among atomic bomb survivors, chronic myelogenous leukemia was most frequently encountered; acute myelogenous leukemia was second in frequency. At the younger age, the acute undifferentiated leukemia showed the most marked increase. In view of the predominance of myeloid leukemias, it must be pointed out that lymphoid leukemias are comparatively rare among Japanese people.

Moloney and Lange (1954) studied the blood changes occurring many months before clinical evidence of leukemia. They noticed a leukocytosis with granulocytosis and a relative lymphopenia. Blood smears revealed the presence of a small percentage of myelocytes and metamyelocytes and a striking increase in the absolute number of basophils. Moreover the alkaline phosphatase was extremely low in the leukocytes. When clinically evident, the radiation-induced leukemias were not different in their behavior from the naturally occurring variety of the disease.

II. Fractionated Irradiation

It appears very difficult to give a comprehensive survey of research performed in this particular field. Although a large amount of work has been done, the results are almost impossible to compare owing to the great diversity in the techniques used. We shall therefore restrict this survey to a few types of experiments, the data of which may easily be analyzed and compared.

A. EXPERIMENTAL RESULTS

1. Hematological Modifications

This section will be devoted to the hematological effects of an irradiation fractionated in daily doses administered for a long period of time. Here again the response to a given dose of radiations varies with the species considered. In Table I we have summarized experiments performed in various species by Stearner et al. (1947), Lawrence (1948), Langendorff (1953), Ingram and Masan (1954). From this table, it appears that dogs are definitely more sensitive than rats and mice. In the dog, a daily irradiation with only 0.5 r produces lymphopenia, whereas in the rat, 2.5 r/day are ineffective in this regard. The rabbit seems to be still less sensitive. The same differences appear in the doses of radiation which are necessary to induce a decrease of granulocytes in the blood. However, the granulocytes are less sensitive than the lymphocytes. For example, 10 r/day are needed to decrease the granulocytes in the rat, whereas 3 r are effective in the dog.

Experiments by Suter (1947) and by Ingram and Masan (1954) have shown that the time necessary to induce an effect with a given daily dose of X-ray also depends on the species: 10 r/day induce anemia in the dog after 16 weeks, whereas 32 weeks are required to obtain a similar effect in the rat. The leukocyte and absolute lymphocyte values of the rat decrease in 4 weeks with 10 r/day but the same elements are decreased in monkeys in 1 to 2 weeks by the same dose of radiation.

TABLE I

EFFECTS OF FRACTIONATED IRRADIATIONS ON PERIPHERAL BLOOD CELLS
IN VARIOUS SPECIES

Species	Dose per day (r)	Effects on			
		Lymphocytes	Granulocytes	Platelets	Erythrocytes
Rat	1	0	0		
	2.5	0			
	7.7	+	0		
	10	+	+		+
	33.5	+	+		+
Mouse	5	+	0		
	10	+	0		
	15	+	0		
	20	+	0		
	25	+	+		
Dog	0.1	0	0	0	0
	0.5	+	0	0	0
	1	+	±	0	0
	3	+	+	±	0
	6	+	+	+	+
Rabbit	10	+	+	+	+

A fractionated irradiation with small daily doses affects mainly the lymphocytes. These cells decrease in the peripheral blood much earlier than the other cells. Furthermore, the doses needed to produce a lymphopenia are smaller than those needed to affect the other cells, whatsoever the species used. The sensitivities of the myelocytic and thrombocytic lines seem to be very comparable. The erythropoietic line is a little less sensitive, for example, in the dog.

It must be pointed out that in mice, which received 8.6 r/day, 6 days per week, and showed only slight hematological changes, if any, there was a significant reduction in the survival rate (Henshaw et al., 1947). These authors expressed the opinion that threshold responses of the peripheral blood are at least 10 times less sensitive than the criterion of survival. Henshaw (1944b) examined the hematopoietic tissues of mice exposed to daily doses ranging from 5 to 25 r. He found that small lymphocytes were present in the lymph nodes of the 5 r sample as in the controls, whereas only swollen reticular cells and connective tissue were present in the 25 r group. The lymph nodes of animals receiving 10, 15, and 20 r/day showed intermediate stages. The bone marrow of the mice receiving 5 r was hyperplastic, whereas the marrow of the 25 r group was extremely hypocellular. The animals of the 15 and 20 r group had, in most cases, a hypoplastic marrow; those receiving 10 r showed both hypoplasia and hyperplasia.

Metcalf and Inda (1954) studied the lesions of the hematopoietic system in rats, rabbits, and dogs chronically exposed to daily doses ranging from 0.1 to 10 r. The rats did not show marked changes. In the 10 r/day group, there was perhaps a slight hypoplasia of the lymphoid follicles in spleen and nodes. There were also some animals dying with hemorrhagic lesions in the bone marrow or in the lymph nodes. In rabbits, the blood-forming system was little affected, with the possible exception of moderate hypoplasia of the bone marrow in the 10 r/day group. In the dogs exposed to daily doses of 10 r, the bone marrow was hypoplastic with a decrease of the number of megakaryocytes. Lymph node hypoplasia was somewhat more frequent and more marked in the animals irradiated with the 3 highest dose levels (0.5, 1, and 10 r). Furthermore, hemorrhages were noted in lymph nodes and intestines of dogs receiving 10 r/day.

In rats exposed to 2.5 r/day during 604 days, Langendorff (1953) found only slight modifications of the spleen follicles. It is noteworthy that according to the observations of Metcalf and Inda (1954), and those of Langendorff (1953), the testicular tissue appears to be more sensitive to small daily doses of X-rays than the hematopoietic system. Testicular lesions were conspicuous in animals which only showed slight hematological changes.

2. Tumor Induction

We have previously seen that a single dose of ionizing radiations is able to induce the development of various types of leukoses. Numerous experiments have been designed in order to investigate the influence of dose fractionation and periodicity of irradiation on the incidence of these tumors. A variety of techniques, schedules, and doses of irradiation have been used.

a. Thymic Lymphoma. Kaplan and Brown (1952a) have carefully studied the influence of dose and fractionation on the occurrence of lymphomas in C57Bl mice. They have shown that a dose of 283 r did not significantly increase the incidence of tumors above the normal level, but some of these tumors appeared earlier. Raising the total dose gradually increases the incidence of lymphomas. For a given total dose, this incidence is not modified by daily fractionation. In contrast, fractionated irradiations at intervals of 4 to 8 days increase the incidence of lymphomas and shorten the latent period. When the interval between successive dose fractions was increased to 16 days, the leukemogenic effect decreased, especially at lower dose levels. Upton and Furth (1958) and Upton et al. (1958) noticed also that the incidence of lymphomas was higher in RF mice exposed to 3 doses of 150 r at intervals of 5 days than in those exposed at the same dose at intervals of 2 days. Using CBA mice, Mole (1956) also found a complex time-intensity relationship.

These results suggest that there exists some correlation of the timing of radiation with the rhythm of thymic injury and repair. Kaplan and his co-workers have studied various physiological conditions which are able to influence the thymic activity and also the incidence of radiation-induced lymphoma.

As we have previously mentioned, the incidence of thymic lymphomas is highest in mice irradiated at the age of one month. Females are more susceptible than males. Castration of males (Kaplan, 1950; Toch et al., 1956), prolonged estrogen treatment (Kirschbaum et al., 1949; Gardner, 1950; Gardner and Rygaard, 1954; Toch et al., 1956), and adrenalectomy (Kaplan et al., 1951) enhance the development of tumors. On the contrary, castration of females (Upton et al., 1958), testosterone treatment during (Kaplan and Brown, 1952b) or after irradiation (Gardner and Rygaard, 1954), cortisone treatment (Kaplan et al., 1951), hypothyroidy induced by thiouracil (Morris et al., 1957) or radioiodine (Nagareda and Kaplan, 1957) decrease the incidence of thymic tumors.

The induction of lymphomas by a whole-body irradiation is prevented by shielding a part of the body (Kaplan and Brown, 1952c; Lorenz et al., 1953; Kirschbaum et al., 1953) or by injecting unirradiated isogenic bone marrow cells (Kaplan et al., 1953) or spleen cells (Cole et al., 1956). On the contrary, the injection of intact thymus cells does not prevent the development of lymphomas (Brown et al., 1953). It is noteworthy that these treatments, which are effective in preventing the development of tumors, also accelerate the regeneration of the injured thymus.

Kaplan and Brown (1957) have studied the histological modifications leading to formation of tumors. There was no correlation between the severity of thymic radiation injury and tumor yield. Nevertheless, these authors found differences in the degree of regeneration. The new thymus cells are derived from large immature cells which gradually differentiate into a smaller, more mature form. This process of maturation is favored by shielding the thigh or by injecting marrow cells (Carnes and Kaplan, 1956; Carnes *et al.*, 1956). When this "marrow factor" is absent, there seems to be a maturation arrest and the thymus cortex remains composed of large immature lymphoid cells with numerous mitoses. These cells look very much like those of lymphoid tumors.

The mechanism by which hematopoietic cells protect against lymphoma induction has been the matter of much discussion. Various possibilities have been suggested: recolonization of the injured thymus; restoration of the immunological mechanisms depressed by irradiation; influence on the maturation process of thymocytes. For further discussion of these hypotheses, see the review by Miller (1961).

It is noteworthy that in mice injected with chemical protectors, like cystamine or cysteinamine, the yield of thymic lymphomas is slightly increased (Mewissen, 1961).

More recently, Lieberman and Kaplan (1959) showed that cell-free filtrates of radiation-induced lymphomas of C57Bl mice produce lymphomas when injected into newborn isogenic animals. Serial passages of such filtrates increased the tumor yield markedly. No such agent could be detected in filtrates prepared from thymic glands of nonirradiated C57Bl mice nor from glands taken 2 to 32 days after irradiation. The activity was first detected 64 days after irradiation. Similar results were obtained by Gross (1957) in C3H and C57 Brown mice and by Latarjet and Duplan (1962) in C57Bl mice.

As Kaplan (1961) has pointed out, thymic lymphomas arise by an indirect mechanism. He has assumed that "the viral agent may have a particular affinity or requirement for these undifferentiated cells as host and that it is not able to proliferate at an equilibrium sustaining level leading to tumor development except in the presence of an adequate reservoir of such immature cells."

b. Extrathymic Lymphoma. This tumor group has been discussed earlier. In the present paragraph, we shall only consider the effect of fractionation of the irradiation dose. In CBA mice, exposed to fractionated doses in the range 500 to 1500 r, Mole (1958) found an increase of extrathymic leukemias whatever the total dose. Later in life, the lowest dose (500 r) had apparently more effect than the higher doses. It must be pointed out, however, that in this study, all types of extrathymic leukosis were pooled in a single group. Cole and Nowell (1963) have irradiated young LAF_1 mice with 260 rads (5 rads $\times$ 52, given weekly) and found an increase of extrathymic lymphomas as compared to controls and to mice given a single exposure of 260 rads. This increased incidence was not reduced by lead shielding of the thigh bone marrow at the time of fractionated irradiation. On the contrary, in mice of strain A receiving 500 to 1500 r given as 100 r weekly, the incidence of nonthymic lymphomas was little affected by irradiation (Duhig and Warren, 1960).

c. *Myeloid Leukemia.* As has been mentioned previously, a total body irradiation increases the incidence of myeloid leukemia. Nevertheless, fractionation of the dose does not favor development of the tumor (Upton *et al.*, 1958).

B. Human Leukosis

The effects of fractionated irradiations in human beings have been studied in patients irradiated for therapeutic purposes.

Court-Brown and Abbatt (1955) and Van Swaay (1955) reported an increased incidence of leukemia in patients treated by X-rays for ankylosing spondylitis. Court-Brown and Doll (1957) have published a thorough study of 13,352 such patients. They found 46 patients who had died with a diagnosis of leukemia, aplastic or hypoplastic anemia, or myelofibrosis; 3 further patients suffering from leukemia were still alive. In 28 of the 46 patients, death was attributable to leukemia, whereas the expected number was 2.9. The increase in leukemia was due to an increase in the chronic myeloid and acute forms; no evidence of an increase in chronic lymphoid leukemia was found. The latent period was most commonly between 3 and 5 years. This study is a very valuable one; there remains nevertheless the possibility of an association between spondylitis and leukemia (Abbatt and Lea, 1958). Nor can the possibility be excluded that patients suffering from spondylitis are more susceptible than normal individuals to the induction of leukemia by X-rays. Court-Brown and Doll (1957) have also attempted to estimate the mean dose delivered to the spinal marrow and to find the relationship between dose and leukemia incidence. The dose-effect curve is clearly linear for the middle dose groups, but there has been much discussion about how the curve should be drawn for the lower doses, particularly with regard to whether or not there is a threshold dose.

In Denmark, Faber (1957) studied the incidence of a former therapeutic irradiation in 828 cases of leukemia. This incidence was 1.8% for chronic lymphatic leukemia, 7.8% for chronic myeloid leukemia, and 8% for acute leukemia. He reported also that the incidence of X-ray exposure in control patients did not differ significantly from that of patients with chronic lymphatic leukemia. Faber's conclusion was that chronic lymphatic leukemia is not increased by X-ray treatment, whereas both chronic myeloid and acute leukemia may be induced by irradiation.

He further concluded that some cases in his series must have been caused by diagnostic X-ray exposure.

Simpson *et al.* (1955), Simpson and Hempelmann (1957), and Simpson (1959) studied the incidence of tumors (mainly leukemias and thyroid tumors) in children irradiated for thymic enlargment. They found a greater incidence of leukemia than would have been expected. Similar observations were made by Polhemus and Koch (1959) and by Murray *et al.* (1960). On the other hand, no increased incidence has been found in children with normal-sized thymus given X-ray treatment (Conti *et al.*, 1960). Although the conditions of irradiation were different in these patients, the possibility could not be excluded that an enlarged thymus during infancy may be associated with a hightened tendency for the development of leukemia.

III. Chronic Irradiation

A. EXPERIMENTAL RESULTS

1. *Hematological Modifications*

Laboratory animals have been exposed to chronic irradiations given daily for from 8 to 24 hours. Lorenz *et al.* (1946, 1950, 1953, 1954) have in this way irradiated mice, guinea pigs, and rabbits. Groups of animals were exposed to doses of 0.11, 1.1, 2.2, 4.4, and 8.8 r for 8 hours per day, during periods reaching more than 3 years. In mice the mean leukocyte count was reduced in the groups receiving 2.2 r and more. This did reflect a reduction of lymphocytes, whereas the granulocytes remained in all groups within normal limits. A questionable reduction in erythrocytes and platelets occurred in mice exposed to 4.4 r/day. On the contrary, erythrocytes, lymphocytes, and platelets were clearly decreased in the 8.8 r/day group. The guinea pig appeared to be more sensitive than the mouse. There was, indeed, a lymphopenia after doses of 0.11 and 1.1 r/day. In the group exposed to 2.2 r and above, a pancytopenia developed. In rabbits, the only noticeable effect was a lymphopenia with relative granulocytosis in all groups except those exposed to 0.11 r. The other blood cells were unaffected.

The histological effects of these irradiations were studied in mice by Spargo *et al.* (1951). There was only a slight decrease in thymic lymphocytes in the 1.1 r/day group. After 4.4 r, the hematopoietic organs with the exception of the lymph nodes underwent a progressive depletion. In the 8.8 r group, depletion was observed in all blood-forming tissues including the lymph nodes; there was also a shift of the cell population towards more immature forms.

Lamerton *et al.* (1960) studied the blood and bone marrow of rats subjected to continuous irradiation at dose rates from 16 to 415 rads/day. The irradiation was given continuously during 23½ hours/day. At 16 and 50 rads/day, there was an initial drop of the number of leukocytes and platelets followed after 20 days by a rise and maintenance at roughly normal values. The dose of 84 rads/day also produced a decrease of leukocytes and platelets. The recovery which occurred at about 20 days was only transient. These animals died with a pancytopenia. The mean survival time of the 84 rads group was 50 days, whereas it was 150–200 days in the 50 rads group and more than 320 days in the 16 rads group. Investigation of the bone marrow has shown that in the 50 and 84 rads groups, the number of nucleated cells decreases rapidly during the 20 days after the beginning of irradiation. Later on, the cell number remains around 50% of the normal values in the 50 rads group and 20% of the controls in the 84 rads group. Furthermore, in the 50 rads group, the mitotic index after an initial drop increases above normal values. The blood-forming system is thus able to maintain a steady state at relatively high dose rates. The mechanisms involved in the establishment of this steady state are very complex. Although the mitotic index is increased after 50 rads/day, the total rate of cell production is under the normal level. There must be further regulatory mechanisms maintaining approximately normal peripheral blood counts in spite of a reduction in the rate of new cell production (Lamerton *et al.*, 1960).

Miller and Sacher (1959) have studied rats exposed to 32 r/day for 107 days. At the end of this period, the erythrocyte count was about 18% below normal. The hemoglobin and hematrocrit values were depressed by about 10%. There was no significant difference in the absolute numbers of circulating reticulocytes, and the Fe_{59} uptake was nearly normal in the irradiated animals.

2. Tumor Induction

A fractionated irradiation does increase the incidence of leukemia in mice. Lorenz (1950) has found a higher percentage of leukemias in mice exposed to 8.8 r daily than in nonirradiated controls. Daily doses of 4.4 r hastened the onset of the disease but did not increase its total incidence. Similar results were obtained by Spargo *et al.* (1951).

B. Observations in Man

1. Hematological Modifications

The development of atomic energy programs in various countries have promoted studies of the effect of small radiation doses in human beings. In order to detect minimal hematological changes in workers exposed to ionizing radiations, many elaborate methods have been described. The granulocytopenia, the hypersegmentation of granulocytes, the increase of bilobed or binucleated lymphocytes, the "shift to the left" in the blood picture, all have been used as criteria to detect the early blood changes (Helde, 1946; Nordenson, 1946; Knowlton, 1948; Ingram and Barnes, 1949). Sievert (1947) found changes in persons exposed to X-rays at levels estimated to be as low as 0.02 to 0.05 r/day. Mayneord (1951) reported a significant depression in leukocytes after chronic exposures probably not exceeding 0.125 r/week and Knowlton (1948) found a decrease in lymphocytes after radiation levels of 0.21 r/week.

Such results seem to indicate a high sensitivity of man to ionizing radiations. However, it is difficult to estimate the effects of low level irradiations in man. One must be very careful in ascribing the observed modifications to the action of radiations. Minimal changes like those reported are not at all specific but may be sometimes produced by any physiological stress. This seems to be the case for binucleated lymphocytes. There is indeed an increase of these cells in the blood of chronically irradiated subjects (Ingram and Barnes, 1949; Dobson and Chupp, 1958). However, such lymphocytes appear also in the blood of animals exposed to heat (Murphy and Sturm, 1919), and have been observed in human patients suffering from various diseases (Dobson and Chupp, 1958). Ingram (1955) has emphasized the importance of considering the general health of an individual when interpreting such hematological responses.

2. Tumor Induction

An example of chronic exposure to X-rays in man is that of radiologists. A number of studies have shown the increased frequency of deaths from leukemia in American radiologists (Henshaw and Hawkins, 1944; March, 1950; Schwartz and Upton, 1958). In contrast, excess cases of leukemia have not occurred in British radiologists who began to practice after 1921; there is evidence of a small increase in mortality from leukemia among those who entered radiological practice before 1921 (Court-Brown and Doll, 1958). This difference could be due to the high British standards of protection introduced in the early days of radiology. In fact, it is difficult to determine the dose of radiation absorbed by X-ray workers. Many factors are involved which may be responsible for large individual variations, e.g., size of the practice, concern for safety, and type of equipment used. It is therefore almost impossible to draw any conclusion on the quantitative aspects of the relationship between exposure and leukemia frequency in radiologists. (See also Chapter 11 by Mathé, in this volume.)

References

Abbatt, J. D., and Lea, A. J. (1958). *Lancet* **II**, 880.
Bennett, L. R., Chastain, S. M., Flint, J. S., Hansen, R. A., and Lewis, A. E. (1953). *Radiology* **61**, 411.
Betz, E. H. (1956). "Contribution à l'étude du syndrome endocrinien provoqué par l'irradiation totale de l'organisme." Masson, Paris.
Brown, M. B., Kaplan, H. S., Weymouth, P. P., and Paul, J. (1953). *Science* **117**, 693.
Carnes, W. H., and Kaplan, H. S. (1956). *Proc. Am. Assoc. Cancer Res.* **2**, 99.
Carnes, W. H., Brown, M. B., and Hirsch, B. B. (1956). *Cancer Res.* **16**, 429.
Cole, L. J., and Nowell, P. C. (1963). *Radiation Res.* **18**, 487.
Cole, L. J., Nowell, P. C., and Ellis, M. E. (1956). *Proc. Am. Assoc. Cancer Res.* **2**, 100.
Cole, L. J., Nowell, P. C., and Arnold, J. S. (1960). *Radiation Res.* **12**, 562.
Conrad, R. A., Meyer, L. M., Sutow, W. W., Moloney, W. C., Lowery, A., Hicking, A., and Riklon, E. (1963). Brookhaven Natl. Lab. Rept. BNL-780 (T-296).
Conti, E. A., Patton, G. B., Conti, J. E., and Hempelmann, L. H. (1960). *Radiology* **74**, 386.
Cottier, H. (1961). "Strahlenbedingte Lebenverkürzung." Springer, Berlin.
Court-Brown, W. M., and Abbatt, J. D. (1955). *Lancet* **I**, 1283.
Court-Brown, W. M., and Doell, R. (1957). *Med. Res. Council Spec. Rept. Ser.* **295**.
Court-Brown, W. M., and Doell, R. (1958). *Brit. Med. J.* **II**, 181.
Cronkite, E. P., Dunham, C. L., Griffin, D., McPherson, S. D., and Woodward K. T. (1955). Brookhaven Natl. Lab. Rept. BNL-384 (T-71).
De Bruyn, P. P. H. (1948). *In* "Histopathology of Irradiation from External and Internal Sources" (W. Bloom, ed.), p. 348. McGraw-Hill, New York.
Dobson, E. L., and Chupp, M. M. (1958). *Proc. 2nd Intern. Conf. Peaceful Uses Atomic Energy, Geneva* Vol. 23, p. 188.
Dowdy, A. H., and Bennett, L. R. (1955). *Am. J. Roentgenol. Radium Therapy Nucl. Med.* **73**, 639.
Duhig, J. T., and Warren, S. (1960). *Radiation Res.* **12**, 173.
Faber, M. (1957). *In* "Advances in Radiobiology" (G. C. De Hevesy, A. G. Forssberg, and J. D. Abbatt, eds.) Oliver & Boyd, Edinburgh and London.
Folley, J. H., Borges, W., and Yamawaki, T. (1952). *Am. J. Med.* **13**, 311.
Furth, J., and Furth, O. B. (1936). *Am. J. Cancer* **28**, 54.
Furth, J., Upton, A. C., and Kimball, A. W. (1959). *Radiation Res. Suppl.* **1**, 243.
Gardner, W. U. (1950). *Cancer Res.* **10**, 219.
Gardner, W. U., and Pfeiffer, C. A. (1943). *Physiol. Rev.* **23**, 139.
Gardner, W. U., and Rygaard, J. (1954). *Cancer Res.* **14**, 205.
Gross, L. (1957). *Proc. Am. Assoc. Cancer Res.* **2**, 209.
Heineke, H. (1903). *Muench. Med. Wochschr.* **50**, 2090.
Helde, M. (1946). *Acta Radiol.* **27**, 308.
Henshaw, F. S. (1944a). *Radiology* **43**, 279.
Henshaw, F. S. (1944b). *J. Natl. Cancer Inst.* **4**, 513.
Henshaw, F. S., and Hawkins, J. W. (1944). *J. Natl. Cancer Inst.* **4**, 339.
Henshaw, F. S., Riley, E. F., and Stapleton, G. E. (1947). *Radiology* **49**, 349.
Heyssel, R. M., Brill, A. B., Woodburg, L. A., Nishimura, E. T., Ghose, T., Hoshino, T., and Yamazaki, M. (1960). *Blood* **15**, 313.

Hollcroft, J. W., Lorenz, E., Matthews, M., and Congdon, C. C. (1955). *J. Natl. Cancer Inst.* 15, 1059.

Ingram, M. (1955). *Proc. 2nd Intern. Conf. Peaceful Uses Atomic Energy, Geneva* Vol. 13, p. 210.

Ingram, M., and Barnes, S. W. (1949). *Physiol. Rev.* 75, 1765.

Ingram, M., and Masan, W. B. (1954). *In* "Biological Effects of External Radiations" (H. A. Blair, ed.), p. 253. McGraw-Hill, New York.

Jacobson, L. O., Marks, E. K., Simmons, E. L., Hagen, C. W., and Zirkle, R. E. (1947). U. S. Atomic Energy Comm. Rept. MDDC-1174.

Jacobson, L. O., Marks, E. K., and Lorenz, E. (1949). *Radiology* 52, 371.

Kaplan, H. S. (1950). *J. Natl. Cancer Inst.* 11, 83.

Kaplan, H. S. (1961). *Cancer Res.* 21, 981.

Kaplan, H. S., and Brown, M. B. (1952a). *J. Natl. Cancer Inst.* 13, 185.

Kaplan, H. S., and Brown, M. B. (1952b). *Cancer Res.* 12, 445.

Kaplan, H. S., and Brown, M. B. (1952c). *Cancer Res.* 12, 441.

Kaplan, H. S., and Brown, M. B. (1957). *In* "The Leukemias: Etiology, Pathophysiology and Treatment" (J. W. Rebuck, F. H. Bethell, and R. W. Monto, eds.), p. 613. Academic Press, New York.

Kaplan, H. S., Marder, S. N., and Brown, M. B. (1951). *Cancer Res.* 11, 629.

Kaplan, H. S., Brown, M. B., and Paull, J. (1953). *J. Natl. Cancer Inst.* 14, 303.

Kikuchi, T., and Wakisaka, G. (1952). *Acta Schol. Med. Univ. Kyoto* 30, 1.

Kirschbaum, A., Shapiro, J. R., and Mixer, H. W. (1949). *Proc. Soc. Exptl. Biol. Med.* 72, 632.

Kirschbaum, A., Shapiro, J. R., and Mixer, H. W. (1953). *Cancer Res.* 13, 262.

Knowlton, N. P., Jr. (1948). U. S. Atomic Energy Comm. Rept. AECO-1021.

Kono, Y. (1957). Paper presented at *Conf. intern. sur l'influence des conditions de vie et de travail sur la santé,* Cannes.

Krebs, C. A., Wagner, A., and Rask-Nielsen, H. C. (1930). *Acta Radiol. Suppl.* 10, 1.

Lamerton, L. F., Pontifex, A. H., Blackett, N. M., and Adams, K. (1960). *Brit. J. Radiol.* 33, 287.

Lange, R. D., Moloney, W. C., and Yamawaki, T. (1954). *Blood* 9, 574.

Lange, R. D., Wright, S. N., Tomonaga, M., Kurasaki, H., Matsuoke, S., and Matsunaga, M. (1955). *Blood* 10, 312.

Langendorff, H. (1953). *Strahlentherapie* 90, 408.

Latarjet, R., and Duplan, J. F. (1962). *Intern. J. Radiation Biol.* 5, 339.

Lawrence, J. S., Dowdy, A. H., and Valentine, W. N. (1948). *Radiology* 51, 400.

Leffingwell, T. B., Melville, G. S., and Young, R. J. (1963). *Radiation Res.* 19, 195.

Lieberman, M., and Kaplan, H. S. (1959). *Science* 130, 387.

Lorenz, E. (1950). *Am. J. Roentgenol.* 63, 176.

Lorenz, E., Heston, W. E., Jacobson, L. O., Eschenbrenner, A. B., Shimkin, M. B., Deringer, M. K., Doniger, J., and Schweisthal, R. (1946). U. S. Atomic Energy Comm. Rept. MDDC-653, p. 654.

Lorenz, E., Jacobson, L. O., and Sutton, H. (1950). U. S. Atomic Energy Comm. Rept. ANL-4401, p. 38.

Lorenz, E., Congdon, C. C., and Uphoff, D. E. (1953). *J. Natl. Cancer Inst.* 14, 291.

Lorenz, E., Jacobson, L. O., Heston, W. E., Shimkin, M., Eschenbrenner, A. B., Deringer, M. K., Doniger, J., and Schweisthal, R. (1954). *In* "Biological Effects of External X and Gamma Radiation" (F. Niggli, ed.), p. 300. McGraw-Hill, New York.

Ludwig, F. C. (1961). Univ. Calif. School Med. San Francisco, Rept. UCSF 21, 41.

March, H. C. (1950). Am. J. Med. Sci. 220, 282.

Mayneord, N. V. (1951). Brit. J. Radiol. 24, 525.

Metcalf, D. (1959). Radiation Res. 10, 313.

Metcalf, R. G., and Inda, F. A. (1954). In "Biological Effects of External Radiation" (H. A. Blair, ed.). McGraw-Hill, New York.

Mewissen, D. J. (1961). "Radiolésions, radiocancers et radioprotection chimique." Arscia, Brussels.

Michaelson, S. M., Thomson, R. A. E., Hasen, C. L., and Howland, J. W. (1960). Radiation Res. 12, 456.

Miller, J. F. A. P. (1961). Advan. Cancer Res. 6, 291.

Miller, M., and Sacher, G. A. (1959). Radiation Res. 11, 455.

Mole, R. H. (1956). In "Progress in Radiobiology" (J. S. Mitchell, B. E. Holmes, and C. L. Smith, eds.), p. 468. Oliver & Boyd, Edinburgh and London.

Mole, R. H. (1958). Brit. Med. Bull. 14, 174.

Moloney, W. C., and Kastenbaum, M. A. (1955). Science 121, 308.

Moloney, W. C., and Lange, R. D. (1954). Blood 9, 663.

Morris, D. M., Wolff, F. F., and Upton, A. C. (1957). Cancer Res. 17, 325.

Murphy, J. B., and Sturm, E. (1919). J. Exptl. Med. 29, 1.

Murray, R. G. (1948). In "Histopathology of Irradiation from External and Internal Sources" (W. Bloom, ed.), p. 243. McGraw-Hill, New York.

Murray, R. G., Heckel, P., and Hempelmann, L. H. (1960). Cited by Hempelmann, L. H. Cancer Res. 20, 18.

Nagareda, C. S., and Kaplan, H. S. (1957). Radiation Res. 7, 440.

Nordenson, N. G. (1946). Acta Radiol. 27, 416.

O'Brien, C. A., Pace, H. B., Austin, J. W., and Adam, G. M. (1963). Radiation Res. 19, 195 (Abstr.).

Polhemus, D. W., and Koch, R. (1959). Pediatrics 23, 453.

Schwartz, E. E., and Upton, A. C. (1958). Blood 13, 845.

Sievert, R. M. (1947). Brit. J. Radiol. 20, 308.

Simpson, C. L. (1959). In "Radiation Biology and Cancer" (M. D. Anderson Hospital Symp.), p. 336. Univ. of Texas Press, Austin, Texas.

Simpson, C. L., and Hempelmann, L. H. (1957). Cancer 10, 42.

Simpson, C. L., Hempelmann, L. H., and Fuller, L. M. (1955). Radiology 64, 840.

Snell, F. M., Neel, J. V., and Ishibaki, K. (1949). Arch. Internal Med. 84, 569.

Spargo, B., Bloomfield, J. R., Glotzer, D. J., Leiter, G. E., and Nichols, O. (1951). J. Natl. Cancer Inst. 12, 615.

Stearner, S. P., Simmons, E. L., and Jacobson, L. O. (1947). U. S. Atomic Energy Comm. Rept. MDDC-1319.

Suter, G. M. (1947). U. S. Atomic Energy Comm. Rept. MDDC-824.

Takeshima, K. (1953). Acta Pathol. Japon. 3, 124.

Toch, P., Hirsch, B., Brown, M. B., Nagareda, C. S., and Kaplan, H. S. (1956). Cancer Res. 18, 890.

Upton, A. C. (1959). In "Ciba Foundation Symposium on Carcinogenesis: Mechanisms of Action" (G. E. W. Wolstenholme and M. O'Connor, eds.), p. 249. Churchill, London.

Upton, A. C. (1961). Cancer Res. 21, 717.

Upton, A. C., and Furth, J. (1958). Proc. 6th Intern. Congr. Soc. Hematol. p. 98.

Upton, A. C., Wolff, F. F., Furth, J., and Kimball, A. W. (1958). Cancer Res. 18, 842.

Valentine, W. N. (1951). Atomic Bomb Casualty Commission Tech. Rept.
Van Swaay, H. (1955). *Lancet* **II**, 225.
Wald, N. (1958). *Science* **127**, 699.
Watanabe, S. (1958). *Acta Haematol. Japon.* **21**, Suppl., 301.
Wohlwill, F. J., and Jetter, W. W. (1953). *Am. J. Pathol.* **29**, 721.
Yamasowa, Y. (1953). *Acta Internal Med.* **91**, 310.

CHAPTER 14

Effects of Radiations on the Coagulation of Blood*

Ioulios A. Iossifides and Philip H. Geisler†

*The Cardeza Foundation for Hematologic Research,
Jefferson Medical College, Philadelphia, Pennsylvania*

* Supported by U. S. Atomic Energy Commission contract AEC AT (30–1) 1982.
† Deceased.

I. General Introduction

Authors who attempt a critical review of the cause and effect relationships between two sets of phenomena, the one physical and the other biological, must be prepared for difficulties arising from the possible controversial nature of their subject matter. In spite of intensive studies of the effects of ionizing radiations on living matter, the mechanisms involved are still only partially known. Only in recent years has the study of radiobiology passed from the early stages of gross clinical observation to the refinements of an intracellular and molecular science, and biochemistry has now become the chief source of new information. Analysis of the effects of ionizing radiation on blood coagulation is compounded by the fact that the physiological and biochemical mechanisms of the normal clotting process are still poorly understood and are subject to many contradictory interpretations. Because of the dynamic nature of the material detailed consideration of the many hypotheses evolved to explain radiation-induced alterations in clotting parameters is beyond the scope of this chapter. We shall attempt to report principally those investigations which have led to generally accepted concepts, and to minimize purely speculative material.

It is obvious that the effects of ionizing radiations on the various factors and elements of blood coagulation cannot be separated from the effects of these same radiations on other bodily functions and structures. For example, the effects of radiation on fibrinogen and fibrinolysin should properly be considered in the light of concomitant impairment of liver functions. The intricate chain-reaction complex of blood coagulation with its enzymes, substrates, activators, inhibitors, energy donors, and autoregulatory mechanisms is dependent upon a balanced system of bodily functions. Ionizing radiations have many different deleterious effects, each one of which could presumably influence directly or indirectly the processes of coagulation. Although review articles on the effects of radiation on blood clotting are indeed few, there is a multitude of excellent publications dealing with specific studies and it has been attempted to include as many of these as possible. Omissions that inadvertently have occurred reflect not the intrinsic value of the omitted work but rather the limitations of the author's capacity to select from the available material.

II. Historical Review

It was not until after the wartime nuclear explosions that the full clinical significance of post-radiation hemorrhagic diathesis was realized and intensively explored. Prior to that the deleterious effects of X-radiation on the blood and the blood forming organs had been described, but no systematic investigation was undertaken. A review of the earlier literature has been published (Jackson et al., 1952a). It appears (Mossberg, 1947) that the first to observe the action of radiation on specific cells in the bone marrow was Heineke (1903, 1904, 1905) who, stimulated by London's observations (1903) investigated the bone marrow cell injuries in animals exposed to roentgen and radium rays. He reported the disappearance of native giant cells from the bone marrow in guinea pigs and rabbits following X-radiation and observed that the phenomenon was reversible if the animal was to survive. Working with rats, rabbits, and dogs, Helber and Linser (1905) could only see unimportant morphological and quantitative changes in the thrombocytes following chronic X-radiation; slight changes in the platelet counts were also reported by Drause and Ziegler (1906–1907). Duke (1915) was the first to observe the rise in the thrombocyte counts following low doses of X-rays, an observation that is accepted nowadays as valid. In long-term total body exposures of guinea pigs to X-rays, Fabricius-Moeller (1922) observed a progressive thrombocytopenia associated with a parallel disappearance of megakaryocytes. This led him to conclude that Wright's theory (1906) correlating the production of platelets to the megakaryocytes was probably correct. He was also the first to conclude that the hemorrhagic diathesis produced by the X-rays was the direct result of the thrombocytopenia and not of other possible changes in the fibrin content of the blood. Death from hemorrhages associated with low platelet counts were also reported in the same year in newborn rabbits following X-radiation of the pregnant mothers (Lacassagne et al., 1922). In 1923 Mottram reported a transient thrombocytopenia following prolonged exposure to radium, and confirmed a transient rise in the platelet numbers with small radiation doses. Summarizing the accumulated experience on the effects of radium or X-rays on the blood elements including the thrombocytes, Minot and Spurling wrote in 1924, "The greater the dose the more profound is the blood damage, the more rapidly it develops and the more slowly it is repaired. The blood response remains quite consistent qualitatively over a wide range of dosage, although massive exposures may obscure the early changes, and small doses sometimes fail to evoke the complete response." Following these initial observations, confirmatory reports on the depressive effects of X-rays on thrombocyte counts (Takacizumi and Ono, 1929; Ducuing *et al.*, 1936; Barnes, 1941; Dunlap, 1942; Neefe, 1936–1937; Craver and MacComb, 1934; Clarkson *et al.*, 1938; Wright and Bulman, 1929), thought in many instances to be more sensitive indices of X-radiation damage than other blood constituents (Shouse *et al.*, 1931; Bignani, 1939), on the megakaryocytes of the bone marrow (Latta and Ehlers, 1931; Langendorf and Papperitz, 1939), and on other parameters of coagulation, became more abundant. In addition, it was slowly realized that X-radiations are indeed dangerous and could result in death even in small doses if the exposure is continued over long periods of time. As early as 1915 the autopsy of the first known human victim of X-rays, an Italian radiologist, was reported (Gawazzeni and Minelli, 1914–1915). In 1937 a review of the literature revealed 32 recorded cases of aplastic anemia among chronically exposed subjects, many of whom presented severe thrombocytopenia and hemorrhages (Engelbreth-Holm, 1957). Systematic work, however, correlating the chronic radiation exposures to thrombocytopenia in humans did not appear until after 1947.

III. Basic Concepts and Definitions

A. Ionizing Radiations

There are many kinds of radiations, originating from both natural and man-made sources, which are physically similar and which exert essentially similar biological effects. The physical and physicochemical properties of these radiations are relatively well known, but much less insight has been gained concerning their effect on living matter and its cellular and subcellular components. This lack of knowledge concerning predictable biological effects of ionizing radiations reflects the still elementary state of our information and may also be an indication of the resistance of living tissues to some types of radiation. Be this as it may, it is true that only a small number of the known actinic energies produce detectable alterations in blood clotting parameters. Among these the more common are the following.

1. X-radiation or Roentgen-Radiation

X-radiation is an electromagnetic radiation generated by the action of fast-moving electrons (cathode rays) upon a target. The X-ray generating energy stems from the replacement of orbital target electrons that happened to be hit by the cathode rays; or it is produced by the retardation of previously accelerated electrons in the anode of an X-ray tube. X-rays originate only from the perinuclear areas of the atom and possess neither a mass nor a charge. Their tissue-penetrating capacity is great and appears to be related to their energy potential, which in turn is directly dependent upon the voltage applied to the generating tube.

2. Alpha-Radiation

Alpha-radiation is produced almost exclusively during the radioactive disintegration of certain radioisotopes, such as radium, uranium, or plutonium. It represents high speed helium nuclei, stripped of their electrons and composed only of two protons and two neutrons; they possess therefore a mass of 4 and a charge of $+2$. This relatively large-size charged particle has a weak penetrating capability, which does not exceed 0.1 mm in tissues; in its short course, however, it creates dense ionization by dislodging orbiting electrons from the atoms found in its path. Consequently, alpha-rays from sources outside the body have little or no biological effect, but when introduced internally, tissue damage may be extensive.

3. Beta-Radiation

Beta-radiation consists of energized negatively charged particles with a very small mass. They are, therefore, indistinguishable from electrons, the only difference being that the latter stem from the perinuclear shells while the beta-rays originate from within the nucleus. Radioisotopes such as strontium-90, yttrium-90, caesium-137, iodine-131, or carbon-14 are among the best known beta emitters. The high speed, light-weight beta particle ionizes less but penetrates deeper than the alpha-rays, reaching a tissue depth from a few millimeters up to eight centimeters depending upon the generating source. As in the case of alpha-rays, beta-rays are much more effective when they are emitted from within the body.

4. Gamma-Radiation

Physically, gamma-rays cannot be distinguished from X-rays since they actually are electromagnetic rays; in contrast, however, to X-radiations, they originate from within the nuclei of radioisotopic elements. Their tissue penetrating capacity is great and the high content of energy they carry results in the creation of dense clouds of electrons (Compton electrons) dislodged from their prospective orbits by direct atom hits and energy transfer. The activated electrons are, therefore, in reality the source of the ionization, and consequently the biological effectiveness of the gamma-rays depends upon the magnitude of the electron cloud they produce. High energy gamma-rays penetrate deeper and ionize extensively; low energy or soft gamma-rays are more readily absorbed and produce small electron fields.

5. Neutron-Radiation

Neutrons are found as natural constituents of atomic nuclei, being ejected only during the disruption of an atom. Their mass is 1, while their zero charge allows them to penetrate easily without creating ionization by direct action. According to their contained energy, neutrons are categorized as fast or slow neutrons, each group acting differently upon the molecules of the tissue target. Fast neutrons ionize by transfer of energy to nuclei of hydrogen; the latter, under the direct impact of the collision, recoil and detach from their molecules. As a result, heavy, charged particles are created which produce a dense secondary ionization. Slow neutrons, on the other hand, ionize by incorporating themselves within the nuclear mass of atoms, thus releasing gamma-rays and charged particles while creating at the same time isotopes, some of which are radioactive.

6. Other Radiations

There are other radiations that might exert some biological effects, such as proton radiation or cosmic radiations, but even a brief discussion of their properties will exceed the purpose of this chapter, since they have no known direct effects on the coagulation of blood.

B. RADIATION ENERGY AND RADIOBIOLOGICAL UNITS

A biological effect is in reality the expression of the balance between the energy conveyed by the acting radiation and the ability of the target tissue to absorb it. The energy contained in a given radiation is usually expressed in electron-volts (ev), or in multiple units (ev $\times$ 10^3 = kev, ev $\times$ 10^6 = Mev). This energy, dependent as it is upon the type of radiation and the intensity of the producing source, manifests itself and is measured in terms of ionizations that it produces. A unit for ionization produced in air by X- or gamma-rays is the roentgen (r) which, however is a rather inadequate unit, since by definition it cannot be related to other than air targets and other than X- or gamma-radiations. A more pragmatic approach is the measurement of the energy absorbed by the unit of target mass. In 1953 the International Commission on Radiobiological Units and Measurements (cf. the ICRU report, 1957) defined the "rad" as the unit for absorbed energy. The rad, representing 100 ergs of energy absorption per gram of radiated material at the target point, is a unit which is applicable to any ionizing radiation if it is calculated within the radiated material. In order to compare the effectiveness on tissues of the absorbed dose of radiation delivered by different sources, the concept of the Relative Biological Effectiveness (RBC) was introduced, signifying that N number of rads delivered as one type of radiation have the biologic effectiveness of $N \times$ RBE factor rads delivered by a second type of ray. The magnitude of the RBE for a certain radiation depends upon the linear energy transfer (LET) from the ionizing particle to the tissues; on this basis the roentgen- and gamma-rays of certain energies are conventionally used as reference radiation and the RBE values in gross calculations are: 1 for X-rays, gamma-rays, and beta-rays, and 10 for alpha-rays. Another important matter is the source of the radiation. Studies of the comparative effectiveness of gamma- and X-radiations from different sources acting upon the same targets show that the RBE values of Co^{60} and 22 Mevp are similar but less effective than that of the 200 kevp rays (Sinclair, 1962; Miceli et al., 1962). For fast neutrons the RBE value calculated through comparisons with X-rays was found to be 6.3. (Jacobson and Mark, 1954; Miceli et al., 1962). For slow neutrons calculation of the RBE is more difficult since a number of gamma-rays and fast neutrons are always present.

The dose unit biologically equivalent to a rad is the "rem" (rad equivalent for man), which, in a formulary way can be represented for any given radiation as:

$$\text{dose in rems} = \text{dose in rads} \times \text{RBE}.$$

The rem as a measuring unit has a limited application since most of the controlled biologic effects are caused by X-rays, gamma-rays, or neutrons from standard sources, which makes the RBE values more or less fixed. The rad is therefore accepted as a preferable unit for radiobiological studies and it will be used as such in this text.

C. GENERAL FACTORS INFLUENCING THE BIOLOGICAL EFFECTS OF IONIZING RADIATIONS

It becomes apparent from the above that the effects of ionizing radiations on living cells, tissues, or whole organisms depend upon the type of radiation, its contained energy and its source. However, other factors such as the rate and duration of the radiation can influence the end result. There is a definite relationship between the dose-rate and the biological effect (Lea, 1947) which is not always directly proportional.

Although it is generally true that within certain limits higher dose-rates will produce faster and more severe biological effects, it seems that the radiosensitivity of certain tissues or functional molecular complexes in tissues can best be expressed by specific dose rates usually in the intermediate range (Clark *et al.*, 1959; Clark and Baker, 1963). Another important factor is the duration of the ionizing effect. Ill defined terms have been introduced attempting to describe the biological effects of radiations, acting for short or prolonged periods of time in single or repeated exposures. The terms acute and chronic radiation are the most confusing of all. Cronkite and Bond (1960a) separate the acute or chronic delivery of the radiation from resulting acute or chronic clinical effects; this distinction is quite helpful. In the text the terms "acute" and "chronic" effects are used only to indicate corresponding clinical pictures. Otherwise the following terminology introduced by the United States National Research Council Subcommittee on the hematological effects of ionizing radiations (Van Lancker, 1963) applies in this discussion.

Short-term exposures—Total or partial exposure of the body over a short period of time (days or weeks). In these terms a total dose higher than 50 rads is defined as a high dose, less than 50 rads as a low dose.

Long-term exposures—Refers to continued or repeated exposures over long periods of time (months or years). Although dose of radiation given in long-term exposures is important, the significance of the dose per unit of time, usually weeks, must not be overlooked. A low weekly dose is defined as exposure to between 100 and 1000 millirads, and a high weekly dose as exposure to greater than 1000 millirads.

D. BIOLOGICAL EFFECTS OF RADIATION

What is finally expressed as a radiation effect upon a biological system is in reality the end product of a series of drastic biochemical changes resulting from the original deposition of minute amounts of energy in the molecules. That these changes take place is an accepted fact; however, very little is known about the actual pathway that the biochemical event follows. In pure liquid systems such as water, the ionization effects are easily detected, but analogies are naive and even dangerous when drawn between these systems and the complex system of the living cell. Effects on purified substrates also hold little analogy to the reactions in the corresponding systems within the body. For example, the radiation dose required to produce a certain deleterious effect on a particular substance is approximately tenfold higher *in vitro* than *in vivo* (Hollaender, 1954; Cronkite and Bond, 1960b). This is one reason for the slow progress in the study of radiobiological phenomena.

During investigations at the cellular level attention was drawn to the inhibitory action of ionizing energies upon deoxyribonucleic acid (DNA) synthesis. The interest in this observation was enhanced by the fact that there was a simultaneous inhibition in the initiation of cellular mitosis. Today it is believed that although factors modified by radiation can influence both of these phenomena (Cronkite and Bond, 1960b), their synchronous appearance is not the result of a cause-effect relationship (Van Lancker, 1963). Synthesis of DNA studied in splenic rat cells is found to be delayed with low doses of roentgen- or gamma-rays and completely inhibited with higher doses. The inhibition is most probably due to a decrease in the phosphorylation of nucleotides and/or to an inhibition of the activity of the specific polymerase (Van Lancker, 1963; Goutier, 1961; Nygaard and Potter, 1962; Vladimirov, 1963). In general it can be said that within certain dose and dose-rate limits there is no direct action on the nucleic acid synthesis, but rather an indirect inhibition, through deleterious effects on the enzymes involved. These biochemical changes cannot as yet be correlated with, but certainly are accompanied by morphological changes at the subcellular (intracellular) level, where shifts in enzymatic activities can be demonstrated histochemically through electron microscopy. It is presumed that changes in enzyme complexes are due to observed ruptures in the limiting membranes of the endoplasmic reticulum as well as to profound changes in the mitochondrial structures (Goldfeder, 1963). These general observations have been made on a variety of cells and have also been confirmed in monkey and dog platelets, following X-radiation of the animals (Toskaia et al., 1961). Unfortunately, no bone marrow cells have been studied as yet.

The biochemical changes in body fluids observed during clinical or subclinical radiation insults to animals or humans have been more thoroughly explored. The extent of the defective nucleic acid metabolism is reflected by the severe aminoaciduria observed in the early stages of radiation injury (Katz and Hasterlik, 1955; Rubini et al., 1959; Pendic, 1961; Shipman, 1961), which occasionally may be found to persist for more than a year following recovery (Radojičic et al., 1961). In humans after accidental exposures the magnitude of the aminoaciduria can be correlated with the severity of the injury. Concerning the proteins, in experimental animals exposed to lethal or sublethal doses of X-rays the general pattern in plasma protein behavior is that of a decrease in the albumin and γ-globulin fractions and an increase in the α- and β-globulins, including fibrinogen. In the rat (Fisher et al., 1955; Winkler and Paschke, 1956) the changes appear dependent upon the dose and post-radiation time. Similar fluctuations in the plasma proteins are observed in hamsters (Ditzel, 1962), rabbits (McLaughlin *et al.*, 1957), goats (Waldschmidt-Leitz and Keller, 1961), and dogs (Muntz *et al.*, 1949; Zaretskaya, 1953). In humans the changes reported are similar in all fatal cases (Shipman, 1960). However, hyperalbuminemia can occur following sublethal exposures (Kyker, 1959). The exact mechanism of these changes is not understood. Inanition was blamed as the cause for the albumin decrease (Fisher *et al.*, 1955). The composition of a- and β-globulins, on the other hand, appears to be directly related to the X-radiation. The amino acid sequence in β-globulins is disturbed and there is an almost complete disappearance of the sulfur-containing groups, with a corresponding increase in histidine and lysine (Waldschmidt-Leitz and Keller, 1961). Increased amounts of fibrinogen are detected in the plasma of X-radiated dogs (Jackson *et al.*, 1952b) as well as humans (Mogilinitski *et al.*, 1962). This increased fibrinogen activity seems to be inversely proportional to the eventual development of a hemorrhagic state, and apparently is not due to a decrease in the concentration of fibrinogenase (Gordeeva, 1962). The lipoproteins are also disturbed in the radiated animal. As early as 1949, an opalescence due to circulating lipids was noted in the serum of radiated rabbits that correlated well with the incidence of death (Rosenthal, 1949; Hayes and Hewitt, 1955). Similar findings were noted in dogs (Prosser *et al.*, 1956; Bogdanoff, 1962a,b). It seems that the observed lipemia is dependent upon both time and radiation dose and is probably due to a conversion of low density lipoproteins to higher density components (Hewitt *et al.*, 1952); it might also be connected with observed changes in heparin levels (Hewitt *et al.*, 1952; Antonini and Salvini, 1953). The serum levels of lipoproteins, glycoproteins, and polysaccharides are modified following X-radiation of dogs (Antonini and Salvini, 1953; Goldwater and Entenman, 1957), while even more specifically the phospholipid level in the plasma of lethally radiated mice, rats, rabbits, guinea pigs, and dogs is found to be substantially increased (Entenman *et al.*, 1955). Increased phospholipid levels with new, as yet unidentified components, have also been observed on paper chromatograms in sublethally gamma-radiated rabbits which received additional gamma-radiation to the liver. All these changes in the plasma lipid profile are important because they may be associated with the appearance of circulating anticoagulants in the plasma of radiated animals.[*]

Other important biochemical alterations occurring in the radiated organism appear in the form of profound changes in the electrolytes as well as in the nonelectrolytic plasma components (Cronkite and Bond,

---

[*] Unpublished data from our laboratories.

1960b). In humans and in animals these observations are difficult to interpret, since the variables involved are multiple. Hemorrhage, infection, nutritional, or digestive disturbances all tend to produce a suboptimal fluid milieu to which each functioning system has to adjust rapidly, if it is to survive. The coagulation system of the blood, therefore, in addition to the direct damage on its formed elements and soluble components must operate in the radiated animals in an unfavorable environment that in itself can indirectly modify the normal outcome of the clotting processes.

E. Outline of Coagulation

Normal hemostasis requires the effective function of three groups of factors: (1) extravascular; (2) vascular; and (3) intravascular.

Extravascular factors are those residing in the tissues surrounding a vessel, and vary to some extent with the location of the vessel. Included are tissue tension and pressure, and the potential thromboplastic activity which varies in different tissues.

Vascular factors are those characteristics of the vessel wall which influence hemostasis. The structure of the vessel, whether thick-walled artery, distensible vein, or thin-walled, fragile capillary; and the ability of the vessel to contract and to retract, are important determinants in the control of bleeding.

Intravascular factors are those substances and elements in the blood itself which influence coagulation. A consideration of the effects of radiation on the various factors involved in blood coagulation requires some familiarity with the nomenclature of these factors and with a generally accepted scheme for the sequence of events leading to the formation of a thrombus. In Table I, the eleven factors officially accepted at the September, 1961, meeting of the International Committee on Blood Clotting Factors are listed, with commonly encountered synonyms. Figure 1 presents an outline of the four phases of blood coagulation leading to formation of a fibrin clot. This conception of the clotting mechanism is, like all such hypothetical schemes, open to argument. Most of the tests of various clotting factors and functions mentioned in the text are widely used and well known. The reader is referred to the original papers and to standard reference works in blood coagulation, such as the recent edition of Biggs and MacFarlane's excellent book (1962).

Naturally occurring inhibitors include those directed against the specific procoagulant factors in Phase II, circulating antithromboplastin and the antithrombins. Heparin inhibits the formation of thromboplastin in the early stages of clotting, opposes the conversion of prothrombin to thrombin, and acts as an antithrombin in the late stages of clotting.

A single schematic representation of the fibrinolytic system is shown in Fig. 2. It should be noted that "activator" is present in tissues and extravascular fluids, but is not normally present in blood, while proactivator is present in both blood and tissues.

TABLE I

FACTORS IN BLOOD COAGULATION

Factor number	Factor name and synonyms
I	Fibrinogen
II	Prothrombin
III	Thromboplastin
IV	Calcium
V	Accelerator globulin; labile factor; AcG
VII	Proconvertin; serum prothrombin conversion accelerator (SPCA); stable factor
VIII	Antihemophilic globulin (AHG, AHF)
IX	Plasma thromboplastin component (PTC); Christmas factor
X	Stuart factor
XI	Plasma thromboplastin antecedent (PTA)
XII	Hageman factor (HF)

IV. Coagulation Defects Produced by Alpha-Rays

The oldest known radioactive element, emitting primarily α-rays is Ra^{226}. Ra^{226} has a half life of 1950 years, and localizes mainly in the bones, provided that it gains entrance into the body through the gastrointestinal system. Inhalation of the element gives a different distribution. Ra^{226} can also be found within the body as a result of transformation of Pu^{239}.

There are no significant hematologic disorders following exposure to Ra^{226} or Ra^{228}, neither are there any significant changes in the coagulation mechanism. Administration in rats of 300 μc per kilogram of body weight of $RaCl_2$, produces within 10 days a 13% drop in the platelet count; lower doses are apparently ineffective (Suter and Boyd, 1950). Similar mild reductions in platelet counts are observed in the rat with intraperitoneal or intravenous doses of 0.94 μg per gram of body weight of $RaCl_2$, while the rabbit appears to be even less sensitive (Jacobson et al., 1954b). In all of the above experiments the dosage administered is maintained below the pharmacological acute toxic level. The slight platelet suppression may be the result of an effect upon the bone marrow but extensive bone marrow studies are not recorded. In humans, the effects on both the blood counts and blood coagulation are either absent or inconspicuous and at any rate reversible. Acute poisoning with Ra^{226} or mesothorium-228 salts have occurred; in such instances the high ionization dose adds to the pharmacological toxicity, but the victims die usually from poisoning before coagulation disturbances can be manifested. In long-term exposures of luminous dial painters that occurred

PHASE I: THE INITIATING OR CONTACT PHASE

Hageman factor (XII) $\xrightarrow{\text{damage to vessel wall}}$ Activated HF (contact factor)

Platelets $\xrightarrow{\text{viscous metamorphosis}}$ Platelet factor 3

PHASE II: FORMATION OF THROMBOPLASTIN

Intrinsic System:

Procoagulants

Platelet factor 3
AHG (VIII)
PTC (IX) $\xrightarrow[\text{Ca}^{2+}]{\text{contact factor}}$ Plasma thromboplastin
PTA (XI)
Stuart factor (X)
AcG (V)

Extrinsic System:

Tissue thromboplastin (incomplete) + V, VII, X $\xrightarrow{\text{Ca}^{2+}}$ Plasma thromboplastin

PHASE III: FORMATION OF THROMBIN

Prothrombin $\xrightarrow[\text{Ca}^{2+}]{\text{plasma thromboplastin}}$ Thrombin

PHASE IV: FORMATION OF FIBRIN

Fibrinogen $\xrightarrow{\text{thrombin}}$ Activated fibrin + Fibrinopeptides

Activated fibrin $\xrightarrow[\text{Ca}^{2+}]{\text{fibrin-stabilizing factor}}$ Fibrin

Fig. 1. System for the coagulation of the blood.

in the past, the clinical and pathologic changes seen up to 40 years post-exposure do not include coagulation defects or thrombocytopenia (Aub *et al.*, 1952; Finkel *et al.*, 1959), although anemia could be present (Baker *et al.*, 1961). Even in cases where the radium content of the body is 40 times above the permissible level, and death can indirectly be attributed to the concentration of the element, there are no significant symptoms or disturbances of the coagulation mechanism (Muth and Schraub, 1957). Neither, it seems, are there any significant changes following local therapeutic application of radium (Rud, 1927).

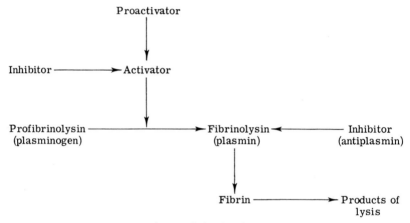

Fig. 2. Scheme of the fibrolytic system.

A second industrially used radioelement is plutonium (Pu^{239}, half-life 2.4×10^4 years), which also localizes in the bones and the liver. Intravenous or intraperitoneal administration of Pu^{239} in rabbits, rats, or mice can cause anemia with thrombocytopenia and death, but no other obvious coagulation defects (Jacobson and Simmons, 1954). In humans, no changes in the system of blood coagulation have been detected in individuals working with the element (Hempelmann, 1962).

In general, it can be said that intrinsic α-radiations do not materially alter the normal processes of blood coagulation.

V. Coagulation Defects Produced by Beta-Rays

Extensive studies on the effects of external administration of beta-rays on the hematological parameters in rodents showed no noticeable post-exposure thrombocytopenia (Raper and Barnes, 1952). These data on animals agree with the data on humans exposed accidentally to gamma- and beta-rays during the atomic explosions on the Marshall Islands. In the victims, skin burns caused by beta-rays could not be correlated with hematological changes (Bond et al., 1956). However, indirect effects in the normal sequence of blood coagulation may be expected from the marked disturbance in the protein metabolism and electrolyte water balance occurring during extensive skin burns. The burned skin itself may play some role. It has been demonstrated that a thromboplastic activity exists in burned skin extracts (Fox et al., 1961). An indirect effect, therefore, could result through the absorption of such thromboplastic substances. However, specific coagulation studies have not been performed, and in the cases in which no serious complications have occurred during the post-radiation period, there is no reason to believe that disturbances in the coagulation system exist. Ingestion of Sr^{90}, a rather common byproduct of nuclear detonation, which is a strong beta-emitter and localizes in the bones, apparently does not produce coagulation defects (Jacobson et al., 1954a). Its destructive effect on the bone marrow is confined only to the immediate area of its localization (Detrick et al., 1961). It has, however, been reported that oral administration to dogs of Sr^{90} in high doses produces massive hemorrhages but no thrombocytopenia (Andersen and Winchell, 1961). In these cases an intravascular basophilic substance observed in post-mortem sections, was held responsible for loss of endothelial integrity and hemorrhage by occlusion of smaller vessels. No other coagulation studies were performed during this investigation.

Yttrium, another beta-emitter, is not known to produce changes in the thrombocyte counts or in blood coagulation (Jacobson et al., 1954a).

Diagnostic or therapeutic doses of I^{131} do not as a rule produce thrombocytopenia. Exceptions do exist (Kafafova, 1959). In this report six patients with thyrotoxicosis developed thrombocytopenia but no hemorrhagic tendency; no other coagulation defects were noted. The erratic response of the thrombocytes to therapeutic doses of I^{131} is attributed to a specific hypersensitivity towards the radioisotope, a hypersensitivity which may also be acquired by persons having a history of long radiation exposure. Indeed in radiologists or patients treated with radiation, diagnostic doses of X-rays or beta-rays from I^{131} can induce significant undulations in the absolute values of platelets, eosinophils or monocytes (Sergel, 1961).

Similar and perhaps greater depressive action upon the bone marrow precursors of platelets can be expected with other beta-emitters, such as radiophosphorus; P^{32} is employed in a variety of diagnostic and therapeutic applications in proliferative diseases, chiefly because of its incorporation in the nucleic acids and its potent interference with the cell cycle. Following therapeutic administration, marked thrombocytopenia with purpura is not uncommon. As far as is known, thrombocytopenia is the most severe coagulation defect in patients treated with P^{32}. However, factor V deficiency was reported in six polycythemic patients, 48 hours following intravenous administration of P^{32} (Vetter and Vinazzer, 1952, 1954); the magnitude of the phenomenon was dose dependent. Interesting is the application of radiophosphorus in thrombocythemias (Kafafova, 1959). Therapeutic doses of P^{32} not only reduce the platelet counts to normal levels, but in cases of idiopathic hemorrhagic thrombocythemia normalize the associated coagulation defects (Coliez et al., 1957). There is no reason to assume that this normalization is other than an indirect result stemming from the action of the radioisotope upon the production of platelets.

Another beta-ray emitter, used because it is removed by the reticuloendothelial system in the body and consequently attacks selectively this tissue, is radiogold (Tocantins and Wang, 1956). Administration of this radioisotope to dogs in high doses produces both a drop in the platelet count and disturbances in the clotting mechanism best detected by the prothrombin consumption test. It seems that similar observations were made on other animals as well as on humans (Ferguson et al., 1952). Extensive studies on the effects of this isotope on all phases of blood coagulation again are lacking.

VI. Coagulation Defects Produced by Neutrons

As mentioned before, ionization by slow neutrons is achieved by the incorporation of the neutron particles within the nuclei of the target tissue. In this process a multitude of secondary components are produced such as gamma-rays, beta-rays, and fast neutrons, and it seems that the biological action of slow neutrons is that of secondarily produced radioactivity. Although there are no specific studies, it seems that the effects of slow neutrons in blood coagulation are substantially similar to the effects produced by fast neutrons.

Fast neutrons given to rabbits in doses of 80–89 n,[*] resulted in an initial abortive rise and subsequently a depression in the platelet count which reached its lower point by the 5th day, while normalization occurred by the 15th day. With higher doses of approximately 100–108 n, a maximum reduction of 72% of normal occurred by the 10th day, while restoration to normal values was not accomplished before the 23rd day

[*] The symbol n represents an arbitrary unit defined as the dose of fast neutrons capable of producing a discharge of one division in a Victoreen-r-meter equipped with a 100 r chamber.

(Jacobson *et al.*, 1949). Dogs exposed to 150 n showed depression of their thrombocyte counts similar to those observed following exposures to X-rays. When the exposure to neutrons was repeated a second time, complete recovery was again observed; following, however, the fourth exposure the platelet levels reached only two-thirds of the normal values and remained there during the rest of the studies (Baum *et al.*, 1961). The pattern of the platelet depressions following X-ray doses of 150 r was similar. It appears that the platelet reaction to high doses of X-rays or fast neutrons is identical. With lower neutron doses given over long periods of time in rats, rabbits, and dogs, no particular pattern of platelet response can be found, although in dogs the count variation observed was almost within the limits of significance (Ely *et al.*, 1954).

Concerning the bone marrow, studies on rabbits with doses lower than the $LD_{50}/30$ days, showed the megakaryocytes decreasing by the 3rd day. During the recovery phase, by the 14th day a striking increase is noted. In mice one can destroy the megakaryocytic population of the bone marrow within 9 days with a dose of 119 n total body radiation (Bloom, 1948). From these experiments it appears again that the mega-karyocytic response to neutrons follows chronologically and quantitatively the pattern of X-rays.

In all the animal studies reported so far, no reference could be found to any direct effect of fast neutrons on any other factors of the coagula-tion system. It is possible, however, that indirect influences through a general biochemical disarrangement of the body could exist. There are no data on human exposures to pure fast neutron energies; fast neutrons do, however, contaminate the X- or gamma-radiations to which human subjects may be accidentally exposed, as for example in the Y-12, or the Los Alamos (Shipman, 1961) or in the Vinča (Yugoslavia) zero-energy reactor accidents (Pendic, 1961). In these cases as in the case of the accidental exposure of the Marshall Islanders to radioactive fallout, the principal components of the ionizing energy were the gamma-rays, to which the severity of the observed injuries were attributed. Undoubtedly though, fast neutrons played some additive role. It should also be noted that the hematologic response, as well as the response of the coagulation complex to the composite radiation in the above accidents, appeared no different from the response noted in subjects exposed to pure X- or gamma-rays. This indirectly confirms the impression gained by compara-tive animal studies that the biological effects of fast neutrons and those of X- or gamma-rays are expressed by similar survival and hematological responses. It seems reasonable therefore to assume that the response of the blood coagulation system would be the same toward all three of these ionizing energies.

VII. Coagulation Defects Produced by X-Rays and Gamma-Rays

The physical similarity of X-rays and gamma-rays results in the production of identical effects on the biological system acted upon by the two types of energy. Although their RBE as we have seen may vary, the end result of their action on a specific system is identical and depends only upon the dose administered from either form of energy. This being the case, the effects of X-rays and gamma-rays upon the coagulation of blood will be considered together and for purposes of simplicity the term X-ray will hereafter be used for both types of radiation.

The result of a high X-ray dose administered to animals or humans over a short period of time will depend upon the body-surface area exposed to the rays. In total or near total body exposures with doses approaching the LD_{99} level, severe hemorrhagic diathesis with profuse bleeding is a common cause of death. Although there are some exceptions (for instance, the rabbit does not bleed copiously under heavy doses of radiation), it can be stated that as a general rule, X-radiation affects the normal coagulation processes of the body in such a fashion as to render the blood incoagulable. A number of coagulation tests thus become abnormal following exposure to X-rays. Whether these changes are the result of the functional or physical impairment of one or more of the coagulation factors is still a matter of discussion. There is, however, agreement that following X-radiation, at least one radical change takes place in the coagulation system and this appears in the form of a more or less pronounced thrombocytopenia. Thrombocytopenia, coupled with alterations in the other elements of coagulation, and with well demonstrated damage to the endothelium of the smaller vessels, forms the basis of the post-radiation hemorrhagic diathesis.

In the ensuing paragraphs a discussion of the qualitative and quantitative *in vivo* effects of X-rays on the platelets will be presented. Following this there will be an analysis of the possible alterations suffered by other factors or systems in the coagulation mechanisms of X-rayed animals and humans.

A. Effects of X-rays on the Platelets and on Clotting Tests
   Relating to Platelets

1. *Effects of X-rays on the Platelet Counts*

a. *High Dose Short-Term Exposures:* (*i*). *Animal studies.* A high dose of X-rays will induce a degree of thrombocytopenia even if it is given in only one exposure. The degree as well as the time of appearance of the thrombocytopenic response depends upon the radiation dose and dose rate, and also upon the species and the size of the experimental animals. Under the usual circumstances in the experimental laboratory a single LD$_{99}$ X-ray dose, delivered from a 250 KVP machine or from a cobalt bomb at a rate between 4 and 85 r per minute, will result in an initial period of unchanged platelet counts which lasts from 1 to 4 days depending upon the animal. During this time it is not unusual to observe a short-lived mild thrombocytosis lasting up to 48 hours, a phenomenon known for many years to investigators but still not completely explained. This slight and abortive increase in platelet counts, thought in the past to represent a direct myelopoietic stimulation from the radiation, appears more prominently with lower doses (Ingram and Masan, 1954; Andrews and Sitterson, 1959; Cronkite et al., 1959), and can occasionally cause a transient hypercoagulability (Panichi and Bonechi, 1958; Levy, 1963). Following the thrombocytosis, thrombocytopenia develops first at a slower rate and then precipitously, reaching minimum values during the second post-radiation week and persisting until death. Although the degree of thrombocytopenia does not always correlate with the magnitude or persistence of hemorrhagic diathesis, failure of platelet recovery faithfully reflects grave damage to the bone marrow and eventual death from either hemorrhage or infection. Death without marked thrombocytopenia occurs only in cases of exposure to high doses over a short period of time, such as atomic bomb explosions (Cronkite, 1950) or under circumstances of continuous high dose level experimental radiation (Wald et al., 1961). In such cases, death precedes the development of thrombocytopenia. In other cases, where the dose delivered is below the lethal range, the fall of the platelet count is less precipitous and the number of platelets usually reaches and remains at a certain level until the initiation of recovery. Recovery starts about the 3rd or 4th week and continues as a gradual but steady process until it reaches pre-exposure levels 4 to 6 weeks later. All the above variations are closely associated with and closely follow the fluctuation on the peripheral blood counts of the granulocytes. The platelets together with the polymorphonuclear granulocytes are truly sensitive and reliable indices of radiation effects on the hematopoietic system, in both the initial post-exposure phase and later during the phase of recovery.

In recent years a variety of animals have been exposed to X-rays and their platelet response has been studied. In monkeys after single total body exposures ranging from 50 to 40,000 r, the platelet counts were either stable or slightly increased during the first two post-exposure days, and then decreased constantly to reach the lowest levels around the middle of the second week. The counts remained at this level for another week and in the animals that survived, the recovery started following the third week. (French et al., 1955; Wald et al., 1961; Eldred and Eldred, 1953). Goats and swine, receiving large amounts of X-radiation during the experimental bomb explosions at Bikini Atoll, showed no disturbances in platelet counts for the first few days and died by the 5th day without marked thrombocytopenia. In animals receiving smaller doses, the counts stabilized at low levels during the second week. In the survivors the upward trend did not start until later (Cronkite, 1950). Burros show a similar type of reaction after exposure to lethal doses, with the difference that the maximum thrombocytopenia appears later during the third post-exposure week (Trum and Rust, 1953). The dog has been used extensively both because of availability and ease of handling and because of the apparent similarity to humans in response to X-radiation (Warren and Draiger, 1946). A multitude of studies have been performed on the various aspects of radiation effects on this animal, and in all the experiments a similar pattern of thrombocytopenic response is found (Cronkite and Brecher, 1954; Jackson et al., 1952b; Ingram and Masan, 1954; Warren and Draiger, 1946; Holden et al., 1949; Shively et al., 1961) commencing during the first week and reaching its maximum during the second and third post-exposure weeks. In lethal cases the dogs die with severe hemorrhagic phenomena. Cats are found to respond in a similar fashion (Reisner and Heating, 1957). Another species of animal used extensively in studies on radiation effects are rabbits (DeLeeuw et al., 1953; Reisner and Heating, 1957; Rosenthal and Benedek, 1950). Rabbits are more tolerant to radiation than other animals of equal size, demonstrating an $LD_{50}/30$ days, around 700–750 r. At this level of radiation the platelets reach their lowest values of about 10% of normal at about day 14, and remain there until day 19 or 20 when recovery begins. With higher doses the cycle is slightly accelerated but the maximum thrombocytopenia is not present earlier than the 12th post-radiation day even in lethal cases. The thrombocytopenic response of the rat is also well described (Ingram and Mason, 1954; Firkin et al., 1959; Fliedner et al., 1958) and this animal because of its easy handling makes an ideal model for the studies of platelet replacement in thrombocytopenia.

  ii. Human studies. The accumulated experience comes mainly from three sources: (1) therapeutic exposures of subjects either to lethal total body radiation followed by bone marrow replacement, or to high radiation doses aimed at specific body areas and given within a relatively short period of time (the extent of the thrombocytopenic response in the latter cases depends upon the size of the radiated body surface); (2) accidental exposures of human beings to high concentrations of radiation in industrial or experimental plants dealing with atomic energy; or (3) war or experimental atomic bomb explosions. Among the first data that appeared in the literature of the hematological changes induced by atomic explosions, are those of Beck and Meissner (1946) on the survivors of Nagasaki, recorded 6 to 7 weeks following the bombing. At that time platelet counts were low, ranging from 30 to 177 $\times$ 10^3 platelets per milliliter, but the data in regard to the radiation dosology were not accurate. The best published reports, those of LeRoy (1950) and Oughtersen and Warren (1956) on the hematological data of the bomb casualties in both Hiroshima and Nagasaki, indicate that in humans exposed to large doses of radiation and presenting grave clinical pictures, death occurred around the 10th post-bombing day while there was moderate to marked thrombocytopenia but no hemorrhagic tendency. In less severe cases the majority of the survivors presented platelet counts below 50,000 per millimeter between the 3rd and 6th post-radiation week; starting with the 7th week the counts increased until they reached normal levels at about the 10th week. There was no platelet recovery in the cases with fatal outcome. The experience gained again showed that depression of the platelet counts is directly dependent on the dose and rate with which the radiation is administered, and that it follows the changes in leukocyte counts. In addition, it was found that diffuse hemorrhage depends upon the degree of thrombocytopenia, being usually absent with platelet counts above 20 $\times$ 10^3/ml. These general patterns were later confirmed during the accidental exposure of human beings in the atomic explosion in the Marshall Islands. In this case thrombocytopenia following radiation with 14 to 175 r reached levels of 60% of normal on the 10th post-exposure day and lower levels of 30% of normal at the end of 4 weeks. The recovery was gradual and continued until the 7th week when a new depression occurred (Bond et al., 1956). Observations on the platelet count of victims of accidental exposures in different laboratories confirm that the first signs of thrombocytopenia appear towards the end of the first post-exposure week and that an initial gradual decline of the platelet counts is replaced by a more accelerated one until a maximum depression is reached by the end of the 4th week. In all accidents in which the calculated radiation dose was below the LD$_{99}$, the platelet counts remained depressed until the 6th or 7th week, at which time recovery began. This is the pattern seen in all cases treated with only general supportive measures (Hempelmann et al., 1952; Andrews and Sitterson, 1959; Jammot et al., 1959; Sise et al., 1961; Howland et al., 1961; Andrews, 1962). In cases of therapeutic total body exposures treated with bone marrow transplantation, the platelet response to radiation reflected the success of the attempted therapy.

Haurani and his co-workers (1960) reported their experience with nine patients with a total of 12 radiation exposures ranging from 50 to 600 r. With these doses the maximum depressive effect on platelets was noted between the 2nd and 3rd week, while recovery took place in from 21 to 31 days. The bone barrow recovered in only three patients, however, and two patients died as a result of pancytopenic hemorrhage. Higher radiation doses were employed by Thomas et al. (1961) who administered approximately 1600 r. The reported results on the platelet counts were within the same range as were the results of other investigators (Pegg et al., 1962; Kurnick et al., 1958). Experience in our laboratory in a patient with a widespread seminoma who received 750 r of gamma-rays in a single total body exposure showed initiation of thrombocytic suppression by the 5th day. The thrombocytopenia progressed without recovery until death on the 32nd day from an overwhelming infection. In a second patient with acute stem-cell leukemia who received 790 r and was transfused with homologous marrow, an upward trend in the platelet count was noted by the 14th post-infusion day and continued until the patient's death from infection by the 21st day. In both instances the hemorrhagic tendency appeared in the form of extensive petechiae and intermittent gastrointestinal bleeding, and in both instances the changes in platelet counts closely correlated with those of the leukocytes.

The magnitude of the thrombocytopenic response depends not only on the radiation dose, but also on the body surface exposed. X-ray therapy aimed at specific limited body-surface targets resulted in marked platelet depressions in 30 patients given therapeutic antitumor doses (DeNicola et al., 1955; DiGuglielmo, 1957). The thrombocytopenia in these cases is apparently associated with other coagulation disturbances, but the degree of bleeding is not significant. In other reports (Csomor et al., 1961b; Bergamaschi and Schiatti, 1962b) platelet count depression, although a constant finding, appears to be variable in magnitude and not always accompanied by other coagulation defects or a hemorrhagic tendency. The degree of thrombocytopenia in therapeutic limited body-surface radiation is independent of the localization of the target area, although some indications exist that radiation of the thorax may produce greatest depression in the platelet counts than equivalent radiation of other areas. It should be noted in this connection that the general state of the patient's health, as well as individual sensitivities to X-rays, plays a significant role in the development of thrombocytopenia. On the other hand, development of a hemorrhagic tendency does not depend on thrombocytopenia alone. Other systems interfere such as the fibrinolytic system, and these may depend upon the functional state of specific organs.

b. Low-Dose, Long-Term Exposures. The influences that long-term exposures to low doses of X-rays exert on biological systems has been repeatedly emphasized. The genetic and somatic effects of such exposures on animals are well recognized. Furthermore, well documented reports exist, dealing with responses to long-term exposures of such specific organs or body constituents as the blood, liver, serum proteins, etc. in both animals (Lorentz *et al.*, 1954; Ingram and Masan, 1954) and humans (Pons and MereGreze-Rueff, 1952; Low-Bee and Stone, 1952). Studies, however, referring to the system of blood coagulation are sparse, and with the exception of the platelet response to prolonged exposures, we have little if any information on the changes or damages inflicted upon the other factors of the blood coagulation apparatus.

From the experience gathered so far it seems that the quality and the magnitude of the platelet response to long-term radiations is a function of both the length and the frequency of exposure, as well as of the fractional and the cumulative dose. Of all the above parameters, the single most important one seems to be the level of the fractional dose and the rate at which it is administered. Anemia, for example, a rather common sequel of the exposure to repeated small doses of X-rays over long periods of time, does not occur in guinea pigs after doses of 1.1 r/day for a total of 2200 r, but does occur following 2.2 r/day for a similar total dose (Lorentz *et al.* 1954). That this is so appears logical in view of the belief that the radiation action is short-lived and is primarily directed against the highly proliferative precursors in the bone marrow. Since the target population is limited, the chance of suffering from the actinic action increases with the dose level of each fractional exposure. The cells hit only once, suffer reversible damages and recover, unless a new hit results in frank cellular sterility or death. In this respect, the frequency of exposures plays a role equally as important as the fractional dose, since long interims between radiations will allow for repairs of the damages inflicted. Another important factor playing a role in the manifestation of long-term, low-dose radiation effects is the total length of the exposure, which will also determine the total given dose. A comprehensive summary in general terms of the effects of such radiation is given by Hekhuis (1961).

(*i*) *Animal studies.* Lorentz and his associates (1954) studied the effects of low-level, long-term exposure in rodents. The platelet response in mice receiving doses of 0.11, 1.1, and 2.2 r/day in 8-hour sessions is not significant, with some possible exceptions in male animals, in which after 119 weeks some suppression in the platelet count is noted. With exposures of 4.4 and 8.8/8 hours/day, a 30% reduction is noted at the end of 79 weeks in either sex. The low counts remain throughout the duration of the experiment. In guinea pigs there is no response with the lowest dose, while with the higher doses thrombocytopenia appears proportionate to the fractional dose. Deaths from thrombocytopenic hemorrhages occur occasionally. Following discontinuation of radiation the pattern of recovery varies in different animals. Some animals do not recover, and in those the platelet counts and the clotting times remain low. The cause of death is not, however, attributed to hemorrhage. In other animals, the platelet counts return to normal only to become thrombocytopenic again and at the same time show changes in the clotting mechanism. These survivors live with low platelet values for the rest of their lives. Finally, a third group of animals can show a steady recovery starting at the 6th post-exposure week and continuing for several months until normal levels are reached. The study of the rabbit proves it to be a more radioresistant animal. Cumulative doses of 12,000 r given at a rate of 1.1 r/8 hours/day do not effect the platelet counts. With higher fractional dose the degree of thrombocytopenia appears proportional to the dose, but only to a certain point, beyond which the platelet counts do not decrease. It can be said in general that following a continuous low-dose radiation exposure, the platelet count in rodents starts to fall gradually after the 3rd week, and this decrease continues until it stabilizes at a low level. The clotting times are prolonged and few petechiae are present, but death is not the result of hemorrhage (Lorentz et al., 1954; Ingram and Mason, 1954). In dogs (Ingram and Masan, 1954), X-radiation in fractional doses from 3 to 10 r given every day for 2 years causes at first an abrupt fall in the platelet counts and then, after the second month, a more gradual decline. With daily doses of 3 r, variations in the platelet counts are insignificant while with lower doses changes occur. These changes reflect actual variations in the number of the bone marrow megakaryocytes. With a high fractional dose of 10 r/day a noticeable suppression of megakaryocytes is present, together with focal hemorrhages seen in an occasional animal (Metcalf and Inda, 1954).

(ii). *Human studies.* A careful follow-up of personnel occupationally exposed to X-rays over long periods of time show a remarkable thrombocytopenia as well as deficiencies in other coagulation factors (Mungo et al., 1962). Micu and his co-workers (1962), in a recent study of 82 physicians and 72 radiology technicians over a period of 9 years, noticed among other changes marked thrombocytopenia resulting from a maturation arrest of the megakaryocytic series. Aplastic pancytopenia, a known sequel among survivors of acute radiation exposure is also known to appear among individuals protractedly exposed to low doses of X-rays. In fact the first known victim of X-rays was an Italian radiologist who died from pancytopenic hemorrhage (Gawazzeni and Minelli, 1914–1915). The clinical picture of such exposures has been repeatedly described (Pons and MereGreze-Rueff, 1952). The gravity of the clinical syndrome and the time of its appearance largely depends upon the frequency and magnitude of the fractional dose. In addition, as already mentioned, individual sensitivities as well as prior exposures to small doses of any type of radiation can induce the clinical manifestation of an otherwise subclinical injury, either as a fully expressed syndrome or only as a thrombocytopenia (Sergel, 1961).

c. *Latent Effects of X-radiation.* Radiation is a severe stress, to which the animal and its functioning units must adapt in order to recover successfully. In the bone marrow, as in other organs, the effect of a single or repeated high doses of radiation will be death or sterilization of the cells in the proliferative compartments. As a result, a gradual bone marrow and peripheral blood depopulation would occur had it not been for adaptive mechanisms which, in an as yet incompletely understood way, compensate for the dead proliferative units and try to maintain a steady state. This being the prime concern of the affected bone marrow, normalization to preinjury levels will be achieved only if increased demands during recovery can be provided for and maintained; in any other eventuality marrow elements will be restored at a lower quantitative and perhaps qualitative level which, of course, must be compatible with life.

Following an exposure to a high radiation dose, it is conceivable that one or more of the components involved in the complex coagulation system could be adjusted to function at a different level. It has for example been shown that the serum proteins in the rabbit, having returned to normal after a single exposure to a high radiation dose, failed to do so following repetitive similar doses, and settled to a steady lower level (McLaughlin *et al.*, 1957). Detailed studies on experimental animals or on humans concerning the coagulation factors other than the platelets are lacking. The platelet response has been studied in rats by Lamerton and co-workers (1960), following continuous exposure to radiation. It appears that with daily doses above 50 rads an initial platelet rise is followed by a gradual decline and an abortive attempt for restoration by the 22nd day, until the platelet counts stabilize at a lower level. With 176 r per day, although an initial rise is seen, the platelets rapidly thereafter reach very low numbers. In humans, changes in the platelet counts have also been observed. According to Misao and his co-workers (1962), the Japanese atomic bomb survivors show lower platelet counts than the average population, though by a degree that is not considered significant. Similar studies by Conrad and his co-workers

(1959) on the exposed population of Rongelap Island showed that 8 years following the incident the platelet counts were persistently lower than the average unexposed population. In these victims platelet counts never reached normal levels, being 75% of the controls by the 6th post-exposure month, and 85–90% by 5 years (Conrad, 1959). Characteristically platelet counts were lower in male children between the age of 8 to 15 than in the rest of the population during the 1962 survey (Conrad, 1958), a fact due perhaps to the smaller body size of the children at the time of exposure resulting in a higher effectiveness of the rays. Similar observations have been recorded in the past in animal experiments (Sorensen *et al.*, 1960), wherein an identically administered radiation dose resulted in ill effects markedly more severe among the smaller size subjects.

The megakaryocytic response to protracted radiation is not dramatic. The megakaryocyte counts in the bone marrow of the X-radiated rat stabilizes quickly at a lower level, showing none of the quantitative fluctuation of the platelets (Lamerton *et al.*, 1960).

2. Effects of X-rays on Platelet Morphology and Function

For many years it has been known that shortly after radiation unusual platelet forms appear in the peripheral blood. Giant platelets are frequently present, measuring sometimes up to 14 μ^2 (Lindell and Zajicek, 1957) seemingly increasing in proportion as the total platelet values decrease (Jacobson *et al.*, 1949). Among the small and middle platelet types, many appear by electron microscopy as degenerated forms with a marked loss of pseudopodia, with smooth surfaces, a loss of distinct border between hyalomere and granulomere, and with noticeable vacuolization (Kikuchi and Wakivaka, 1952). These "radiation forms" (Bagdasarov *et al.*, 1959) rise to levels of approximately 60% of the total number during the first post-radiation days. The routine staining characteristics of the thrombocytes are also changed; the uptake of the dye appears weak, and the azurophilic granules are no longer visible (Kikuchi and Wakisaka, 1952). These changes in morphology and staining characteristics have been seen frequently (Eldred and Eldred, 1953; Brinnitzer, 1935) and it appears that they are invariably associated with increased fragility and a marked tendency to fragmentation, a fact repeatedly observed in our laboratories.

Most important, however, is the question as to whether and to what extent the observed morphological disturbances reflect existing functional injuries. It is known that the clot-retracting capacity of radiated platelets is defective. In a radiated animal the restoration of platelet counts to normal noticeably precedes a return to normal of the clot-retracting activity. Clot-retracting ability of platelets harvested and tested during the degenerative phase following radiation is considerably less than that of platelets accumulated during the phase of regeneration. The exact nature of the changes are not known. Histochemical studies performed on platelets from radiated monkeys and dogs show grave functional disorders in the content of cytochromoxidase as well as in the content of glycogen, histidine, lipids, and sulfhydryl groups. Interestingly enough, these studies indicate that in addition to qualitative disturbances there is actually a marked shifting of the active groups within the platelets. The histochemical disturbances return to normal only if the radiated subject is to survive. The regeneration of platelets is associated with restoration of their functional capacity (Toskaia *et al.*, 1961). These are interesting studies and should be confirmed. The question, however, as to whether these results represent damage inflicted directly as the result of the rays upon the platelets or its precursors, or whether they are merely results of the biochemical disarrangement of the entire body, must be answered before a final evaluation can be accepted. It has been reported that platelet alterations occur after radiation *in vitro* and that these alterations are influenced by the composition of the suspending medium. Addition of sodium succinate or α-glycerophosphate in the suspending medium seems to furnish protection of the succinic dehydrogenase activity of the platelets (Wagner *et al.*, 1957).

3. Effects of X-rays on the Megakaryocytes

The hematological changes appearing following exposures to ionizing radiations are not the result of direct action upon the formed elements of the peripheral blood. These elements, representing the end forms of a long maturation process, are remarkably radioresistant, and as far as is known can effectively perform their usual functions after exposures to ionizing energies of much higher dose level than would be required to kill a whole organism. The response, however, to radiations is quite different when the hematopoietic organ is considered. The bone marrow is extremely radiosensitive, ranking second only to the gonads and the lymphatic tissue. Reduction of the formed elements or the peripheral blood, therefore, is primarily the result of direct damage to bone marrow components, and more specifically the result of an insult to the reproductive integrity of the cells; indeed there is every reason to believe that the process of maturation continues unhampered, at least at the midlethal or lethal levels of radiation that are frequently used in experimental studies.

The work of a number of investigators points towards the conclusion that within a certain radiation dose range the radiosensitivity of cells in reference to maintenance of their reproductive integrity is unrelated to their origin, their benign or malignant nature, or to the *in vivo* or *in vitro* conditions under which they are exposed to the radiation (Lajtha, 1961). On this basis, and although the great majority of observations and specific studies of the kinetics of marrow cells are concerned with the erythropoietic series, general conclusions can be drawn concerning megakaryocytes and the hypothesis explaining radiation-induced marrow cell damage can be expanded to include platelet precursors. There is no doubt at present that the sequence of events in maturation leads from an as yet unidentified precursor cell to the bone marrow megakaryoblast, to the promegakaryocyte and to the megakaryocyte from whose cytoplasm platelets are detached and eventually carried into the peripheral circulation. Mitotic divisions in this sequence take place in the stem cell, the megakaryoblastic and the promegakaryocytic stage, while megakaryocytes do not divide but differentiate towards the late megakaryocytic stage by four or at the most five nuclear divisions and a synchronous cytoplasmic maturation. Of these steps in platelet production, radiation energies most probably act upon the stages characterized by their pronounced mitotic activity and, depending upon the dose, result in either a temporary or permanent inhibition of mitosis, or in an immediate or delayed cell death. With radiation doses at the midlethal range, the resulting injury is probably inflicted during the sensitive interphase of the mitotic cycle, while the actual process of DNA synthesis seems to be less affected (Neary *et al.*, 1959; Lajtha *et al.*, 1958). It is, therefore, expected that an inhibition of mitotic divisions will take place while maturation processes will continue. All these point towards an expected delay in the disappearance of the late megakaryocytes from the bone marrow and to an even greater delay in the disappearance of the platelets from the peripheral blood, following exposure to radiation energies. This hypothesis, as expressed by Lajtha (1961) is in reality justified by Osgood's (1942) original *in vitro* observations and by the extensive and elaborate *in vivo* studies on the bone marrow of radiated rats (Hulse, 1957, 1959), guinea pigs (Harris, 1956), or other animals (Bloom, 1948). Further indications supporting the hypothesis derive from the fact that stimulation of the megakaryocytes prior to radiation results in a delayed and also less severe thrombocytopenia, presumably because of the increased stock of the nondividing radioresistant megakaryocytic forms (Cserhati, 1961; Traskunova, 1962). Concerning the kinetics of the megakaryocyte following radiation, Lindell and Zajicek (1957) found that this cell faithfully follows the fate of the granulopoietic series; the response, therefore, of the megakaryocyte to the damaging influences of radiation appears later than that of the lymphopoietic and erythropoietic series. Accordingly, megakaryocytes decline slowly in the bone marrow of the radiated animal, the first morphological and quantitative changes appearing by the 3rd day, and complete disappearance by the 6th day. The early morphological changes in the megakaryocytes are characterized by nuclear pyknosis, deepening of the nuclear basophilia, marked irregularity in the nuclear shape, cytoplasmic condensation associated with surface diminution, and in some instances vacuolization. Experience with human cases is similar. With sublethal doses of radiation slight morphological changes are demonstrable during the second post-radiation day, sometimes associated with a mild increase in the number of megakaryocytes and subsequently of the platelets (Andrews and Sitterson, 1959). Following this elevation there is a gradual decline and the number of megakaryocytes reaches its lowest point by the 24th or 25th post-exposure day. At this time the few remaining cells show marked degenerative changes (Andrews and Sitterson, 1959). Recovery of the megakaryocytes starts soon thereafter, and in most cases of sublethal radiation is completed by the 8th week. The new megakaryocytes appear morphologically normal and they can be observed producing normal platelets. It is not unusual during the recovery phase and before a normal state is obtained to observe an actual increase over the normal number of megakaryocytes, an overshoot (so to speak) above the regular values, which indicates a strong generative stimulation. Such a stimulation exists in radiated animals in the form of a humoral serum factor which is capable of inducing increase in the numbers of megakaryocytes as well as a thrombocytosis when given to normal subjects (Rak et al., 1962; Czerhati et al., 1962).

B. Effects of X-rays on Whole Blood Clotting Times

1. Animal Studies

The clotting time of native blood in glass or silicone is the fundamental test for an alteration in the clotting system. Prolongation indicates a defect in the mechanism, while shortening is the result of acceleration at some point in the process. Being a simple test, it has been widely used as a screening as well as an investigative tool of the radiation effects on the coagulation of blood. However, as it is with all basic screening tests, the whole blood clotting time failed to pinpoint the abnormal among the systems involved, thus leaving the door open to many interpretations.

Abnormally prolonged whole blood clotting time usually appears in X-radiated subjects synchronously to a marked thrombocytopenia. Although this is not always so, (Allen and Jacobson, 1947a; Cronkite, 1950; Cohn, 1952), the majority of the investigators actually believe that thrombocytopenia is the most important factor in the production of the post-radiation prolonged clotting times. This concept was first introduced by Shouse and co-workers (1931), although Lacassagne et al. (1922, 1928) had already noted the existing relation between the two phenomena. Others, (Cronkite and Brecher, 1952; Allen, 1952; Verwilghen and Peremans, 1955; Kudryashov et al., 1957; Petrova, 1958, 1959; Lagutina, 1960) also presented convincing evidence that in a variety of animals prolongation of the whole blood clotting times is related to the degree and duration of the post-radiation thrombocytopenia. It was, however, pointed out that a number of interfering factors, such as the quality and duration of the radiation, or development of anticoagulants by radiation-induced protein denaturation, can modify the degree of this correlation (Zunz and LaBarre, 1927; Cohn, 1952; Allen, 1952). A better correlation seems to exist between the chronological development of prolonged clotting times and that of a hemorrhagic diathesis in the exposed animal, although again individual sensitivities of the animals or animal species, interfere (Fulton, et al., 1954; Rosenthal, 1955).

In addition to the thrombocytopenia, a number of other etiological factors have been introduced to explain the prolongation of the clotting time. Allen and Jacobson in 1947 and again in 1948 introduced evidence that a heparin-like substance acting as a second and third phase anticoagulant was responsible for the long coagulation time seen in the whole blood of X-radiated dogs (see discussion below). Although the hypothesis later proved nonrealistic, at the time it generated a great deal of enthusiasm because it offered a quick, simple, and presumably effective tool to combat post-radiation blood hypocoagulability and hemorrhage. Tocantins also based on experimental evidence obtained by in vitro dilution techniques of blood from radiated dogs, theorized that the main defect in the prolongation of whole blood clotting times was the potentiation of the thrombocytopenia by an antithromboplastin-like anticoagulant (Tocantins, 1952). Defective or abnormal thromboplastin generation was also considered as an important etiological factor in the production of abnormal clotting times (Holden, 1949), either because of loss of an essential platelet-derived factor following qualitative changes of the thrombocytes (Toskaia et al., 1961; Lagutina, 1960) or because of the parallel appearance or disappearance of other substances. The serum 5-hydroxytryptamine, for example, was found decreased in dogs following 600 r of total body radiation and a chronological association with the prolongation of whole blood clotting times was suggested (Panasewicz et al., 1961). In other experiments with rats a mild correction could be observed in the coagulation time following administration of a splenic extract from a normal animal (Pelishenko and Rudakova, 1959).

With exposures to other types of radiation such as alpha or beta rays derived from intrinsic sources, the observations were similar. In dogs, prolongation of whole blood clotting time can be induced by an intravenous dose of 20 μc per kilogram of radiogold (Ferguson et al., 1952). Phosphorus-32 as injectable sodium phosphate can produce hypocoagulability of whole blood when given in rats in doses sufficient to generate approximately 1000 r of total body radiation. The survivors demonstrated abnormally prolonged clotting times from the 4th to the 15th post-radiation day (Kudryashov et al., 1957). With Sr^{90} and Po^{210}, despite the low-dose-prolonged nature of the radiation, longer than normal whole blood clotting times were also observed (Petrova, 1959).

Szirmai (1962) found a shortening of the whole blood clotting times in rats the third day following X-radiation, presumably because of a release of clotting factors from the tissues. However, it seems that generally and within the limits of the dose-response relationship of each animal species, the usual finding is a prolongation of the whole blood clotting time in the radiated animal. This coagulation defect is apparently closely associated with, but not necessarily dependent upon the degree of the post-radiation thrombocytopenia and the time of its appearance. Qualitative changes of the radiated thrombocytes may play some role. In addition, there is accumulated evidence suggesting that following radiation the generation of plasma thromboplastin is defective, either because of functional impairment of the factors involved or because of the appearance of anticoagulant substances acting as anti-thromboplastin.

2. Human Studies

Among the first to report a prolongation of whole blood clotting times in cancer patients receiving X-ray therapy were Reding (1935), Mallet (1936), and Otuka (1938). A transient lengthening of coagulation time in patient with uterine carcinoma was also reported shortly thereafter, following either X-ray or radium therapy (Bignani and Pizetti, 1939). In an elaborate review of the literature and report on his studies on the hematological parameters of 53 patients receiving radiation therapy, Mossberg (1947) found no prolongation of whole blood clotting times, not even in cases (seven) that developed thrombocytopenia. Similar results were reported by others (Teschendorf, 1931; Donati, 1928; Rud, 1925, 1927; Wald, 1957). It seems that with local therapy and fractionation of the dose, the total X-ray dose must reach levels of 2000 r before a mild prolongation of the whole blood clotting time can be observed. It must be emphasized, however, that no correlation exists between the long clotting times and the degree of thrombocytopenia, the development of a hemorrhagic diathesis and the dose of X-rays, although a relation between the degree of prolongation and the total body surface exposed can be observed (DeNicola *et al.*, 1954, 1955; Pavero and Caviglia, 1957).

In contrast to the above, Casassa and associates (1957) found shortening of the whole blood clotting times in their group of locally radiated patients. Twenty-four of the subjects studied received local deep X-ray and ten received beta radiation for neoplasms of the lung. The observation of acceleration of clotting is especially interesting in view of the marked thrombocytopenia which developed in all cases. No differences were seen in clotting parameters between the group receiving X-rays and that receiving beta rays. Actually, this is an old observation dating back to 1922 when Giraud and Pares (1922) and Joltrain and Bernard (1922) described acceleration of the coagulation of blood as part of the syndrome following radiation. Further evidence that local radiation may result in acceleration of coagulation is presented by Panichi and Bonechi, who studied the effects of a single high dose (150 r) to the sternal region, and noted in 30 clinically normal subjects a shortening of the whole blood clotting times (Panichi and Bonechi, 1958).

The five individuals involved in the Y-12 accident at Oak Ridge, Tennessee, received doses ranging from 62 to 96 of mixed neutron energy, and from 174 to 269 of gamma energy, or 236–365 r total energy. Laboratory examinations were performed 11, 29, and 67 days after exposure. At no time was there alteration of the clotting times of whole blood, even during the period of most severe thrombocytopenia (Gauthier *et al.*, 1959; Sise *et al.*, 1961).

There is general agreement that the total body radiation to which the Japanese atomic bomb victims were exposed did produce prolongation of whole blood clotting times. No laboratory data are available on those receiving the highest doses, all of whom died in the first 10 days after exposure, but clinical manifestations of severe hemorrhagic diatheses were observed. In individuals exposed to lower doses of radiation, subacute symptoms developed from the 3rd to the 8th week after exposure. Kikuchi and Wakisaka in their report have divided these victims into four groups, graded by symptoms from severe to slight. In the most severely exposed cases they report moderate prolongation of whole blood coagulation times. Less severely exposed groups showed no deviation from the accepted normal range. It is interesting to note that a few of the survivors retained symptoms and signs of hemorrhagic diathesis one and even 2 years after exposure (Kikuchi *et al.*, 1945, 1946, 1947, 1952; Cronkite *et al.*, 1952).

Although Aubertin in 1932 failed to detect changes in whole blood coagulation time in radiologists who, as a result of occupational exposures, had developed severe anemia and thrombocytopenia (Aubertin, 1932), DeNicola (1961), in an article summarizing the studies on coagulopathies resulting from occupational exposure to ionizing radiation, includes prolongation of whole blood clotting times as one of the characteristic manifestations of the condition; however, DeNicola describes a transitory state of hypercoagulability observed to occur first under certain experimental conditions, presumably a "biphasic reaction." The nature of effects on whole blood clotting times may be related more to differences in dose than to differences between local radiation and total body exposure.

Recent studies on the effects of long-term occupational exposure have produced evidence of hypocoagulability. Mungo and his colleagues report prolongation of clotting times in all members of the occupationally exposed group which they studied (Mungo *et al.*, 1962), as did Shevchenko (1962) in his investigation of 70 workers chronically exposed to radiation.

C. Effect of X-rays on the Skin Bleeding Time

1. Animal Studies

Prolonged skin bleeding was one of the first effects of ionizing radiation to be reported in experimental animals. Lacassagne *et al.* (1922, 1928) observed prolonged skin bleeding times in rabbits after radiation of the uterus, a phenomenon later thought to be due to a secondary thrombocytopenia (Shouse *et al.*, 1931). Since that time additional investigations have added to the belief that prolonged bleeding times on radiated animals are indeed well correlated with and, it seems, dependent upon the degree of developing thrombocytopenia (Ducuing *et al.*, 1936, 1950; Allen, 1952). Other factors, however, play an equally important role, such as the extent of damage to the vascular endothelium. In this respect the observation that an apparent association exists between a progressive decrease in the serum 5-hydroxytryptamine (serotonin) and a prolongation of skin bleeding time in radiated dogs is of great interest (Panasewicz *et al.*, 1961).

2. Human Studies

Hegler and Griesbach in 1931, reported studies of a patient who developed prolonged skin bleeding time during a course of tangential whole body radiation for generalized skin disease. Prolonged bleeding time in this case probably represented a change at the skin level rather than a constitutional effect. Prolonged skin bleeding time after chronic occupational exposure in radiologists was reported by Aubertin (1932). Mossberg (1947) found prolonged skin bleeding times in only two of his series of 53 patients receiving roentgen therapy. In both prolongation concurred with thrombocytopenia, but in 5 other patients who became thrombocytopenic, skin bleeding times remained normal.

The Japanese report on the hematological effects of the atomic bombings indicates that concomitant with the onset of generalized hemorrhages there was marked prolongation of skin bleeding times in the more severely exposed individuals. Increased bleeding times were observed when the platelet count fell below 100,000/mm³, and the degree of prolongation was proportional to the decrease in platelet count. As the platelet count returned towards normal levels during the recovery phase, bleeding times became correspondingly shorter, and all had returned to normal by the 9th week after exposure. Less severely exposed individuals did not show these changes (Kikuchi, 1952).

In the seventy persons studied by Shevchenko who were exposed to chronic radiation occupationally, bleeding times were not prolonged (Shevchenko, 1962).

D. Effects of X-rays on Clot-Retracting Activity

1. Animal Studies

Clot retraction has been of particular interest because of its functional relationship to thrombocytes. Ducuing et al. (1936) reported that total body radiation of dogs caused a progressive decrease in clot-retracting activity as the platelet counts decreased. Mossberg noted suppression of clot retraction after whole body radiation (Mossberg, 1947), as did Allen and Jacobson (1947a) in their studies. Ferguson et al. (1952) found impairment of clot-retraction to occur in dogs following intravenous injections of radiogold (Au¹⁹⁸) in doses of 10 or 20 mc per kilogram, but saw no effect at lower doses. Cohn (1952) observed a decrease in clot retracting activity paralleling thrombocytopenia in radiated rats. Savitsky and Sherry (1954), however, described decreases in clot-retracting activity concomitant with progressive loss of platelet adhesiveness (as measured by the Moolten method), and noted that these changes occurred before the onset of thrombocytopenia or prolongation of bleeding times. Subsequent studies indicated the presence on the 8th day after exposure of a circulating anticoagulant in the radiated dogs which appear to inhibit clot-retracting activity and platelet adhesiveness (Savitsky, 1954). In later dog studies, Savitsky found that a protein extract of bovine spleen contained a tissue clot-retraction accelerator which was capable of neutralizing inhibitor of clot-retraction induced by radiation (Savitsky, 1955).

The rate of clot retraction became longer in guinea pigs on the 3rd day after exposure, according to Rosenthal, and by the 9th day clot retraction was absent. Recovery of clot-retracting ability was observed in animals receiving 200 or 400 r but in those receiving 600 r the change was apparently irreversible (Rosenthal, 1955). Petrova observed loss of clot-retracting activity concomitant with thrombocytopenia and prolongation of whole blood clotting times in rabbits and dogs receiving short- or long-term radiation, respectively, and regarded the thrombocytopenia as the primary defect (Petrova, 1958, 1959). Giordano and associates (1959) found a direct correlation between decreased rate of clot retraction and platelet count in radiated rabbits.

2. Human Studies

Aubertin (1932) reported suppression of clot-retracting activity in radiologists when they developed anemia and thrombocytopenia as a result of occupational exposure. Mossberg (1936), however, found that radiation therapy did not alter the clot-retracting activity in the fifty-three patients in his series.

Cronkite and his colleagues report defective clot retraction as part of the hemorrhagic syndrome in the Japanese victims of the atomic bomb attacks (Cronkite *et al.*, 1952). Schevchenko (1962) did not observe changes in clot-retracting activity in the seventy persons occupationally exposed to radiation whose blood he studied, despite changes in certain other parameters of coagulation.

It can be said that poor retraction of the clot following exposure to radiation faithfully parallels and reflects the degree of quantitative and qualitative platelet changes in both animals and humans. This, of course, is to be expected because of the close functional relationship of platelets to clot retraction.

E. Effects of X-rays on Coagulation Proteins

1. Effects of X-rays on Fibrinogen

a. Animal Studies. The investigations of Allen and his colleagues (1948) led them to report that total body radiation did not appear to induce a deficiency of fibrinogen. On the contrary, Cronkite and co-workers (1952) claimed that plasma fibrinogen concentration may be either normal or increased by total body radiation, and Allen (1952) also observed increased fibrinogen concentration in totally radiated dogs.

Cronkite and Brecher relate the rise in fibrinogen concentration to the onset of bacterial infection following exposure to gamma rays (Cronkite *et al.*, 1952).

Verwilghen and Peremans X-radiated 17 dogs with total doses of either 400 or 600 r; measurement of fibrinogen before and after exposure by a colorimetric procedure showed an increase in the concentration in all of the animals (Verwilghen and Peremans, 1955). On the other hand, Lagutina (1960), in her experiments with acute radiation sickness in dogs and monkeys, observed no alterations in fibrinogen concentration.

The effects of intravenous injection of radionuclides into adult beagles were studied by Dougherty and his co-workers. Substances injected included Ra^{226} and Ra^{228}, Pu^{239}, Th^{228}, and Sr^{90}. All produced elevation of fibrinogen values (Dougherty *et al.*, 1962). Shaber and Miller studied the turnover rate of I^{131}-labeled rat fibrinogen injected into radiated and control nonradiated rats. The turnover rate was found to be the same for both groups, but there was evidence that the labeled fibrinogen left the plasma and entered the tissues more rapidly in the radiated rats (Shaber and Miller, 1963).

b. Human Studies. Reports of the Y-12 accident at Oak Ridge described the elevation of plasma fibrinogen levels to be slight but distinct, by the 11th day after the exposure (Gauthier *et al.*, 1959; Sise *et al.*, 1961). Csomor and his fellow investigators describe, as part of the syndrome of hypocoagulability in patients receiving roentgen therapy for genital cancer, an increase in the reactivity of fibrinogen B (labile, non-heat-coagulable component of fibrinogen), which became more intense as the treatment progressed (Csomor, 1961a,b).

c. In Vitro Studies. Purified bovine fibrinogen exposed *in vitro* to X-ray doses of 25–500 r shows a logarithmic increase of the thrombin clotting time. The fibrin clots so formed are more labile in concentrated urea solution than are those formed by addition of thrombin to non-radiated fibrinogen (Rieser, 1956). The thrombin-induced release of fibrinopeptide is also found decreased, but there is no decrease in clotable protein (Rieser and Rutman, 1956). Further studies indicate that radiation alters the fibrinogen molecule in such a way as to decrease its capacity to react with thrombin, consequent upon a reduction in release of fibrinopeptide, but without altering the clotability of the fibrinogen. These findings are in accord with accepted concepts of the mechanics of polymerization (Rieser and Rutman, 1957).

Latallo *et al.* (1958) tested the effects of *in vitro* X-radiation of plasma and various blood-clotting factors. They found the thrombin time to be prolonged both when radiated plasma and radiated purified fibrinogen were used, and attributed this alteration to effects of X-rays on fibrinogen.

Gordeeva and her colleagues (1960) observed that fibrinogen from radiated dogs clotted normal dog serum more slowly than that from control nonradiated dogs despite the tendency of fibrinogen concentration to increase after radiation. These investigators also noted that when fibrinogen was salted out of radiated plasma it formed coarse floccules. They isolated fibrinogen from plasmas of radiated and nonradiated dogs, lyophilized it, and tested a number of basic properties: (1) there was no difference in isoelectric point; (2) there was no difference in uptake of a dye designed to measure amino acid chromophore groups; (3) distinct differences were seen in ultraviolet absorption characteristics; (4) rate of clotting was slower with fibrinogen from radiated dogs; and (5) the sedimentation rate of salted-out fibrinogen from radiated animals was greater than that of fibrinogen from control animals. The authors concluded that one of the effects of radiation leading to defective blood coagulation is the qualitative changes in fibrinogen produced by radiation.

Koenig and his associates (1960) subjected bovine fibrinogen, both lyophilized and in solution, to gamma rays from cobalt-60, and looked for changes in physical properties—viscosity, sedimentation, and light scattering. They observed decrease in the concentration dependence of the sedimentation constant with increasing radiation. There was also decrease in intrinsic viscosity when the fibrinogen had been radiated in the dry state, and decrease of solubility of both dry and solubilized fibrinogen. The fibrinogen molecule appeared to be both fragmented into lighter units and aggregated into heavier complexes by radiation. When the bovine fibrinogen was radiated in solution, progressive gel formation occurred.

DiBenedetto and Cioffi (1962) obtained thromboelastographic and electrophoretic patterns of bovine fibrinogen dissolved in Veronal buffer before and after exposure to X-rays. The results showed that maximal amplitude of the tracing was progressively decreased as the dose of radiation was increased. Between 50,000 and 80,000 r there was abrupt worsening of the pattern indicating a marked slowing of the clotting process and progressively poorer quality of the clot formed. The electrophoretic data showed increased velocity of migration, an indication of modification of the fibrinogen molecule following radiation.

Next to platelets, fibrinogen is perhaps the most radiosensitive clotting factor. As the *in vitro* studies indicate, radiation doses, well within the clinical and experimental ranges, can produce changes in the fibrinogen molecule which possibly will modify its capacity to react with thrombin. Consequently, the formation of the clot might be impaired. The fibrinogen change is qualitative; apparently its production in the radiated subject remains unaltered and fibrinogen levels increase when thrombocytopenia or other complicating factors reduce the prothrombin utilization and prolong the clotting time of the whole blood.

2. Effects of X-rays on Prothrombin

a. *Animal Studies.* In 1941, Barnes investigated plasma prothrombin time in mice and rats before and after total body radiation. He found no alterations in prothrombin times after radiation, even when severe thrombocytopenia had developed. Adams (1942a) supported this observation in his report on experiments in dogs, published the following year and Allen and his associates in 1948 found no evidence of prothrombin deficiency.

In his report on the animals exposed as part of the atomic bomb tests at Bikini, Cronkite (1950) states that in the four surviving swine among the ones receiving 20,000 r, the prothrombin times were "inexplicably prolonged from 10 to 16 seconds on the fifth day after exposure." Swine exposed to 1300 to 1500 r, showed prolongation of the prothrombin times of pooled whole blood, a change which occurred after the whole blood clotting times had become prolonged. Penick and his co-workers (1951) observed impairment of prothrombin utilization in 10 dogs exposed to whole body X-radiation. In a systematic study of the pathogenesis of radiation hemorrhage in dogs, Cronkite's group found no evidence of prothrombin deficiency by the one-stage and two-stage prothrombin tests, except in the terminal 24 hours in some animals. Prothrombin utilization, however, was decreased proportionately with the platelet count (Cronkite et al., 1952). Allen (1952), in his discussion of the pathogenesis of radiation hemorrhage, likewise cites defective prothrombin conversion as one of the probable etiological factors. His experimental results have shown prothrombin utilization to be reduced in most animals after radiation, without concomitant loss of prothrombin activity. Allen considered loss of thromboplastic activity due to thrombocytopenia as the most likely explanation for the decreased rate of prothrombin to thrombin conversion (Allen, 1952). Cronkite and Brecher (1952) also noted an inverse relationship between residual prothrombin and degree of thrombocytopenia after total body radiation of dogs. They noted that the defect in prothrombin utilization was not corrected by antiheparin substances.

Ferguson and associates (1952) describe impairment of prothrombin utilization following intravenous injection of radiogold (Au[198]) in dogs. The defect was most marked in the dog receiving the highest dose (20 mc per kilogram). The authors considered the two-stage prothrombin consumption test as a sensitive indicator of the severity of the defect. Jackson, Cronkite, and their associates also reported in 1952 that total body radiation in dogs did not significantly affect the prothrombin level, while prothrombin utilization approached the zero mark as the post-radiation period progressed (Jackson *et al.*, 1952a,b).

The effect on prothrombin consumption appears to be the same in large animals. Following exposure of burros to gamma-rays, Trum (1953) observed progressive decrease in prothrombin utilization. There was, however, acceleration of the one-stage prothrombin time; the author attributes this either to conversion of prothrombin precursor or to activation of serum accelerator factors. Stender and Elbert (1953) subjected rabbits to 500 and 1000 r of total body radiation, and observed acceleration of prothrombin activation in the first 24 hours after exposure; there was no alteration in the level of circulating prothrombin. Cornatzer and his colleagues exposed 6 dogs to 500 r of total body radiation, and reported no significant changes in the Quick one-stage prothrombin time (Cornatzer *et al.*, 1953). White and his colleagues were interested in the possible usefulness of soybean phosphatide as a substitute for platelet tranfusions in the management of post-radiation hemorrhage. *In vivo* administration of soybean phosphatide to the radiated dog temporarily shortened the clotting times and increased prothrombin utilization (White *et el.*, 1953). Brecher and Cronkite (1953) again used dogs to demonstrate the correlation between radiation, thrombocytopenia, and decreased prothrombin utilization. Transfusion of platelets appeared to prevent bleeding, but did not efficiently correct the defect in prothrombin utilization.

Verwilghen and Peremans (1955) performed coagulation studies on dogs before and after total body radiation in the 600-r dose range. In contrast to the findings of other investigators, they observed prolongation of one-stage prothrombin times in most of the dogs, and a decrease in circulating prothrombin level in 10 of 15 dogs studied. They attributed these defects to deficiency in thromboplastin formation, due either to radiation-induced thrombocytopenia, Factor VII deficiency, or both. Prolongation of one-stage prothrombin times was also seen by Rosenthal (1955) in his studies in guinea pigs. The animals were exposed to 200, 400, or 600 r. Prolongation of prothrombin times was low in the group receiving the lowest dose, but much more marked in the other two groups. Recovery was rapid in the 200-r animals, slow in the 400-r group, and absent in 600-r group. Thrombocytopenia seemed to parallel these changes.

Davis and his colleagues (1955), in their investigations of the combined effects of thermal burns and radiation in female rats, reported no alterations in prothrombin times in any of the groups—those receiving radiation alone, those exposed to burns alone, and those exposed to both.

Tripodo and Del Buono (1955) demonstrated the expected etiological relationship between radiation damage to the liver and prothrombin level. Daily doses of 500 r to the liver areas of rabbits were followed by gradual, progressive decrease in prothrombin levels, paralleling the progression of hepatic lesions in histological controls.

Gunther and his colleagues (1958) exposed rats to 1200 r of total body radiation, and made serial measurement of concentration of prothrombin, Factor V and Factor VII. After 48 hours, the concentrations of all three factors began to rise, as a prelude to death of the animals, which occurred shortly thereafter.

In the comparative study of high- or low-level radiation exposures conducted by Petrova (1959), prolongation of prothrombin times resulted in all three groups of dogs, although it was less pronounced in the animals exposed over a long period of time by implantation of strontium-90 or polonium-210 than by the high single dose of 600 r gamma rays. The platelet count varied in inverse proportion to the prothrombin time.

The splenic extract administered to radiated rats by Pelishenko and Rudakova (1959) partially corrected the decrease in prothrombin consumption; the latter was considered by the authors as a sensitive parameter of a post-radiation coagulation defect.

In the twenty dogs subjected to 600 r of total body radiation by Lagutina (1960), no alteration of prothrombin times was seen, despite prolongation of whole blood clotting times and microheparin times. When twice this dose, 1200 r, was administered to rats by Szirmai (1962), a rise in plasma prothrombin level was observed, due apparently to accummulation of unutilized prothrombin.

b. Human Studies. In 1942 Adams reported that the prothrombin level was found to decrease by 30% in the plasma of patients receiving radium treatment for carcinoma of the female genital tract, but remained unaltered in patients treated by roentgen therapy to the same area (Adams, 1942b). A few years later, Kaufmann (1946) concluded from a study of persons engaged in radiological work that continuous exposure led to gradual prolongation of the prothrombin times to a maximum of double the normal control time. Mossberg (1947), among his group of 53 patients receiving radiation therapy, found no alterations in the Quick one-stage prothrombin times. Birkner et al. (1952) reporting on a group of patients similarly exposed to local radiation, observed an initial prolongation in one-stage prothrombin times, followed during continued exposures by a shortening in some cases. After radiation was discontinued, there was a temporary drop to below normal levels, followed by a return to the normal range.

Study of the severely exposed victims of the Hiroshima and Nagasaki atomic bombings revealed decrease in the plasma prothrombin. This change was not observed in the less severely exposed cases (Kikuchi and Wakisaka, 1952).

DeNicola, DiGuglielmo, and Timossi have studied coagulation changes in a large series of patients treated with roentgen therapy for neoplastic diseases. They observed a general tendency to hypocoagulability, including a consistent, significant decrease in plasma prothrombin activity (DeNicola *et al.*, 1955; DiGuglielmo *et al.*, 1957; DeNicola *et al.*, 1958; DeNicola, 1961a). Wald, on the other hand, followed 41 patients with metastatic carcinoma, who received low-dose total body radiation, and observed no change in one-stage prothrombin times and an increase in prothrombin consumption within 10 days after exposure. He notes that this is not in agreement with the results of the animal experiments of Jackson, Cronkite, and others, but points out that the dose was much lower in his human subjects, and no thrombocytopenia was produced (Wald, 1957).

In their comparative study of patients being treated for malignancy either with deep alpha-rays or with beta-rays, Casassa *et al.* (1957) described a shortening of the prothrombin time during the early stages of treatment, accompanied by thrombocytopenia. No differences in the two groups of patients were observed. Despite high local doses, up to 2000–2500 r, and thrombocytopenia, Pavero and Caviglia observed no changes in prothrombin activity in their group of 12 patients treated with X-ray for malignancy.

An increase in prothrombin consumption following low-dose local radiation to the sternum was observed by Panichi and Bonechi (1958). The results are similar to those described by Wald. The changes were transitory, and were accompanied by a rise in platelet count. Sise, Gauthier, and their co-investigators observed no changes in prothrombin time, or in serum or plasma prothrombin levels in the individuals exposed in the Y-12 accident (Sise *et al.*, 1961; Gauthier *et al.*, 1959).

Csomor *et al.* (1961a,b) reported on coagulation changes in 34 women receiving high doses of X-ray alone or X-ray and radium combined for genital carcinoma. Decreases in prothrombin consumption were related to dose and to thrombocytopenia. Pozzi studied patients receiving either X-ray or radium therapy, and found decreased prothrombin activity in both groups (Pozzi, 1961).

Shevchenko (1962) and Mungo and his colleagues (1962) reported on chronic occupational exposures among X-ray workers. In both studies, decreases in prothrombin activity were found.

c. *In Vitro Studies.* In their studies of the effects of addition of soybean phosphatide to post-radiation dog blood *in vitro,* White and his associates (1953) observed that this "platelet substitute" produced a marked increase in prothrombin utilization. This increase was more pronounced and longer maintained than was that following addition of tissue thromboplastin. Latallo *et al.* (1958) observed that radiation of plasma *in vitro* did not affect the rate of prothrombin conversion.

Caprino and his colleagues (1962a,b) reported that X-radiation of blood or plasma samples in various doses from 500 to 32,000 r produced prothrombin times at the upper limits of normal, except at the two highest doses, i.e., 4000 r, which produced moderate but distinct prolongation, and 32,000 r, which produced marked prolongation.

In summary it can be stated that the experimental and clinical data indicate that the prothrombin is not altered by radiation and that only unusually high *in vitro* doses disrupt its functional capacity. Disturbances of the prothrombin conversion or the prothrombin utilization can be attributed to a defective formation or action of the plasma thromboplastin and not to quantitative or qualitative changes in the plasma prothrombin. The only possible exception appears during the terminal 24 hours when actual prothrombin deficiencies can be detected, constituting an almost certain prognostic sign of imminent death. The exact cause of this prothrombin deficiency is not known, but it is probably related to liver failure.

3. Effects of X-rays on Thromboplastin

a. Animal Studies. Holden and his colleagues (1949) applied a method for the assay of plasma thromboplastin to studies of total body X-radiation in dogs. They found evidence of hypothromboplastinemia, and considered this to be an important etiological factor in post-radiation hemorrhage. Later this observation was confirmed and the hypothromboplastinemia in radiated dogs was explained as the result of existing thrombocytopenia (Cronkite and Brecher, 1952). In the experiments performed in connection with the atomic bomb tests at Bikini, it was also noted that the prolonged whole blood clotting times of the swine that survived long enough to develop the fatal hemorrhagic syndrome, could be corrected *in vitro*, at times to normal levels, by addition of thromboplastin (Cronkite, 1950). Studies of the antithromboplastic activity of canine plasma before and after radiation gave evidence that an excess of antithromboplastic activity exists after total body radiation. Furthermore, it was found that dilution of the post-radiation plasma shortened the previously prolonged clotting times to normal levels, while addition of plasma from radiated dogs to normal canine or human plasma prolonged the clotting times of these mixtures. Thrombocytopenia was again believed to be the principle defect, the effects of which were potentiated by a raise in antithromboplastin (Tocantins, 1952); however, later attempts to apply the same technique in the study of anti-thromboplastic activity of rabbit plasma before and after radiation met with failure (Caprino *et al.*, 1962a).

White and his co-workers (1953) reported that although the addition of soybean phosphatide to post-radiation thrombocytopenic canine plasma was more effective in increasing prothrombin utilization, thromboplastin proved to be the better agent for shortening plasma clotting times. Stender and Elbert (1953) found disturbed thromboplastic activity in rabbits 3 days after exposure to 1000 r. Verwilghen and Peremans (1955), using the thromboplastin generation test of Biggs and Douglas (cf. Biggs and McFarlane, 1962), also found a severe disturbance in thromboplastin formation in dogs following 400 or 600 r of total body radiation. It was also reported that similar radiation of dogs produced a marked decrease in both plasma and platelet thromboplastic activity during the period of most severe hemorrhage (Lagutina, 1960). The deficiency of "prothrombokinase" reported by Kudryashov and his group (1957) following exposure of white rats to whole body X-ray and to injections of P^{32} may also be interpreted as a defect in thromboplastic generation.

b. Human Studies. No abnormalities in thromboplastin generation were observed in five individuals exposed during the Y-12 accident at Oak Ridge. Studies 1, 11, and 29 days after exposure showed only slight prolongation of partial thromboplastin times as compared with normal control values (Gauthier *et al.*, 1959; Sise *et al.*, 1961).

Coliez *et al.* (1957) studied 8 patients treated for thrombocythemia with radioactive phosphorus. During therapy, the platelet counts returned to normal and hemorrhages and thromboses disappeared. The thromboplastin generation test prolonged in five of the six cases before treatment, returned to a normal rate after a course of P^{32}, to become again abnormal when the thrombocytopenia recurred. The clot-accelerating effects of single low-dose radiation to the sternum described by Panichi and Bonechi (1958) was attributed by them to increased thromboplastin formation and the rise in the platelet count. In his review of coagulation changes in patients receiving radium or roentgen therapy for gynecological malignancies, Pozzi (1961) reported defective thromboplastin generation as part of the general picture of hypocoagulability. The seventy persons subjected to chronic occupational exposure to X-radiation in Shevchenko's study also showed impaired thromboplastin formation in the thromboplastin generation test (Shevchenko, 1962).

c. In Vitro Studies. When Latallo and his colleagues subjected plasma to X-rays *in vitro*, generation of thromboplastin was slightly impaired by doses of 6600 and 13,200 r (Latallo et al., 1958). Caprino et al. (1962a,b) also investigated the effects of X-radiation in doses varying from 4000 to 512,000 r on a solution of rabbit brain thromboplastin, but did not observe any direct effect of radiation on the tissue thromboplastin. In this and subsequent in vitro studies of the effects of ionizing radiation on the optical density of clotting plasma, they consider the post-radiation coagulation defect to be due to a low level of thromboplastin formation, secondary to radiation-induced platelet abnormalities.

As a general conclusion, it can be said that accidental or therapeutic radiation on humans or experimental radiation on animals may result in an impaired generation of thromboplastin. This change is primarily due to a deficiency in Factor III, but deficiency in other factors cannot be excluded. Furthermore, there is some evidence of an increase in a lipid anticoagulant having anti-thromboplastic activity, a possibility which clinically is important enough to warrant further experimental exploration. It seems, however, that restoration of the platelet counts by means of transfusion compensates for any adverse effect of the circulation anticoagulant.

4. Effects of X-rays on Factors V, VII, VIII, IX, X, XI, and XII

a. Animal Studies. Penick and his co-investigators (1951) exposed dogs to acute total body X-radiation, and performed assays of Factor VIII (antihemophilic factor—AHF) activity. Despite development of prolonged whole blood clotting times and impaired prothrombin utilization, Factor VIII activity remained normal, and plasma from radiated dogs corrected the clotting defect in hemophilic dogs, as it had done before the radiation. It is interesting to note that AHF activity was not reduced despite extensive radiation damage to the lymphoid tissue, and in previous experiments to the liver, indicating that AHF activity is apparently not dependent on an intact liver or lymphatic system.

In his discussion of the pathogenesis of radiation hemorrhage in 1952, Allen reported that studies on the clotting factors in radiated dogs had failed to provide evidence of defects in activities of either Factor V or Factor VII (Allen, 1952). Jackson, Cronkite and their colleagues, and Cronkite and Brecher, agree that their experiments in dogs have shown no change in Factor V (Ac-globulin) after radiation. They did observe, however, that Factor VII (SPCA) levels varied directly as did the conversion of prothrombin, and tended to be decreased when this activity was impaired (Cronkite and Brecher, 1952; Cronkite et al., 1952; Jackson et al., 1952a,b).

The effect of radiation on the rabbit liver was studied by Tripodo and Del Buono, (1955). They found decreases in Factor VII levels; there was an unaccountable rise between the second and third daily doses, then Factor VII dropped as did the prothrombin. The results contribute support to the concept of the hepatic genesis of Factor VII. Verwilghen and Peremans (1955) observed in their studies of the post-radiation clotting changes in dogs that the defective generation of thromboplastin appeared to be primarily a deficiency in Factor VII in some of the dogs, correctable by normal canine serum, while a platelet deficiency was primarily responsible in other dogs. They found Factors VIII and IX to be unaffected by radiation.

Gunther and his colleagues (1958) exposed rats to 1200 r total body radiation, and observed increases in Factors V and VII, as well as prothrombin. The increases occurred shortly before death of the animals. Szirmai (1962) likewise gave 1200 r to rats, and observed no changes until 3 days after exposure, when there were elevations in the levels of prothrombin and Factors V and VII. Szirmai considers tissue damage as the basis for these increases.

b. *Human Studies.* In their series of investigations of alterations in the clotting factors in patients treated for chronic leukemia or other neoplastic diseases by radiotherapy, and of healthy individuals occupationally exposed to radiation, DeNicola et al. (1954, 1955, 1958, 1961a) have consistently found that both Factors V and VII decrease after radiation. By contrast, Pavero and Caviglia (1957) studied patients who had received local radiation for malignancies in divided doses to a total of 2000–2500 r, and found no changes in either Factor V or Factor VII activities.

In the eight thrombocythemic patients studied by Coliez and his coworkers (1957), a decrease in platelet count to normal levels occurred following a course of P^{32} therapy; this was accompanied by correction of a Factor V deficit which had been present when the patients were thrombocythemic. The authors believe that the radioactive phosphorus acted to suppress the production of excessive numbers of apparently dysfunctional platelets by the bone marrow.

The reports of laboratory studies done by Gauthier et al. (1959) and Sise et al. (1961) following the Oak Ridge Y-12 accident include the observation of slight elevation in Factor V in 4 of the 5 individuals exposed, and of marked elevation in Factor VIII activity in all five when the thrombocytopenia was most severe. Further studies in patients with primary and secondary thrombocytopenia indicate that Factors V and VIII may be characteristically elevated during the thrombocytopenic state. Two possible hypothetical explanations are offered: (1) these factors may be absorbed on platelets, thus, when there are less platelets, less absorption can take place; (2) the decreased rate of intravascular clotting related to thrombocytopenia may permit these factors to accummulate in the plasma. No changes were observed in Factors VII and X levels.

Finally, in studies of chronic occupational exposure to X-rays, it was found that decreases in Factor V and Factor VIII activities were among the alterations observed as a result of such exposure (Shevchenko, 1962; Mungo *et al.*, 1962).

c. Studies in Vitro. According to Latallo and his colleagues, irradiation *in vitro* produced slight impairment of Factor IX activity, but did not affect Factors V, VII, or VIII.

No studies have been reported in reference to the fate of Factors XI and XII following X-radiation.

F. Effects of X-rays on Other Systems Related to Coagulation

1. Effects of X-rays on the Fibrinolytic System

a. Animal Studies. Although some interesting observations have been made, the effects of radiation on fibrinolysis and its precursors have not been thoroughly studied, despite the great potential for fruitful investigations that lies in this field.

In the course of observations of goats and swine exposed during the atomic bomb tests at Bikini, Cronkite (1950) noted indications of increased fibrinolytic activity, but no reassurements were made. Ferguson and co-workers (1952) administered radiogold intravenously to dogs, and reported that clot lysis was absent 24 hours after injection.

Levels of fibrinolysin in the serum and urine of dogs exposed to high doses of total body X-radiation were measured by Colgen *et al.* (1952). They observed a rapid rise in both serum and urine fibrinolytic activity levels 4 to 5 days prior to death in those dogs that died with massive pulmonary hemorrhage. A similar elevation was seen in the dogs that survived, with return to control levels by the 24th post-radiation day. The authors hypothesize that the rise in fibrinolytic activity may be accounted for by release of tissue kinase due to radiation damage. Copley's studies of the relationship of fibrinolysin to the integrity of capillaries are briefly described in the section of vascular permeability. The animals appeared to be able to develop resistance to the "capillorhagic" effect of fibrinolysin, but radiation weakened this resistance (Copley, 1954).

Fleming and his colleagues (1960, 1962) concentrated in their investigation on the effects of gamma-rays on the fibrinolytic activity in the canine lung. They found that total body X-radiation caused a decrease in the activator of profibrinolysin in the lung, and that in the radiated animals there was an abnormal persistence of the hyaline membrane. When cobalt-60 gamma-radiation was administered to the right hemithorax of dogs in single doses of 1000–2000 rads, there was development of radiation pneumonitis in most of the dogs, accompanied by decreased activation of lung profibrinolysin. When the physiological fibrinolytic system in the lungs fails to remove fibrin deposits, hyaline membrane formation and fibrosis result. Cortisone and heparin had no significant effect on the production of these pathological changes, but intravenous administration of actinomycin D did appear to exert a protective effect on the lungs.

b. *Human Studies.* DiGuglielmo, DeNicola, and Timossi include increased fibrinolytic activity as part of the complex syndrome of hemostatic defects resulting from therapeutic exposure to radiation (DiGuglielmo et al., 1957; DeNicola et al., 1958), but DeNicola states that by thrombelastographic measurement fibrinolytic activity following radiation of humans is variable (DeNicola, 1961?). Sise, Gauthier, and their co-investigators also observed elevated fibrinolytic activity in only one of the five persons exposed in the Oak Ridge Y-12 accident (Sise et al., 1961).

Yamashita and his group (1959) conducted a study of the activation of fibrinolysin in the urine of nurses who were chronically exposed to small doses of radiation during roentgentherapy of patients. The sources of gamma-rays included cobalt-60 tubes, needles, and cells, and radium tubes and needles. The measurement of urinary fibrinolytic activity indicated that seven such minor exposures to ionizing radiation causes significant activation of fibrinolysin. Administration of ε-aminocaproic acid before exposure appeared to reduce the activation. In a later study, fibrinolytic activity was measured in the blood and urine of seventy patients receiving radiation therapy for cancer. The results indicated that in the majority of these patients, blood and urine fibrinolytic activity was elevated above control normal levels before radiation exposure; however, in two-thirds of the patients studied, a further rise was detected after radiation, usually at the time of onset of symptoms of radiation sickness. Again, administration of ε-aminocaproic acid appeared to control fibrinolysin activation and prevent radiation sickness, without side effects (Yamashita et al., 1959, 1961).

2. Effects of X-rays on Heparin and Other Anticoagulant Substances

a. *Animal Studies.* In 1947 and 1948 publications, Allen, Jacobson, and their fellow investigators reported the results of studies of total body X-radiation in dogs. They concluded from their studies that thrombocytopenia is of secondary importance in the genesis of post-radiation hemorrhage and that the primary cause is the production of an excessive amount of circulating heparin. They based this conclusion on observation of: (1) a clot-delaying effect of radiated dog plasma on normal dog plasma, indicating the presence of a circulating anticoagulant; (2) apparent return of the clotting times to normal values *in vivo* or *in vitro* by such antiheparin agents as protamine sulfate and toluidine blue; (3) isolation of an anticoagulant with characteristics of heparin from the blood of radiated dogs; (4) inconsistencies in the times of onset of hemorrhage and thrombocytopenia (Allen and Jacobson, 1947a; Allen *et al.*, 1948). Jacobson and co-workers (1948a,b, 1949) pointed out that prolongation of clotting times by a heparin-like anticoagulant is not exclusively a radiation effect, and reported similar observations in animals and man following administration of a nitrogen mustard compound. They believed that such a substance may be released in response to severe damage to the hematopoietic system from any cause. In the report on the animals exposed during the atomic bomb test at Bikini, Cronkite (1950) described shortening of the prolonged whole blood and plasma clotting times following addition of toluidine blue. He ascribes prolonged coagulation time in fatally radiated animals to a circulating anticoagulant with heparin-like properties.

In a subsequent paper, however, again dealing with the pathogenesis of radiation hemorrhage, Allen (1952) discussed later studies on radiated dogs in whom a clotting inhibitor was detected in only a minority of the animals. This led Allen to revaluate his earlier results, with the realization that transfusion reactions in some of the dogs probably created an erroneous interpretation of the results. On the basis of results in the two studies, it appeared that two types of anticoagulant might develop following radiation: one not responding to toluidine blue or protamine, which occurs in a minority of untransfused animals, and one seen in the trasfused animals which does respond to protamine or toluidine blue (Allen, 1952). Two reports by Cronkite and his co-workers in the same year also refuted their earlier findings of a heparin-like anticoagulant. Their assays for such a substance were negative, and protamine and toluidine blue failed to correct either prolonged clotting times or defects in prothrombin utilization. The authors concluded that there was no convincing evidence for a circulating second-phase anticoagulant, but that a first-phase anticoagulant could not be ruled out (Cronkite and Brecher, 1952; Cronkite *et al.*, 1952). Preston and Parker (1953) administered the antiheparin agent Polybrene to radiated dogs; they observed no effect of Polybrene on the coagulation defect.

Nevertheless, interest in heparin has continued; Hewitt and his colleagues (1953) radiated rabbits and produced elevated levels of serum lipoprotein which they attributed to an acute heparin deficiency. They noted that injection of heparin accelerated return to normal levels of lipoprotein, and injection of the antiheparin agent toluidine blue caused changes in the lipoprotein patterns similar to those seen in the rabbit after radiation.

Stender and Elbert (1963) exposed rabbits to 500 or 1000 r total body radiation, and after an initial period of acceleration of clotting times, they observed prolongation of the thrombin time, due apparently to increases in substances resembling antithrombin. In the lethally radiated higher dose animals a thrombin inhibitor with heparin-like properties was elaborated, the effects of which could be offset by toluidine blue or protamine sulfate. Antonini and Salvini (1953) suspected a connection between increases in plasma heparinoid substances and alterations in lipid and lipoprotein patterns in the radiated rabbit, although definite proof of such a relationship was lacking.

Fulton and his colleagues (1954) hypothesized that the prolongation of clotting times in radiated hamsters might be related, at least in part, to release of heparin into the circulation. These authors observed disrupted mast cells in the hamsters' cheek pouches 3–10 days after radiation. Dogs totally radiated by Verwilghen and Peremans (1955) exhibited decreased tolerance for heparin as part of the general syndrome of hypocoagulability. Rosenthal's studies of radiated guinea pigs revealed prolonged heparin clotting times, even when whole blood clotting times were not affected; the heparin clotting time thus appeared to be a more sensitive test for radiation injury (Rosenthal, 1955). Lagutina (1960) likewise reported prolongation of the microheparin times in dogs 7 days after exposure to 600 r of total body radiation, and a concomitant rise in the level of free circulating heparin in 12 of the dogs, which reached a maximum 8 to 15 days after exposure. Szirmai (1962), on the other hand, reported shortening of the thrombin times in his radiated rats, corresponding to the shortening of the whole blood clotting times. The acceleration of the thrombin times, with or without addition of toluidine blue, indicated a decrease in heparinoid antithrombins.

b. Human Studies. Of particular importance as part of the general tendency of hypocoagulability observed in patients receiving roentgen therapy for leukemia and malignancies is an increased sensitivity to heparin (and to urea as well), that is attributed to a complex defect involving multiple clotting factors not necessarily including heparin itself (DeNicola et al., 1954, 1955, 1958). In another study of 34 patients therapeutic gamma- or beta-radiation produced no changes in "heparinoid" substances (Casassa et al., 1957). However, Pavero and Caviglia (1957) report that in their group of 12 patients, who received divided doses of X-ray up to a total of 2000–2500 r for local treatment of malignancy, there was an increase in "heparin-like" anticoagulant activity, and hyperplasia of "heparin-forming" tissue.

In the report of the Oak Ridge Y-12 accident, it is stated that no evidence for development of a circulating anticoagulant was found (Gauthier et al., 1959). Similarly Shevchenko (1962), in his series of 70 individuals occupationally exposed to chronic radiation found no changes in the level of free circulating heparin.

3. Effects of X-rays on Vascular Permeability

a. *Animal Studies.* The capacity of ionizing radiations to damage blood vessels resulting in loss of integrity and increased permeability of the capillaries has attracted the interest of investigators for many years. Moon and associates (1941) pointed out the similarities between the symptoms and pathology of the post-radiation syndrome and those resulting from other forms of shock. Dogs were subjected to 1400–2800 r of gamma-radiation to the abdomen. The resulting generalized severe mucosal hemorrhages were related to dilatation and increased permeability of the capillaries. The swine exposed to radiation during the atomic bomb tests at Bikini exhibited, as the first stage in the development of a hemorrhagic diathesis, scattered petechiae and positive tourniquet tests, indicating decreased capillary resistance. These findings appeared before prolongation of clotting times or thrombocytopenia. By the 10th day after exposure, capillary fragility was severe (Cronkite, 1950).

Within the range of the usual experimental X-ray doses, the increased capillary permeability in animals appears as an immediate but transient effect of radiation (McCutcheon, 1952). It becomes evident within the first 24 to 48 post-radiation hours (Lenskaya, 1961), but the peak of capillary change as shown by the degree of erythrocyte spillage into the lymph of radiated dogs is reached on the 13th or 14th post-exposure day, at which time an accompanying anemia is also present (Furth et al., 1951; Bigelow et al., 1951). Brecher and Cronkite (1953) correlated the post-radiation thrombocytopenia with the appearance of red blood cells in lymph and found that transfusion of platelets appeared to be helpful in preventing bleeding; this report was later substantiated in radiated rats and dogs. It seems that following radiation, the vascular integrity is adversely affected by a low concentration of platelets in the blood (Woods et al., 1953).

Copley (1954) became interested in the concept that fibrin is involved in the integrity of capillaries. He could produce a "capillorhagic" effect by injection of fibrinolysin in the nictitating membranes of rabbits. This effect became weaker with repeated injections, but when the animals were radiated it again became strong as though radiation had overcome whatever mechanism of resistance to capillary rupture by fibrinolysin had been developed.

Fulton and his co-workers (1954), in their comparative study of hematological alterations in radiated hamsters, noted that petechiae appeared before the development of thrombocytopenia or prolongation of clotting times, suggesting that damage to small vessels precedes other changes. They studied vascular effect of radiation on the hamster in three ways: (1) single dose total body X-ray; (2) local X-radiation of the cheek pouch; and (3) long-term exposure of the cheek pouch to imbedded beta-emitting strontium-90 glass beads or gamma-emitting cobalt-60 needles. Techniques of negative pressure and injections of mocassin venom revealed increased capillary permeability (increased petechia formation) resulting from all three types of radiation. Platelet thrombi were observed as a result of prolonged but not short-term, high-dose radiation (Fulton et al., 1956). Increased capillary permeability was also demonstrated by the rate of disappearance of labeled proteins from the circulation of radiated dogs and tracer movements in the lymphatics. Although the rate of disappearance is similar, the slower rate of lymph flow causes the tracer to reappear in the plasma of the radiated animals later than in the nontreated controls. This may explain the post-radiation drop in plasma protein concentration (Szabo et al., 1958a,b,c). Finally increased vascular permeability was domonstrated in the vessels of the gastrointestinal tract of rats by the use of I^{131}-labeled polyvinylpyrrolidone (Sullivan, 1961).

Using a microinjection technique, Rieser (1955) made direct readings of intracapillary pressure and endothelial resistance in the intestinal capillaries of the leopard frog. Roentgen radiation (and heparin injection, and peptone and trypsin shock) caused increased fragility of the mesenteric capillaries, as determined by observation of lower breaking pressure. Concomitant petechiae and hemorrhages occurred. Similar conclusions of increased capillary fragility were reached by Kudryashov and his colleagues (1957) following radiation of 3000 white rats. In addition to increased fragility, radiation can also produce a decrease in the vascular response to arterenol with an accompanying increased tendency to edema; these changes appear distinct from those produced by purely inflammatory agents (Heite and Schrader, 1955).

The capillary damage following X-radiation is apparently a localized phenomenon unrelated to the innervation of the regional vascular bed. Elegant investigations on the vessels of the anterior chamber of the rabbit showed that the capillary reaction to radiation is identical in both innervated and surgically denervated eyes. Similar are the results in the skin (Arlashenko, 1959, 1963).

In 1952 Cronkite and his colleagues cited references to previous animal studies by others, the results of which indicated that increased vascular fragility could be controlled by the administration of flavonones to decrease capillary permeability (Rekers and Field, 1948; Sokoloff et al., 1950). Their own experiments with administration of flavonoids to radiated animals had not supported these findings (Cronkite et al., 1949; Cronkite and Brecher, 1952).

b. *Human Studies.* Mossberg (1947) reported that of the fifty-three patients in his study receiving radiation therapy for a variety of conditions, only two showed a positive test for decreased capillary resistance.

The more severely exposed of the victims of the atomic bombings in Japan showed decreased resistance of the capillary wall, as indicated by Rumpel-Leedes and Borberry tests (Kikuchi et al., 1952).

Neumayer and Thurner (1952) studied capillary permeability in eighty patients treated with localized X-radiation. They found evidence of increased capillary permeability in tissue distant from the site radiated. Pretreatment of the patient with rutin and antihistamines appeared to decrease this effect.

It can be concluded that radiation produces an increase in the permeability of the smaller blood vessels and the capillaries. Although many explanations have been offered, the exact mechanism of the phenomenon is not completely understood and the exact point of the actinic action or the vascular wall is not known. It appears that treatment of the thrombocytopenia drastically improves, but does not completely remove the cause for the increased permeability, a fact suggesting a complex of factors acting upon the vessel following a high dose of radiation.

G. Effects of X-rays on Blood Coagulation Studied by Specialized Techniques

Thrombelastographic measurements in blood from patients therapeutically exposed to radiation show a decrease in maximal amplitude, and evidence of increased fibrinolytic activity as the most constant and significant changes (DiGuglielmo et al., 1957; DeNicola et al., 1960). The magnitude of these changes depends upon the fractional and total dose and perhaps the site of the radiation. In some instances reaction time and K values are also affected (Bergamaschi and Schiatti, 1962a,b). There are, however, other times that therapeutic radiation does not alter significantly the thrombelastographic parameters (Pozzi, 1961).

Levy (1963) exposed rabbits to whole body X-radiation in doses of 25, 50, and 950 r, and studied platelet-rich and platelet-poor plasma samples in the thrombelastograph. Comparison with nonradiated controls indicated that all three thrombelastographic parameters—reaction time, K value, and maximal amplitude—were altered by radiation. The alterations were interpreted as being in the direction of hypocoagulability, except that with the 950-r dose a slight tendency of hypercoagulability was seen first.

As part of his studies of the effects of whole body radiation on blood coagulation in the rat, Cohn (1952) measured the electrical resistance of the blood. He found that the electrical resistance of the blood during clotting decreased in the radiated animals as compared with nonradiated controls. Giordano and his co-workers (1959) also observed significant decreases in electrical resistance in radiated rabbits that they considered were related to concomitant decreases in numbers of red cells. DeNicola and his colleagues (1960) used a resistance bridge type of apparatus to measure changes in electrical resistance in the blood of patients receiving X-ray therapy. They observed no changes in those being treated for external tumors or lumbosacral arthroses, but in the group receiving therapy for deep internal malignancies, a decrease in electrical resistance occurred. The authors correlate this decrease with erythrocyte concentrations, but saw no relationship to clotting factors.

Finally, Caprino *et al.* (1962a) applied the technique for studying variations in the optical density of clotting plasma *in vitro*, called thrombodensitography, to investigation of the effects of radiation. They observed an increasing tendency to hypocoagulability as the dose increased, which they considered to be due to an radiation-induced platelet abnormality, resulting in a decreased rate of thromboplastin formation.

VIII. Conclusions

Major changes in the normal processes of blood coagulation are primarily caused by the action of the penetrating energies such as X-rays, gamma-rays, or neutrons. Alpha- or beta-radiations emitted from extrinsic sources are ineffective while their effectiveness from inside the body is rather limited.

Based on experimental studies and with the experience accumulated from the human exposures, it can be generally stated that the fundamental response of the coagulation apparatus and its related or accessory systems is basically similar in animals and humans. This allows for some generalizations and also for deductions in the areas where experience with human beings is limited.

Following a relatively high dose of radiation, the blood may become incoagulable. Mainly responsible for this effect is the difficulty of the body in generating thromboplastin. Of all the factors involved in this initial phase of coagulation, the most vulnerable to the effects of radiations seems to be the platelet factor, both quantitatively and qualitatively. Thrombocytopenia, therefore, and thrombasthenia, both being the indirect result of actinic action upon the megakaryocyte, play the role of protagonist in the genesis of post-radiation hypocoagulability. The extent of damage suffered by Factors V, VII, VIII, IX, or X is not completely known, but it seems that at least Factors VIII, IX, and X are radio-resistant, while Factors V and VII are more labile. The generation and the stability of thromboplastin in the post-radiation period is also subjected to unfavorable influences by substances with demonstrable anti-thromboplastic activities that are found to circulate in the serum. It is believed that they are lipoproteins, perhaps phospholipids, and that their presence potentiates the effects of the thrombocytopenia.

Although prothrombin seems unaffected by the radiation, the fibrinogen suffers qualitative changes. Whether this reflects liver damage or a direct molecular effect on the protein itself is not known. It is a fact, however, that next to the megakaryocyte-platelet complex, fibrinogen is most sensitive to the action of X-rays. Hypocoagulability with poor clot formation may be the result of a qualitatively inferior fibrinogen.

Thrombocytopenia and hypocoagulable blood are not solely responsible for the post-radiation hemorrhage. It has been established that an increased capillary fragility and an increased capillary permeability become evident shortly after the exposure. Again, it is not known whether the damage is the result of a direct action on the capillary endothelium, or is effected through the action of released toxic substances, such as serotonin. The result of the damage is a considerable loss of erythrocytes from the available blood volume, a fact that adds insult to the existing impairment in the red cell production. Marked anemia or exsanguination ensues. Serum proteins may be also lost because of the increased vascular permeability.

The most effective tool available at present to combat hypocoagulability and hemorrhage following high X-ray doses is the replacement of lost platelets. Stored platelets are perhaps as good as freshly harvested ones. The transfused thrombocytes not only correct defects in the generation of thromboplastin, but apparently act beneficially in limiting damage to the capillary endothelium. Promising also is the use of the newly introduced ε-aminocaproic acid as an agent neutralizing the effects of fibrinolysin activators. Although this substance has not been widely tested, its preliminary therapeutic applications are encouraging.

Finally, it must be emphasized that persons receiving localized X-ray treatment or those who are professionally exposed with low doses of rays over long periods of time, are not immune to potential damages in their coagulation apparatus. Although the changes only rarely pose an immediate threat to the life of these subjects, the X-ray effects are nevertheless cumulative and may become irreversible. Thrombocytopenia and other concomitant changes in the factors and systems of the coagulation complex must, therefore, be included among the accountable complications of long professional exposures to penetrating energies.

REFERENCES

Adams, W. (1942a). *Strahlentherapie* **71**, 114.

Adams, W. (1942b). *Strahlentherapie* **71**, 248.

Allen, J. G. (1952). *In* "Transactions of the Fifth Conference on Blood Clotting and Allied Problems" (J. E. Flynn, ed.) pp. 213–246. Josiah Macy, Jr. Foundation, New York.

Allen, J. G., and Jacobson, L. O. (1947a). *Proc. Inst. Med. Chicago* **16**, 376.

Allen, J. G., and Jacobson, L. O. (1947b). *Science* **105**, 388.

Allen, J. G., Sanderson, M., Milham, M., Kirschon, A., and Jacobson, L. O. (1948). *J. Exptl. Med.* **87**, 71.

Anderson, A. C. (1957). *Radiation Res.* **6**, 361.

Anderson, A. C., and Winchell, H. S. (1961). U. S. Atomic Energy Comm. Rept. UCD 101–104, p. 108.

Andrews, G. A. (1962). *J. Am. Med. Assoc.* **179**, 191.

Andrews, G. A., and Sitterson, B. W. (1959). *In* "The Acute Radiation Syndrome." (Compiled by Marshall Brucher). At. Energy Comm. Tech. Inform. Serv.

Andrews, G. A., Sitterson, B. W., Kretchmar, A. L., and Brucer, M. (1961). *In* "Diagnosis and Treatment of Acute Radiation Injury," World Hematol. Organ. Publ. Grune, Stratton, New York.

Antonini, F. M., and Salvini, L. (1953). *Arch. Studio Fisiopatol. Clin. Ricambio.* **17**, 299.

Arlashenko, N. I. (1959). *Med. Radiol.* **4**, 12–20.

Arlashenko, N. I. (1963). *Bull. Exptl. Biol. Med.* **54**, 835.

Aub, J. C., Evans, R. D., Hempelmann, L. H., and Martland, H. S. (1952). *Medicine* **31**, 221.

Aubertin, C. (1932). *J. Belge Radiol.* **21**, 148.

Bagdasarov, A. A., Raushenbalk, M. O., Abdullaev, G. M., Baliaeva, B. F., and Lagutina, N. (1959). *Probl. Hematol. Blood Transfusion* (*USSR*) (*English Transl.*) **4**(8), 1.

Baker, W. H., Bulkley, J. B., Dudley, R. A., Evans, R. D., McCluskey, H. B., Reeves, J. D., Ryder, R. H., Salter, L. P., and Shanahan, M. M. (1961). *New Engl. J. Med.* **265**, 1023.

Barnes, W. A. (1941). *Am. J. Roentgenol. Radium Therapy Nucl. Med.* **46**, 356.

Baum, S. J., Davis, A. K., and Alpen, E. L. (1961). *Radiation Res.* **15**, 97.

Beck, J. S. P., and Meissner, W. A. (1946). *Am. J. Clin. Pathol.* **16**, 586.

Bergamaschi, P., and Schiatti, E. (1962a). *Arch. Ostet. Ginecol.* **67**, 101.

Bergamaschi, P., and Schiatti, E. (1962b). *Arch. Ostet. Ginecol.* **67**, 106.

Bigelow, R. R., Furth, J., Woods, M. C., and Storey, R. H. (1951). *Proc. Soc. Exptl. Biol. Med.*

Biggs, R., and MacFarlane, R. G. (1962). "Human Blood Coagulation and Its Disorders," 3rd ed. Davis, Philadelphia, Pennsylvania.

Bignani, C. (1939). Radiol. Med. 26, 1015.

Bignani, C., and Pizzetti, F. (1939). Ser. Ital. Radiobiol. 6, 229.

Birkner, R., Frey, J. G., and Trautmann, J. (1952). Strahlentherapie 88, 44.

Bloom, M. A. (1948). In "Histopathology of Irradiation from External and Internal Sources" (M. Bloom, ed.), p. 162. McGraw-Hill, New York.

Bogdanoff, M. L. (1962a). Presbyterian–St. Luke's Hospital Med. Bull. 1(1), 8–11.

Bogdanoff, M. L. (1962b). Radiology 78, 263.

Bond, V. P., Cronkite, E. P., Farr, J. J., and Hechter, H. H. (1956). U. S. Atomic Energy Comm. Rept. TID 5358, p. 45.

Brecher, G., and Cronkite, E. P. (1953). N. Y. State J. Med. 53(1), 544.

Brinnitzer, H. N. (1935). Strahlentherapie 52, 699.

Buckwalter, J. A., Blythe, W. B., and Brinkhous, K. M. (1949). Am. J. Physiol. 159, 316.

Caprino, G., Cittadini, G., and Maggioni, L. (1962a). Boll. Soc. Ital. Biol. Sper. 38, 1321.

Caprino, G., Cittadini, G., and Maggioni, L. (1962b). Boll. Soc. Ital. Biol. Sper. 38, 1326.

Casassa, P. M., Borio, C. D., and DelMaestro, G. P. (1957). Arch. Sci. Med. 104, 819.

Clark, G. M., and Baker, D. G. (1963). Laval Med. 34, 44.

Clark, G. M., Baker, D. G., and Heddle, J. (1959). Can. J. Genet. Cytol. 1, 142.

Clarkson, J. R., Mayneord, W. B., and Parson, L. D. (1938). J. Pathol. Bacteriol. 46, 221.

Cohen, S. H. (1952). Blood 7, 225.

Colgen, J., Gates, E., and Miller, L. L. (1952). J. Exptl. Med. 95, 531.

Coliez, R. T., Tubiana, M., and Alagille, D. (1957). J. Radiol. Electrol. Med. Nucl. 38, 405.

Coniglio, J. G., Darby, W. J., Efner, J. A., Fleming, J., and Hudson, G. W. (1956). Am. J. Physiol. 184, 113.

Conrad, R. A. (1958). Brookhaven Natl. Lab. Publ. BNL 534 (T-135).

Conrad, R. A. (1959). Brookhaven Natl. Lab. Publ. BNL 609 (T-179).

Copley, A. L. (1954). Arch. Intern. Pharmacodyn. 99, 426.

Cornatzer, W. E., Englestad, O., and Davison, J. P. (1953). Am. J. Physiol. 175, 153.

Craver, L. F., and MacComb, W. S. (1934). Am. J. Roentgenol Radium Therapy Nucl. Med. 32, 654.

Cronkite, E. P. (1950). Blood 5, 32.

Cronkite, E. P., and Bond, V. P. (1960a). "Radiation Injury in Man," p. 39. Thomas, Springfield, Illinois.

Cronkite, E. P., and Bond, V. P. (1960b). "Radiation Injury in Man," p. 84. Thomas, Springfield, Illinois.

Cronkite, E. P., and Brecher, G. (1952). In "Transactions of Fifth Conference on Blood Clotting and Allied Problems" (J. E. Flynn, ed.), p. 171. Josiah Macy, Jr. Foundation, New York.

Cronkite, E. P., and Brecher, G. (1954). Acta Radiol. Suppl. 116, 376.

Cronkite, E. P., Eltzholtz, D. C., Sipe, C. R., Chapman, W. H., and Chambers, F. W. (1949). Proc. Soc. Exptl. Biol. Med. 70, 125.

Cronkite, E. P., Jacobs, G. J., Brecher, G., and Dillard, G. (1952). Am. J. Roentgenol. 67, 796.

Cronkite, E. P., Moore, C. V., Valentine, W. N., Bond, J. P., Moloney, W., LeRoy, G. V., Brecher, G., and Nickson, J. S. (1956). *Natl. Acad. Sci.—Natl. Res. Council Publ.* **452**, Appendix 1, pp. 1–7.

Cronkite, E. P., Bond, V. P., and Conrad, R. A. (1959). *In* "Atomic Medicine" (E. Behreus ed.) p. 160. Williams & Wilkins, Baltimore, Maryland.

Cserhati, I. (1961). *Nature* **190**, 544.

Cserhati, I., Krizsa, F., Sovenyi, C., and Rak, K. (1962). *Z. Ges. Exptl. Med.* **135**, 355.

Csomor, S., Hunka, R., and Szinnyai, M. (1961a). *Magy Radiol.* **13**(2), 93.

Csomor, S., Szinnyai, M., and Hunka, R. (1961b). *Radiobiol. Radiotherap.* **2**, 55.

Dahl, B. (1936). "De l'éffet des rayons x sur les os long en dévelopment et sur la formation de cal." Jacob Dylwood Publ., Oslo.

Davis, W. M., Davis, A. K., Lee, W., and Alpen, E. L. (1955). *Am. Surgeon* **142**, 66.

DeLeeuw, N. K. M., Wright, C. S., and Morton, J. L. (1953). *J. Lab. Clin. Med.* **42**, 592.

DeNicola, P. (1961a). *Thromb. Diath. Hemorrhag.* **7**, Suppl. 1, 347.

DeNicola, P. (1961b). *Hemostase* **1**, 16.

DeNicola, P., DiGuglielmo, L., and Timossi, G. (1954). *Boll. Soc. Ital. Hematol.* **2**, 186.

DeNicola, P., DiGuglielmo, L., and Timossi, G. (1955). *Haematol. Arch.* **40**, 187.

DeNicola, P., DiGuglielmo, L., and Timossi, G. (1958). *Am. J. Roentgenol. Radium Therapy Nucl. Med.* **79**, 142.

DeNicola, P., Giordano, A., Trenta, A., and Caprotti, M. (1960). *Haematologica* **452**, 933.

Detrick, L. G., Upham, H. C., Miles, C. P., Dunlap, A. K., and Haley, T. J. (1961). *Radiation Res.* **15**, 467.

DiBenedetto, C., and Cioffi, L. A. (1962). *Boll. Soc. Ital. Biol. Sper.* **38**, 1370.

DiGuglielmo, L., DeNicola, P., and Timossi, G. (1956). *Radioterap. Radiobiol. Fis. Med.* **12**, 371.

DiGuglielmo, L., DeNicola, P., and Timossi, G. (1957). *Radioterap. Radiobiol. Fis. Med.* **12**, 371.

DiLuzio, N., and Simon, K. A. (1957). *Radiation Res.* **7**, 79.

Ditzel, J. (1962). *Radiation Res.* **17**, 694.

Donati, G. S. (1928). *Boll. Soc. Med. Chir. Prov. Vavese* **6**, 1131.

Dougherty, T. F., Stover, B. J., Dougherty, J. H., Jee, W. S. S., Mayo, C. W., Rehfeld, C. E., Christensen, W. R., and Goldthorpe, H. C. (1962). *Radiation Res.* **17**, 625.

Ducuing, J., Marques, P., and Miletzky, O. (1936). *J. Radiol.* **20**, 177.

Ducuing, J., Marques, P., and Miletzky, O. (1937). *J. Radiol.* **21**, 250.

Ducuing, J., Marques, P., and Miletzky, O. (1950). *J. Radiol. Electrol. Med. Nucl.* **31**, 666.

Duke, W. (1915). *J. Am. Med. Assoc.* **65**, 1600.

Dunlap, C. E. (1942). *Arch. Pathol.* **34**, 502.

Eldred, E., and Eldred, B. (1953). *Blood* **8**, 262.

Ely, J. O., Ross, M. H., Metcalf, R. G., Inda, F. A., Barnett, T. B., and Casarett, G. W. (1954). *In* "Biological Effects of Internal Radiation" (H. A. Blair, ed.), p. 419. McGraw-Hill, New York.

Engelbreth-Holm, J. (1957). *Bibl. Laeg.* **129**, 59.

Entenman, C., Neve, R. A., Supplee, H., and Olmsted, C. A. (1955). *Arch. Biochem. Biophys.* **59**, 97.

Fabricius-Moeller, J. (1922). "Experimentelle Studier Over Haemorrhagick Diathese, Fremkaldt Med. Roentgenstegalen." Levin and Muksgaard, Copenhagen.

Ferguson, J. H., Andrews, G. A., and Brucer, M. (1952). *Proc. Soc. Exptl. Biol. Med.* **80**, 541.

Finkel, A. J., Miller, C. E., and Hasterlik, R. J. (1959). *Radiation Res.* **11**, 442.

Firkin, B. G, Aremura, G., and Harrington, W. J. (1959). *Proc. 3rd Conf. on Platelets.* Natl. Acad. Sci.–Natl. Res. Council, Washington, D.C.

Fisher, M. A., Magee, M. Z., and Coulter, E. P. (1955). *Arch. Biochem.* **56**, 66.

Fleming, W. H., Szakacs, J. E., Hartney, T. C., and King, E. R. (1960). *Lancet* **11**, 1010.

Fleming, W. H., Szakacs, J. E., and King, E. R. (1962). *J. Nucl. Med.* **3**, 341.

Fliedner, T. M., Sorensen, D. K., Bond, V. P., Cronkite, E. P., Jackson, D. P., and Adamik, E. (1958). *Proc. Soc. Exptl. Biol. Med.* **99**, 731.

Fountain, J. R., and Losowsky, M. S. (1962). *Quart. J. Med.* **31**, 207.

Fox, Ch. L., Jr., Singer, H., and Holder, I. A. (1961). "Effects toniques et thromboplastiques d'entrair de peau brulée et de peau normale," Vol. 1, p. 275.

French, A. B., Migeon, C. J., Samuels, L. T., and Bowers, J. Z. (1955). *Am. J. Physiol.* **182**, 469.

Frenkel, L., and Barinstein, L. (1927). *Novaja Chir.* **4**, 406; *Zentr. Ges. Rad.* **3**, 700.

Fulton, G. P., Joftes, D. L., Kagan, R., and Lutz, B. R. (1954). *Blood* **9**, 622.

Fulton, G. P., Lutz, B. R., and Kagan, R. (1956). *Circulation Res.* **4**, 133.

Furth, J., Bigelow, R. R., Kahn, J. B., Knoohuizen, M. M., and Ross, M. H. (1951). *Am. J. Pathol.*

Gauthier, J., Becker, R., Sise, H. S., and Bolger, J. (1959). U.S. Atomic Energy Comm. Rept. ORINS 25, 11.1.

Gawazzeni, S., and Minelli, S. (1914–1915). *Strahlentherapie* **5**, 309.

Giordano, A., Trenta, A., and Mazza, L. (1959). *Radioterap. Radiobiol. Fis. Med.* **14**, 450.

Giraud, A., and Pares, L. (1922). Quoted by Holthusen in Lazarus Handbook, 1928. (See Mossberg, 1947).

Goldfeder, A. (1963). *Laval Med.* **34**, 12.

Goldwater, W. H., and Entenman, C. (1956). *Radiation Res.* **4**, 243.

Goldwater, W. H., and Entenman, C. (1957). *Am. J. Physiol.* **188**, 409.

Gordeeva, K. V. (1962). *Bull. Exptl. Biol. Med.* **53**, 39.

Gordeeva, K. V., Kosiakov, K. S., Pavlova, L. M., and Popel, L. V. (1960). *Probl. Hematol. Blood Transfusion* (*USSR*) (*English Transl.*) **5**, 588.

Goutier, R. (1961). *Progr. Biophys. Biophys. Chem.* **11**, 53.

Graham, J. B., Collins, D. L., Godwin, I. D., and Bzinkhous, K. M. (1951). *Proc. Soc. Exptl. Biol. Med.* **77**, 294.

Gunther, P. G., Gunther, E., and Horn, W. (1958). *Strahlentherapie* **107**, 309.

Hagen, C. W., Jr., and Zirkle, R. E. (1954). *In* "Histopathology of Irradiation from External and Internal Sources" (W. Bloom, ed.). McGraw-Hill, New York.

Haigh, M. V., and Patterson, E. (1956). *Brit. J. Radiol.* **29**, 148.

Harris, P. F. (1956). *Brit. J. Haematol.* **2**, 1032.

Haurani, F. I., Repplinger, E., and Tocantins, L. M. (1960). *Am. J. Med.* **28**, 794.

Hayes, T. L., and Hewitt, J. E. (1955). *Am. J. Physiol.* **181**, 280.

Hegler, C., and Griesbach, W. (1931). *Roentgen–Lab. Praxis* **3**, 75.

Heineke, H. (1903). *Muench. Med. Wochschr.* **50**, 2090.

Heineke, H. (1904). *Muench. Med. Wochschr.* **51**, 1382.

Heineke, H. (1905). *Deut. Z. Chir.* **78**, 196.

Heite, H. J., and Schrader, W. (1955). *Strahlentherapie* **97**, 3955.

Hekhuis, G. (1961). *U. S. Air Force School Aerospace Med.* **61–93**, 1.

Helber, E., and Linser, P. (1905). *Muench. Med. Wochschr.* **52**, 689.

Hempelmann, L. H. (1962). *Health Phys.* **8**, 753.

Hempelmann, L., Lisco, H., and Hoffman, J. G. (1952). *Ann. Internal Med.* **36**, 279.

Hewitt, J. E., and Hayes, T. L. (1956). *Am. J. Physiol.* **185**, 257.

Hewitt, T. E., Hayes, T. L., Gofman, J. W., Jones, H. B., and Pierce, F. T. (1952). *Cardiologia* **21**, 353.

Hewitt, J. E., Hayes, T. L., Gofman, J. W., Jones, H. B., and Pierce, F. T. (1953). *Am. J. Physiol.* **172**, 579.

Holden, W. D., Cole, J. W., Portmann, A. F., and Storaasli, J. P. (1949). *Proc. Soc. Exptl. Biol. Med.* **70**, 553.

Hollaender, A. (1954). *In* "Radiation Biology," Vols. I–III. McGraw-Hill, New York.

Hornykiewytsch, T., Seydl, G., and Thiele, O. W. (1954). *Strahlentherapie* **95**, 523.

Howland, J. W., Ingram, M., Mermagen, H., and Hensen, C. L., Jr. (1961). *In* "Diagnosis and Treatment of Acute Radiation Injury." World Health Org. Publ., Geneva.

Hulse, E. V. (1957). *Brit. J. Haematol.* **3**, 348.

Hulse, E. V. (1959). *Brit. J. Haematol.* **5**, 278.

Ingram, M., and Masan, W. B. (1954). *In* "Biological Effects of Internal Radiation" (H. A. Blair, ed.), p. 58. McGraw-Hill, New York.

International Commission on Radiobiological Units and Measurements (ICRU) (1957). "Report of the ICRU, 1956." Handbook No. 62, U. S. Nat. Bur. Standards, Washington, D.C.

Invernizzi, G. (1957). *Arch. Patol. Clin. Med.* **5**, 616.

Jackson, D. P., Cronkite, E. P., Jacobs, G. J., and Behrens, C. F. (1952a). *Am. J. Physiol.* **169**, 208.

Jackson, D. P., Cronkite, E. P., LeRoy, G. V., and Helpern, B. (1952b). *J. Lab. Clin. Med.* **39**, 449.

Jacobson, L. O., and Mark, E. K. (1954). *In* "Histopathology of Irradiation from External and Internal Sources" (W. Bloom, ed.) McGraw-Hill, New York.

Jacobson, L. O., and Simmons, E. L. (1954). *In* "Histopathology of Irradiation from External and Internal Sources" (W. Bloom, ed.) McGraw-Hill, New York.

Jacobson, L. O., Marks, E. K., Gaston, E. O., Allen, J. G., and Block, M. H. (1948a). *J. Lab. Clin. Med.* **33**, 1566.

Jacobson, L. O., Allen, J. G., Smith, T. R., Spurr, C. L., and Block, M. H. (1948b). *J. Clin. Invest.* **27**, 541.

Jacobson, L. O., Marks, E. K., and Lorenz, E. (1949). *Radiology* **52**, 371.

Jacobson, L. O., Marks, E. K., and Lorenz, E. (1951). *In* "Industrial Medicine in the Plutonium Project" (R. Stone, ed.), Chapter 5. McGraw-Hill, New York.

Jacobson, L. O., Simmons, E. L., and Block, M. H. (1954a). *In* "Histopathology of Irradiation from External and Internal Sources" (W. Bloom, ed.) McGraw-Hill, New York.

Jacobson, L. O., Simmons, E. L., and Sacher, G. (1954b). *In* "Histopathology of Irradiation from External and Internal Sources" (W. Bloom, ed.) McGraw-Hill, New York.

Jammet, H., Mathé, H. G., Pendic, B., Duplan, J. F., Maupin, B., Latarjet, R., Kalic, D., Schwarzenberg, L., Djukic, Z., and Vigne, J. (1959). *Rev. Franc. Etudes Clin. Biol.* **4**, 210.

Joltrain, and Bernard, (1922). Quoted by Holthusen in Lazarus Handbook, 1928, (see Mossberg, 1947).

Kafafova, D. D. (1959). *Probl. Hematol. Blood Transfusion (USSR) (English Transl.)* **4**, 26.

Katz, E. J., and Hasterlik, R. J. (1955). *J. Natl. Cancer Inst.* **15**, 1085.

Kaufmann, J. (1946). *Am. J. Roentgenol.* **55**, 464.

Kikuchi, T., and Wakisaka, G. (1952). *Acta Schol. Med. Univ. Kyoto* **30**, 1.

Kikuchi, T., and Wakisaka, G. (1952–1953). *Acta Schol. Med. Univ. Kyoto* **30**, 205.

Kikuchi, T., Okubo, T., Nishiyame, S., Sasaki, T., Wakisaka, G., Setsuda, T., Anzai, S., Itoi, S., Hamanashi, J., Ishigami, H., Nasa, T., Shiokawa, Y., Takeda, M., and Fujimura, S. (1945). Report to the Special Research Committee on the Atomic Bomb Disasters.

Kikuchi, T., Wakisaka, G., Setsuda, T., Anzai, S., Oga, T., Hiracka, T., Murata, K., Itoi, S., Umeda, T., Okamoto, J., Hama, O., Murakami, T., Sawada, T., Ilshigami, R., Tajima, Y., and Akigama, S. (1946). Report to the Special Committee on the Atomic Bomb Disasters.

Kikuchi, T., Wakisaka, G., Setsuda, T., Yokolyama, T., Uba, B., Nishikawa, M., Tanaka, J., Yamasowa, Y., and Akigama, S. (1947). Report to the Special Committee on the Atomic Bomb Disasters.

Kocholaty, W., Ellis, W. W., and Jensen, H. (1952). *Proc. Soc. Exptl. Biol. Med.* **80**, 36.

Koenig, V. L., Sowinski, R., Oharenko, L., Freling, V., and Wei, G. C. (1960). *Radiation Res.* **13**, 432.

Kohn, H. J., Robinett, R. W., and Cupp, M. N. (1948). U. S. Atomic Energy Comm. Rept. D-2176.

Kornblum, K., Boerner, F., and Henderson, S. G. (1938). *Am. J. Roentgenol.* **39**, 235.

Krause, F., and Ziegler, S. (1906–1907). *Fortschr. Roentgenstrahlen* **10**, 126.

Kudryashov, B. A., Andreenko, G. V., Bazazyan, G. G., Pastorova, V. E., Sytina, N. P., Kalishevskaya, T. M., and Shimonaeva, E. E. (1957). *Probl. Gematol. i Pereliv Krovi* **23**.

Kurnick, N. B., Montano, A., Gerder, J., and Feder, B. H. (1958). *Ann. Internal Med.* **49**, 973.

Kyker, G. C. (1959). In "The Acute Radiation Syndrome" (compiled by M. Bruce). U. S. Atomic Energy Comm. Tech. Ref. Serv., Washington, D.C.

Labram, C. (1963). *Concours Med.* **85**, 849.

Lacassagne, A. (1928). *Progr. Med.* **56**, 1077.

Lacassagne, A., Lavedan, A., and deLeombardy, J. (1922). *Compt. Rend. Soc. Biol.* **86**, 668.

Lagutina, N. I. (1960). *Probl. Hematol. Blood Transfusion (USSR) (English Transl.)* **5**, 583.

Lajtha, L. G. (1961). *Progr. Biophys. Biophys. Chem.* **11**, 79.

Lajtha, L. G., Oliver, R., Kumatori, T., and Ellis, F. (1958). *Radiation Res.* **8**, 1.

Lamerton, L. F. (1963). *Laval Med.* **34**, 156.

Lamerton, L. F., Pontifex, A. H., Blackett, N. M., and Adams, K. (1960). *Brit. J. Radiol.* **33**, 287.

Langendorff, H., and Papperitz, W. (1939). *Strahlentherapie* **65**, 624.

Latallo, Z., Dancewicz, A. M., and Musialowicz, T. (1958). *Acta Biochim. Polon.* (*English Transl.*) **5**, 225.

Latta, E., and Ehlers, G. (1931). *Am. J. Anat.* **47**, 447.

Lea, D. E. (1947). "Actions of Radiations on Living Cells." Macmillan, New York.

Lee, T. C., Salmon, R. J., Loken, M. K., and Mosser, D. G. (1962). *Radiation Res.* **17**, 903.

Lenskaya, R. V. (1961). *Med. Radiol.* **9**, 26.

LeRoy, G. V. (1950). *Arch. Internal Med.* **86**, 691.

Levy, C. (1963). *Hemostase* **III**, 59.

Liebow, A. A., Warren, S., and DeCoursey, G. (1949). *Am. J. Pathol.* **25**, 853.

Lindell, B., and Zajicek, J. (1957). *In* "Advances in Radiobiology" p. 376. Oliver & Boyd, Edinburgh and London.

Linser, P., and Helber, E. (1905). *Deut. Arch. Klin. Med.* **83**, 479.

London, E. S. (1903). *Berlin Klin. Wochschr.* **40**, 523.

Lorentz, E., Jacobson, L. O., Heston, W. E., Shimkin, M., Eschenbrenner, A. B., Deringer, M. K., Doniger, J., and Schweisthal, R. (1954). *In* "Biological Effects of External X- and Gamma Radiation" (R. E. Zirkle, ed.), p. 24. McGraw-Hill, New York.

Low-Bee, B. V. A., and Stone, R. S. (1952). *In* "Industrial Medicine in the Plutonium Project" (R. S. Stone, ed.), p. 338. McGraw-Hill, New York.

McCutcheon, M. (1952). *J. Cellular Comp. Physiol.* **39**, 113.

McLaughlin, M. M., Nury, F. S., and Vrent, R. L. (1957). *Radiation Res.* **7**, 436.

Malamos, B., Miras, C. and Mead, J. (1963). *Nature* **198**, 401.

Mallet, L. (1936). *Arch. Elect. Med.* **44**, 337.

Meffered, R. B., Jr., Webster, W. W., and Hymans, M. A. (1958). *Radiation Res.* **8**, 461.

Metcalf, R. G., and Inda, F. A. (1954). *In* "Biological Effects of External Radiations" (H. A. Blair, ed.), p. 268. McGraw-Hill, New York.

Merialdi, A. (1961). *Quad. Clin. Ostet. Ginecol.* **16**, 580.

Miceli, R., Corinaldesi, A., and Rimondi, C. (1962). *Radioterap Radiobiol. Fis. Med.* **17**, 109.

Micu, D., Maximilian, S., Eremia, R., and Pilat, L. (1962). *Stud. Carcet. Med. Intern.* (*Bucharest*) **3**, 225.

Milch, L. J., Yarnell, R. A., Stinson, J. V., and the Cardiovascular Res. Group. (1954). *Science* **120**, 713.

Minot, G. R., and Spurling, R. G. (1924). *Am. J. Med. Sci.* **168**, 215.

Misao, J., Hattori, K., Ito, M., Kuraoka, S., Kamatani, T., Fukuta, H., Mikawa, R., Histuanoto, S., Endo, N., and Kishikawa, Y. (1962). *J. Radiation Res.* (*Tokyo*) **3**, 79.

Mogilinitski, B. N., Goldberg, A. F., and Shekhonin, V. P. (1962). "Problems in Roentgenology," p. 268. Moscow, U. S. S. R.

Moon, V. H., Kornblum, K., and Morgan, D. R. (1941). *J. Am. Med. Assoc.* **116**, 489.

Mossberg, H. (1947). *Acta Radiol. Suppl.* **67**, 5.

Mottram, J. G. (1923). *Proc. Roy. Soc. Med.* **16**, 9.

Mungo, A., Chiariello, G., and Piccolli, P. (1962). *Folia Med.* **45**, 1214.

Muntz, J. A., Baron, E. S. G., and Prosser, G. L. (1949). *Arch. Biochem.* **23**, 434.

Muth, H., and Schraub, A. (1957). *Strahlentherapie* **102**, 577.

Neary, G. J., Evans, H. J., and Tokinson, S. M. (1959). *J. Genet.* **56**, 363.

Neefe, J. (1936–1937). *Zentr. Ges. Radiol.* **23**, 315.

Neumayer, A., and Thurner, B. (1952). Strahlentherapie 86, 207.

Nygaard, O. F., and Potter, R. L. (1962). Radiation Res. 16, 243.

Osgood, E. G. (1942). Am. J. Roentgenol. 48, 214.

Otuka, M. (1938). Mitt. Med. Ges. Chiba 16, 40.

Oughtersen, A. W., and Warren, S. (1956). "Medical Effect of the Atomic Bomb in Japan." McGraw-Hill, New York.

Panasewicz, J., Lopaciuk, S., and Lubiarz, F. (1961). Polski Tygod. Lekar. 162, 1270.

Panichi, S., and Bonechi, I. (1958). Minerva Nucl. 2, 199.

Pavero, A., and Caviglia, E. (1957). Arch. Maragliano Patol. 13, 521.

Pegg, D. E., Humble, J. G., and Newton, K. A. (1962). Brit. J. Cancer 16, 417.

Pelishenko, I. A., and Rudakova, V. V. (1959). Med. Radiol. 4, 7, 20.

Pendic, B. (1961). In "Diagnosis and Treatment of Acute Radiation Injury." World Health Organ. Publ., Geneva.

Penick, G. D., Cronkite, E. P., Godwin, I. D., and Brinkhouse, K. M. (1951). Proc. Soc. Exptl. Biol. Med. 78, 732.

Perman, V., Cronkite, E. P., Bond, V. P., and Sorensen, D. K. (1962). Blood 19, 724.

Petrova, A. S. (1958). Med. Radiol. 3, 25.

Petrova, A. S. (1959). Probl. of Hematol. Blood Transfusion (USSR) (English Transl.) 4, 14.

Pons, H., and MereGreze-Rueff, P., (1952). J. Radiol. Electrol. (Med. Nucl.) 33, 734.

Pozzi, V. (1961). Quad. Clin. Ostet. Ginecol. 16, 877.

Preston, F. W., and Parker, R. P. (1953). A. M. A. Arch. Surg. 66, 545.

Prosser, G. L., Painter, E. E., Swift, M. N., and Jacobson, L. O. (1954). NNES Div. IV, Vol. 22C.

Prosser, G. L., Painter, E. E., and Swift, M. N. (1956). U. S. Atomic Energy Comm. Rept. TID-5220, p. 1.

Raccuglia, G., and Zarafonetis, C. J. (1962a). Am. J. Med. Sci. 244, 152.

Raccuglia, G., and Zarafonetis, C. J. (1962b). Proc. Soc. Exptl. Biol. Med. 110, 641.

Radojicic, B., Hajdukovic, S., and Antic, M. (1961). "Diagnosis and Treatment of Acute Radiation Injury." World Health Org. Publ., Geneva.

Raper, J. R., and Barnes, K. K. (1952). In "Histopathology of Irradiation from External and Internal Sources" (W. Bloom, ed.) McGraw-Hill, New York.

Rak, K., Krizsa, F., and Cserhati, I. (1962). Kiserl. Orvostud. 14, 212.

Reding, R. (1935). Compt. Rend. Soc. Biol. 119, 342.

Rehnborg, C. S., Ashikawa, J. K., and Nichols, A. V. (1962). Radiation Res. 16, 860.

Reisner, E. H., and Heating, R. P. (1957). Proc. Soc. Exptl. Biol. Med. 96, 112.

Rekers, P. E., and Field, J. B. (1948). Science 107, 16.

Rieser, P. (1955). Proc. Soc. Exptl. Biol. Med. 89, 39.

Rieser, P. (1956). Proc. Soc. Exptl. Biol. Med. 91, 654.

Rieser, P., and Rutman, R. J. (1956). Nature 178, 257.

Rieser, P., and Rutman, R. J. (1957). Arch. Biochem. Biophys. 66, 247.

Rosenthal, R. L. (1949). Science 110, 43.

Rosenthal, R. L. (1955). Blood 10, 510.

Rosenthal, R. L., and Benedek, A. L. (1950). Am J. Physiol. 161, 505.

Rubini, J. R., Cronkite, E. P., Bond, V. P., and Fliedner, T. M. (1959). Proc. Soc. Exptl. Biol. Med. 100, 130.

Rud, E. (1927). Strahlentherapie 25, 195.

Savitsky, J. P. (1955). Blood 10, 52.

Savitsky, J. P., and Sherry, S. (1954). *Proc. Soc. Exptl. Biol. Med.* **85**, 587.

Schjeide, O. A., Ragan, N., and Simons, S. (1958). *Radiation Res.* **9**, 327.

Sergel, O. S. (1961). *Med. Radiol.* **9**, 17.

Shaber, G. S., and Miller, L. L. (1963). *Proc. Soc. Exptl. Biol. Med.* **113**, 346.

Shevchenko, V. V. (1962). *Med. Radiol.* **7**, 49.

Shipman, T. L. (1961). *In* "Diagnosis and Treatment of Acute Radiation Injury" p. 113. World Health Org. Publ., Geneva.

Shitikova, M. G., and Kozinets, G. I. (1962). *Med. Radiol.* **7**, 41.

Shively, J. M., Michaelson, S. M., and Howland, J. W. (1961). *Radiation Res.* **15**, 319.

Shouse, S. S., Warren, S. L., and Whipple, G. H. (1931). *J. Exptl. Med.* **53**, 421.

Sinclair, W. K. (1962). *Radiation Res.* **16**, 394.

Sise, H. S., Gauthier, J., Becker, R., and Bolger, J. (1961). *Blood* **18**, 702.

Sokoloff, B., Redd, J. B., and Dutcher, R. (1950). *Proc. Soc. Exptl. Biol. Med.* **75**, 6.

Sorensen, D. K., Bond, V. P., Cronkite, E. P., and Perman, V. (1960). *Radiation Res.* **13**, 669.

Stefanini, M., and Crosby, W. H. (1950). *Proc. Soc. Exptl. Biol. Med.* **73**, 301.

Stender, H. S., and Elbert, O. (1953). *Strahlentherapie* **90**, 625.

Sullivan, M. F. (1961). *Am. J. Physiol.* **201**, 951.

Suter, G. M., and Boyd, G. A. (1950). In "Biological Studies with Polonium, Radium and Plutonium" (R. M. Field, ed.), p. 282. McGraw-Hill, New York.

Szabo, G., Magyar, S., Kertai, P., and Zadory, E. (1958a). *Nature* **182**, 885.

Szabo, G., Magyar, S., Kertai, P., and Zadory, E. (1958b). *Orv. Hetilap* **99**, 1566.

Szabo, G., Magyar, S., Kertai, P., and Zadory, E. (1958c). *Z. Ges. Exptl. Med.* **130**, 452.

Szirmai, E. (1962). *Z. Ges. Inn. Med. Ihre Grenzgebiete* **17**, 359.

Takacizumi, M., and Ono, Y. (1929). *Trans. Japan Pathol. Soc.* **18**, 161.

Teschendorf, W. (1931). *Fortschr. Roentgenstrahlen* **43**, 510.

Thomas, E. D., Herman, E. C., Jr., Greenlough, W. B., III, Hager, E. B., Cannon, J. H., and Sahler, O. D. (1961). *Arch. Internal Med.* **107**, 829.

Tocantins, L. M. (1952). *In* "Blood Clotting and Allied Problems" (J. E. Flynn, ed.), pp. 247–279 Josiah Macy, Jr. Foundation, New York.

Tocantins, L. M., and Carroll, R. T. (1949). *In* "Blood Clotting and Allied Problems" (J. E. Flynn, ed.), pp. 11–27. Trans. 2nd Conf. Josiah Macy, Jr. Foundation, New York.

Tocantins, L. M., and Wang, G. C. (1956). *In* "Progress in Hematology: Methods of Study" (L. M. Tocantins, ed.), p. 138. Grune & Stratton, New York.

Toskaia, A. A., Terenteva, E. I., and Abdullaev, G. M. (1961). *Med. Radiol.* **6**, 29.

Traskunova, N. V. (1962). *Med. Radiol.* **7**, 45.

Tripodo, C., and Del Buono, G. (1955). *Radioter. Radiobiol. Fis. Med.* **10**, 228.

Trum, B. F. (1953). *Mil. Surg.* **112**, 333.

Trum, B. F., and Rust, J. H. (1953). *Proc. Soc. Exptl. Biol. Med.* **82**, 347.

United Nations Committee on the Effects of Atomic Radiation, New York. (1958). Suppl. No. 17(A3838).

Van Lancker, J. L. (1963). *Laval Med.* **34**, 63.

Verwilghen, R. L., and Peremans, J. M. (1955). *U. S. Air Force Med. J.* **6**, 645.

Vetter, H., and Vinazzer, H. (1952). *Wien. Z. Inn. Med. Grenzgebiete* **33**, 455.

Vetter, H., and Vinazzer, H. (1954). *Blood* **9**, 163.

Vladimirov, V. G. (1963). *Bull. Exptl. Biol. Med.* **54**, 1236.

Wagner, R., Meyeric, K., and Berman, C. Z. (1957). *Blood* **12**, 733.

Wald, N. (1957). *Proc. Soc. Exptl. Biol. Med.* **96**, 294.

Wald, N. Woodward, K. T., Boone, I., and Thoma, G. E., Jr. (1961). *In* "Hematology" (J. E. Pickering, ed.), Chapter 60. U. S. Air Force Aerospace Med. Center, Banks Air Force Base, Texas.

Waldschmidt-Leitz, C., and Keller, L. (1961). *Strahlentherapie* **116**, 610.

Warren, S. (1947). *Cancer Res.* **6**, 449.

Warren, S., and Draiger, R. H. (1946). *U. S. Naval Bull.* **46**, 1349.

Weiner, N., Albaum, H. G., Milch, L. J., and the Cardiovascular Res. Group. (1955). *A. M. A. Arch. Pathol.* **60**, 621.

Weiner, N., Milch, L. J., and Shults, G. E. (1956). *J. Appl. Physiol.* **9**, 88.

Winkler, C., and Paschke, G. (1956). *Radiation Res.* **5**, 156.

White, S. G., Lagen, J. B., Aggeler, P. M., and Geyer, R. P. (1953). *Proc. Soc. Exptl. Biol. Med.* **83**, 384.

Wolff, K. (1935). *Strahlentherapie* **54**, 68.

Woods, M. C., Furth, J., Gamble, F. N., and Bigelow, R. R. (1953). *Blood* **8**, 545.

Wright, J. H. (1906). *Boston Med. Surg. J.* **154**, 643.

Wright, S., and Bulman, H. A. (1929). *Lancet* **II**, 217.

Yamashita, H., Kobayashi, K., Suzuki, S., and Hashimoto, S. (1959). *Keio J. Med.* **8**, 331.

Yamashita, H., Igari, S., and Tanaka, T. (1961). *Keio J. Med.* **10**, 195.

Zaretskaya, I. V. (1953). Dissertation, Odessa (Abstr.).

Zirkle, R. E. (1947). *Radiology* **49**, 271.

Zunz, E., and La Barre, J. (1927). *Compt. Rend. Soc. Biol.* **96**, 125.

CHAPTER 15

Nuclear Hematology and Blood Transfusion

Volkmar Sachs

Hygiene-Institut der Universität Kiel, Kiel, Germany

I. Introduction

There has always been a strong interaction between blood transfusion and hematology, since blood transfusion developed into a special branch after the discovery of blood groups (Landsteiner, 1900) and the method of using sodium citrate to prevent clotting (D'Agote, 1915; Hustin, 1914; Lewisohn, 1915), and especially since it played an important role in clinical therapy. The relationship between immune hematology and transfusion serology is particularly important.

Even in the newest branch of hematology, namely nuclear hematology, blood transfusion is an essential factor in treating radiation damage of the hematopoietic organs. All reports about radiation damage caused by atomic bombings, nuclear therapeutic operations, or nuclear accidents tell about employment of blood transfusion and infusion of plasma. Therefore, Miller (1962) has called for the extension of blood banks to be ready for the requirements of an atomic disaster.

Although there are numerous points of contact between research in nuclear hematology and blood transfusion—possibly more will eventually become apparent—at present the therapy of radiation damage is mainly important from the point of view of blood transfusion. Practically, radiation damage is a hematological problem, because the neurological and gastrointestinal types of damage are fatal in every case. Only the hematological type can be treated successfully. There has been a great increase of knowledge in the field of nuclear hematology in the last 10 or 20 years, which has enlarged and improved the possibilities of effective treatment of radiation damage, e.g., regarding the character of metabolism and proliferation of hematopoietic organs, the dependence of the effect of rays on the dose and kind of radiation, the nature of direct and indirect influence on cell function, and the mechanisms preventing damage by ionizing radiation. During the same period transfusion research has been initiated—Hässig (1962) called it "hemotherapy made to measure"—which aims to make transfusion therapy more effective and expedient by the application of isolated corpuscles and plasma of the blood.

No one has yet written the chapter on "specific hemotherapy of radiation damage" in a book on nuclear disasters, and we hope it will never be necessary. But the threatening dangers in the age of atomic bombs should lead to discussion of the therapeutic possibilities arising from both branches of research. Hopefully, this may stimulate further experiments.

II. Hemotherapy of Radiation Damage

A. Elimination of Ionizing Substances by Exchange Transfusion

Before discussing the different possibilities of transfusion therapy, another problem should be discussed here, namely, exchange transfusion. It was introduced by Bayliss (1919), and it was recommended again 38 years later by Bessis and Bernard (1947). At the same time Wiener and Wexler (1946) used it to treat morbus hemolyticus neonatorum. Transfusion therapy serves to remove undesired and injuring substances or cells from the circulation and the organism. It has been applied successfully in erythroblastosis of the new-born, after transfusion of incompatible blood, in uremia, poisonings, leukemia, and pregnancy anemia (Ocklitz and Schmitz, 1950; Rudert, 1951; Karcher, 1953; Fullerton and Turner, 1962). Since we have to reckon with uptake of radioactive substances during irradiation accidents as well as during nuclear therapeutic treatment, and especially during nuclear disasters, exchange transfusion is thought to be a suitable means to remove these substances. This is true particularly when using the method of Fullerton and Turner (1962), supported by the transporting property of albumin. Nevertheless we do not know whether the exchange-transfusion will ever gain high importance for this purpose, because large quantities of blood, belonging to the same group, are needed. It will be difficult to get the necessary blood when numerous and repeated exchange transfusions are required. Moreover, pharmaceutical methods of removal of radioactive substances have advanced to such an extent (Catsch and Le, 1957, 1958; Haley, 1963) that exchange transfusion can be considered as only an additional possibility in this field.

B. TRANSFUSION THERAPY OF ACUTE RADIATION SYNDROME

What are the conditions necessary to make transfusion therapy of radiation damage successful? And what are the problems the doctor should pay attention to?

Acute irradiation syndrome shows a characteristic development (Becker and Fliedner, 1957; Stodtmeister et al., 1958): in the beginning one finds an influence on the marrow circulation combined with hyperemia, damage of the vascular walls, bursting of the sinus, marrow edema, nonthrombocytopenic marrow hemorrhage, cell dissociation, marrow destruction, lipid infiltration, decrease of cellularity, reticulocytosis, and plasmacytosis during the first 24 hours. Next the lymphocytes decrease rapidly, obviously by direct radiation action, until they have a nearly constant value depending on the radiation dose (Andrews et al., 1959; Hulse, 1963). During the first few days the number of leukocytes increases because of disturbed marrow circulation. As a sign of temporary recovery they decrease (appearance of giant cells) and reach a minimum at the 30th to 35th day, then rising gradually again. The minimum levels of platelets are observed from the 28th to the 30th day. There is a delay of diminution caused by proliferation processes, indicating the disproportion between production and reduction. The number of platelets will again rise on about the 30th day. The reticulocytes behave like granulocytes. Anemia will develop only slightly because of the long life of the red cells, and because of the mixing of degenerative and regenerative processes. If there is much bleeding as a result of thrombocytopenia, however, anemia can occur owing to the additional loss of blood. This eventuality, as well as individual variations, will determine the requirements of therapy. If the diagnosis (examination of marrow, and radioiron clearance, if possible) shows that the regenerative power of the marrow is still retained, it is primarily necessary to bridge the functional disturbance (infections and hemorrhages) resulting from leukopenia and thrombopenia by means of transfusion therapy, until spontaneous regeneration commences.

Platelet transfusion may be utilized to combat the hemorrhagic tendency caused by lack of regeneration of thrombocytes. As Jackson et al. (1959) showed, transfusion of thrombocytes is effective only if the platelet suspension is prepared from recently collected blood, and if the platelets are not destroyed by the method of isolation. Most methods of isolation cause a lesion of thrombocytes because of centrifugation and washing procedures. If there is no arrangement to isolate the platelets carefully it would be better to use a pooled buffy coat of 10 or 20 fresh units of preserved blood (Vergoz, 1961). As a last resort, one can fall back on the method of transfusing fresh whole blood, especially when the hematocrit or hemoglobin concentration is decreasing simultaneously.

The same rules are valid for the selection of the donor blood and the management of transfusions as are known for any other transfusion. If there is no group-compatible blood available (this could happen with the rare blood groups B and AB) in emergency treatment blood of group O without hemolysins can be used; in the treatment of isolated platelets, blood of group O can also be used. It does not matter whether fresh whole blood or direct transfusion is used (Blum, 1962). There are advantages as well as disadvantages in both cases. Direct transfusion is combined with completely physiological conditions, but it is difficult to find donors, and it is time consuming and expensive because of the high number of persons concerned. The application of fresh preserved blood, especially if large quantities are needed, will occasionally require supplementary calcium by administration of glucose-calcium; but we are not forced to produce it at the place of application, it can be transported quickly, and it can be transfused with a minimum of expense of personnel and time. Of course, every transfusion must be prepared carefully with respect to typing of ABO groups and Rh factor, identification of irregular antibodies of donor and acceptor, and serological cross-match.

The second factor that is important for the clinical picture of acute irradiation syndrome is the infection caused by leukopenia. In this case the primary treatment is therapy with antibiotics, but this will be more efficient when combined with blood transfusion, as Skalta (1962) showed by animal tests. That attempt to influence leukopenia by infusion of isolated leukocytes is hopeless has been known for a long time (Strumia, 1934; Dausset and Maupin, 1956). Preparations of γ-globulin have proved successful in many bacteriological and viral infections (Schultze and Heide, 1960; Stampfli et al., 1960) because they are produced from the serum of a number of donors and because they contain about 20 times as much antibodies as normal blood generated by the organism during several manifest and latent infections against different pathogenic agents.

Apart from the characteristic course of the syndrome there is no difference between the transfusion therapy of the acute radiation syndrome and the usual transfusion treatment of conditions caused by other injuries. It would hardly be possible to get the needed quantity of fresh blood, and the production of large quantities of platelet suspension is quite impracticable (Manstein, 1963).

As to the question of whether the modern blood transfusion system guarantees an effective treatment of radiation damage, even under the conditions of a catastrophe, we must remember one of the most important facts in the therapy of hematological radiation damages. Numerous examinations of biological therapeutic methods concerning radiation damage (e.g., bone marrow transfusion; see Chapter 16) lead to the conclusion that its effect depends on the stimulation of the body's own hematopoiesis (Van Bekkum, 1959).

It has been known for a long time that the application of blood and plasma, and blood and plasma ingredients has a stimulating effect in addition to a substituting effect. Our knowledge about this stimulating effect is not yet complete and is based mainly on speculation, but there are several concrete inferences. A specific erythropoietic effect of plasma was already supposed by Carnot and Déflandre (1906) and later on it was verified by many other authors (e.g., Linman and Bethell, 1956, 1957; Linman and Long, 1958; Jacobson et al., 1956; Stohlman and Brecher, 1956; Hatta et al., 1962). Cazal et al. (1956) and Hässig et al. (1959), as well as Gugler (1961, 1962) showed that bleeding can be stopped with the help of Cohn's fraction I when thrombocytopenic hemorrhagic tendency exists. Neither this effect nor the effect of Cohn's fraction I on angiohemophilia can be viewed as a mere substitution. The observations of Bagdassarov (1957) and Peter (1954) about the regular fluctuations of the leukocyte numbers and of Polak and Polakova (1956) about the increase of ameboid mobility of leukocytes after blood and plasma transfusions lead in the same direction. Finally Waitz and Sachs (1964) saw surprising recoveries in hopeless cases of panmyelophtisis after cytostatic treatment when Cohn's fraction I and packed red blood cells were applied simultaneously; this effect could not be interpreted as substitution alone.

All these observations have something in common, namely, that the effect of plasma or plasma components is obtained with preparations which can be produced simply and in large quantities and can be preserved with the help of freeze-drying or deep freezing. These preparations can be stored for a long time and are permanently available. In addition they have the advantage that they can be applied without extensive serological preparations and require no additional personnel (Hässig *et al.*, 1959).

Until now the question has not been settled as to whether plasma and plasma ingredients have the same success as fresh whole blood and platelets suspension, because not much attention has been paid to this special branch of experimental and clinical inquiry; however, it is obvious that hemotherapy during nuclear disasters must be based entirely on these stored preparations.

The few scattered and not yet clear results about the effect of plasma and plasma components on hematopoiesis which have been obtained suggest that plasma transfusion would have a beneficial effect on the hemolytic disorders of the acute radiation syndrome, particularly because hemolytic radiation damage is not specific for the type of radiation, but is organ-specific.

During a nuclear disaster, the platelet suspension or fresh whole blood will be replaced by Cohn's fraction I (because it is so much easier to obtain) in treatment of the initial thrombocytopenic hemorrhagic tendency, and when erythropoiesis is damaged as well it will be replaced by packed red blood cells. The same preparations, as well as units of preserved blood and plasma, assisted by γ-globulin, might be beneficial in the treatment of leukopenia and its consequences.

Certainly these statements are only speculative. There are no specific experiments and clinical tests to prove their correctness. It would seem to be an urgent and worthwhile task to carry out these experiments.

C. Transfusion Therapy of the Sequelae of Acute Radiation Syndrome

Höhne *et al.* (1952, 1953, 1955); Künkel (1955), and Winkler and Paschke (1955, 1956) called attention to the alterations of the protein content in the plasma after the acute radiation syndrome has developed. The alteration consists of a reduction of the whole protein, caused by a decrease of the γ-globulin and of albumin. The diagnosis leads to substitution therapy. Plasma, stable plasma protein solution (SPPS) (Surgenor, 1952; Surgenor and Pennel, 1960; Nitschmann and Kistler, 1954; Nitschmann *et al.*, 1956), albumin, and γ-globulin are indicated. If protein is to be replaced generally, SPPS is better than plasma (Hässig *et al.*, 1959), because SPPS which is received by removing the γ-globulin from the plasma can be pasteurized. Thus the hepatitis virus can be made inactive, and the preparation can be applied without danger.

The solution of albumin is the best remedy owing to its osmotic properties. Albumin has all the advantages of SPPS and in addition it can be pasteurized, does not cause hepatitis, may be stored, and has the highest osmotic activity. It is available in different concentrations, about 5% and about 15 to 20%. Therefore, the doctor in charge is able to adapt the therapy to every particular case. Albumin of high concentration proved to be effective for flushing out ascites in cirrhosis of the liver (Post et al., 1951; Hartmann, 1952; Siede, 1953) and for dehydration during the treatment of cerebral edema (Reissigl, 1961). It could also become important in the treatment of the cerebral edema caused by radiation (Wende, 1963).

As the physiology of clotting does not really belong to the hematological field, the transfusion therapy of nonthrombocytopenic defective clotting resulting from radiation will only be briefly mentioned here (see Szirmai, 1954, 1958; Farkass, 1962; and Chapter 14 of this volume). Besides fresh whole blood and plasma preparations activating clotting such as Cohn's fraction I, prothrombin–proconvertin–Stuart factor–antihemophilic factor B (PPSB) of Blatrix and Soulier (1959), accelarin-convertin (Acc 76) of Deutsch (1962), and others can be applied. Results of an analysis of the clotting process will determine which of the different preparations activating clotting should be used.

D. TRANSFUSION THERAPY OF CHRONIC RADIATION DAMAGE AND OF LATE SYMPTOMS

The transfusion of blood and plasma as well as of blood and plasma ingredients can be essential in the treatment of chronic radiation injury. The main symptoms of illness originating from chronic radiation damage are less characteristic than those of the acute radiation syndrome, because the reactions are organ and not radiation specific. There are no strict rules of treatment. The therapy is executed according to the rules which are generally valid for the characteristics of the illness; this is true for transfusions and hemotherapy, also. All the precautions are to be observed which are necessary in transfusions and hemotherapy, if the sequelae of chronic radiation effect have to be treated.

Transfusion (in the form of an exchange transfusion) will not be indicated in the future for the purpose of eliminating a source of radiation which leads to a chronic radiation damage, because the method of antagonizing by chemical means has made great strides during the last years (Catch and Le, 1957, 1958; Haley, 1963).

Transfusions and general hemotherapy can be useful in treatment of one of the most frequent consequences of chronic radiation influence, namely the failure of hematopoiesis, which first occurs as pancytopenia and sometimes as leukemia (Fliedner and Stodtmeister, 1962). The clinical picture will determine whether fresh whole blood, units of preserved blood, packed red blood cells, washed red blood cells, plasma, or a combination of several preparations are preferred. Though fresh whole blood promises the best results when the whole hematopoietic system fails, packed red blood cells and possibly washed erythrocytes are thought to be acceptable. If substitution has to be continued intensely for a long time, the danger of a transfusion reaction arises with every whole blood transfusion, in spite of careful serological preparation, because the complement added with the donor plasma can activate resting antigen-antibody reactions (Kolb, 1961, 1963). This risk can be avoided or reduced to a minimum by use of packed red blood cells and washed red blood cells (Baumgarten, 1963).

Leukemia is a very frequent late sequela of acute and chronic radiation. Other sequelae are observed less often, e.g., aplastic anemia, pancytopenia, and panmyelopthisis (Cronkite et al., 1960; Moloney, 1959; Heyssel et al., 1960; Brill et al., 1962; Kimball, 1958; Lange et al., 1955). During leukemic disease, blood transfusion will play a role only when anemia occurs simultaneously (Wilkinson, 1963). It does not matter whether it is caused by radiation or not. It mainly depends on the clinical facilities, whether fresh whole blood is used, or units of preserved blood or packed red blood cells and washed red blood cells are applied in case of incompatibility not caused by differences in blood groups. The transfusion is indispensable for the treatment of pancytopenic conditions. Because the substitution must be continued over a long period of time it is recommended to transfuse packed red blood cells even in the beginning to avoid reactions caused by incompatibility (Mollison, 1963; Bagdassarov and Guljaew, 1958). One is forced to use fresh whole blood and concentrations of leukocytes (Fleischhacker and Stacher, 1963) or perhaps Cohn's fraction I connected with packed red blood cells, if the granulocytopenia is the most striking symptom of the illness.

As hemotherapy and blood transfusion of radiation damage play the most important roles in the field of radiation hematology the indications and the theoretical possibilities are given in Table I.

III. Labeling with Radioactive Substances for Estimation of the Quality of Preserved Blood

Although transfusion therapy is most important for the irradiation hematology, some relations between nuclear hematology and blood transfusion will be mentioned that play a less important role, but still constitute important advances in knowledge.

TABLE I

HEMOTHERAPY OF RADIATION DAMAGE

	Hemotherapeutic treatment	Other hemotherapeutic treatment	Remarks
Elimination of ionized substances	Exchange transfusion, partial exchange transfusion		Chemical elimination
Acute hematological radiation syndrome			
(a) Thrombocytopenic hemorrhagic tendency:			
without anemia	Platelet suspension, pooled buffy coat	Cohn's fraction I	
with anemia	Fresh whole blood, platelet suspension, pooled buffy coat	Cohn's fraction I, units of preserved blood, packed red blood cells, plasma	Splenectomy
(b) Leukopenia	Fresh whole blood, leukocytes suspension, pooled buffy coat, γ-globulin	Cohn's fraction I, packed red blood cells, units of preserved blood	Antibiotica
Early sequelae			
Plasma protein displacements	Plasma, albumin, γ-globulin		
Not thrombocytopenic clotting defects	Fresh whole blood, plasma, Cohn's fraction I, PPSB, and other		Cysteine
Late sequelae			
Leukemia	Fresh whole blood, units of preserved blood	Packed red blood cells, washed red blood cells	Cytostatica
Pancytopenia (agranulocytosis)	Packed red blood cells, units of preserved blood, fresh whole blood (leukocyte-suspension)	Plasma, Cohn's fraction I, packed red blood cells	Corticosteroids, antibiotics
Chronic irradiation			
Failure of hematopoiesis	Fresh whole blood, units of preserved blood, packed red blood cells, washed red blood cells	Plasma	Corticosteroids
Late symptoms	Same as for acute irradiation syndrome		

Transfusion of specifically labeled blood cells contributes to the study of the functional dynamics of the hematopoietic cell systems (for a summary see Stohlmann, 1959). The research of Wendell and Gurney (1959) on the Pelger-Huet anomaly should also be noted. The most important advance was made possible by the use of radioactive isotopes (Pribilla, 1959; Owen, 1959). This technique is not only valuable for diagnosis in nuclear hematology, but is also used in research on blood transfusion. Our knowledge of the aging processes of preserved blood, and the influence of stabilization, duration, and other conditions of storage on its biological value are in part based on investigations dealing with the transfusion of blood labeled by radioactive chromium (cf. Strumia, 1958; Mollison and Veall, 1956; Schmidt *et al.*, 1960; and Chapters 3, 4, 6, 7, 9, and 10 of this treatise).

IV. Extracorporeal Irradiation of Blood

Finally, a new method of radiation therapy should be noted that is beginning to show its value for the treatment of certain hematological disorders: the extracorporeal irradiation of blood (Lajtha *et al.*, 1962).

By a nonhemolysing pump, the blood is withdrawn from a suitable vein, conducted in a closed system through a chamber in which it is exposed to radiation, and back to another vein (axillary, cubital, or external jugular vein). Until now we have not been able to draw definite conclusions concerning the results of experimental and therapeutic tests, but probably the extracorporeal radiation treatment of blood will have several applications in the future. There is likelihood of its use during treatment of acute leukemia if the number of peripheral cells does not exceed $10,000/mm^3$, if the bone marrow is not yet completely overgrown by blastocytic cells, and if the blastocytes of the blood and those of the bone marrow are of the same type. Possibly it could be used during the treatment of lymphatic leukemia in which a high number of cells occur that are resistant to cytostatic drugs. The method gives in addition a possibility of eliminating long-lived populations of cells found in the circulation and thereby influencing certain immunity reactions. Finally, radiation treatment of the peripheral blood is possible without the risk of whole body irradiation.

REFERENCES

Andrews, G. A., Sitternson, B. W., Kretschmar, Al. L., and Brucer, M. (1959). *Health Phys.* **2,** 134.

Bagdassarov, A. A. (1957). *Therap. Arch.* (*Moscow*) **29,** No. 10.

Bagdassarov, A. A., and Guljaew, A. W. (1958). "Die Bluttransfusion." Volk und Gesundheit, Berlin.

Baumgarten, K. (1963). *Wien. Med. Wochschr.* **113**, 10.

Bayliss, W. M. (1919). *Spec. Rept. Ser. Med. Res. Commun.* (*London*) No. 25.

Becker, J., and Fliedner, T. M. (1957). *Med. Klin.* (*Munich*) **34**, 1956.

Bessis, M., and Bernard, J. (1947). *Bull. Acad. Med.* **131**, 615; *Bull. Soc. Med. Hop.* **63**, 871.

Blatrix, Ch., and Soulier, J. P. (1959). *Pathol. Biol. Semaine Hop.* **7**, 2477.

Blum, K. U. (1962). *Med. Klin.* (*Munich*) **57**, 267.

Brill, A. B., Tomonaga, M., and Heyssel, R. M. (1962). *Ann. Internal Med.* **56**, 590.

Carnot, P., and Déflandre, C. (1906). *Compt. Rend. Acad. Sci.* **143**, 432.

Catsch, A., and Le, D. K. (1957). *Strahlentherapie* **104**, 494.

Catsch, A., and Le, D. K. (1958). *Strahlentherapie* **106**, 606.

Cazal, P., Graafland, R., Izern, P., Mathieu, M., Palaeisac, G., and Fischer, M. (1956). *Acta Haematol.* **15**, 337.

Cronkite, E. P., Mc Coney, W., and Bond, V. P. (1960). *Am. J. Med.* **28**, 673.

Dausset, J., and Maupin, B. (1956). *Sang* **27**, 20.

D'Agote, L. (1915). *Ann. Inst. Mod. Clin. Med. B. Aiv.* **1**, 25.

Deutsch, E. (1962). *Ärztl. Praxis* **14**, 1287.

Farkass, E. (1962). *Nucl. Haematol.* Sept./Nov., p. 9.

Fleischhacker, H., and Stacher, A. (1963). *Paediat. Praxis* **2**, 219.

Fliedner, T. M., and Stodtmeister, R. (1962). "Experimentelle und klinische Strahlenhaematologie." Lehmanns Verlag, Munich.

Fullerton, W. T., and Turner, A. G. (1962). *Lancet* **I**, 75.

Gugler, E. (1961). In "Ergebnisse der Bluttransfusionsforschung" (G. W. Orth, ed.), Vol. VI, p. 270. Karger, Basel, Switzerland.

Gugler, E. (1962). *Med. Hyg.* **20**, 1000.

Hässig, A. (1962). *Triangel Sandoz J. Med. Sci.* **5**, 234.

Hässig, A., Barandun, S., and Stampfli, K. (1959). In "Ergebnisse der Bluttransfusionsforschung" (W. Hasse, ed.), Vol. IV, p. 42. Karger, Basel, Switzerland.

Haley, T. J. (1963). *Nucl. Haematol.* Sept./Nov., p. 3.

Hartmann, F. (1952). *Deut. Med. Wochschr.* **77**, 801.

Hatta, Y., Muruyama, Y., Tsuruoka, N., Yamaguski, A., Kukita, M., Sho, Ch. T., Sugata, F., and Skimizu, M. (1962). *Acta Haematol. Japan.* **25**, 8.

Heyssel, R. M., Brill, A. B., Woodbury, L. A., Nishimura, E. T., Chose, T., Hoshino, T., and Yassasaki, M. (1960). *Blood* **15**, 313.

Höhne, G., Jaster, R., and Künkel, H. A. (1952). *Klin. Wochschr.* **30**, 952.

Höhne, G., Jaster, R., and Künkel, H. A. (1953). *Klin. Wochschr.* **31**, 910.

Höhne, G., Jaster, R., and Künkel, H. A. (1955a). *Klin. Wochschr.* **33**, 907.

Höhne, G., Künkel, H. A., and Anger, R. (1955b). *Klin. Wochschr.* **33**, 284.

Hulse, E. V. (1963). *Brit. J. Haematol.* **9**, 365, 376.

Hustin, A. (1914). *J. Med. Bruxelles* **12**, 436.

Jackson, D., Sörensen, D. K., Cronkite, E. P., Bond, V. P., and Fliedner, T. M. (1959). *J. Clin. Invest.* **38**, 1689.

Jacobson, L. O., Plzak, L., Fried, W., and Goldwasser, G. (1956). *Nature* **177**, 1240.

Karcher, G. (1953). *Langenbek's Arch. Klin. Chir.* **274**, 423.

Kimball, A. W. (1958). *J. Natl. Cancer Inst.* **21**, 383.

Kolb, H. (1961). In "Ergebnisse der Bluttransfusionsforschung" (G. W. Orth, ed.), Vol. VI, p. 64. Karger, Basel, Switzerland.

Kolb, H. (1963). In "Transfusionspraxis" (P. Dahr and M. Kindler, eds.), pp. 206–212. Schattauer, Stuttgart, Germany.

Künkel, H. A. (1955). *Strahlentherapie Suppl.* **33**, 31.

Lajtha, L. G., Lewis, C. L., Oliver, R., Gunning, A. J., Sharp, A. A., and Callender, S. (1962). *Lancet* **I**, 353.

Landsteiner, K. (1900). *Zentr. Bakteriol. Parasitenk.* **27**, 357.

Lange, R. D., Wright, S. W., Tomonaga, M., Kurasaki, H., Matsuoka, S., and Matsunaga, H. (1955). *Blood* **10**, 312.

Lewisohn, R. (1915). *Med. Record* (*Am.*) **87**, 141.

Linman, J. W., and Bethell, F. H. (1956). *Blood* **11**, 310 (1957); **12**, 123; *J. Lab. Clin. Med.* **49**, 113.

Linman, J. W., and Long, M. J. (1958). *J. Lab. Clin. Med.* **51**, 8.

Manstein, B. (1963). "Atomare Gefahr und Bevölkerungsschutz." Fink, Stuttgart, Germany.

Miller, G. W. (1962). *Can. Med. Assoc. J.* **87**, 1193.

Mollison, P. L. (1963). "Blood Transfusion in Clinical Medicine." Blackwell, Oxford, England.

Mollison, P. L., and Veall, N. (1956). *Brit. J. Haematol.* **1**, 62.

Moloney, W. C. (1959). "Induction of Leukemia in Man by Radiation." Symposium on Radiation Biology and Cancer. M. D. Anderson Hosp. and Tumor Inst., Houston, Texas; *Blood* **14**, 1137.

Nitschmann, H., and Kistler, P. (1954). *Helv. Chim. Acta* **7**, 176.

Nitschmann, H., Kistler, P., Renter, H. R., Hässig, A., and Joss, A. (1956). *Vox Sanguinis* **1**, 183.

Ocklitz, H. W., and Schmitz, H. (1950). *Monatschr. Kinderheilk.* **98**, 375.

Owen, C. A., Jr. (1959). *Postgrad. Med.* **25**, 83.

Peter, H. (1954). *Proc. 5th Intern. Congr. Blood Transfusion, Paris*, p. 578.

Polak, H., and Polakova, K. (1956). *Acta Haematol.* **16**, 385.

Post, I., Rose, I. V., and Shore, S. M. (1951). *Arch. Internal. Med.* **87**, 775.

Pribilla, W. (1959). *Med. Klin.* (Munich) p. 1332.

Reissigle, H. (1961). *In* "Die Bluttransfusion." (H. Reissigl, ed.), pp. 108–124. Wilhelm Maudrich, Vienna.

Rudert, P. O. (1951). *Kongr. Zentr. Inn. Med.* **128**, 66.

Scheffler, W. (1963). *Deut. Gesundheitsw.* **18**, 596.

Schmidt, H. A. E., Schmitt, H., Kleiderling, W., Mathes, M., and Feiser, W. (1960). *Acta Haematol.* **23**, 96, 150, 208.

Schultze, H. E., and Heide, K. (1960). *In* "Medizinische Grundlagenforschung" (K. Fr. Bauer, ed.), Vol. III. Georg Thieme, Stuttgart, Germany.

Siede, W. (1953). *Muench. Med. Wochschr.* **95**, 535.

Skalta, M. (1962). *Nature* **193**, 240.

Stampfli, K., Kaiser, M., and Barandun, S. (1960). *In* "Ergebnisse der Bluttransfusionsforschung" (G. W. Orth, ed.), Vol. VI, p. 260. Karger, Basel, Switzerland.

Stodtmeister, R., Sandkühler, S., and Fliedner, T. M. (1958). *Proc. 2nd Intern. Conf. on Peaceful Uses of Atomic Energy, Geneva* Vol. 22, p. 238.

Stohlman, E. (1959). "The Kinetics of Cellular Proliferation." Grune & Stratton, New York.

Stohlman, F. Y., and Brecher, G. (1956). *Proc. Soc. Exptl. Biol. Med.* **91**, 1.

Strumia, M. M. (1934). *Am. J. Med. Sci.* **187**, 527.

Strumia, M. M. (1958). *Proc. 6th Congr. Intern. Soc. Blood Transfusion* (L. Holländer, ed.), Vol. VII, p. 303. Karger, Basel, Switzerland.

Surgenor, D. M. (1952). *Chem. Eng. News* **30**, 2218.

Surgenor, D. M., and Pennel, R. B. (1960). *Vox Sanguinis* **5**, 272.

Szirmai, E. (1954). *Milli Türk. Tip. Kongr. tutanagindau syri baski, Istambul–Ismir–Kongressbuch.* Vol. XIII.

Szirmai, E. (1958). Rept. of the United Nations Sci. Comm. on the Effects of Atomic Radiation Suppl. XVII, A 3838. U. N., New York.

Van Bekkum, D. W. (1959). *Proc. Europ. Conf. Haematol. (London),* p. 153.

Vergoz, D. (1961). *In* "Transfusion sanguine: Problèmes d'actualité" (R. André, G. David, G. Duchesne, Ch. Salmon, and D. Vergoz, eds.). Masson, Paris.

Waitz, R., and Sachs, V. (1964). In preparation.

Wende, S. (1963). *Fortschr. Röntgenstr. u. Nuklearmed.* **98,** 594.

Wendell, F. R., and Gurney, C. W. (1959). *Blood* **14,** 170.

Wiener, A. S., and Wexler, I. B. (1946). *J. Pediat.* **31,** 871.

Wilkinson, J. F. (1963). *Proc. Roy. Soc. Med.* **56,** 644.

Winkler, C., and Paschke, G. (1955). *Klin. Wochschr.* **33,** 1011.

Winkler, C., and Paschke, G. (1956). *Radiation Res.* **5,** 156.

CHAPTER 16

Problems of Bone Marrow Transplantation in Radiation Damage

E. Szirmai*

*Division of Nuclear Hematology, Medical Section,
The Institution of Nuclear Engineers, London, England*

I. Introduction

The object of this chapter is, to report, on the basis of the literature and the author's own experience, on some of the theoretical and experimental problems of bone marrow transplantation.

The most successful approach to the problem of recovery from whole-body irradiation injury in mammals is bone marrow transfusion (Cong-

* *Permanent address:* Division of Nuclear Hematology, Medical Section, the Institute of Nuclear Engineering, Adolf Kroner Strasse 11, Stuttgart, Germany.

don, 1959a). According to immunological laws, it was impossible to imagine that these results on animals could be applicable to man. It was known that, under certain physiological conditions, it should be possible eventually to transplant autologous and isologous cells. This is of great practical importance and interest, due to the increase in radiation hazard and damage and the unpleasant prospect of an atomic war or an accidental atomic explosion, and atomic hazards in industry. Thus, it is important to seek new therapeutic possibilities, and further research in this field is necessary.

A transfusion of the hematopoietically active stem cells of the blood may also be necessary after destruction of the bone marrow due to physiological and cytostatic (chemical) influences, or as a result of chemotherapeutic or physical effects within the bone marrow during treatment of malignant cell proliferation in the marrow tissue or in other marrow diseases. After many difficulties and failures, it was possible to see that, in certain cases, success could be achieved. This success resulted from improved methods of homogenization and storage at $-70°C$ to make transfusion possible whenever it was needed. Such transfusion is a result of the application of theoretical and practical knowledge. There exists today the possibility of following the path of the transfused cells in the organism of the receptor, and of a carefully undertaken hematological, cytological, and clinical examination of the progress and vitality of the transplant and its effects in man and animals.

II. Short Historical Survey

The first experimental bone marrow transfusion on animals was made about 18 years ago, although there were earlier experiments by Chiari (1912) and Fabricius-Möller (1922). The implications of their work were not generally recognized for many years. Chiari (1912) placed autologous femoral bone marrow in the spleen of rabbit and after two months exposed the animal to whole-body irradiation, while shielding the splenic region. At necropsy, 5 months later, a well-defined bone marrow nodule was observed in the spleen. This nodule was considerably larger than those arising from intrasplenic marrow transplants in nonirradiated rabbits. Fabricius-Möller (1922) observed a severe thrombopenia 7–8 days after exposure, preceded by a reduction in the number of megakaryocytes in the bone marrow. When the extremities, head, and pelvis were shielded with lead, thrombopenia was prevented, but it did develop if only the abdomen was shielded. It was concluded that shielding of the bones prevented destruction of megakaryocytes and subsequent thrombopenia.

The first successful bone marrow transplantations were those of Lorenz and his associates (1951). They secured the survival of mice and other animals after a normally lethal whole-body irradiation, by injections of isologous bone marrow. These experiments were actually the logical sequel to the earlier research of Jacobson et al. (1949, 1951a,b). These authors irradiated the animals only after protection of the spleen, so that there was very little destruction of essential blood-forming elements in the pulp. From 1951 to the present there have been various experiments involving lethal irradiation of rats, rabbits, and dogs; they were all unsuccessful. Failures were due to insufficient preparation and faulty techniques of application, storage, etc. Through the screening (protection) of the bone marrow, Talbot and Pinson (1951) and Talbot and Elson (1958) have attained a high survival rate. Hilfinger et al. (1953) have made successful bone marrow transplantations in rabbits, and Fishler and his associates (1954) in rats. In recent years, there have been reports of bone marrow transfusion also in monkeys, hamsters, and other animals. Important experiments in this field will be discussed in the following pages.

III. Preservation, Survival, and Dosage of Preserved Hematopoietic Cells

A. PRESERVATION OF SPLEEN AND BONE MARROW CELLS

One of the most important problems of bone marrow transfusion is preservation of the cells; it may be possible to store them in a "bank" as is done for blood, and draw on them when needed.

In the reports on bone marrow preservation, one must distinguish between experimental transplantation in animals and clinical transfusion in man. Short- and long-term preservation of bone marrow cells has been successful when judged by the cells' ability to improve survival of lethally irradiated animals. Both the temperature and the diluent solution used are essential factors in the preparation of bone marrow suspensions. Suspended mouse bone marrow cells were effective after two-day storage at room temperature in Tyrode's Solution and after 5 days at 2°–5°C or, according to some authors (Mathé, 1961; Witte, 1963), in physiological saline solution at room temperature also after 5 days. Recovery efficiency was reduced, however, if marrow was used from stored intact excised femurs or from femurs retained in the dead animal (Urso and Congdon, 1957). According to Jankay (1962) the cell suspension was effective if kept at 2°–5°C for 7 days. Billen (1959) reported that the isologous mouse bone marrow kept at 25°C could, after 24 days, influence a radiation effect. The same author—as Congdon (1959a) reported—stated that in tissue culture medium, the suspensions were effective after 7 days at 2°–5°C, but Nagy and Petrányi (1961) observed that during this time the bone marrow had lost its therapeutic effect.

It was later reported that frozen material is preferable for long-term preservation. The preservation in glycerol frozen at −70°C, had been carried out by Barnes and Loutit (1955) with fragments of baby mouse spleens. These fragments were effective after 83 days storage. Glycerol two-stage freezing was eventually recognized as the best technique; it has been further explored by Ferrebee and his associates (1958).

Adult bone marrow can be stored successfully under similar conditions (Schwartz et al., 1957a,b). This author found that glycerol is not necessary for preservation of adult mouse marrow at −80°C. The slow-freezing technique reported by Congdon (1959a) makes use of a protein solution. Polge et al. (1949) were able with the technique of Barnes et al. (1957), to preserve the radiation-protection effect also with the slow-freezing technique. Ferrebee and his associates (1958) found that it was best to combine a protein solution with one of 45% glycerol in the slow-freezing process. A higher percentage of glycerol was harmful to the cells.

Another technique of bone marrow cell preservation is the use of a 10% serum and phenol-free heparin solution for suspension of centrifuged and sedimented marrow cells. Water-free glycerol is added to give a 15% final concentration. The following freezing procedure should be used: between +20°C and −20°C the temperature could be lowered 1° per minute; between −20° and −70°C, 10° per minute.

Porter and Murray (1958) preserved rabbit marrow by slow-freezing in glycerol and storage at −70°C. Bone marrow preserved for 1 week was as efficient as fresh marrow in establishing homografts and subsequent recovery in lethally irradiated rabbits.

Tran and Bender (1960) replaced glycerol by polyvinylpyrrolidine dissolved in saline. After addition of NaCl, the efficacy of preservation was found to be better, because the survival time of the isologous treated mice was prolonged. A 0.13 M NaNO$_3$ solution was quite effective. Ashwood-Smith (1961) has found in the mousetest with colloidal dimethylsulfoxide that the increase of leukocytes and reticulocytes was faster than with glycerol.

Richards and Persidsky (1962) applied 10% solution of polyvinylpyrrolidine of molecular weight 300,000. Mannitol, sorbitol, ribose, and lactose were excellent substitutes for glycerol if optimal concentrations were used. Dimethylsulfoxide has, after parenteral injection, caused a better permeation of the capillary wall, than glycerol.

Bender *et al.* (1960) made a study of the effect of protective additives for mouse bone marrow. Bone marrow was slow-frozen ($-1°$C/minute) and thawed rapidly, and given to lethally irradiated mice to determine viability of the cells. At $-70°$C, after 22 weeks storage, the marrow was fully effective although many cells were lost by clumping. Dextran, mouse serum, bovine serum albumin, Tyrode solution, glucose, and polyvinylpyrrolidine gave little or no protection at the concentrations tested, whereas several polyhydroxy alcohols (isoerythritol, isoinositol, D-sorbitol, D-mannitol, and D-ribitol), and sucrose, lactose, or choline chloride were effective. Tests of marrow frozen in 15% glycerol were made after storage at three temperature levels for various lengths of time. Bone marrow stored at $-30°$C showed signs of reduced effectiveness after 4 weeks and was ineffective after 25 weeks. After being stored for 26 weeks at $-196°$C, marrow was fully effective although many cells were lost by clumping. Bone marrow tissue culture offers an approach to the problem, the rationale being that a cell line, continuously and selectively cultured, should have consistent biological properties.

Great care is needed in the defreezing process, as cells frozen in glycerol are very fragile; the thawing must be done quickly. The glass with the frozen bone marrow must be put in a vessel filled with water at $37°$C. Naturally, these cells will show some damage.

Many efforts have been made to determine the efficacy of cultured hematopoietic tissue as a recovery agent. Embryonal mouse liver and 2-day-old cultures of infant spleen—as Miller (1956) reported—were able to cause survival of lethally irradiated mice. But 4-day-old cultures of these tissues were less effective. Isologous bone marrow cultures retained their recovery activity at $37°$C for 14 days when injected into lethally irradiated mice and, as Billen (1957) reported, 24-day-old cultures, if kept at $25°$C, were also effective. McCulloch and Parker (1957) have reported that altered cell lines maintained in culture were thought to have some recovery but not an effective survival activity. Van Putten (1964) recently reported on the effectiveness of different freeze storage techniques for mouse bone marrow cell suspensions, and Lewis and Trobaugh (1964) on the transplantation potential of fresh and stored bone marrow by two *in vivo* systems.

B. SURVIVAL ACTIVITY AND DOSAGE OF PRESERVED BONE MARROW

The effect of bone marrow transfusion is measured by the survival activity and the dosage of bone marrow cells. The amount of bone marrow given an irradiated recipient is often expressed as the number of nucleated cells injected. Dose response between the amount of the intravenously injected isologous, homologous, and heterologous* bone marrow and 30-days survival has been shown after X-ray exposure. Jacobson et al. (1955) and Van Bekkum et al. (1956) reported that threshold doses of bone marrow cells in the isologous experiment with supralethally irradiated mice are about 50,000 nucleated cells for vigorous hybrid mice. With the dose of about 500,000 nucleated cells in some types of mice, optimal 30-day survival is seen. But a considerably smaller number of dividing cells in the injected bone marrow are actually responsible for the 30-day survival, because the nondividing and maturing cells do not contribute significantly to the effect. According to Congdon (1959a,b) it has not been determined experimentally what these stem cells are and how many are needed to repopulate the destroyed marrow.

The highest dose, 237×10^6 nucleated cells, returned the bone marrow to normal in about 4 days but also the lowest dose of bone marrow used, 17,000 nucleated cells, gave some response. Urso and Congdon (1957) demonstrated a relationship over a greater range of intravenous bone marrow. These authors used the bone marrow response of the irradiated host as the dose-response end point instead of the survival time.

Van Bekkum and Vos (1957) and Hamilton (1964) have published detailed work on bone marrow cell dose survival, in isologous, homologous, and heterologous bone marrow. But in the homologous and heterologous experiments, larger doses of bone marrow are necessary for survival. Here is also a dose response for an end point with 30-days survival.

To obtain maximum survival of supralethally irradiated mice, one femur-equivalent of isologous mouse marrow cells from a 12 to 17-week-old mouse (12×16^6 cells) has often been used. The maximum survival with certain irradiated hybrid mice can be obtained with doses ranging from 0.5×10^6 to 5.0×10^6 nucleated cells. The threshold dose of bone marrow cells in the IBM experiments is, however, lower than 12×10^6 cells. Some increase in survival has been obtained with adult isologous marrow in the range of 0.137 to 0.925×10^6. Jacobson et al. (1955) and van Bekkum and Vos (1957) reported some survival with as few as 0.050×10^6 IBM cells. These authors compared (van Bekkum and Vos, 1957) equivalent numbers of isologous, homologous and heterologous rat marrow cells. As Smith and Congdon (1960) reported, it has become

---

* The terms used in this chapter are defined as follows: autologous (ABM)—tissue from the same individual; isologous (IBM)—tissue from a member of the same inbred strain; homologous (HBM)—tissue from the same species but a different strain; and heterologous—tissue from a different species.

apparent from these and other studies that the number of blood forming cells whether isologous, homologous or heterologous, required to give a particular level of survival is partially dependent on the mouse strain used as the recipient as well as on the source of the donor cells.

As we know, survival is only one criterion that can be used for evaluation of the response of an irradiated animal to graded doses of bone marrow. According to Brown *et al.* (1955) and Hirsch *et al.* (1956), the recovery of thymic weight is related to the dose of injected marrow cells. Jossifides *et al.* (1964) reported on enhanced survival of skin homografts in mice with a bacterial infection.

IV. Technical Problems of Bone Marrow Transfusion

A. SOURCE AND PREPARATION OF CELLS

In the experiments used on mice and rats, the bone marrow is obtained from the long tubular bones, especially the femur. To extract the marrow, the bone is either opened longitudinally or the marrow washed out with a solution. One can isolate the cells from the solution by filtering the suspension through needles of different diameters. As a suspending medium, Earle's Solution, T.C. 100, Hank's Solution, and others (cf. Witte, 1963) can be used. It is recommended that a blood-clotting inhibitor be added to the solution, usually heparin (20–70 μg/ml. Also a salt solution such as Tyrode's, could be used with addition of antibiotics. The addition of 5–10% of blood serum is essential, if the material is to be frozen.

In big animals, such as monkeys and dogs, the preparation of bone marrow is similar to man, that is, by multiple punctures. By the same process, one can obtain homologous bone marrow from larger animals, also by the addition of heparin and exsanguination of the long bones of the animals, and also the ribs and vertebrae. The marrow can also be washed out from the diaphysis of the long bones with salt solution. In dogs and rabbits, the technique of making a window of 1.5 × 0.5 cm in the femur has also been used. With this procedure, it is possible to obtain bone marrow more than once from the same animal (Witte, 1963; Mannick *et al.*, 1960).

B. ROUTE, TIME OF INJECTION, AND LOCALIZATION OF INJECTED CELLS

1. *Route of Injection*

Several different routes of injection of the bone marrow are known but in experimental studies intravenous administration is much more effective than intraperitoneal injection with regard to the number of marrow cells required to give comparable survival of lethally irradiated animals. The intraperitoneal injection though effective, requires more cells and the survival, as Congdon (1959a,b) stated, may be erratic. However, despite the obvious advantages of the intravenous route, intraperitoneal injection provides a means of giving certain preparations of hematopoietic tissue that tend to kill by embolism when injected intravenously. Lorenz et al. (1954) and van Bekkum et al. (1956) reported other effective injection routes, e.g., intracardial, intrasplenic, and intrathoracic. Intramuscular, subcutaneous, intracerebral, and intratesticular injections (van Bekkum, 1958) have not proved successful.

2. Time of Injection

It is known that, after a supralethal irradiation in mice, the bone marrow given intravenously may be delayed several days and still promote survival. It was reported by Lorenz and Congdon (1954a) that mortality was reduced in irradiated strain A mice when bone marrow was given 72 hours after exposure. In (L&A)Fl mice given fresh or frozen bone marrow as late as 4 days after exposure, Schwartz et al. (1960) reported good 30-day survival. In the irradiated host, the limiting factors would be expected to be the time of onset of bacterial infection and hemorrhage. Isologous bone marrow given several months after the start of the exposure promoted recovery of the irradiated animals in chronically irradiated guinea pigs (Lorenz et al., 1954; Congdon, 1957). According to some investigators, a 24- to 48-hour delay of the time of injection, until there is some depletion of the host animal's bone marrow, is advantageous.

A delay in the time of injection, in treatment with homologous bone marrow, has been advocated on the grounds that a more depressed immune response 1 or 2 days after exposure would favor transplantation. It is, of course, logical that a bone marrow injection before irradiation is not effective. According to Lorenz and Congdon (1954a) survival of lethally irradiated mice has been increased by marrow given 3 or 4 (Schwartz et al., 1957a,b), or 5 days (Jacobson et al., 1955) after exposure. Smith and Djerassi (quoted in Smith and Congdon, 1960), obtained survival with large doses of bone marrow given 7 days after irradiation. Two advantages have been advocated for delaying the bone marrow injection: (a) the injected cells have a greater chance to accumulate and proliferate in the hypocellular marrow of the host; (b) delaying the marrow injection until the immune system is maximally depressed would favor establishment of homologous or heterologous transplants. Gengozian and Makinodan (1958) also worked on this problem in the X-radiated mouse (710 r). When rat erythrocytes (antigen) were given at intervals of 5 minutes to 1 day after exposure, a progressive increase in immunological efficiency was apparent.

3. Localization of Injected Cells

The localization of the injected cells is essential for the evaluation of success. Brown et al. (1955) injected P^{32}-labeled marrow cells into irradiated mice and, at different intervals, checked the radioactivity of the tissue. The result of this experiment suggests that some cells temporarily accumulated within 20 to 30 minutes after injection in the lungs and possibly in the liver. The radioactivity in bone marrow and spleen reached a peak after 90 min. Nowell et al. (1956, 1957) found rat cells in the recipients' marrow within 2 hours after injecting irradiated mice with rat bone marrow. Urso and Congdon (1957) found that the nucleated cell counts of the recipients' bone marrow had increased within 20 minutes after the injection of large doses of IBM into irradiated mice. Odell and Smith (1958) observed labeled marrow cells in lungs of irradiated recipients within 15 minutes after injection. These authors used S^{35}-methionine in conjunction with autoradiography and found that many cells were localized in the marrow, spleen, lymph nodes, and thymus within 4 hours. In hematopoietic tissue marrow cells were detected up to 72 hours after injection. Mauri (1961) used H^3-thymidine with the autoradiographic technique to determine DNA-synthese in the bone marrow erythroblasts. With P^{32}, it is possible to follow the fate of the transplanted cells but, with H^3-thymidine it is possible also to identify the proliferative cells again after reinjection. It may be added that the radioisotope can damage the cells. Iron-59 labeling in vivo has also been used in isologous transplantations. According to Hodgson (1962) Fe^{59}, when injected some days after marrow transfusion, appears in the erythrocytes within 24 hours. So one can distinguish the erythrocytes of rats (Lindsley et al., 1955), rabbits (Cohen, 1958), and monkeys (Summary of Conference, etc., 1960). The hemoglobin variants of mice (Popp et al., 1958) and monkeys (Newsome, 1961) can also be differentiated by electrophoresis. There are at present many ways of labeling cells experimentally and one can conclude that these methods are very valuable, especially in examination after total body irradiation.

Dragić et al. (1960), Hajduković and Stoisić (1962), Hajduković (1964), Rasković et al. (1963–1964), Fleischhacker and Stacher (1963–1964), Aleksandrowicz et al. (1958, 1963–1964) have reported on several nuclear hematological problems. Rasković et al. (1963–1964) have studied bone marrow regeneration in irradiated, bled mice by H^3-thymidine incorporation. According to their data, derived from autoradiograms, a large number of cells are clearly labeled, but a certain number remain unlabeled. The occurrence of unlabeled cells is probably due, on the one hand, to the asynchronous manner in which hematopoietic cells undergo division and, on the other hand, to the too short period of time allowed for tritiated thymidine incorporation (only 1 hour). This study of the proliferative activity of bone marrow cells by means of thymidine incorporation has shown that bleeding after irradiation stimulates the process. This confirms earlier results showing an increase of the mitotic index and Fe^{59} incorporation in bone marrow cells of mice bled after irradiation. All these observations show a stimulative effect of post-irradiation bleeding on the activity of bone marrow cells and on the state of peripheral blood in mice (Rasković et al., 1963–1964). Fliedner et al. (1964) have reported on the rate of transfused H^3-thymidine labeled bone marrow cells in irradiated recipients.

V. Bone Marrow Transfusion after Whole-Body Irradiation

In the bibliographies compiled by Fortuine and Baxter (1959), Fortuine et al. (1960), and Witte (1963) about 1200 references to publications in all fields of radiation injury and bone marrow transplantation are listed. Twelve years of intensive research have been invested in studies on bone marrow transplantation in experimental animals and man since the first experiments by Jacobson et al. (1951a) and Lorenz et al. (1951). These authors (Jacobson et al., 1951a; Lorenz et al., 1951) came to the conclusion that spleen or marrow therapy prevented acute radiation death in mice. A great part of the research during the first 4 years after the initial experiments was undertaken to determine whether the injected marrow replaced and repopulated the hematopoietic tissues of the irradiated recipient, or whether it provided humoral factors that stimulated cellular repair in the host (Congdon, 1962; Witte, 1963). Later on, different investigators (van Bekkum, 1960; Kay and Koller, 1960) demonstrated transplantation repopulation by the injected marrow in the irradiated recipient and production of blood cell elements of the donor animal's type (Smith and Congdon, 1960). According to Congdon (1958, 1962), no substantial evidence has been forthcoming to demonstrate the existence of humoral factors in bone marrow that will stimulate repair of blood-forming cells after they have been exposed to supralethal doses of radiation. In the initial period of research, it was realized that foreign donor bone marrow kept few lethally irradiated animals alive for more than a short period of time, when compared with the excellent results obtained when the donor and irradiated recipient were genetically identical. After whole-body radiation injury with ionizing radiation, different dosages of bone marrow are needed for different types of damage (Fliedner and Stodtmeister, 1962). As Congdon et al. (1952) also reported, various bone marrow preparations were used to treat some blood dyscrasias in laboratory animals and human beings.

The current approach to the experimental treatment of acute lethal whole-body radiation injury is based (Congdon, 1957; Szirmai, 1963a,b,c; Witte, 1963), on the concept of transplanting normal tissues and cells to replace those damaged by the exposure. Spontaneous recovery of bone marrow can be supported therapeutically by "tiding-over" measures such as administration of antibiotics and blood transfusions. As stated by Cronkite and Brecher (1955), Perman et al. (1959), Sorensen and his associates (1959), and Szirmai (1961a) tiding-over techniques constitute an important practical aspect of the therapy of radiation injury. Experimental bone marrow therapy, as indicated by the histological and autoradiographical experiments of Fliedner and Stodtmeister (1962), have shown that bone marrow damage caused by radiation with midlethal dosages is also reversible.

A. THE MECHANISM OF ACUTE RADIATION DEATH

After whole-body irradiation, one of the most frequent causes of death is injury to the hematopoietic system. Early changes of the ultrastructure in the myelopoietic series are shown in Figs. 1 and 2.* Ionizing radiation with 500 rads of Co^{60} gamma-rays produces dilatations and ruptures in the membrane systems [nuclear membrane, ergastoplasm (Fig. 1)] and swelling and degeneration of the mitochondria (Fig. 2). Bone marrow, spleen, thymus, and the lymphatic tissues make up this organ system. The most critical event in the nearly total loss of the hematopoietic system after a lethal exposure is destruction of bone marrow (Cronkite and Brecher, 1955; Smith and Congdon, 1960; Szirmai, 1963a; Witte, 1963). Following the terminology of Smith and Congdon (1960), the terms sublethal, lethal, midlethal, and supralethal exposure are herein used as follows: sublethal—an exposure that does not result in any acute death; lethal—an exposure that results in acute deaths of some or all of the animals, and which may be divided into (a) midlethal—an exposure that results in some but not 100% acute deaths, and (b) supralethal —an exposure that always results in 100% acute deaths. As Cronkite and Brecher (1955), Jacobson (1954), Patt and Brues (1954), and Szirmai (1963b) reported, these and all major aspects of the pathogenesis of

---

* The author is greatly indebted to Dr. Hans E. Bauer (Czerny Radiation Clinic of the University of Heidelberg) for permission to include here these unpublished electron microphotographs and their interpretation.

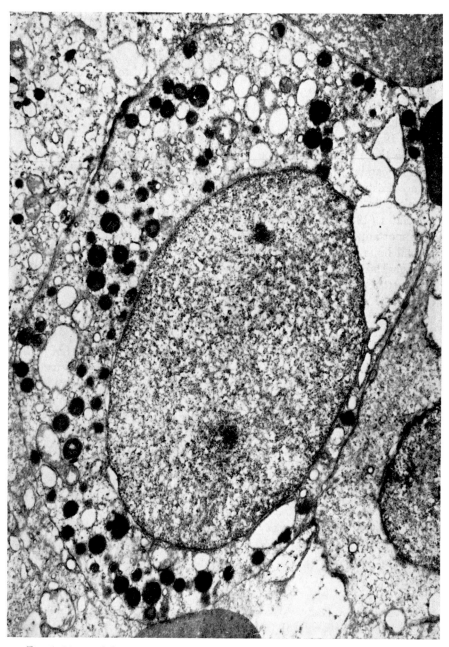

Fig. 1. Neutrophil promyelocyte from the femoral bone marrow of a rat 1 hour after whole-body irradiation with 500 rads of Co⁶⁰ gamma-radiation. Detachment of the outer (plasmatic) nuclear membrane which surrounds empty spaces. Partial dilatation of the ergastoplasm. Fixation in 1% osmium tetroxide solution; dehydration in alcohol. Methylacrylate embedding. Sections treated with uranylacetate. Electron microscopic magnification: 2000×; total magnification: 13,600×. Reproduced with the kind permission of Dr. Hans E. Bauer (unpublished).

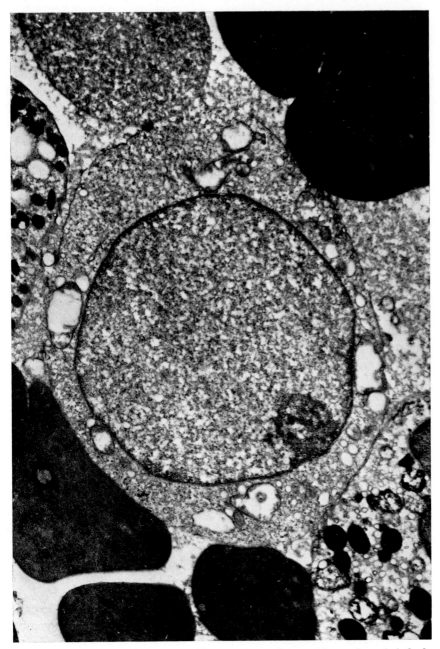

Fig. 2. Myeloblast from the femoral bone marrow of a rat 1 hour after whole-body irradiation with 500 rads of Co⁶⁰ gamma-radiation. Swelling of mitochondria, fragmentation, and clumping of cristae. A great part of the interior of the mitochondria appears empty. (Fixation, etc., as in Fig. 4.) Electron microscopic magnification: 4000×; total magnification 12,700×. Reproduced with the kind permission of Dr. Hans E. Bauer (unpublished).

acute radiation death need to be known in order that the treatment of radiation injury be undertaken, whether by the transplantation technique or another approach.

The major cause of radiation death is, according to a great number of studies, the inability of the bone marrow to replace granulocytes and platelets, leading to an extremely small number of these elements in the peripheral blood. Miller *et al.* (1951), Cronkite and Brecher (1955), Boche (1960), and Szirmai (1963a) have reported that, since granulocytes play a major role in clearing the blood stream and tissues of bacteria, their absence is followed by bacterial invasion. The more immediate cause of acute radiation death is bacterial infection and hemorrhage caused by low blood platelet levels. In many mammals (Conard, 1956; Quastler, 1956) deaths that occur 3–5 days after exposure are associated with severe and continuous diarrhea. The major cause of diarrhea and sometimes also of severe vomiting is the damage to the intestinal mucosa. According to Gerstner and Kent (1957) and Smith and Congdon (1960) there are also signs of injury to the central nervous system and animals may die within minutes or hours after exposure to still higher, supralethal radiation doses of kiloroentgen range. This type of death is characterized by convulsions and other motor disturbances, as well as sensory phenomena. The radiation dose determines whether the primary cause of death will be due to injury of the hematopoietic, intestinal, or central nervous system. Naturally, for intestinal and central nervous system damage, the transplantation technique has not been used. Andrews and Brace (1956), Conard *et al.* (1956), and Taketa (1959) have described palliative results with certain tiding-over techniques.

B. Type of Radiation

In the following parts dealing with autologous, isologous, homologous, and heterologous bone marrow therapy, we shall find all types of experimental irradiation. But in this short summary we shall only deal with the important types of irradiation.

Most of the work on bone marrow transplantation has been done after X-ray injury, but some authors used irradiation with neutrons, gamma-rays, etc. As Lorenz and Congdon (1954a) and other authors (e.g., Randolph *et al.*, 1957) reported, lethal exposure to 14-Mev neutrons could be treated by bone marrow therapy but not with results as good as observed after X-ray injury. Bone marrow therapy has very little effect on death caused by exposure to 2-Mev cyclotron neutrons (Cole and Ellis, 1957). According to Congdon (1959a) there was also no effect on death caused by 8-Mev neutrons. The therapy used was intravenous bone marrow (1×10^6 cells) or intraperitoneal baby mouse spleen. Vogel *et al.*

(1956) found no effect with intraperitoneal spleen therapy in injury caused by fission neutrons, but this therapy was effective against Co^{60} gamma-ray exposure. The same authors suggest that streptomycin therapy be added to the treatment with blood-forming cells, which effectively influences survival after exposure to fission neutrons. In a single experiment (Lorenz and Congdon, 1957), survival after bone marrow therapy of mixed irradiation from intravenously administered radon was good.

C. AUTOLOGOUS AND ISOLOGOUS BONE MARROW TRANSFUSION

1. Autologous Bone Marrow Transfusion

Autologous bone marrow transfusion is technically only possible in large animals. In the smaller animals, only isologous transfusion between individuals of the same inbred strain is possible.

Autologous bone marrow transfusion has been studied mainly in dogs. The technique of the application of bone marrow is the same in all experiments. One has to transfuse intravenously the fresh marrow immediately after the whole-body irradiation. It can be given also intra-arterially (Sullivan et al., 1959). According to Alpen and Baum (1958) and Mannick et al. (1960) after 400 r, which is a sublethal dose for dogs, all animals survived in an experiment after one transfusion of 1.4–1.8 × 10^9 bone marrow cells. In another experiment on eight animals, seven survived after having received 0.26–0.64 × 10^9 cells (Sullivan et al., 1959). After exposure to fast neutron in a dosage of 470 rads, seven out of eleven dogs stayed alive after a 1–2 × 10^9 autologous bone marrow cell transplantation. With the above therapy, radiation with 310 rads was lethal for all animals. After a whole-body radiation with 600–1500 r conventional X-ray or Co^{60} gamma-ray, a dose of 1 × 10^6 autologous bone marrow cells did not prevent lethal bone marrow damage. With 1.7–3.7 × 10^9 cells, nine out of eleven animals have been effectively protected. Therefore, it is difficult to make a comparison in different radiation experiments, because the fast neutrons are biologically more effective than the conventional X-ray or the gamma-radiation of a Co^{60} source; 1–5 × 10^9 cells in dimethylsulfoxide of frozen (−80°C) autologous marrow cells protected sixteen dogs after irradiation with 1200 r (Cavina et al., 1962).

In experiments on calves, it was shown that, after an exposure of 250 r total-body irradiation (about midlethal) 1.2 × 10^9 cells of fresh autologous bone marrow, when given 1 hour after irradiation, were sufficient for survival of ten out of fifteen animals that, for several weeks afterwards, had a serious leukopenia (Mizuno et al., 1960).

2. Isologous Bone Marrow Transplantation (IBM)

The successful experiments of Lorenz et al. (1952) and Congdon et al. (1952) have provided a large amount of data on this field. In mice the lethal exposure is 100% by a total body irradiation of 800–900 r.

It is known that in irradiated marrow-treated animals a transient depression in cellularity of hematopoietic tissues occurs; it results, as Smith and Congdon (1960) reported, in leukopenia and thrombopenia (Witte, 1963). Depending on the amount of marrow injected, by the end of the second week or sooner, the hematopoietic tissues are largely restored, thus preventing pancytopenia and death. In the splenic red pulp, marked hyperplasia of the blood-forming elements occurs during marrow regeneration. Lymph nodes, Peyer's patches, thymus, and splenic white pulp return to their normal morphological appearance somewhat more slowly. Depending on the strain of animals, IBM intravenously injected into lethally irradiated mice gives a 30-day survival of up to 100%. As the above authors reported, although loss of body weight occurs in the irradiated animals, it is rapidly restored. Control mice continue to lose weight until death. The repopulation of bone marrow is faster as more isologous bone marrow cells are given (Congdon, 1959a; Witte, 1963). It has not yet been proved that the bone marrow injection is better when given 24 hours after radiation exposure (summarized in Witte, 1963) than the injection given immediately after the radiation. But the 4–7 days post-irradiation situation is worse and it is necessary to apply 8–10 times more isologous bone marrow to improve the survival rate (Congdon, 1959a,b; Djerassi, 1960).

In inbred lines of guinea pigs exposed to lethal X-ray doses, isologous bone marrow also proved effective (Lorenz and Congdon, 1954a). According to van Bekkum and Vos (1957) isologous rat marrow affords good survival. As Congdon (1959a,b), Witte (1963) and Szirmai (1963b) reported, isologous hematopoietic tissues other than marrow also enhance survival of lethally irradiated animals. Whole embryos (Jacobson, 1952), suspension of fetal liver (Jacobson et al., 1955; Duplan, 1958), suspension of spleen (Cole et al., 1957a,b), as well as leukocyte-containing blood (Congdon et al., 1956) are also effective in mice. Woodruff (quoted in Congdon, 1962) stated that lymph nodes are generally ineffective, although the injection of isologous cellular preparations obtained from cannulation of lymphatic vessels is moderately beneficial in promoting survival of irradiated rats. Residual clumps of bone marrow adhering to the fragments could not be completely discounted as the active agent in intraperitoneally injected cortical bone fragments, which were also effective (Lorenz and Congdon, 1954a). Congdon (1962) found (cf. also

Smith and Congdon, 1960) that tissue from all major organs of the mouse, except tissues of hematopoietic potential, have not been successful in promoting survival of lethally irradiated mice. Brown *et al.* (1955), using thymic weight as a criterion of recovery after whole-body irradiation, reported that injection of suspensions of brain, kidney, lymph node, or intestine was not effective in mice. Witte *et al.* (1963) found that also a relatively small number of 5×10^6 isologous bone marrow cells could cure the radiation damage of 1000 r of gamma-radiation in rats which, without treatment, would certainly be lethal. Delormé (1961) found a similar but smaller effect also in rats with isologous lymphocyte concentrate from ductus thoracicus after 1000 r irradiation.

To summarize, one may say that the problems of experimental prevention of lethal hematopoietic damage after total-body irradiation of animals is apparently solved by the autologous and isologous bone marrow tranfusion. It is possible to prevent or to cure pancytopenia by bone marrow cell suspension and so to prevent death. Frozen cells can be as effective as fresh bone marrow cells. The mechanism of therapy is apparently repopulation with functioning hematopoietic bone marrow cells. Until now, it is not definitely known which of these methods is the fastest in effectively restoring bone marrow regeneration.

D. HOMOLOGOUS AND HETEROLOGOUS BONE MARROW TRANSFUSION

We know that transplantation of foreign bone marrow is possible because severe radiation injury interferes with the reactivity of the immune system. Homologous and heterologous bone marrow transplantation may cause different immunological complications. According to the time of transplantation, we could distinguish two kinds of complications: (1) early reactions occurring about 5–21 days after the transfusion; and (2) late reactions, after about 21–60 days (see Chapter 15 in this volume).

1. Homologous Bone Marrow Transplantation (HBM)

Considerable information about the application of homologous bone marrow has been obtained from experiments with several species of animals, but much of the fundamental work has been done on the mouse.

Homologous bone marrow (HBM) therapy has been successfully used with lethally irradiated mice (Lorenz *et al.*, 1952), rats (Fishler *et al.*, 1954), guinea pigs (Lorenz and Congdon, 1954a), rabbits (Porter, 1957), hamsters (Smith and Ruth, 1955), dogs (Ferrebee *et al.*, 1958; Porter and Couch, 1959), and monkeys (Crouch and Overmann, 1957). There are indications that, under certain conditions, it might be useful in humans.

Lorenz *et al.* (1954) have shown that HBM, and Rabotti (1964) that

HBM and spleen were effective in increasing survival of lethally irradiated mice. Although homologous hematopoietic tissues prevented acute radiation deaths, many animals died during the subsequent 2–5 weeks.

Mice injected with HBM show essentially the same hematological recovery during the second and third weeks after irradiation as that of mice after IBM injection. Lethally irradiated CBA mice given CBA infant spleen homogenate show good 30-day and long-term (400-day) survival, as pointed out by Barnes and Loutit (1955). But irradiated CBA animals given homologous spleen (strain A) show relatively poor 30-day survival and a high mortality rate during the second month (Barnes and Loutit, 1955). Denko (1956), Trentin (1956a,b), and Congdon and Urso (1957), also observed that death was delayed when HBM was given to irradiated mice.

In lethally irradiated rats, rabbits, and dogs, homologous bone marrow has afforded moderately good survival. According to Smith and Congdon (1960), radiation injury to the intestines of these species, however, is apparently a limiting factor because many animals die when exposed to the radiation dose range required to permit successful use of IBM.

Mice injected with HBM during the second and third weeks after irradiation show the same hematological recovery as that of IBM. Many HBM-treated animals during and after the third week begin to lose weight and become emaciated. Deaths resulting from foreign bone marrow reaction usually begin during the third week after irradiation and by the end of three months many of the animals are dead. Congdon and Urso (1957) in experiments on homologous bone marrow in the treatment of radiation injury in mice found the pathological basis for this disease in the lymphatic tissues. Law (1954), Porter et al. (1958), and Porter and Murray (1958) observed similar lymphatic tissue change associated with delayed deaths in lethally irradiated rabbits given HBM.

Congdon and Urso (1957) and Denko et al. (1959), working on homologous bone marrow in the treatment of radiation injury in mice and on the histopathology of delayed death in irradiated mice treated with homologous cells, found that delayed deaths are not usually the result of hematopoietic failure because the repopulated marrow persists in most animals. A small percentage of the treated animals escape death or recover from this disease and behave as if they had been treated with IBM.

Porter (1957) observed that homologous bone marrow injections in X-radiated rabbits improved the survival rate, but the beneficial effects attributed to marrow treatment were probably partially (Porter, 1957) upset by gastrointestinal damage despite good recovery of hematopoietic tissue.

The radiosensitivity of the rat intestine, as Fishler *et al.* (1954) suggested, might partially interfere with the efficacy of HBM. Taketa (1959) by shielding a loop of the intestine, found the lethal dose required to kill 50% of the animals (LD_{50}) for HBM treated rats was increased from 850 to 1200 r. Swift *et al.* (1956) in experiments on the efficacy of hematopoietic protective procedures in rats X-radiated with the intestine shielded, reported that relative to the amount of IBM used for mice, more rat marrow was necessary for optimal survival in the rat despite intestinal shielding. Lacassagne *et al.* (1955) reported that the rat fetal liver cells moderately improved survival of rats exposed to 725 r without intestinal shielding. Maisin *et al.* (1955a) indicate that the improved survival afforded the rat by marrow shielding after 500 r of total body X-irradiation was largely offset when the dose was increased to 700 r, and that concomitant intestinal and marrow shielding was required for a maximum 30-day survival.

Sullivan *et al.* (1959) found no beneficial effect in dogs with homologous hematopoietic tissues after supralethal doses of radiation to the whole body. Porter and Couch (1959) also studied dogs and observed that 3 of 16 dogs exposed to 450 or 500 r survived more than 30 days ($LD_{50}/30$ days, 315 r). But none of the marrow-treated dogs exposed to 600 or 700 r survived, as death was mainly brought about by gastrointestinal injury. Ferrebee *et al.* (1958) and Thomas *et al.* (1959) reported that HBM improves survival of lethally irradiated dogs. These authors generally administered either 800 r in 2 daily doses of 400 r, or 1200 r in 3 daily 400 doses, to reduce intestinal damage. The same investigators (Ferrebee and associates, 1958) in the United States and Porter and his associates (1958) in Great Britain, observed that many of the salient features of bone marrow experiments in small rodents have been seen in rabbits and dogs.

As Smith and Congdon (1960) reported, only a limited amount of information is available on attempted marrow transplantation in irradiated primates other than man. Other investigators, e.g., Crouch and Overmann (1957) and Newsome and Overmann (1959) in their work on the effect of homologous marrow transplantation on survival of monkeys following sublethal whole-body X-radiation, describe success in the irradiated monkeys. Ambrus *et al.* (1959) reported success also with autologous bone marrow in monkeys that had been irradiated or given lethal doses of nitrogen mustard. In observation of chimpanzees after whole-body irradiation and homologous bone marrow treatment, Rothberg *et al.* (1959) have seen that one of the chimpanzees exposed to 900 r and then given HBM, survived 170 days with excellent hematological recovery. Further studies on irradiation and the effect of bone marrow transplantation in dogs and primates have been published by Alpen and Baum (1958), Stodtmeister (1962), Hager et al. (1961), Witte (1963), Mathé et al. (1962a,b, 1963), Szirmai (1963a,b,c, 1965), and many others.

2. Heterologous Bone Marrow Transplantation

Heterologous bone marrow transplantation has been reviewed by Hajdukovič (1964), Witte (1963), Szirmai (1963a), and many other authors. Foreign bone marrow reaction occurs (Congdon, 1957) in the same manner as with HBM therapy. In irradiated mice, rat bone marrow is effective (Congdon and Lorenz, 1954; Cole et al., 1955) and, although variable in 50%, 30–day survival is frequently obtained. But the successful use of heterologous marrow in mammals has been confined to irradiated mice. Van Bekkum and Vos (1957) reported that the time of death of irradiated mice can be delayed with guinea pig or hamster marrow. Lorenz and Congdon (1957) claimed limited success with guinea pig marrow. Marrow transplantation in mice has not been successful of the following cells: human (Hollingsworth, 1958); dog (Lorenz and Congdon, 1954a); rabbit (van Bekkum and Vos, 1957; Lorenz and Congdon, 1954b); chicken marrow (Makinodan, 1957); and a variety of all types of young chicks or chicken embryos (Simmons et al., 1957). Shekarchi and Makinodan (quoted in Smith and Congdon, 1960) have extended the survival of a small percentage of mice beyond 30 days by using hamster marrow. Heterologous bone marrow from related species is, apparently, moderately or slightly effective in mice, whereas marrow from more distant species is not.

Salvidio et al. (1958) reported survival of irradiated rats given cellular suspensions of calf lymph nodes with good regeneration of bone marrow. The injection of baby mouse liver or embryonic spleen cells improved the survival of irradiated rabbits but the regeneration of hematopoietic tissues was poor (Jacobson et al., 1949). Porter and Moseley (1958) in experiments on the effect of newborn rabbit and mouse liver suspension on X-radiated rabbits, could not confirm this.

In work on immunological aspects of homologous and heterologous bone marrow transplantation in irradiated animals, van Bekkum and Vos (1957) found that up to 15×10^7 mouse bone marrow cells did not improve the survival of irradiated rats, but the dose of 650 r radiation may not have sufficiently suppressed the immune system to permit successful hetero-grafting. Witte (1963) also mentioned that the bone marrow experiment has been extended to a class of vertebrates other than mammals.

In investigations of the immunogenetic effects of homologous and heterologous bone marrow treatment in pigeons (Columbia livia) exposed to 2500 rads X-radiation and on modifications of irradiation effects in the pigeon, Shaw and Vermund (1959a,b) found that homologous and heterologous bone marrow improved survival of lethally X-radiated pigeons. According to Smith and Congdon (1960), hematopoietic tissue therapy in other vertebrate classes could conceivably provide useful information.

To summarize, we can say that studies on homologous and heterologous bone marrow transplantation have shown that transplantation of homologous and heterologous hematopoietic bone marrow cells can be successful. This has mainly been shown in rodents, and especially in heterologous transplantations from the rat to the mouse.

The secondary syndrome or foreign bone marrow reaction after bone marrow transplantation has been discussed earlier in this volume (see Chapter 11).

E. CHEMICAL TREATMENT OF RADIATION DAMAGE

Urso et al. (1958) have found that an injection of S-2-aminoethylisothiuronium-Br-HBr (AET) reduced the bone marrow damage induced by irradiation; AET was more effective when given intraperitoneally than orally (Simmons and Lartigue, 1964). According to Smith (1957) this drug, when injected on the day of irradiation or 3 days thereafter promoted recovery in lethally irradiated mice. Doherty and Burnett (1955) reported earlier that, by combining the protective effect of AET with an antibiotic and bone marrow therapy, some mice survived 2600 r of gamma-radiation up to 2 months after exposure (Burnett and Doherty, 1955). Meyer et al. (1964) have reported on autologous bone marrow transfusion following chemotherapy.

Maisin et al. (1955a,b) studied erythropoietic activity in irradiated rats injected with homologous and heterologous bone marrow, using Fe^{59}. These authors observed better survival than with either treatment alone, when both mercaptoethylamine and spleen tissue were given. According to Congdon (quoted from Smith and Congdon, 1960), treatment of X-radiated mice with both bone marrow and AET increased the $LD_{50}/30$ days from 750 to about 1800 r.

The monographs of Witte (1963) and Hamilton (1964) contain complete reviews of the literature on the field of chemical treatment of radiation damage and chemical protection and especially on the work in experimental leukemia and tumors.

VI. Shielding Procedures of Organs

It is possible to shield various organs before irradiation. According to Smith and Congdon (1960), the development of the use of intravenously injected blood-forming tissues for prevention of hematopoietic deaths after lethal radiation is primarily based on the success obtained with spleen or leg shielding. Szirmai (1963a) reported on the effect of shielding the appendix. Leg shielding increases survival in most species of mammals. The effect of spleen shielding varies among different species, but is uniformly beneficial in the irradiated mouse in preventing hematopoietic death. In the studies of Jacobson et al. (1950) and Jacobson (1952), the influence of the spleen on hematopoietic recovery after radiation injury confirms that spleen shielding in the irradiated rat is less successful; in the rabbit, it does not appreciably affect survival, although there is some regeneration of blood-forming tissues.

Jacobson et al. (1950) found that the shielding of liver or intestine of the irradiated mouse also increased survival. Concomitant spleen and leg shielding gave better 30-day survival than did intestinal shielding to the midlethally irradiated rat. But Jacobson et al. (1950) could not increase survival of irradiated mice by shielding one exteriorized kidney. Kidney shielding has an effect on survival following whole-body irradiation (Bohr et al., 1955). Survival of rats, after X-radiation (Edelmann, 1951) is improved following adrenal shielding, but the possibility of concurrent protection of hematopoietic tissue by shielding complicates interpretation of these data; data concerning the effects on survival of partial-body shielding are also available. The chances of any species surviving a lethal radiation dose are improved by shielding a critical portion of the hematopoietic system, provided (Smith and Congdon, 1960; Szirmai, 1963b; Hamilton, 1964) that the radiation dose is not so high as to cause death through damage to other tissues. The studies of Congdon et al. (1952, 1957), Witte (1963), Hamilton (1964), and others contain many other old and new data on this aspect.

References

Aleksandrowicz, J., Urbánczyk, J., Ostrowska, A., and Sierko, J. (1958). Blood 13, 652.

Aleksandrowicz, J., Sznajd, J., Urbánczyk, J., and Schiffer, Z. (1963–1964). Nucl. Hematol. 2–3 III-X.

Alpen, E. L., and Baum, S. J. (1958). Blood 13, 1168.

Ambrus, C., Feltz, E. T., and Byron, J. W. (1959). Proc. Assoc. Cancer Res. 3, 2.

Andrews, H. L., and Brace, K. C. (1956). Am. J. Physiol. 187, 378–380.

Ashwood-Smith, M. J. (1961). Proc. 8th Congr. Europ. Soc. Haematol., Vienna No. 68.

Barnes, D. W. H., and Loutit, J. F. (1955). J. Natl. Cancer Inst. 15, 901–905.

Barnes, D. W. H., Ford, C. E., Ilbery, P. L. T., Koller, P. C., and Loutit, J. F. (1957). J. Cellular Comp. Physiol. 50, 123–138.

Bender, M. A., Phan The Tran, and Smith, L. H. (1960). *In* "Radiation Protection and Recovery" (L. H. Smith and C. C. Congdon, eds.), Vol. 9, p. 242. Macmillan (Pergamon), New York.

Billen, D. (1957). *Nature* **179**, 574–575.

Billen, D. (1959). *In* "Die Knochenmarktransfusion" (S. Witte, ed.), p. 100. Lehmanns, Munich, Germany.

Boche, R. D. (1960). "Radiation and Susceptibility to Infection," Spec. Rept. Contract No. AF:33(038)27353. Obtainable from GOP; *in* "Radiation Protection and Recovery" (L. H. Smith and C. C. Congdon, eds.), pp. 242–302. Macmillan (Pergamon), New York.

Bohr, D. F., Rondell, P. A., Palmer, L. E., and Bethell, F. H. (1955). *Science* **128**, 202–203.

Brown, M. B., Hirsch, B. B., Nagareda, C. S., Hakstetler, S. K., Farghan, W. G., Tock, P., and Kaplan, H. S. (1955). *J. Natl. Cancer Inst.* **15**, 949.

Burnett, W. T., and Doherty, D. G. (1955). *Radiation Res.* **3**, 217.

Cavina, J. A., Kasakura, S., Thomas, E. D., and Ferrebee, J. W. (1962). *Blood* **20**, 730.

Chiari, O. M. (1912). *Muench. Med. Wochschr.* **59**, 2502–2503.

Cohen, C. (1958). *Transplant. Bull.* **5**, 21.

Cole, L. J., and Ellis, M. E. (1957). *Federation Proc.* **16**, 23–24 (Abstr.).

Cole, L. J., Habermeyer, J. G., and Bond, V. P. (1955). *J. Natl. Cancer Inst.* **16**, 1–9.

Cole, L. J., Habermeyer, J. G., and Nowell, P. C. (1957a). *Am. J. Physiol.* **188**, 555–558.

Cole, L. J., Habermeyer, J. G., and Nowell, P. C. (1957b). *Radiation Res.* **7**, 139.

Congdon, C. C. (1957). *Radiation Res.* **7**, 310.

Congdon, C. C. (1958). *Radiation Res.* **9**, 102.

Congdon, C. C. (1959a). *In* "Progress in Hematology" (L. M. Tocantins, ed.), pp. 21–46. Grune & Stratton, New York.

Congdon, C. C. (1959b). *Proc. 21st Intern. Congr. Physiol. Sci., Buenos Aires (Symp. on Radiation Protection and Recovery)*, pp. 119–123.

Congdon, C. C. (1962). *Ann. Rev. Med.* **13**, 203, 212.

Congdon, C. C., and Lorenz, E. (1954). *Am. J. Physiol.* **176**, 297–300.

Congdon, C. C., and Urso, I. S. (1957). *Am. J. Pathol.* **33**, 749–767.

Congdon, C. C., Uphoff, D., and Lorenz, E. (1952). *J. Natl. Cancer Inst.* **13**, 73–107.

Congdon, C. C., McKinley, T. W., Jr., Sutton, H., and Urso, I. S. (1956). *Radiation Res.* **4**, 424–434.

Congdon, C. C., Makinodan, T., and Gengozian, N. (1957). *J. Natl. Cancer Inst.* **18**, 603–613.

Conrad, R. A. (1956). *Radiation Res.* **5**, 167–188.

Conrad, R. A., Cronkite, E. P., Brecher, G., and Strome, C. P. A. (1956). *J. Appl. Physiol.* **9**, 227–233.

Cronkite, E. P., and Brecher, G. (1955). *Ann. N. Y. Acad. Sci.* **59**, 815–833.

Crouch, B. G., and Overmann, R. T. (1957). *Federation Proc.* **16**, 27.

Delormé, E. J. (1961) *Proc. 8th Congr. Europ. Soc. Haematol., Vienna* No. 70.

Denko, J. D. (1956). *Radiation Res.* **5**, 607.

Denko, J. D., Simmons, E. L., and Wissler, R. W. (1959). *Radiation Res.* **11**, 557, 571.

Djerassi, L. (1960). *In* "Radiation Protection and Recovery" (L. H. Smith and C. C. Congdon, eds.), Vol. 9, p. 242. Macmillan (Pergamon), New York.

Djerassi, L., Woodruff, R., and Farber, S. (1960). *Radiation Res.* **12**, 505.

Doherty, D. G., and Burnett, W. T., Jr. (1955). *Proc. Soc. Exptl. Biol. Med.* **89**, 312–314.

Dragić, M. B., Adamović, M. G., Hajduković, S. J., and Radotić, M. M. (1960). *Bull. Inst. Nucl. Sci. "Boris Kidrich" (Belgrade)* **10**, 127–136.

Duplan, J. F. (1958). *Compt. Rend. Acad. Sci.* **247**, 662–664.

Edelmann, A. (1951). *Am. J. Physiol.* **165**, 57–60.

Fabricius-Möller, J. (1922). "Experimentelle Studier over Haemorrhagisk Diathese Femkaldt Ved Rontgenstraaler." Levin & Munksgaards Forlag, Copenhagen.

Ferrebee, J. W., Lochte, H. L., Jr., Jaretzki, A., Sahler, O. D., and Thomas, E. D. (1958). *Surgery* **43**, 516–520.

Fishler, M. C., Cole, L. J., Bond, V. P., and Milne, W. L. (1954). *Am. J. Physiol.* **177**, 236–242.

Fleischhacker, H., and Stacher, A. (1963–1964). *Nucl. Hematol.* **2**, XI-XIV.

Fliedner, T. M. (1958). *Strahlentherapie* **106**, 212.

Fliedner, T. M., and Stodtmeister, R. (1962). "Experimentelle und klinische Strahlenhämatologie." Lehmann, Munich, Germany.

Fliedner, T. M., Thomas, E. D., Meyer, L. M., and Cronkite, E. P. (1964). *In* Physical Factors and Modification of Radiation Injury" (L. P. Hamilton, ed.), *Ann. N. Y. Acad. Sci.* **114**, 510–528.

Fortuine, R., and Baxter, H. (1959). *Transplant. Bull.* **6**, 438–450.

Fortuine, R., Mathé, G., and Baxter, H. (1960). *Transplant. Bull.* **7**, 434–441.

Gengozian, N., and Makinodan, T. (1958). *J. Immunol.* **80**, 189–197.

Gerstner, H. B., and Kent, S. P. (1957). *Radiation Res.* **6**, 626–644.

Goh, K., Miller, D. G., and Diamond, H. D. (1961). *J. Immunol.* **86**, 606.

Hager, E. B., Mannick, J. A., Thomas, E. D., and Ferrebee, J. W. (1961). *Radiation Res.* **14**, 192.

Hajduković, S. (1964). Unpublished data.

Hajduković, S., and Stosić, Lj. (1962). *Proc. 8th Congr. Europ. Soc. Haematol., Vienna, 1961,* p. 75. Karger, Basel, Switzerland.

Hamilton, L. D., ed. (1964). "Physical Factors and Modification of Radiation Injury." *Ann. N. Y. Acad. Sci.* **114**, 716 pp.

Hilfinger, M. F., Jr., Ferguson, J. H., and Riemenschneider, P. A. (1953). *J. Lab. Clin. Med.* **42**, 581–591.

Hirsch, B. B., Tock, P., Melbye, R. W., Nagareda, C. S., and Kaplan, H. S. (1956). *Radiation Res.* **5**, 483.

Hodgson, G. S. (1962). *Blood* **19**, 460.

Hollingsworth, J. W. (1958). *Yale J. Biol. Med.* **31**, 157–163.

Jacobson, L. O. (1952). *Cancer Res.* **12**, 315–325.

Jacobson, L. O., (1954). *In* "Radiation Biology" (A. Hollaender, ed.), Vol. 1, pp. 1029–1090. McGraw-Hill, New York.

Jacobson, L. O., Marks, E. K., Robson, M. J., Gaston, E. O., and Zirkle, R. E. (1949). *J. Lab. Clin. Med.* **34**, 1538–1543.

Jacobson, L. O., Robson, M. J., and Marks, E. K. (1950). *Proc. Soc. Exptl. Biol. Med.* **75**, 145–152.

Jacobson, L. O., Simmons, E. L., Marks, E. K., and Eldredge, J. H. (1951a). *Science* **113**, 510–511.

Jacobson, L. O., Simmons, E. L., Marks, E. K., Gaston, E. O., Robson, M. J., and Eldredge, J. H. (1951b). *J. Lab. Clin. Med.* **37**, 683–697.

Jacobson, L. O., Marks, E. K., and Gaston, E. O. (1955). *In* "Radiobiology

Symposium" (Z. M. Bacq and P. Alexander, eds.), pp. 122–133. Butterworth, London and Washington, D. C.

Jankay, I. (1962). *Blood* **20**, 637.

Jossifides, J. A., Gutzait, L., Brand, U., and Tocantins, L. M. (1964). *In* "Physical Factors and Modification of Radiation Injury" (L. P. Hamilton, ed.), *Ann. N. Y. Acad. Sci.* **114**, 487–496.

Kay, H. E. M., and Koller, P. C. (1960). *In* "Cancer Progress" (R. W. Raven, ed.), Vol. 32, p. 258. Butterworth, London and Washington, D. C.

Lacassagne, A., Duplan, J. F., and Buu-Hoi, N. P. (1955). *J. Natl. Cancer Inst.* **15**, 915–921.

Law, L. W. (1954). *Cancer Res.* **14**, 695–709.

Lewis, J. P., and Trobaugh, F. E., Jr. (1964). *In* "Physical Factors and Modification of Radiation Injury" (L. D. Hamilton, ed.), *Ann. N. Y. Acad. Sci.* **114**, 667–686.

Lindsley, D. B., Odell, T. T., Jr., and Tausche, F. G. (1955). *Proc. Soc. Exptl. Biol. Med.* **90**, 512–515.

Lorenz, E., and Congdon, C. C. (1954a). *Proc. 4th Intern. Congr. Intern. Soc. Hematol.* pp. 192–211. Grune & Stratton, New York.

Lorenz, E., and Congdon, C. C. (1954b). *J. Natl. Cancer Inst.* **14**, 955–965.

Lorenz, E., and Congdon, C. C. (1957). *Rev. Hematol.* **10**, 476–484.

Lorenz, E., Congdon, C. C., and Uphoff, D. (1952). *Radiology* **58**, 863–877.

Lorenz, E., Congdon, C. C., and Uphoff, D. (1953). *J. Natl. Cancer Inst.* **14**, 291–301.

Lorenz, E., Law, L. W., and Congdon, C. C. (1954). *In* "Ciba Foundation Symposium on Leukaemia Research" (G. E. W. Wolstenholme and M. P. Cameron, eds.), pp. 189–195. Churchill, London.

Lorenz, E., Uphoff, D., Reid, T. R., and Shelton, E. (1951). *J. Natl. Cancer Inst.* **12**, 197–201.

McCulloch, E. A., and Parker, R. C. (1957). *In* "Canadian Cancer Conference" (R. W. Begg, ed.), Vol. 2, pp. 152–167. Academic Press, New York.

Maisin, J., Maisin, H., and Dunjuć, A. (1955a). "Radiobiology Symposium" (Z. M. Bacq and P. Alexander, eds.), pp. 154–169. Butterworth, London and Washington, D. C.

Maisin, J., Maisin, H., Dunjuć, A., and Maldague, P. (1955b). *J. Belge Radiol.* **38**, 394–429.

Makinodan, T. (1957). *J. Cellular Comp. Physiol.* **50**, Suppl. 1, 327.

Mannick, J. A., Lochte, H. L., Jr., Ashley, C. A., Thomas, E. D., and Ferrebee, J. W. (1960). *Blood* **15**, 255.

Mathé, G. (1961). *In* "Diagnosis and Treatment of Acute Radiation Injury," pp. 191–223. World Health Organization, Geneva.

Mathé, G., Amiel, J. L., Schwarzenberg, L., and Méry, A. M. Presented by Binet, L. M. (1962a). *Compt. Rend. Acad. Sci.* **255**, 2863–2865.

Mathé, G., Amiel, J. L., Matsukura, M., and Méry, A. M. Presented by Debré, R. (1962b). *Compt. Rend. Acad. Sci.* **255**, 3480–3482.

Mathé, G., Amiel, J. L., Schwarzenberg, L., and Méry, A. M. (1963). *Blood* **22** (1), 44–52.

Mauri, C. (1961). *Folia Haematol.* **6**, 1–3.

Meyer, M., Fliedner, T. D., and Cronkite, E. P. (1964). *In* "Physical Factors and Modification of Radiation Injury" (L. D. Hamilton, ed.), *Ann. N. Y. Acad. Sci.* **114**, 499–510.

Miller, C. L. (1956). *Nature* **178**, 142.

Miller, C. P., Hammond, C. W., and Tompkins, M. (1951). *J. Lab. Clin. Med.* **38**, 331, 343.

Mizuno, N. S., Perman, V., Joel, D. D., Bates, F. W., Sautter, J. H. and Schultze, M. O. (1960). *Proc. Soc. Exptl. Biol. Med.* 105, 317.

Nagy, S., and Petranyi, J. (1961). *Klin. Wochschr.* 39, 815.

Newsome, F. E. (1961). *Blood* 17, 785.

Newsome, F. E., and Overmann, R. R. (1959). *Physiologist* 2, 90.

Nowell, P. C., Cole, L. J., Habermeyer, J. G., and Roan, P. L. (1956). *Cancer Research* 16, 258.

Nowell, P. C., Cole, L. J., Roan, P. L., and Habermeyer, J. G. (1957). *J. Natl. Cancer Inst.* 18, 137.

Odell, T. T., Jr., and Smith, L. H. (1958). *Acta Haematol.* 19, 114–120.

Owen, R. D. (1945). *Science* 102, 400.

Patt, H. M., and Brues, A. M. (1954). *In* "Radiation Biology" (A. Hollaender, ed.), Vol. I, pp. 959–1028. McGraw-Hill, New York.

Permann, V., Cronkite, E. P., Bond, V. P., and Sorensen, D. K. (1959). *Radiation Res.* 11, 459–460.

Polge, C., Smith, A. U., and Parkes, A. S. (1949). *Nature* 166, 666.

Popp, R. A., Cosgrove, G. E., Jr., and Owen, R. D. (1958). *Proc. Soc. Exptl. Biol. Med.* 99, 692–694.

Porter, K. A. (1957). *Brit. J. Exptl. Pathol.* 38, 401–412.

Porter, K. A., and Couch, N. P. (1959). *Brit. J. Exptl. Pathol.* 40, 52–56.

Porter, K. A., and Moseley, R. (1958). *Brit. J. Exptl. Pathol.* 39, 128–132.

Porter, K. A., and Murray, J. E. (1958). *Cancer Res.* 18, 117–119.

Porter, K. A., Moseley, R., and Murray, J. E. (1958). *Ann. N. Y. Acad. Sci.* 73, 819–824.

Quastler, H. (1956). *Radiation Res.* 4, 303–320.

Rabotti, G. F. (1964). *In* "Physical Factors and Modification of Radiation Injury" (L. D. Hamilton, ed.), *Ann. N. Y. Acad. Sci.* 114, 468–480.

Randolph, M. L., Congdon, C. C., Urso, I. S., and Parrish, D. L. (1957). *Science* 125, 1083–1084.

Rašković, D., Hajduković, S., and Karanović, J. (1963–1964). *Nucl. Hematol.* 2, XV–XVI.

Richards, V., and Persidsky, M. (1962). *Blood* 19, 521.

Robins, M. M., and Noyes, W. D. (1961). *New Engl. J. Med.* 265, 974.

Rothberg, H., Blair, E. B., Gomez, A. C., and McNulty, W. (1959). *Blood* 14, 1302–1321.

Salvidio, E., Oliva, L., and Pierotti, P. (1958). *Acta Haematol.* 19, 173–178.

Schwartz, E. E., Upton, A. C., and Congdon, C. C. (1957a). *Proc. Soc. Exptl. Biol. Med.* 96, 797–800.

Schwartz, I. R., Repplinger, E. F., Congdon, C. C., and Tocantins, L. M. (1957b). *J. Appl. Physiol.* 11, 22–23.

Schwartz, R., Misra, D. K., and Dameshek, W. (1960). *Blood* 15, 137.

Shaw, D. H., and Vermund, H. (1959a). *Radiation Res.* 11, 466.

Shaw, D. H., and Vermund, H. (1959b). *Proc. Natl. Acad. Sci. U. S.* 45, 23–30.

Shekarchi, I. C., and Makinodan, T. (1960). *In* "Radiation Protection and Recovery" (L. H. Smith and C. C. Congdon, eds.), pp. 242–302. Macmillan (Pergamon), New York.

Simmons, E. L., and Lartigue, O. (1964). *In* "Physical Factors and Modification of Radiation Injury" (L. P. Hamilton, ed.), *Ann. N. Y. Acad. Sci.* 114, 607–613.

Simmons, E. L., Jacobson, L. O., and Denko, J. (1957). *In* "Advances in Radiobiology" (G. C. de Hevesy, A. G. Forssberg, and J. D. Abbatt, eds.), pp. 214–220. Oliver & Boyd, Edinburgh and London.

Smith, F., and Ruth, H. J. (1955). *Proc. Soc. Exptl. Biol. Med.* **90**, 187–191.
Smith, L. H. (1957). *Exptl. Cell Res.* **13**, 627–630.
Smith, L. H., and Congdon, C. C. (1960). *In* "Radiation Protection and Recovery" (A. Hollaender, ed.), pp. 242–302. Macmillan (Pergamon), New York.
Sorensen, D. K., Bond, V. P., Cronkite, E. P., and Perman, V. (1959). *Radiation Res.* **11**, 469.
Stodtmeister, R. (1962). Probleme der Knochenmarktransplantation. Lecture, 2nd Meeting deut. Strahlenschutzärzte, Essen, Germany.
Sullivan, R. D., Stecher, G., and Sternberg, S. S. (1959). *J. Natl. Cancer Inst.* **23**, 367–383.
Summary of Conference on Chemical Protection and Bone Marrow Transplantation, Oak Ridge (1960). *Blood* **16**, 1499.
Swift, M. N., Taketa, S. T., and Bond, V. P. (1956). *Radiation Res.* **4**, 186–192.
Szirmai, E. (1961a). *Schweiz. Med. Wochschr.* **91**, 1153.
Szirmai, E. (1961b). *Nucl. Haematol.* **1** (1), 4–5.
Szirmai, E. (1963a). *Z. Inn. Med.* **18**, 37–40.
Szirmai, E. (1963b). *Nucl. Hematol.* **2** (2), Lecture II.
Szirmai, E. (1963c). Introduction à l'Hématologie Nucléaire, Conf. Faculty of Science, University of Dijon, France.
Szirmai, E. (1965). *Nuclear Energy* **6**, 124.
Taketa, S. T. (1959). *Radiation Res.* **11**, 471.
Talbot, J. M., and Pinson, E. A. (1951). *Military Med.* **108**, 412–417.
Talbot, T. R., and Elson, L. A. (1958). *Nature* **181**, 684–686.
Thomas, E. D., Ashley, C. A., Lochte, H. L., Jr., Jaretzki, A., III, Sahler, O. D., and Ferrebee, J. W. (1959). *Blood* **14**, 720–736.
Tran, P. T., and Bender, M. A. (1960). *Proc. Soc. Exptl. Biol. Med.* **104**, 388.
Trentin, J. J. (1956a). *Proc. Soc. Exptl. Biol. Med.* **92**, 688–693.
Trentin, J. J. (1956b). *Proc. Soc. Exptl. Biol. Med.* **93**, 98–100.
Urso, P., and Congdon, C. C. (1957). *Blood* **12**, 251–260.
Urso, P., Congdon, C. C., Doherty, D. G., and Shapira, R. (1958). *Blood* **12**, 665, 676.
van Bekkum, D. W. (1958). *Semaine Hop. Paris* (*Rev. Gen.*) July.
van Bekkum, D. W. (1960). "Mechanisms in Radiobiology" (M. Errera and A. Forssberg, eds.), Vol. 2, pp. 297–360. Academic Press, New York.
van Bekkum, D. W., and Vos, O. (1957). *J. Cellular Comp. Physiol.* **50**, 139–156.
van Bekkum, D. W., Vos, O., and Weyzen, W. W. H. (1956). *Rev. Hematol.* **11**, 477, 485.
van Bekkum, D. W., Vos, O., and Weyzen, W. W. H. (1959). *J. Natl. Cancer Inst.* **23**, 75.
van Putten, L. M. (1964). *In* "Physical Factors and Modification of Radiation Injury" (L. P. Hamilton, ed.), *Ann. N. Y. Acad. Sci.* **114**, 695–701.
Vogel, H. H., Jr., Clark, J. W., Jordan, D. L., Bink, N., and Barhorst, R. R. (1956). *U. S. Atomic Energy Comm. Rept.* ANL–5597, pp. 61–64.
Witte, S., ed. (1963). "Die Knochenmarktransfusion." Lehman, Munich, Germany.
Witte, S., Barth, G., Gräbner, Z., and Henning, N. (1963). *Strahlentherapie. In* "Die Knochenmarktransfusion" (S. Witte, ed.), Lehman, Munich, Germany.

CHAPTER 17

Nuclear Hematology: Based on Experience with Atomic Explosions

Susumu Watanabe

*Research Institute for Nuclear Medicine and Biology,
Hiroshima University, Hiroshima, Japan*

I. Introduction

There are many reports dealing with the somatic effects of the atomic bomb written both in English and Japanese, but most of them deal with the acute effects. Concerning the chronic effects, which resulted almost exclusively from radiation injuries, we do not have sufficient information as yet, since these effects are still progressing among persons who were exposed to the atomic bombs in Hiroshima and Nagasaki 19 years ago. Moreover, we are not sure whether other injuries, which are still unknown, may not develop in the future.

It has long been known that hematopoietic cells and tissues are highly sensitive to radiation, and are severely injured by it. Therefore, it is essential to investigate the consequences of the atomic bomb, particularly in the field of hematology, to elucidate the mechanism of radiation effects on human beings.

Among the late effects that resulted from exposure to the atomic bomb, leukemia and anemia, especially the former, are considered to be the most important hematological disorders, and much attention will be directed to studies of leukemia in the following sections. Although our knowledge of the somatic effects of atomic radiation is not sufficient today, we are convinced that data obtained from studies of atomic bomb victims will contribute much to medical utilization of atomic energy in the future.

II. Outline of Atomic Bomb Explosions and Their Effects on Human Beings in Hiroshima and Nagasaki

A. SCOPE OF DAMAGE AND CASUALTIES CAUSED BY ATOMIC BOMB EXPLOSION

1. A Brief Description of the Atomic Bomb Explosions

In Hiroshima, an atomic bomb composed of uranium (U^{235}) exploded at a height of 600 meters from the earth's surface above the center of the city at 8:09 A.M. on August 6, 1945. It was the time to prepare breakfast, so that not only the heat from the atomic bomb but also fires from charcoal braziers contributed much to the conflagration. Approximately 6000 youngsters and older students as well as adults were on the streets engaged in voluntary tasks of clearing the ground or on their way to work. The city of Hiroshima is situated in the delta of the Ohta River and is flat except for Hijiyama Hill, about 70 meters high, in the northeastern part of the city. The atomic bomb exploded over the heart of the city and almost two-thirds of the 90,000 buildings within 25 square km were destroyed. The fires which followed immediately after the explosion became a major conflagration and spread in all directions covering a circular area of some 11 square km. Most of the fires were extinguished by evening. At the instant of the explosion, the sky was filled with a bluish-white flash, and this was followed by a sound like that of thunder. The sun was obscured and the sky was covered with yellow, white, and brown smoke for about 20 minutes. Twenty to sixty minutes after the explosion, rain began to fall, chiefly in the northwestern part of the city, which lasted until evening at the hypocenter (a point on the earth's surface just under the point in the sky where the atomic bomb exploded). The rain-water appeared blackish in the first 1–2 hours and then gradually changed to ordinary transparent rain.

In Nagasaki, an atomic bomb composed of plutonium (Pu^{239}) exploded at a height of 500 meters from the earth's surface above the Uragami valley, which is situated in the northern section of the city, at 11:03 A.M. on August 9, 1945.

The city of Nagasaki is spread out around the harbor situated on the south shore of the city. One valley runs east and another, the Uragami valley, runs northwest and is flanked on both sides by hills, 270–400 meters high. The Uragami district was the center of the industrial area and also had a high concentration of dwellings, but most parts of the business center and some other residential areas of the city escaped from the severe damage of the bombing. The hillsides offered good shielding, so that the extent of the damage caused by the bombing differed greatly from one part of the city to another. Although two-thirds of the industrial plants and buildings were destroyed, the fires were mostly restricted to the Uragami valley area and did not develop into a major conflagration. Most fires were extinguished by the next morning. There is no precise record concerning rainfall following the bombing in Nagasaki.

2. Damage

Wooden houses were instantaneously shattered into pieces within an area having a radius of 1 km from the hypocenter, completely destroyed within an area of 1–2-km radius, severely damaged within an area of 2–3-km radius, and moderately damaged within an area of 3–4-km radius; window panes were broken up to 10 km from the hypocenter. Most concrete buildings escaped destruction. For more detailed information concerning this and following sections, a report by Oughterson and Warren (1956) should be very useful.

3. Casualties and Survivors

There are no precise data concerning the casualties caused by the atomic bombings in both cities. Estimated data concerning damage and casualties in both cities resulting from the atomic bombings were published by Hiroshima City officials in 1953 (Table I). The distribution of persons who were exposed to the atomic bomb but were still living at the time of the national census on October 1, 1950 are shown in Table II.

TABLE I

DAMAGE BY THE ATOMIC BOMB IN HIROSHIMA AND NAGASAKI[a]

	Hiroshima	Nagasaki
Razed area	4,000,000 tsubos[b]	2,030,000 tsubos
Razed houses	56,111	11,574
Totally destroyed houses	6,820	1,326
Partially destroyed houses	3,750	5,509
Half-razed houses	2,290	0
Number of dead	260,000 persons	73,884 persons
Number of injured	163,298 persons	74,904 persons

[a]As compiled by the Hiroshima City Hall, April, 1953
[b]1 tsubo = 3.306m^2

TABLE II

MUNICIPAL AND PREFECTURAL DISTRIBUTION OF PERSONS
EXPOSED TO THE ATOMIC BOMB[a]

Hokkaido	686	Shiga	432
Aomori	118	Kyoto	964
Iwate	169	Osaka	2,996
Miyagi	283	Hyogo	2,501
Akita	149	Nara	300
Yamagata	175	Wakayama	439
Fukushima	289	Tottori	605
Ibaragi	389	Shimane	1,734
Tochigi	278	Okayama	1,928
Gumma	259	Yamaguchi	4,576
Saitama	426	Tokushima	500
Chiba	678	Kagawa	815
Tokyo	3,702	Ehime	1,615
Kanagawa	1,141	Kochi	569
Niigata	291	Fukuoka	4,576
Toyama	123	Saga	1,989
Ishikawa	202	Kumamoto	2,342
Fukui	221	Oita	1,537
Yamanashi	163	Miyazaki	1,119
Nagano	294	Kagoshima	1,909
Gifu	370	Hiroshima	125,485
Shizuoka	508	Nagasaki	112,325
Aichi	1,060		
Mie	471	Total	283,508

[a]From the Japan National Census, Oct. 1, 1950.

The numbers of exposed persons who were living in Hiroshima prefecture on October 1, 1960 are shown in Table III, and those of Nagasaki prefecture are shown in Table IV. When we compare the numbers of the atomic bomb survivors in the two prefectures according to the distance from the hypocenter (Table V), we find that in Hiroshima, the largest number of survivors belong to the 1.5–2-km group, which composed about 26% of total survivors, followed by the 1–1.5-km group which had about 18% of total survivors. In total, 52,675 out of 108,110, i.e., approximately one-half of the exposed population, belong to groups who were exposed

TABLE III

NUMBER OF EXPOSED PERSONS WHO WERE LIVING IN HIROSHIMA PREFECTURE
ON OCTOBER 1, 1960

Exposure distance from hypocenter in kilometers	Hiroshima City		Hiroshima Prefecture excluding Hiroshima City		Total in Hiroshima Prefecture	
	Male	Female	Male	Female	Male	Female
< 0.5	124	139	158	114	282	253
0.5 – 1	1,370	1,604	1,320	726	2,690	2,330
1 – 1.5	5,783	8,427	2,632	2,613	8,415	11,240
1.5 – 2	8,169	10,879	4,570	3,847	12,739	14,726
2 – 2.5	4,897	7,288	1,596	1,577	6,493	8,865
2.5 – 3	4,841	7,181	1,558	1,521	6,399	8,702
3 – 4	4,633	6,612	2,362	2,451	6,995	9,063
4 <	3,418	4,468	647	385	4,065	4,853
	33,235	46,598	14,843	13,434	48,079	60,032
	79,833		28,277		108,110	

to the atomic bomb within 2 km from the hypocenter. Therefore, it seems quite logical to assume that late effects of atomic radiation, such as neoplasms, will be induced at a higher rate among the Hiroshima survivors than that of the Nagasaki survivors, more than two-thirds of whom were exposed at more than 2 km from the hypocenter.

B. PRINCIPAL INJURIES CAUSED BY ATOMIC BOMB EXPLOSIONS

1. Introduction

Tsuzuki (1951) classified atomic bomb injuries (the atomic bomb disease) into 3 groups: atomic burns, atomic bomb traumas, and atomic

TABLE IV

NUMBER OF EXPOSED PERSONS WHO WERE LIVING IN NAGASAKI PREFECTURE
ON OCTOBER 1, 1960

Exposure distance from hypocenter in kilometers	Nagasaki City		Nagasaki Prefecture excluding Nagasaki City		Total in Nagasaki Prefecture	
	Male	Female	Male	Female	Male	Female
< 0.5	191	173	150	110	341	283
0.5 - 1	1,555	1,702	834	621	2,389	2,323
1 - 1.5	1,163	1,279	594	374	1,757	1,653
1.5 - 2	2,624	3,790	767	880	3,391	4,670
2 - 2.5	2,898	4,318	702	666	3,600	4,984
2.5 - 3	3,472	5,190	694	693	4,166	5,883
3 - 4	9,213	13,008	1,613	1,768	10,826	14,776
4 <	8,701	13,381	861	909	9,562	14,290
	29,817	42,841	6,215	6,021	36,032	48,862
	72,658		12,236		84,894	

TABLE V

NUMBER OF ATOMIC BOMB SURVIVORS IN HIRO-
SHIMA AND NAGASAKI ACCORDING TO THEIR
EXPOSURE DISTANCES[a]

Exposure distance from hypocenter in kilometers	Hiroshima Prefecture	Nagasaki Prefecture
< 0.5	535	624
0.5 - 1	5,020	4,712
1 - 1.5	19,655	3,410
1.5 - 2	27,465	8,061
2 - 2.5	15,358	8,584
2.5 - 3	15,101	10,049
3 - 4	16,058	25,602
4 <	8,918	23,852
	108,110	84,894

[a]Surveyed on October 1, 1960.

bomb radiation injuries. This classification seems to have been used by Kajitani and Hatano (1953), and brief definitions of each group were given. Kajitani and Hatano (1953) suggested a fourth group, i.e., atomic bomb gas injury. This group was included to comprehend the remaining radioactivities or internally and externally induced radioactivities. The classification of Liebow et al. (1949) differs from other classifications in that it divides radiation, which is the main source of energy, into thermal and ionizing radiations. Nevertheless, the types of injuries are likewise divided into the groups of wounds, burns, and radiation injuries. We prefer to follow Tsuzuki's classification, but in regard to radiation injuries, some confusion may occur in its original form, and, therefore, the classification shown in Table VI was devised by us in 1952, and then revised slightly (Watanabe, 1953a).

TABLE VI

CLASSIFICATION OF INJURIES CAUSED BY THE ATOMIC BOMB[a]

I. Atomic bomb burns (thermal injuries)
   a. Primary: flash burns
   b. Secondary

II. Atomic bomb traumas (mechanical injuries)
   a. Primary: blast injuries
   b. Secondary

III. Atomic bomb radiation injuries
   a. Primary: radiation injuries due to fission products
   b. Secondary:

   1) Radiation injuries due to internal induction of radioactivity
   2) Radiation injuries due to external induction of radioactivity

[a]From Watanabe (1953a).

2. Thermal Injuries

The intensity of heat generated by the atomic bomb explosion was extremely high and was presumed to have been over 6000°C above ground level in the hypocenter area, but later studies revealed it to be much lower, from 3000 to 4000°C. Another peculiarity aside from the severity of the heat intensity was that the duration of the action was markedly short, and was calculated to have occurred within several seconds, and the total amount of radiation heat energy was said to have been emitted within a period of 3 seconds. Thermal injuries were inflicted as burns on exposed skin that was unprotected from the source of heat, and, due to the fact that the duration of thermal action was so short, the lesions tended to be circumscribed to the superficial layer of the skin. In other words, the burns were superficial and localized. Furthermore, the great number of cases in which the skin peeled off can be explained by the occurrence of a subepidermal explosion of steam or by the divestment of epidermis by the blast. Viewing, as the standard, persons who were standing in the open air, unprotected by any shelter, it was seen that those within 1 km from the hypocenter suffered severe burns, those within 2 km suffered moderate burns, and those within 4 km suffered mild burns. Keloids usually appear from about the thirtieth day after exposure, and reached their peak in the third month. That is, according to Hatano and Watanuki (1953), the rate of incidence rapidly increased from the thirtieth to the ninetieth day, after which time, it gradually decreased with a gently sloping curve. Furthermore, people within an area 2 to 2.5 km from the hypocenter had the highest rate of incidence. Hatano and Watanuki (1953) further stated that the greatest incidence of keloids was seen when the burns began to heal. According to Hatano and Watanuki (1953), the principal cause of keloid was intense heat acting superficially upon the skin, i.e., "flash burn." However, there are some workers (Tamagawa, 1950; Tamagawa et al., 1951) who placed great stress upon the action of radioactivity as the cause since the state of vacuole formation in the epidermal layer was similar to changes seen in the epidermis, apparently caused by radiation. Hatano and Watanuki (1953) further reported that keloids after the atomic bomb reached a maximum in May, 1946 and called this the prolifreative or acme stage; the period following December, 1946 may be called the period of decline, and, thereafter, the keloids were transformed into ordinary scars and the symptoms became less pronounced. In late 1947, we could not find exposed persons with prominent keloids on the streets of Hiroshima.

According to a brief summary of Tsuzuki (1956b), two kinds of abnormalities of the burn scars formed as late effects of atomic bomb injury could be distinguished, i.e., hypertrophic scar and true keloid. The former not only involved whole layers of the skin but also underlying deep tissues, and the scar became thick and hard. True keloid is a thickening of the scars of the primary flash burn which developed among persons exposed within 2 km from the hypocenter that healed relatively smoothly. This thickening process was limited to scar tissue of the skin. This keloid was distinctly broader and thicker than that of ordinary burn scars. As to the pathogenesis of the hypertrophy and keloid formation of the atomic bomb burn scar, Tsuzuki presented four hypotheses: (a) maltreatment hypothesis, (b) diathesis hypothesis, (c) thermal hypothesis,

and (d) radioactive hypothesis. He favored the thermal hypothesis, but
Shriabe (1953) inclined to the diathesis and radioactive hypotheses, and
emphasized the insufficiency of internal secretory activities, especially of
the adrenal glands, that resulted from radiation injuries.

3. Mechanical Injuries

The blast pressure resulting from the explosion of the atomic bomb was
said to be 4.5–6.7 tons per m² in Hiroshima, and 6.7–10 tons per m² in
Nagasaki. The duration of action was estimated to be 0.4 second. Indirectly, the blast caused many instantaneous deaths, but many facts
still remain obscure as to the degree of direct injury. At any rate, we do
not have any typical findings of death caused by the blast.

4. Radiation Injuries

Little is known about severe radiation injuries that cause immediate
death. People who escaped without any serious burns complained of lassitude, nausea, vomiting, thirst, anorexia, headache, vertigo, diarrhea, or
insomnia within hours to a few days after exposure. Most individuals who
received massive irradiation died within a few days with severe symptoms. Less severely injured patients expired by the end of the second
week with continued fever, hemoptysis, hematemesis, bloody diarrhea,
and hematuria, which developed about 2 days after the exposure. In
cases of early deaths, marked anemia was observed, but the incidence of
hemorrhagic diathesis in this stage was uncertain.

Most of those who suffered from severe burns and traumas died within
2 weeks, and those who died later were more or less affected by radiation
injuries. The main symptoms seen in the subacute stage as a result of
radiation injuries were epilation, fever, hemorrhage, oral symptoms, gan-
grene, mucosanguinous diarrhea, etc., and approximately one-half of the
cases with such symptoms expired in this stage. Epilation was therefore
feared as a prodromal sign of death. Subcutaneous petechiae and other
signs of hemorrhagic diathesis were prominent in this stage. Moreover,
bone marrow activity tended toward the aplastic state, so that the defense
mechanism against infection was lowered and gangrenous processes developed in the oral cavity and gastrointestinal tract, which presented
clinical signs resembling dysentery. Deaths were largely due to aplasia
and its complications. In the next stage, all who were injured showed
signs of recovery. However, the so-called "cachectic state" reported by
Tsuzuki (1951), characterized by malfunctions of the liver and kidneys,
developed at this stage. Still, at this stage, functions of the gonads,
especially spermatogenesis, were disturbed (Tsuzuki, 1951).

C. Course and Sequence of the Injuries of Atomic Bomb Explosions

1. *Introduction*

Tsuzuki (1951) classified the clinical course of atomic bomb injuries into the stages shown in Table VII, which was first established by him in 1946, but not released for publication until 1951. He presented another classification (Tsuzuki, 1954) suitable for long-term studies (shown in

TABLE VII

Course of the Atomic Bomb Injuries[a]

I. Initial period	4 months
a. Acute stage	(2 months)
b. Chronic stage	(2 months)
II. After period	Several years and more
a. Sequela stage	
b. Influence stage	
III. Heredity period	After many years

[a]From Tsuzuki (1951)

Table VIII) which had been established by him in 1950. Miyake (1953b) proposed a classification of atomic bomb injuries from the pathological point of view (Table IX). Liebow *et al.* (1949) divided atomic bomb patients into 4 groups according to the time of survival. Concerning the effects of radiation on the human body in general, not confined to cases

TABLE VIII

Clinical Course of Atomic Bomb Injuries[a]

Period	Term	Symptoms
First period (Early stage)	Immediately after the explosion to the end of second week (2 weeks)	Acute
Second period (Middle stage)	Third to eighth week (6 weeks)	Subacute, complicated
Third period (Late stage)	Third to fourth month (8 weeks)	Lessening
Fourth period (After stage)	Fifth month and on	Sequela

[a]From Tsuzuki (1954).

of atomic bomb radiation injuries, Prosser et al. (1947) postulated that it is most suitable to divide them into primary, acute, and chronic reactions. The classification by clinical stages naturally differs with the type of injury taken as the indicator, but, from the standpoint of long-range observations, this can be done most precisely when radiation injury is taken as the primary indicator. With chronic injuries, there are those which have remained from the primary stage as sequelae of primary injuries or have manifested themselves only after a latency of several years, or even of several generations. Therefore, we believe it is quite correct to classify the injuries as shown in Table X.

TABLE IX

CLASSIFICATION OF THE STAGES OF ATOMIC BOMB INJURIES[a]

Stages	Days
Acute	0–14
Subacute	15–35
Subchronic	36–60
Chronic	61–120 and beyond

[a]From Miyake (1953)

2. Acute Injuries

Injuries of the acute stage consist usually of the two or three kinds already mentioned. Radiation injuries in this stage initiate chiefly with injuries of the central nervous system; injuries of the gastrointestinal tract follow. Hematological injuries develop later although the extent and magnitude of injuries in the blood-forming organs are far more important. In the subacute stage, hematological injuries are fully manifested and aplasia of the bone marrow is very prominent at this stage.

Epilation, which began to develop in the earlier stage, was observed

TABLE X

CLASSIFICATION OF THE ATOMIC BOMB INJURIES[a]

A. Primary injuries		
I. Acute stage	Up to the second week	⎫
II. Subacute stage	Up to the fifth week	⎬ Acute injuries
III. Subchronic stage	Up to the second to fourth month	⎭
IV. Chronic stage	After the fourth month	
(Sequela)		⎫ Chronic injuries
B. Late injuries	Developing several years after	⎭

[a]From Watanabe (1953).

in about 70% of the persons exposed within a 1-km radius of the hypocenter, and persisted from 1 to 2 weeks; then a regenerative process took
place.

In the subchronic stage, recovery processes were prominent in various
organs and tissues, especially in the hematopoietic organs. But atrophy
of the gonads and other endocrine organs was still apparent in this stage.

3. Chronic Injuries

In the chronic stage, we observed the formation of hypertrophic scars
and keloids, and these manifestations gradually became obscure in this
stage, although contractive scars from severe burns and wounds were still
apparent as the sequelae of acute injuries. Radiation cataracts were first
noticed in 1950, i.e., 5 years after the atomic bombing, by Hirose and
Fujino (1950) in Nagasaki, and later by Masuda (1956) in Hiroshima;
Sinskey (1955) made extensive studies on exposed persons of both cities.
As a rule, among exposed persons within a 2-km radius of the hypocenter,
these changes were found in approximately 50% of these persons, while
among the exposed population beyond 2 km from the hypocenter the
incidence of radiation cataracts decreased sharply. As to the late effects
of atomic bomb injuries, except for a high incidence of leukemia, we have
not obtained sufficient data to establish a definite correlation between
atomic radiation and induction of neoplasia, although there are some
preliminary data suggesting this. The Hiroshima City Medical Association in cooperation with Atomic Bomb Casualty Commission made a
preliminary survey on the incidence of neoplasia in survivors in Hiroshima (Harada and Ishida, 1960) from May 1, 1957 to December 31,
1959. They found that, among persons who were exposed to the atomic
bomb within a radius of 1 km from the hypocenter, the incidence of
neoplasia had increased to approximately 4 times that of nonexposed
persons, and they noticed that neoplasia of the lung, stomach, uterus, and
ovary was more frequently found among exposed persons than nonexposed. Concerning the shortening of the life span of exposed persons,
Tabuchi and associates (Tabuchi, 1956; Nishida, 1956, 1957) made extensive surveys, and they found that the mortality rate of exposed persons, especially of males, was higher than that of nonexposed persons.
They also found that the mortality rate of exposed persons with neoplasia
was much more frequent than that of nonexposed persons.

As to the hereditary effects, we do not yet know exactly whether
atomic radiation will cause a high incidence of malformation among
descendants of exposed persons although an increase in the incidence of
microcephalia with retarded intelligence has been noted among children
exposed to the atomic bomb in utero.

III. Hematological Changes Caused by Atomic Bomb Explosions

A. INTRODUCTION

Cases of radiation injuries of human beings caused by single total-body irradiations belong to the following four categories: (a) Hiroshima and Nagasaki cases irradiated by atomic bomb radiations; (b) Bikini cases irradiated by fallout produced from a hydrogen bomb test explosion; (c) cases of accidental irradiations of researchers and employees working in atomic laboratories and atomic plants; and (d) cases of therapeutic irradiations with high radiation doses. Moreover, concerning radiation injuries of human beings caused by multiple total- and partial-body irradiations, experience has been gained with those who have been occupationally, diagnostically, and therapeutically irradiated. Cases of radiologists, X-ray technicians, or nurses belong to the first group and patients to the latter two. As for internal irradiations, the instances of dial painters, miners in radioactive mines, or laboratory workers should be considered. Data gathered from single total-body irradiations will contribute much to studies of acute and subacute radiation injuries, while data gained from the multiple irradiations, especially those of internal irradiations, will promote studies of chronic radiation injuries.

In human beings, as previously mentioned, we do not have sufficient data concerning radiation effects on the hematopoietic system. But as we have considerable data concerning radiation-produced hematological changes in experimental animals, it will be very useful to compare findings gained from human observations and from experimental studies. Here it becomes necessary to understand the types of radiation produced by the atomic bomb and how they react on the organism and result in acute or chronic injuries. Table XI was prepared by the author in 1955. Major radiations of the atomic bomb consisted of gamma radiation, neutron radiation, and radiation of the fission products originating from atomic bomb explosions. The two radiations which contribute to the induction of acute and subacute radiation injuries are external irradiation from gamma radiation (A) and from neutron irradiation (C); however, the external irradiation resulting from radioisotopes produced by irradiation of gamma or neutron radiation of the various elements in the air and on the earth's surface are considered insufficient to result in distinct radiation injuries to the organism (B and D). Amano (1953) emphasized the importance of the radiophosphorus produced by internal induction of phosphorus contained in the bone by neutrons, and he considered the hematological changes of the early stages to be due to such reactions. Such radiation (E) also contributed to development of acute and subacute hematological changes. We postulated that the elements in the air and on the earth's surface first acquired externally induced radioactivity by neutron radiation from the atomic bomb, and then these radioisotopes were deposited in the organs and tissues of the organisms after they were inhaled, ingested, or absorbed (Watanabe, 1953[a]). This radiation contributes to the development of chronic injuries or late effects, but not much to acute injuries. Radiation from fission products also contributes to the establishment of chronic injuries when these substances are inhaled,

TABLE XI

PROCEDURES OF THE ACTIONS OF THE RADIATIONS FROM THE ATOMIC BOMB
EXPLOSIONS TO THE ORGANISM[a]

	External irradiation	Internal irradiation
1. Gamma irradiation	A $\gamma \rightarrow$ External irradiation B $\gamma \rightarrow$ Elements in the surrounding sphere $\downarrow$ Formation of radioisotopes $\downarrow$ External irradiation	
2. Neutron irradiation	C N $\rightarrow$ External irradiation	E N $\rightarrow$ Bone $\downarrow$ Mobilization of P^{32} (Amano, 1953)
	D N $\rightarrow$ Elements in the surrounding sphere $\downarrow$ Formation of radioactive isotopes $\downarrow$ External irradiation	F N $\rightarrow$ Elements in the surrounding sphere $\downarrow$ Formation of radioisotopes $\downarrow$ Inhalation, ingestion, absorption $\downarrow$ Deposition in the tissues, especially in the bone (Watanabe, 1953)
3. Irradiation from the fission products		G Fission products $\downarrow$ Inhalation, ingestion, absorption $\downarrow$ Deposition in the tissues

[a]From Watanabe (1955)

ingested, or absorbed, and then deposited in organs and tissues. All factors A, B, C, D, E, F and G contribute to the development of radiation injuries of persons exposed to the atomic bomb explosion. Factors B, E, F, and G are responsible for the development of radiation injuries of persons who were not exposed to the atomic bomb explosions but who entered the cities shortly after the explosions and stayed there for a certain period. In these cases, the effects from the factors B and D are considered to be rather negligible; factors F and G, especially factor F, are presumed to be more important. As will be stated later in the section on leukemia (Section III, E), it is only by this explanation that the development of leukemia among early entrants into the bombed cities can be understood.

Hematopoietic organs have been known to be extremely sensitive to radiation as the classical experiments of Heineke (1903) have shown, and following his experiments, many contributions have appeared in the field of radiation hematology, especially during the last 15 years.

Changes of the peripheral blood picture reflect the effects of radiation on hematopoiesis. Even very small doses of radiation disturb the functions of hematopoiesis, and these disturbances are reflected in the peripheral blood picture. The preipheral blood is therefore a sensitive indicator of radiation injury. Changes of cell constituents of the peripheral blood result from primary injuries of hematopoiesis, and might be modified by certain neuro-hormonal alteration which is also caused by irradiation.

The bone marrow is highly sensitive to radiation, although not as sensitive as lymphoid tissues. Changes in the bone marrow begin soon after irradiation with high doses (several hundred roentgens); the cessation of mitotic activity and degeneration of hematopoietic cells are observed within 30 minutes after irradiation. Heineke (1903) observed that the destruction of bone marrow cells began 3 hours after irradiation and reached a maximum 11 hours after irradiation. Early regeneration occurred within 5 to 6 days after irradiation. After irradiation with higher doses progressive destruction and hypoplasia were observed continuously. Detailed descriptions of disturbances of the bone marrow by radiation are found in the following papers (Töppner, 1941; Dunlap, 1942; Bloom, 1948; Jacobson, 1954).

The sensitivity of hematopoietic cells differs from one type of cell to another. Usually the erythroblast is more sensitive than the granulocyte, and the latter is more sensitive than the megakaryocyte. The most sensitive blood-forming cells are the lymphocyte and lymphoblast. The macrophage, the reticular cell, and the fat cell of the bone marrow are resistant to radiation. After irradiation, active marrows are replaced by dilated sinusoids and fat or gelatinous tissues, often combined with edema or hemorrhages, and an increase in reticular cells is frequently observed.

After internal irradiation with radioisotopes, bone marrow failures develop more slowly than after external irradiation.

Total-body irradiation produces extensive decreases of RNA and DNA in the cells of the bone marrow. In the early stage after irradiation, one can detect a decrease of RNA in the cytoplasm of the cells in which no morphological changes are found, but, at the stage of complete destruction of cells, RNA disappears, although small amounts of DNA are still found.

Extensive regenerative activity in the bone marrow begins in the early stage after irradiation. Even when experimental animals receive doses approximately corresponding to the LD50 (in 30 days), one can detect signs of regeneration 1–2 weeks after irradiation. In the rat and rabbit, recovery of erythropoiesis takes place earlier than that of granulopoiesis. All peripheral blood cells, with the exception of lymphocytes, are relatively resistant to radiation. Therefore, a decrease of peripheral blood cells is not a result of direct injury to mature cells in the peripheral blood but is a reflection of bone marrow injury which causes the cells produced by the injured marrow to have a short life span. The mean life span of normal lymphocytes in the peripheral blood is estimated to be 1–2 days, that of granulocytes 4–7 days, and that of erythocytes 120 days.

A decrease in the number of lymphocytes in the peripheral blood has been considered as one of the most sensitive indicators of radiation injury. The number of lymphocytes in the peripheral blood decreases within 1 hour after irradiation; the magnitude and duration of this decrease depend on the dose of radiation received. In humans, with as low a dose as 250 millirems, a temporary decrease of the lymphocytes was detected by Clemedson and Nelson (1960). Furthermore, with 100 r, a distinct decrease occurred, and with 300 r or over, an extensive decrease of the lymphocytes was observed; it takes 2 months or more to confirm the complete regeneration of lymphocyte formation. After multiple irradiations with small doses, we can observe occasional morphological changes of lymphocytes, such as an increase in binucleated cells (Dobson and Chupp, 1957) or the appearance of the bilobulated cells (Clemedson and Nelson, 1960).

Granulocytes behave somewhat differently than do lymphocytes. Granulocytes increase slightly in the peripheral blood within 24 hours after irradiation with moderate or high doses, probably due to the stimulative action of radiation; then they begin to decrease, reaching the minimum value at 3–5 days after irradiation. Often, we find abnormally large granulocytes in the peripheral blood, which are considered to be the probable products of abnormal cell divisions. Although, during the recovery process, we can observe a fluctuation in the number of granulocytes, often, the granulocyte count exceeds the normal value at this stage. In the guinea pig, eosinophilia is often observed during the recovery phase (Haigh, and Paterson, 1956).

Erythroblasts also suffer severe damage, and the process is similiar to that in granulocytes. Anemia will reach a maximum 2 weeks after irradiation. Recently, the utilization of radioiron (Fe^{59}) has been highly recommended for following the kinetics of erythropoietic cells. After irradiation, the number of blood platelets in the peripheral blood also decreases. The decrease in number of blood platelets and the lowering of the thrombokinase value are considered as the main causes of prolongation of the blood clotting time and of disturbances in the clotting mechanism (Jackson et al., 1952; Cronkite et al., 1952).

After total-body irradiation with high doses, all hematopoietic elements are severely affected. Consequently, a progressive cytopenia and finally complete aplasia of the bone marrow develop 5–6 days after irradiation. It is well known that hematopoietic organs of younger persons are more sensitive to radiation than those of older persons. Other morphological and biological changes, combined with the previously mentioned decrease of hematopoietic cell elements, interfere with the functions of various organs and tissues; for example, the albumin-globulin ratio usually rises above normal, and the values of electrolyte balance show a fluctuation. Concerning these changes, reference should be made to Patt and Brues (1954). As to changes in enzymic activities of the blood, the lowering of activity of cholinesterase has been most conclusively reported (Ord and Stocken, 1953).

Lymphoid tissues, i.e., lymph nodes, tonsils, Peyer's patches, and other lymphoid apparatus in the intestinal tract, are highly sensitive to radiation. After irradiation, one observes acute destruction of lymphocytes which is manifested as lymphopenia in the peripheral blood stream. Atrophy of the tonsils, complicated by ulcerative processes, and atrophy of lymphoid tissues are the major acute injuries produced by massive irradiation; these extensive destructive changes result not only from the direct action of radiation, but also from the stress due to disturbances of the internal secretory system. For details on the changes in lymphoid tissues, the report of De Bruyn (1948) will be useful. Irradiation of the spleen of experimental animals with a dose of LD_{50} (in 30 days) resulted in the arrest of mitosis of the lymphocytes and their destruction within 1 hour, just as in the marrow, followed by clearance of fragments of the destroyed cells by phagocytes. After irradiation, the spleen became temporarily atrophic, and then regeneration began about 1 week after irradiation and proceeded for 3–4 weeks (Murray, 1948).

The thymus gland is also highly sensitive to radiation. Within 24 hours after irradiation, pyknosis and destruction of thymus cells can be detected, followed by regeneration of the cells in the medulla, extending to the cortex. Decrease of weight of the thymus gland is correlated with the radiation dose, and modified by the interference of internal secretory activities.

B. Course of the Disease

Since injuries caused by atomic bomb explosions are due to radioactivity, the classification of the course of the atomic bomb injuries may be based mainly on radiation effects (as shown in Table X). In the following paragraphs, various manifestations observed in each stage will be reviewed mainly from the hematological point of view.

1. Early Stage

Approximately 90% of the individuals killed by atomic bomb injuries succumbed within this early period due to severe burns, traumas, and massive irradiation.

A violent change was observed in the circulating blood and the hematopoietic tissues, which consisted of highly radiosensitive elements. As has been pointed out by American investigators (Oughterson and Warren, 1956), however, the principal handicap in evaluating the hematological changes, especially in the circulating blood, is that most of the data available are rather fragmentary. Admittedly, the performance of a systematic analysis was almost impossible under the extremely confusing circumstances.

According to Nakao (1953a,b), a marked anemia and especially a pronounced decrease in hemoglobin content were observed in cases of early death. However, the thrombocytopenia was rather mild during this stage, in accord with the fact that development of hemorrhagic diathesis was not prominent. The circulating granulocytes and lymphocytes showed a severe decrease in number. Examination of the bone marrow of two patients with severe leukopenia disclosed the disappearance of almost every parenchymal cell, with the proliferation of reticular cells and plasma cells.

Pathological studies (Miyake, 1953a,b; Miyake and Sugano, 1956) revealed that the bone marrow of patients dying in this stage were in an aplastic state, and the development of hemorrhagic thrombi in the spleen and mesenterium and the development of pulmonary emphysema that may have been caused by thermal radiation were observable. Furthermore, degenerative changes in liver and kidneys were seen among patients with burns.

Amano (1953, 1956) observed the occurrence of pulmonary emphysema, posttraumatic collapse of the circulatory system, vacuolar degeneration of the epidermis and germinative layer of the hair follicles, degeneration and atrophy of the alimentary tract and endocrine glands, atrophy of the lymphatic organs and agranulocytosis in the circulating blood, etc. He also pointed out that the development of serous hepatitis, hemorrhagic diathesis, and nephrosis was the result of these changes. Amano also assumed that pulmonary emphysema resulted from the blast.

2. Intermediate Stage

Most of those who suffered from severe burns or wounds died at the early stage, i.e., within 2 weeks following exposure, and those patients dying during this stage were all more or less affected by radioactivity.

The peripheral blood picture examined by Nakao (1953a,b) indicated that there was moderate to severe anemia and marked thrombocytopenia, which was one of the factors causing hemorrhagic diathesis. Progressive leukopenia with relative lymphocytosis and marked granulocytopenia was characteristic in this stage. Although the bone marrow in most cases was still aplastic, there were some cases with regenerating bone marrow.

Comprehensive hematological surveys of 861 exposed individuals in Hiroshima taken by Mashimo and associates (1953) and Wakisaka (1953) during the middle of the second month after the atomic bomb explosion should be cited here. The subjects were individuals who were exposed in the zone 300 to 3000 meters from the hypocenter. Decreases of erythrocyte count and hemoglobin content were common and were particularly marked among severely affected cases. The color index was within normal range or slightly elevated. There was no distinct anisocytosis, poikilocytosis, polychromatophilia, or basophilic stippling of the erythrocytes among severely affected cases, indicating insufficiency of regenerative activity in the bone marrow. However, an increase of the reticulocytes and nucleated erythrocytes was observed in some recovering cases.

Development of a drastic leukopenia was one of the prominent features in this stage. Leukocyte counts of severe cases were usually less than 1000. The decrease in numbers of erythrocytes and leukocytes showed a parallel relation, but the decrease of the former was less marked than the latter. A severe granulocytopenia with disappearance of eosinophils, and a relative lymphocytosis and plasmacytosis were commonly observed among severe cases. Most granulocytes in the circulating blood were of mature form with various signs of degenerative process. A plasmacytosis and a monocytosis were seen in some of less severely affected cases. An eosinophilia and a mild leukocytosis were encountered in some recovering cases. The phagocytotic activity of the neutrophils was tested 1½ months after the explosion in 12 patients, and it was indicated that the activity was weaker in every tested case than in nonexposed individuals.

In the bone marrow, a sharp drop in nucleated cells, to approximately one-tenth of the normal value, was observed among serious cases. Erythrocytopoiesis was severely affected and the immature form was rarely seen. Granulocytopoiesis was also seriously impaired and most of the cells were mature forms, such as metamyelocytes, banded or segmented granulocytes with various degenerative changes like those observed in the peripheral blood; whereas, the ratios of lymphocyte, monocyte, and plasma cell-like reticular cells were increased. Patients with hemorrhagic diathesis showed a severe thrombocytopenia, with a count 10,000 or less. Accordingly, the prolongation of bleeding and coagulation times, a moderate decrease of plasma thrombin, and an elevation of capillary permeability (with a positive Rumpel-Leede sign) were demonstrated. Furthermore, the erythrocyte sedimentation rates of severely injured patients were highly accelerated.

Pathological findings of Miyake (1953a,b) and Miyake and Sugano (1956) disclosed aplasia of bone marrow, general hemorrhagic diathesis, gangrenous-hemorrhagic pseudomembranous inflammation in the oral cavity and alimentary tract (these findings in the large intestine resembled dysentery), and atrophy of reproductive and endocrine organs. Epilation was understood to be caused by degeneration of the external sheath of hair roots. Amano (1953, 1956) considered that panmyelophthisis, pyknosis, vacuolar degeneration of the epidermis and the germinative layer of the hair root, and degeneration and atrophy of lymphoid tissue and endocrine organs were induced by the direct action of radioactivity emitted from the atomic bomb; induction of gangrenous angina and stomatitis, focal pneumonia, pseudomembranous colitis, miliar necrosis in various organs, and hemorrhagic diathesis was the indirect effect. Furthermore, he emphasized that the effect of neutrons, especially the thermal slow neutron by which the induced radioactivity was conferred to the calcium phosphate of bony tissue, should not be overlooked as one of the causative factors of various pathological changes observed during the subacute stage, and that these changes could not be fully attributable to the primary change in the bone marrow due to gamma irradiation. If this hypothesis is taken into account, it is possible to explain the fact that the clinical signs of the disease shifted to subacute phase in the second week, reached a peak at the middle of the fourth week, with gradual recovery by the seventh week.

3. Subacute Stage

During this stage, various symptoms took a course for recovery. The most characteristic change manifested in the circulating blood during this stage, as pointed out by Nakao (1953a,b), was the relatively rapid recovery from leukopenia. He stated also that both the granulocyte and lymphocyte showed signs of rapid increase but the recovery rate of the latter appeared to be less vigorous than the former.

Pathological studies by Miyake (1953a,b) and Miyake and Sugano (1956) revealed a marked regenerative activity of hematopoietic cells in the bone marrow and hemosiderosis in the spleen. Also, coinciding with the "cachectic state" observed clinically, the development of jaundice and enlarged white kidney were confirmed. In some cases, the formation of miliary abscesses or gangrenous areas were seen in the lungs.

4. Late Stage

Together with the delayed or late effects, the clinical and pathological changes of this stage consisted of chronic injuries.

The injuries in the circulating blood and hematopoietic organs began to heal. According to many fragmentary reports, the leukocyte count was generally restored to the normal level. Some cases even showed a transient leukocytosis. The restoration of the granulocyte count was more vigorous than that of other elements, and a transient eosinophilia was encountered in some cases.

The recovery of erythrocytopoiesis was slower than that of leukocytopoiesis, and anemia was still evident in some of the survivors. The bone marrow was in the proliferative phase both in granulo- and erythrocytopoiesis.

5. Late Effects (Delayed Effects)

Injuries of the hematopoietic organs, alimentary tract, gonads, and skin were most prominent, as previously mentioned, but these gradually subsided by the late stage, except for the development of keloids from burns.

Damage to the circulating blood and hematopoietic organs had almost disappeared by the end of the late stage and an apparent recovery, with some anemia and a transient leukocytosis, was achieved. Most of the survivors returned to their social activities. However, a sudden prevalence of leukemia among these survivors became evident a few years after the explosion. This is one of most characteristic events occurring as the sequelae of exposure to atomic radiation.

The prevalence of leukemia together with other delayed blood disorders which have been observed among the survivors will be discussed in Section III,E.

Concerning chromosome aberrations in human blood cells after irradiation, Bender and Gooch (1962) reported on results gained from accidentally irradiated employees of an atomic processing plant, but among persons exposed to the atomic bomb these aberrations of blood cell chromosomes have not yet been confirmed.

C. APLASIA AND REGENERATION

Detailed histopathological descriptions of findings in atomic bomb victims during the acute and subacute stage are rather scarce because of the general confusion and poor medical facilities. Among those available, an exhaustive study by Amano (1956) is most valuable in analyzing the development of aplasia and subsequent regeneration of hematopoietic organs. He analyzed 25 autopsy materials which had been examined in Hiroshima 4–5 days after the explosion (3 cases) and 4–6 weeks after (22 cases). They were exposed within 650 meters and about 1000 meters from the hypocenter, respectively. In addition to the histopathological study, he also utilized clinical hemo-myelograms and values of beta radioactivity in the various organs of the autopsied materials measured by a Geiger-Müller counter.

Bone marrow was tested in femur and spine. Every femur marrow examined was aplastic and fatty; some showed diffuse hemorrhage. The findings in the spinal marrow were rather complicated and Amano classified them into 4 types: (a) aplastic, (b) aplastic with varied regenerating foci, (c) maturation-arrest, and (d) normal. Regenerating foci of these cases consisted of uniform groupings of one cell series instead of mixtures of diverse cells seen in ordinary aplastic anemia. In general, the most vigorous regeneration was observed in the neutrophilic series, while there was retardation in the erythroblastic and the megakaryocytic series. Two cases of subacute death presented aplastic-type marrow showing hemorrhage and reduction of the parenchymal cells with scattered perivascular plasmacytic reaction. Bone marrow of four cases of subacute death showed the aplastic-type marrow with varied regenerating foci that mostly consisted of cells of the neutrophilic series. Amano (1956) pointed out that a proliferation of monocytic series was infrequently observed besides the neutrophilic foci. One of these cases showed 50% monocytosis among 430 white cells in peripheral blood. An examination of the localization of these regenerating cell foci disclosed that there was no definite relation between the foci and the original structure of the marrow. The most vigorous regeneration was represented by a diffuse infiltration by granulocytes with polyploid nuclei and abundant mitosis by which the sinusoidal structure was compressed as in leukemia. Two other cases of subacute death displayed the maturation-arrest-type. The marrow findings of this category were represented by uneven regeneration of diverse cell series accompanied by the appearance of fatty islets and fibrosis with a remnant of atrophied bone lamellae. It is noteworthy that the immature cell proliferation mainly consisted of nodular hyperplasia of the neutrophlic series, indicating excessive regenerating potency of this series following an aplastic state. The maturation-arrest-type was quite different in various aspects from that seen in the maturation-arrest-type of ordinary aplastic anemia. Therefore, this mode of atypical regeneration observed among atomic bomb victims appeared to be peculiar, and might be referred to as a preleukemic-like change. Furthermore, the possibility could not be neglected that development of leukemia would ensue from this marrow in the future.

The lymph nodes showed cortex atrophy and sinus catarrh in all examined cases.

The spleen was atrophic and destruction of its red pulp was observable. Especially in cases of acute death, disappearance of white pulp and red pulp cells and remnants such as endothelial cells of sinusoids and reticulum trabecles in the spongy mesh were characteristic.

In subacute victims, the structural changes were milder and there were signs of regeneration of lymphopoiesis which fit well with the observed relative lymphocytosis in the peripheral blood in some cases.

From the foregoing descriptions, it is clear that changes in myelopoiesis were most conspicous even during the subacute stage. In order to explain the retardation of myelopoiesis, one should not overlook the effect of internal irradiation of phosphorus by the beta rays, as mentioned before. This possibility was confirmed by a physical examination of autopsy materials with a Geiger-Müller counter.

D. ANEMIA

The development of anemia among heavily irradiated individuals in Hiroshima during the acute and subacute stages was clinically demonstrated, as described previously.

Many practicing physicans in Hiroshima who have been treating survivors have emphasized that severe anemia is a frequent occurrence in exposed persons. On the other hand, there is a report published by the Atomic Bomb Casualty Commission (1955) in which no statistical significance was observed between the exposed and nonexposed persons as far as the incidence of anemia is concerned, and they also did not establish a correlation between the development of aplastic anemia and exposure to atomic radiation. Before drawing any conclusion, our survey (Yamamoto *et al.*, 1953; Hirose *et al.*, 1954; Yokoro *et al.*, 1955; Yamada *et al.*, 1956; Wada *et al.*, 1957; Yokoro *et al.*, 1958) on hematological findings in citizens of Otake City, a small town located in the western Hiroshima Prefecture, will be presented.

The survey was performed in 6 consecutive years starting in 1952 on approximately 250 individuals each year. These people had been uniformly exposed to atomic radiation on a street about 2300 meters away from the hypocenter and were overtaken by the so-called "black rain" that was heavily contaminated with radioactive fission products; they have resided in Otake City thereafter.

The observations of the first year will be summarized as follows: the highest value of erythrocyte count they showed was 526×10^4 and the lowest 216×10^4, and approximately 50% of the subjects showed 320–400×10^4 indicating the existence of a mild to moderate anemia. The hemoglobin content (Sahli %) showed considerable variation ranging from 23 to 121, and, in about half the cases, the range was from 61 to 80% indicating a mild decrease. On the color index, the majority of cases were within normal range, and, it was concluded, that there was a mild orthochromic anemia in this population 7 years after exposure to atomic radiation. Concerning the leukocyte count, the maximum and minimum values were 10,600 and 1600, respectively, and approximately 50% were below 5000. There were 14 cases or 9% with counts below 3000, and, thus, a moderate leukopenia was observed. Futhermore, there were a relative increase of lymphocytes and a relative decrease of neutrophils. Cytologically, in 44% of cases, immature granulocytes were found in the peripheral blood. Based on the foregoing finding, it was clearly demonstrated that hematological abnormalities still existed in these individuals 7 years after exposure.

The yearly change of these figures for the next 5 years, namely, 1953 to 1957 can be briefly described as follows. Figure 1 shows erthrocyte counts from 1952 to 1955. As can be seen, the highest value was observed in 1955, in which approximately 60% were 361–460×10^4. In 1957, that is 12 years after exposure, 70% were 361–480×10^4 indicating the existence of a mild anemia with an apparent improvement. As shown in Fig. 2, a favorable turn in hemoglobin content was also evident as in the erthrocyte count. In the leukocyte count, the recovery was not noticeable until 1955, in which approximately 40% were still in the range of 4001–6000, as shown in Fig. 3. However, a distinct improvement was demonstrated in 1957, that is 77% of cases were in the range of 4501–8000, and the immature granulocytes, sometimes seen in peripheral blood in 1952, were not demonstrated in any case. From the above-mentioned facts, it might be concluded that the improvement in erythrocytopoiesis had been favorable and had reached a normal level with some slight anemia by 1957. On the other hand, the recovery in granulocytopoiesis had been rather slower than that of erthrocytopoiesis, but it had also apparently improved by 1957. Here, we shall consider the character of anemia from a different point of view. It has been pointed out that the peculiarity of changes in erthrocytes due to exposure to ionizing radiation seems to be the induction of fragilocytes, macrocytes, and spherocytes. Thus, most of the radiation-induced anemia should be of the hyperchromic type com-

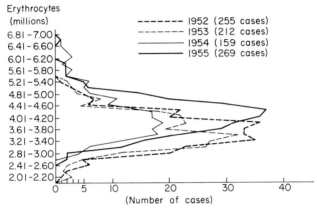

Fig. 1. Trends in the erythrocyte count of the inhabitants of Otake City who were exposed to atomic bomb radiation in Hiroshima in 1945.

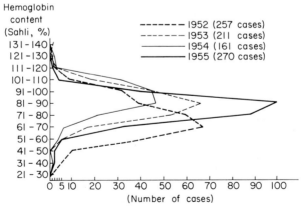

Fig. 2. Trends in the hemoglobin content of the inhabitants of Otake City who were exposed to atomic bomb radiation in Hiroshima in 1945.

monly observed in radiologists. Taking these findings into consideration, an examination for hyperchromic anemia was performed on our subjects. It was demonstrated that, in 1955, there were 12 cases or 4.4% of hyperchromic anemia (hemoglobin: above 90%; erthrocyte count: below 370 × 10⁴; color index: below 0.9), whereas, in 1957, there were 4 cases or 1.3% indicating a gradual decline of the hyperchromic anemia in these exposed individuals. This finding is in accord with those reported by Kikuchi (1957), who examined the survivors living in the Kyoto area, and by Hibino (1957), who studied the survivors living in the Nagoya area. However, it can not be confirmed that hyperchromic anemia is exclusively due to exposure to atomic radiation because it can also be seen among nonexposed persons. As mentioned before, there has been some

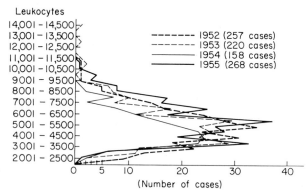

Fig. 3. Trends in the leukocyte count of the inhabitants of Otake City who were exposed to atomic bomb radiation in Hiroshima in 1945.

argument as to whether anemia still existed among the survivors as a delayed effect of atomic radiation. These conflicting views have resulted from at least the following two factors. The first is that the blood pictures of the survivors have gradually improved in recent years, making it difficult to find any significant difference between exposed and nonexposed persons. The second, as revealed by a survey carried out by Hibino (1956) on the survivors visiting the Atomic Bomb Casualty Commission, is that iron-deficiency anemia was rather commonly seen among them. This also makes it difficult to obtain a significant result by statistical analysis under the improved economical and social situation of today.

Besides the usual anemia, there have been some reports of severe aplastic anemia that took a fatal course among survivors, as described by Shigeto (1955). These cases were complicated by abnormal manifestations, not only in the erythrocytic series, but also in the thrombocytic and granulocytic series. Aplastic anemia with aplasia in bone marrow was commonly seen in exposed persons during the acute and subacute stages, as mentioned previously. But the development of this type of aplastic anemia as a delayed manifestation of radiation injury was unexpected; and attention should be directed to the maturation-arrest or the proliferative types, the etiology of which may possibly be attributable to atomic radiation. It should be emphasized that further analysis with a greater number of cases will be necessary before any conclusion can be drawn.

E. LEUKEMIA AND ALLIED DISORDERS

1. Incidence of Leukemia among Hiroshima and Nagasaki Survivors

Injuries induced by exposure to atomic radiation have been roughly classified into two categories, i.e., acute and chronic injuries, as already shown in Table X. Regarding chronic injuries, including the delayed effect which will be the major subject of our present study, a report from the Atomic Bomb Casualty Commission (ABCC) (1955) is of considerable interest. Table XII indicates disorders which have been observed among atomic bomb survivors in comparison to known sequelae of irradiation, both in man and experimental animals. According to that survey, there are only four disorders that are definitely attributable to sequelae of exposure to atomic radiation, namely, induction of leukemia, cataracts, microcephalus due to exposure during early embryonic life, and hypoplasia of dental enamel; others have not been established. Among these four disorders, the prevalence of leukemia is most prominent, and numerous reports dealing with the disease observed in Hiroshima and Nagasaki have been published. First of all, the fact that atomic radiation would cause a subsequent elevation of leukemia incidence in the exposed population had already been foreseen by experts. This was based on the available data indicating a substantial increase of leukemia incidence among physicians (Henshaw and Hawkins, 1944), radiologists (March, 1944, 1950), and irradiated animals (Krebs et al., 1930; Furth et al., 1933; Furth and Furth, 1936; Heuper, 1934; Henshaw, 1944; Furth, 1946; Lorenz et al., 1947). In fact, a sudden rise of leukemia incidence has been observed in both cities since 1947. Study on leukemia incidence in Hiroshima was initiated by one of our colleagues, Yamawaki, and a close correlation between high incidence of leukemia in the Hiroshima survivors and exposure to atomic radiation was confirmed by his $6\frac{1}{2}$ year survey of leukemia incidence in Hiroshima from 1946 to 1951 (Yamawaki, 1953, 1954). However, it was not easy for him to publish his original data until 1954 because of the occupation after World War II. During the period from 1951 to 1959, several reports dealing with the same subject were published by American investigators (Valentine, 1951; Folley *et al.*, 1952; Lange *et al.*, 1954; Moloney and Lange, 1954; Moloney and Kastenbaum, 1955; Wald, 1957, 1958a,b; Heyssel *et al.*, 1959), and in some of the earlier reports, the name of Yamawaki appears as one of the coauthors.

Succeeding the pioneer work of Yamawaki we have been engaged in surveying the incidence of leukemia among the Hiroshima survivors for several years (Watanabe, 1957ab, 1960, 1961, 1962a, 1964; Watanabe and Ito, 1959; Watanabe *et al.*, 1958, 1960), and have obtained complete data for the 17-year period from 1946 to 1962. The summarized data will be given here.

TABLE XII

A COMPARISON OF DISORDERS THAT HAVE BEEN OBSERVED AMONG ATOMIC BOMB
SURVIVORS WITH THE KNOWN SEQUELLAE OF IRRADIATION

Abnormality	Animal experimentation	Humans	
		X-ray over-exposure	ABCC findings
Leukemia	Yes	Yes	Yes
Aplastic anemia	Yes	—	—
Cataracts	Yes	Yes	Yes
Genetic mutation	Yes	—	?
Infertility of individual irradiated *in utero*	Yes	—	—
Microcephaly following exposure of young fetus	Yes	Yes	Yes
Retarded bone growth	Yes	Yes	?
Hypoplasia of dental enamel	Yes	Yes	Yes
Increased dental caries	—	—	?
Premature aging			
Loss of vigor	Yes	—	—
Early greying of hair	Yes	—	—
Increased frequency of hypertension	Yes	—	—
Diminished resistance to infection	Yes	—	—
Reduced life span	Yes	—	—
Tumors			
Lung	Yes	—	—
Ovary	Yes	No(?)	—
Uterus	Yes	—	—
Breast	Yes	—	—
Skin	Yes	Yes	—
Bone	Yes	Yes	—
Pituitary	Yes	—	—

The yearly change of the total and exposed population in Hiroshima City during the period of 1946 to 1962 is shown in Table XIII. After the general census taken by the Japanese government in 1960, the total population of Hiroshima City numbered 431,285; the exposed population in the city was estimated as 95,684 based on the concurrent local census taken by the Hiroshima City officials. According to the previous census in 1950, total population in the city was 285,712, while the exposed population was 98,102. The numbers in the Table are based on these four figures.

TABLE XIII

CHANGE IN POPULATION OF HIROSHIMA CITY

Year	Gross population	Exposed population (Estimated)
1946	171,204	99,069
1947	222,434	98,827
1948	246,134	98,586
1949	262,832	98,344
1950	285,712[a]	98,102[a]
1951	297,758	97,860
1952	321,973	97,618
1953	339,432	97,377
1954	361,367	97,135
1955	360,808	96,893
1956	382,011	96,651
1957	396,730	96,409
1958	412,707	96,168
1959	426,564	95,926
1960	431,285[b]	95,684[b]
1961	459,301	95,442
1962	479,379	95,200

[a]Figures from census on October 1, 1950
[b]Figures from census on October 1, 1960

The number of leukemia cases that developed and the incidence per 100,000 in Hiroshima in each year during the past 17 years are indicated in Table XIV and Fig. 4. The total number of leukemia cases that developed in the city in 1960 was 15 in which only 4 cases were derived from survivors. Accordingly, it appeared that the incidence of leukemia among survivors in 1960 was much lower compared with that of previous years. There were 12 cases among survivors in 1961 and 8 cases in 1962. Thus, the mean value of the leukemia that developed in survivors in these

3 years was 8 cases. From these figures, it might be said that there has been a gradual decline in the incidence of leukemia among the survivors in recent years.

TABLE XIV

INCIDENCE OF LEUKEMIA IN HIROSHIMA

Year of onset	Total cases		Exposed cases (Within 5000 meters)	
	Number of cases	Incidence per 100,000	Number of cases	Incidence per 100,000
1946	2	1.17	1	0.01
1947	6	2.70	5	5.06
1948	15	6.09	11 (1)	11.16
1949	21	7.99	12 (1)	12.20
1950	13	4.55	12	12.23
1951	20	6.72	17 (1)	17.37
1952	17	5.28	9	9.22
1953	22	6.48	16 (2)	16.43
1954	17	4.70	13 (1)	13.38
1955	22	6.10	14 (1)	14.45
1956	18	4.71	13 (1)	13.45
1957	17	4.29	10	10.37
1958	21	5.09	11	11.44
1959	26	6.10	16	16.84
1960	15	3.48	4	4.18
1961	22	4.79	12	12.63
1962	14	2.92	8	8.42

[a]Numbers in parentheses indicate the number of cases exposed at a distance of 5,001–10,000 meters from the hypocenter.

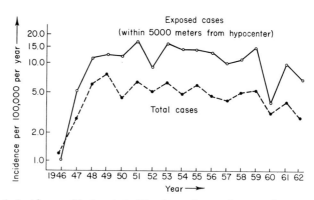

Fig. 4. Incidence of leukemia in Hiroshima during the period 1946–1962.

The number of deaths and the death rate due to leukemia during the same period is shown in Table XV and is visualized in Fig. 5. In 1962, the total number of deaths from leukemia was 13 of which 7

TABLE XV

DEATH RATE OF LEUKEMIA IN HIROSHIMA

Year	Total cases		Exposed cases (Within 5000 meters)		Death rate of all Japan per 100,000
	Number of cases	Death rate per 100,000	Number of cases	Death rate per 100,000	
1946	2	1.17	1	1.01	
1947	4	1.80	3	3.04	1.07
1948	6	2.44	4 (1)	4.06	1.19
1949	15	5.71	8 (1)	8.13	1.37
1950	13	4.55	11	11.21	1.47
1951	14	4.70	14 (1)	14.31	1.58
1952	18	5.59	14	14.34	1.67
1953	21	6.19	12 (1)	12.32	1.91
1954	13	3.60	11 (1)	11.32	2.12
1955	19	5.27	12 (1)	12.38	2.28
1956	20	5.24	14 (4)	14.49	2.41
1957	16	4.03	13 (1)	13.48	2.44
1958	21	5.09	9	9.36	2.65
1959	22	5.16	14 (1)	14.59	2.67
1960	21	4.87	8	8.36	28.0
1961	22	4.79	11	11.52	—
1962	13	2.71	7	7.36	—

[a]Numbers in parentheses indicate the number of cases exposed at a distance of 5,001–10,000 meters from the hypocenter.

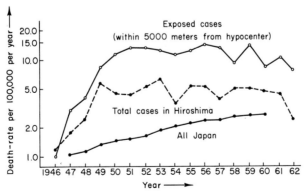

Fig. 5. Death rate from leukemia in Hiroshima during the period 1946–1962.

were from the exposed cases. The death rates per 100,000 were 2.71 and 7.36, respectively. The latter is still fairly high as compared with that of the mean value for all Japan. On the other hand, the death rate from leukemia in Japan is steadily increasing in recent years, as indicated in the right-hand column of Table XV. Although data are available only up to 1960, the trend may be extrapolated up to the present. Therefore, it is most likely that the death rate from leukemia in both the total population and exposed cases in Hiroshima has been decreasing in recent years.

These observations are summarized in Table XVI. During the past 17 years, 288 cases of leukemia occurred in Hiroshima; 184 of these cases

TABLE XVI

INCIDENCE AND MORTALITY OF LEUKEMIA IN HIROSHIMA
DURING THE PERIOD OF 1946–1962

	Total cases	Exposed cases (Within 5,000 meters)	All Japan	Cases entered within a week after explosion[a]
Number of cases of leukemia	288	184		33
Incidence per 100,000 per year	4.87	11.15		6.90
Number of deaths from leukemia	260	166		28
Deathrate per 100,000 per year	4.28	10.07	1.97[b]	6.06

[a]This section was inserted for reference.
[b]This figure is for the period 1947–1960.

were derived from people who were exposed to the atomic bomb within 500 meters from the hypocenter. Thus, the total incidence of leukemia per 100,000 per year during this period was 4.87, whereas that of exposed persons was 11.15. The individual locations of exposure to the atomic bomb of these leukemia cases are indicated in Fig. 6, from which it can readily be observed that most cases were exposed at short distances from the hypocenter.

The total number of deaths from leukemia was 260, of which 166 were in the exposed group. The total death rate from leukemia per 100,000 per year during this period was 4.28, whereas that of exposed cases was 10.07. The mean value of the death rate from leukemia in all Japan within the same period was 1.97; in Hiroshima and in exposed cases it was, respectively, about 2.2 and 5.1 times as high as that of all Japan.

The type of leukemia developed among the survivors in Hiroshima in relation to the onset of the disease is shown in Table XVII. There were

98 cases of the acute form and the majority of them belonged to the myeloid-type. Only 3 cases were definitely diagnosed as the lymphoid-type. A similar trend was also obvious in cases of subacute and chronic forms, that is, 8 cases of subacute myeloid and 1 of lymphoid-type, and 75 cases of chronic myeloid and only 2 of lymphoid-type have been observed. On the other hand, there is no distinct correlation between the latent period and the form of leukemia developed. In other words, both the acute and chronic forms are almost equally distributed in each year throughout the observed period.

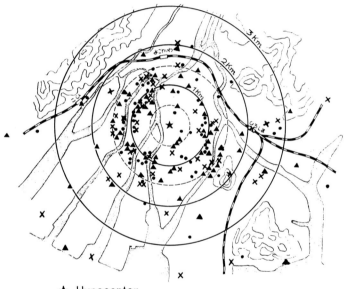

★ Hypocenter
• Cases with onset of leukemia during 1946-1952
▲ Cases with onset of leukemia during 1953-1957
× Cases with onset of leukemia during 1958-1962

Fig. 6. Locations of exposure to the atomic bomb of individuals who later developed leukemia in Hiroshima (1946–1962).

The type of leukemia developed in Hiroshima during the past 17 years in relation to the exposure distance was studied and a significant observation has been made, as shown in Table XVIII. Among cases exposed within 2000 meters from the hypocenter there was an increase in the chronic form as compared with those exposed beyond 2000 meters or nonexposed cases.

Table XIX summarizes the observation. The ratio of the acute and chronic forms among cases exposed within 2000 meters was about 1 : 0.81. In contrast, in the cases exposed beyond 2000 meters, the value of the ratio rises as the exposure distance increases, approaching the ratio of nonexposed cases of 1 : 0.12. Although no data are available on the accurate ratio of these two forms of leukemia in all Japan, it is to be set somewhere between 1 : 0.20 and 1 : 0.17 judging by the statistics made by the leading clinics in Japan.

TABLE XVII

Type of Leukemia Developed Among the Exposed in Hiroshima, According to the Year of Onset

Year	Acute[a]	Subacute myeloid	Subacute lymphoid	Chronic myeloid	Chronic lymphoid
1946	1	0	0	0	0
1947	3	0	0	2	0
1948	6	0	0	5	0
1949	6	0	0	5	1
1950	6	1	0	5	0
1951	8 (1)	1	0	8	0
1952	6	0	0	3	0
1953	10	0	0	6	0
1954	7	0	0	6	0
1955	4	0	1	9	0
1956	4	3	0	6	0
1957	8	0	0	2	0
1958	5	0	0	6	0
1959	11	0	0	4	1
1960	2	1	0	1	0
1961	6 (1)	2	0	4	0
1962	5 (1)	0	0	3	0
	98	8	1	75	2

[a]Numbers in parentheses indicate cases that were diagnosed definitely as lymphoid-type.

In analyzing these findings, there is no doubt about the causative role of the atomic radiation in induction of leukemia among the Hiroshima survivors. Furthermore, it appears to be true that an increase in incidence of chronic myeloid-type leukemia is the most characteristic among leukemia developed in the Hiroshima survivors.

Tables XX and XXI show the prevalence of leukemia among the Hiroshima survivors by age. In the groups both near and far from the explosion, the highest incidence was observed among the age group of

10 to 19 years at the time of the exposure, and the second rank was in age group of 50 to 59. A rather low incidence was found among children who were less than 10 years of age at the time of the exposure which was somewhat peculiar in comparison with that of same generation of non-exposed children, in which the highest incidence is observed. The dura-

TABLE XVIII

TYPE OF LEUKEMIA DEVELOPED IN HIROSHIMA DURING THE PERIOD OF 1946–1962

Distance from hypocenter in meters	Acute[a]	Subacute myeloid	Subacute lumphoid	Chronic myeloid	Chronic lymphoid
Within 500	3	0	0	2	0
501–1000	24 (2)	3	1	17	1
1000–1500	38	1	0	38	0
1501–2000	13 (1)	2	0	11	0
2001–2500	5	0	0	2	1
2501–3000	6	1	0	2	0
3001–3500	2	0	0	1	0
3501–4000	4	0	0	2	0
4001–4500	0	1	0	0	0
4501–5000	3	0	0	0	0
Non-exposed cases	84 (1)	9	0	11	0
Cases entered within a week after explosion[b]	12 (1)	2	1	18	2

[a]Numbers in parentheses indicate cases that were diagnosed definitely as lymphoid-type.
[b]This section was inserted for reference.

TABLE XIX

RATE OF ACUTE AND CHRONIC LEUKEMIA IN HIROSHIMA SURVIVORS BY EXPOSURE DISTANCE

Distance from hypocenter in meters	Acute form[a]	Chronic form	Ratio of acute/chronic
Within 2000	85	69	1 : 0.81
2001–3000	12	5	1 : 0.41
3001–5000	10	3	1 : 0.30
Nonexposed	93	11	1 : 0.12
Mean of all Japan			1 : 0.20–0.17
Cases entered within a week after explosion[b]	13	20	1 : 1.46

[a]Subacute form is included.
[b]This section was inserted for reference.

TABLE XX

Age at exposure	Exposed population estimated[a]	Number of cases of leukemia		Incidence per 100,000		Mean duration between exposure and onset in years	
0–4	1134	10		881.0		7.9	
			20		1038.0		8.0
5–9	791	10		1264.0		8.1	
10–14	817	17		2079.1		13.0	
			33		1335.0		10.3
15–19	1446	16		1105.6		7.6	
20–29	1836	19		1033.6		8.7	
30–39	1924	18		934.2		8.9	
40–49	2034	17		834.7		8.8	
50–59	1243	14		1125.6		10.5	
60 and over	614	6		976.8		6.8	

[a]Figures from ABCC Technical Report (March, 1959, 02–59).

TABLE XXI

Age of exposure	Exposed population estimated[a]	Number of cases of leukemia		Incidence per 100,000		Mean duration between exposure and onset in years	
0–4	10,135	16		157.8		8.0	
			30		170.6		8.6
5–9	7,466	14		189.0		9.3	
10–14	6,564	19		289.0		12.6	
			37		345.9		10.5
15–19	4,132	18		435.6		8.5	
20–29	10,870	30		276.0		8.8	
30–39	12,027	27		224.5		9.6	
40–49	12,311	28		227.4		10.8	
50–59	7,865	21		265.9		9.5	
60 and over	5,154	10		192.0		8.8	

[a]Figures from ABCC Technical Report (March, 1959, 02–59).

tion between exposure and the onset of the disease varied from 7 to 13 years with longest duration in age group of 10 to 14 years.

The incidence of leukemia by sex is given in Table XXII. The ratio of leukemia incidence in the male and female appeared to be 4 : 2.62 among cases exposed within 1500 meters from the hypocenter, while it was 4 : 2.79 among cases exposed at distances of 1501 to 5000 meters from the hypocenter. As the mean ratio of all Japan is approximately 4 : 2.8, it was concluded that there is no significant difference between exposed and nonexposed as far as sex ratio is concerned.

TABLE XXII

SEX DIFFERENCE IN LEUKEMIA INCIDENCE AMONG HIROSHIMA SURVIVORS (1946–1962)

Distance from hypocenter		Exposed population estimated[a]	Number of cases of leukemia	Incidence/ 10^5/ year	Ratio
Less than 1500 meters	Male	4,903	67	80.38	4
	Female	6,936	62	52.57	2.62
1501 to 5000 meters	Male	29,275	28	5.63	4
	Female	40,410	27	3.93	2.79
Total	Male	34,178	95	16.34	4
	Female	47,346	89	11.05	2.71
All Japan	Male				4
	Female				2.8

[a]Figures from ABCC Technical Report (March 1959, 02–59).

Heyssel and associates (1959) also came to the similar conclusion, based on their independent survey, that a great increase in leukemia incidence has been observed among Hiroshima survivors who were exposed within 2000 meters from the hypocenter, and that chronic granulocytic leukemia was predominant in these cases.

An exhaustive survey of Court-Brown and Doll (1957) on the incidence of leukemia in X-ray treated spondylitis patients revealed that the majority of the cases were of the acute myeloid-type. Moloney (1959) observed a similar tendency among cases exposed to therapeutic irradiations. On the contrary, chronic myeloid leukemia predominated among cases exposed to the occupational irradiations. Based mainly on our data on the exposed leukemia and taking their surveys into consideration,

Miyake and Sugano (1962) discussed the possibility that total-body irradiation might contribute to the development of the chronic form of
leukemia while partial-body irradiation might play some role in induction of the acute form. This hypothesis seems to be reasonable in general.
We still assume, however, a possible role of partial-body irradiation
which will contribute to the development of acute leukemia even in the
cases of total-body irradiation. Some acute forms of leukemia seen among
the Hiroshima survivors might come under this category.

On the incidence of leukemia among Nagasaki survivors, many reports have been published by Tomonaga and associates (Tomonaga,
1952, 1953, 1956, 1957a,b, 1958, 1962; Tomonaga et al., 1959a,b; Kageura
et al., 1955, 1956, 1960). According to their surveys during the 13 years
from 1947 to 1959, the total cases of leukemia exposed to the atomic bomb
in Nagasaki was 67 and the incidence per 100,000 of exposed population
per year was 6.0, while the corresponding values of the nonexposed
population was 40 and 1.7, respectively. Although the incidence of leukemia among the exposed population in Nagasaki was not as high as in
Hiroshima, still the value is evidently higher than that for all Japan
(Table XXIII). Regarding the type of leukemia, we find some discrepancies between data for Nagasaki and results of our survey in Hiroshima,
which are probably due to different interpretations of the morphological
features of leukemic cells. According to these studies, the predominant

TABLE XXIII

INCIDENCE OF LEUKEMIA IN RESIDENTS OF NAGASAKI AND HIROSHIMA,
ACCORDING TO DISTANCE FROM HYPOCENTER, 1947–1959

Exposure distance from hypocenter in meters	Nagasaki		Hiroshima[a]	
	Cases	Rate[b]	Cases	Rate[b]
0– 999	6	100	20	100
1000–1499	22	54	40	27
1500–1999	5	10	19	7.1
2000 and over	34	3.4	18	1.8
Total exposed	67	6.0	97	7.0
Nonexposed	40	1.7	53	2.0
Total exposed + nonexposed	107	3.0	150	3.4
Incidence for all Japan, 1947–58	Cases = 20,305		Rate = 1.9	

[a]Hiroshima data from Watanabe et al. (1960).
[b]Rate per 100,000 population per year.

type was granulocytic-type as in Hiroshima, followed by the monocytic-type, while lymphocytic or lymphoid-type was rarely found. Chronic myeloid-type did not evidently increase in cases exposed within 2000 meters from the hypocenter (Table XXIV), chiefly due to the fact that, in Nagasaki, the intensity of radiation, especially neutron radiation, was not as intense as that of Hiroshima. Moreover, the complicated structure of the terrain of Nagasaki makes an analysis more difficult.

TABLE XXIV

DISTRIBUTION OF ALL LEUKEMIA CASES AMONG SURVIVORS EXPOSED TO ATOMIC BOMB RADIATION AT NAGASAKI, BY TYPE AND DISTANCE FROM HYPOCENTER, 1947–1959

Type of leukemia[a]	Exposure distance in meters					Total
	0–999	1000–1499	1500–1999	2000–2999	3000 and over	
AGL	3	17		6	19	45
AML	1	6	1	2	11	21
ALL		4	1	1	6	12
AUL		2	1		6	9
CGL	2	9	3	2	5	21
CLL						
	6	38	6	11	47	108

[a] AGL: Acute granulocytic leukemia; AML: Acute monocytic leukemia; ALL: Acute lymphocytic leukemia; AUL: Acute leukemia, type unspecified; CGL: Chronic granulocytic leukemia; CLL: Chronic lymphocytic leukemia.

2. Incidence of Leukemia among the "Early Entrants"

In Hiroshima, thousands of people entered into the city shortly after the atomic bomb detonation and they stayed there for rescue work, ground clearing, or to obtaining information about their relatives. Of course, estimation of radiation doses received by these people is almost impossible, and there is a tendency to ignore the existence of appreciable residual radioactivity in the city. As already discussed, there are various possible modes of radioactivity being given to the human body and in cases of B, D, F, and G, as indicated in Table XI, radiation injury might have occurred not only to exposed people but also to early entrants. Concerning the mode of irradiation which possibly confers delayed effects to early entrants, we have emphasized the importance of factor F in the paragraph of the introduction of this section. In fact, it has been known that some of the early entrants showed various acute radiation syndromes such as hemorrhagic diatheses and epilation. Therefore, the incidence of leukemia among these early entrants has been investigated by us as well. In order to carry out an accurate survey on the leukemia incidence in early entrants, it was essential to ascertain their exact number, which was very difficult. However, a dependable figure was provided by a survey concurrent with the general census taken by Hiroshima City officials in 1960, shown in Table XXV.

TABLE XXV

NUMBER OF THE EARLY ENTRANTS IN HIROSHIMA[a]

Interval between explosion and entrance in days	Number of early entrants	Accumulated number of early entrants
0	5,784	
within 3	20,015	25,799
within 7	11,001	36,800
within 14	7,326	44,126

[a]Figures from general census, October 1, 1960.

The incidence and death rate of leukemia among early entrants are shown in Table XXVI. It is remarkable that of 39 cases 27 were derived from people who entered the city within 3 days following the explosion. Since the number of people who entered the city within 3 days following the atomic bomb explosion was estimated as 25,799, the incidence of leukemia per 100,000 early entrants per year comes to 8.05. Although this figure is not as high as that of people directly exposed within 5000 meters from the hypocenter, it greatly exceeds that of the nonexposed population.

These leukemia cases are classified by type of disease as shown in

TABLE XXVI

INCIDENCE AND MORTALITY OF LEUKEMIA DEVELOPED AMONG THE EARLY ENTRANTS INTO HIROSHIMA AFTER EXPLOSION

	Cases entered within 3 days	Cases entered within 1 week	Cases entered within 2 weeks
Population	25,799	36,800	44,126
Number of cases of leukemia	27	32	39
Incidence per 100,000 per year	8.05	6.68	6.79
Number of deaths from leukemia	23	28	35
Deathrate per 100,000 per year	6.85	5.85	6.10

Table XXVII. The ratio of types in these cases is rather unique. There were 18 cases of acute leukemia including 3 subacute against 21 of chronic leukemia. The ratio of leukemia incidence by sex was studied among the early entrants who had entered the city within 1 week after the explosion. In these cases, a significant increase in female population was evident and the ratio of the male and female was 4 : 4.19, which is rather unusual compared with those directly exposed or all Japan. The meaning of this has not been determined. According to our survey, no leukemia had developed among these people until 1950. Ever since then,

TABLE XXVII

TYPE OF LEUKEMIA DEVELOPED AMONG THE EARLY ENTRANTS INTO HIROSHIMA AFTER EXPLOSION (1950–1962)

	Acute	Subacute myeloid	Subacute lymphoid	Chronic myeloid	Chronic lymphoid	Total
Male	12	2	0	12	2	28
Female	3	0	1	6	1	11
	15	2	1	18	3	39
Number of cases entered within 1 week	11	1	1	17	2	32
Number of cases entered within 3 days	10	1	1	13	2	27

however, leukemia has begun to appear among them, showing a slight upward curve every year. In other words, it might be speculated that the incidence will reach a maximum a few years later than those of directly exposed cases. Although we know little about the explanation of the high incidence of chronic leukemia in these cases, it brings to mind the fact that the same tendency has been observed in cases exposed within 2000 meters from the hypocenter. Thus, the leukemias occurring among early entrants could be considered as possessing the same character of those occurring among heavily irradiated people.

In an attempt to demonstrate the possible role of internal irradiation in induction of leukemia among early entrants, we performed a series of experiments in which small doses of diverse radioactive isotopes such as P^{32}, Sr^{89}, or Ce^{144} were administered to mice. As expected, leukemias developed in some of the experimental animals after a latent period. Among these, the incidence was highest in P^{32}-treated mice, and most of the induced leukemias were of the myeloid-type (Watanabe, 1955, 1957c,d, 1958, 1962b).

3. Correlation of Incidence of Leukemia and Exposure to Radiation

Correlation of the incidence of leukemia and exposure to ionizing radiation in human beings has been definitely established today based on the following five facts: (a) high incidence of leukemia among physicians, radiologists, and X-ray technicians; (b) high incidence of leukemia among people exposed to the atomic bombs in Hiroshima and Nagasaki; (c) high incidence of leukemia among X-ray-treated ankylosing spondylitis patients in Great Britain; (d) high incidence of leukemia among X-ray-treated infants with enlarged thymus glands; and (e) high incidence of malignant neoplasia (including leukemia) among X-ray-treated infants in utero. Among reports involved in the first category, those of Henshaw and Hawkins (1944) and March (1944, 1950) have been often cited in the literature; more recently, Lewis (1958) stated that from 1938-1952, 17 leukemia deaths in radiologists in the United States were confirmed, and after correction for age distribution it was found that the incidence was about 5 times more frequent as compared with the whole population. The investigation of Court-Brown and Doll (1957) is the unique one which constitutes the third category. Here, among 13,352 cases of ankylosing spondylitis treated with X-ray in the United Kingdom from 1935 to 1954, they found 37 proved and 4 probable cases of leukemia and 4 cases of aplastic anemia, while the expected cases of leukemia was 2.9 and that of aplastic anemia was 0.3. So the incidences of leukemia and aplastic anemia were very high in the patients treated with X-rays as compared with the corresponding nontreated population. Among 30 acute cases, unclassified-type was found in 7 cases, myeloid-type in 14, lymphatic-type in 2, and monocytic-type in 7. Among 7 chronic cases, 6 cases were myeloid-type and 1 was lymphatic. Besides these cases, 2 unclassified myeloid cases and 2 unspecified-type cases were also recorded. Thus, the leukemia that developed among X-ray-treated spondylitis patients was predominately acute leukemia, while only approximately 15–17% of total cases were counted as chronic leukemia. As to the type of leukemia, 22 cases were myeloid, 7 were monocytic, 4 unclassified, and only 4 were lymphatic. From these data, we can expect that therapeutic partial-body irradiation may contribute much to the development of acute rather than chronic leukemia; after such irradiations, by which the bone marrow of the spine was severely injured, mostly myeloid leukemia developed. In each case, data concerning the doses received were adequately provided, furnishing good material for study of the incidence-dose relationship of leukemia induced by radiation, and comparison with leukemia cases following exposure to the atomic bomb. When the mean veretebral marrow dose was 500–1250 rads, the relationship between incidence of leukemia and mean vertebral marrow dose was constant in the irradiated spondylitis cases, but under 500 rads, the question of whether such linearity exists between incidence and dose remains unsettled. Similarly, in regard to leukemia cases following the atomic bomb exposure, many investigators are inclined to favor the linearity theory of incidence-dose relationship. However, at present, this relationship has not been convincingly established.

Under the fourth category, an increase of leukemia has been observed in children given radiation of the thymus as reported by Simpson and associates (Simpson et al., 1955; Simpson and Hempelmann, 1957; Simpson, 1959). They found 21 cases of malignancy instead of 3.6 expected among 2393 treated children, and 9 confirmed and 1 unconfirmed leukemia instead of 1 expected, while in 2722 untreated siblings they found no significant difference between expected and observed incidence of malignancy or leukemia. According to their latest report (Pifer et al., 1963), no new cases of leukemia have occurred since their previous survey although several cases of other neoplasms have been observed. Since there are some reports in which no significant differences were found between treated and nontreated siblings, further studies are needed to confirm this relationship definitely. Concerning the fifth category, Stewart et al. (1958) made extensive investigations on 677 children under 10 years of age, who were certified as having died of leukemia in England; the authors found a higher incidence among children whose mothers had diagnostic X-ray pelvimetry during pregnancy than children from nonexposed mothers. Ford et al. (1959) also came to the same conclusions as Stewart et al. However, studies of Court-Brown and associates (Court-Brown et al., 1960; Court-Brown and Doll, 1960) following up 39,166 children whose mothers had been irradiated in the abdominal or pelvic regions during pregnancy, revealed that 9 were found to have died of leukemia, instead of the expected number estimated to be 10.5. Consequently, the evaluation of these conflicting data needs further investigation.

Some papers dealing with induction of leukemia by ionizing radiation in experimental animals have already been mentioned. Pertinent reviews and articles published thereafter are as follows: Furth and Lorenz (1954), Furth and Upton (1954), Kaplan (1952, 1954), Kaplan et al. (1954), Loutit (1957), Upton (1959), Furth et al. (1959), Upton et al. (1960), Kaplan (1959), and Watanabe and Hirose (1963).

4. Myelofibrosis

Among exposed persons in Hiroshima and Nagasaki, Yamamoto (1957) found 3 autopsy cases of myelofibrosis from Hiroshima and 1 autopsy case from Nagasaki. In 2 cases, he found hyperplasia of all blood-forming elements with fibrosis in the bone marrow, and he considered that these cases were consistent with those of panmyelosis. In the bone marrow of the third case, proliferation of granulocytic, erythroid, and thrombocytic series was noted with marked fibrosis. Proliferating immature granulocytic cell clumps were found along the bone trabeculae, and these changes were thought to be preleukemia. In the fourth case, the bone marrow showed the mosaic-like pattern of aplastic, fibrotic, and hyperplastic areas, and this case was thought to be one of atypical leukemia. The findings of these 4 cases differed from those of nonexposed patients, and, although it was impossible to say definitely that this was an effect of the atomic bomb, some relation was suspected. Recently Yamamoto and Anderson (1963) reported 12 cases of myelofibrosis which included the 4 cases previously reported. In the 12 cases, 8 were typical, 1 was considered atypical, and the remaining 3 were thought to be transitional to leukemia. Furthermore, 10 of these 12 cases were derived from the persons exposed to the atomic bomb. The mean distance from the hypocenter in these 10 exposed cases was 1190 meters, and there was a correlation between incidence of myelofibrosis and distance from the hypocenter. Moreover, the incidence of myelofibrosis in exposed persons was approximately 5 times more frequent than in nonexposed persons, and 18 times more frequent than the mean value for all Japan. Therefore, it is very probable that radiation plays an important role in the induction of such disturbances. Clinically, anemia and splenomegaly were the chief complaints, with a blood picture of leukoerythroblastosis accompanied by erythroblasts in the blood stream in all cases. In the bone marrow, there was moderate or extensive hyperplasia complicated by definite hyperplasia of the megakaryocytes. When the fibrosis was extensive, granulo- and erythropoiesis were involved. Without exception, splenomegaly and moderate or distinct extramedullary hematopoiesis were observed. Hematopoiesis was more pronounced in the sinusoids than in the portal areas. Twelve cases were classified as the proliferative, extensive, fibrosing-type, and Yamamoto and Anderson thought that, from this proliferative-type, leukemia might develop, although they mentioned the possibility that it also might develop from the fibrotic-type. It was also postulated that myelofibrosis and myeloid leukemia might develop from polycythemia vera. Consequently, they expected the development of leukemia both from fibrotic and proliferative-types. In connection with the severe anemia observed among exposed persons during the early stage, the relation between anemia, myelofibrosis, and leukemia should be studied more extensively in the future. In some cases of leukemia of exposed persons, anemic and/or myelofibrotic processes may precede development of leukemia, but we consider that in other exposed cases leukemia may develop without preceding severe anemia or myelofibrosis.

5. Malignant Lymphomas

A possible role of atomic radiation in induction of reticulum cell sarcoma, which is one of malignant tumors derived from lymphatic tissue, should not be neglected.

We have published a paper dealing with this problem (Watanabe, 1957a) in which several reported cases were reviewed. The original foci of most of these reported cases were observed in the cervical and mediastinal regions. Whether the peculiarity of location was due to the fact that the region was nakedly exposed or that the region was a pathway of radioactive substances entering into the body has not been determined. But no positive relation has yet been demonstrated statistically between exposed and nonexposed individuals, and a further analysis with more cases will be necessary before reaching the final conclusion.

F. HEMORRHAGIC DISORDERS

The etiology of hemorrhagic diathesis is complicated and various causative factors are involved. Appearance of hemorrhagic diathesis seems to be due to one or more of the following disturbances: (a) vasopathy, due mainly to disturbance of the blood capillary; (b) thrombopathy, due to disturbance of the thrombocyte series; and (c) coagulopathy, due to deficiency of plasma-promoting factor or excess of plasma-inhibiting factor.

Some of these disturbances are commonly induced by heavy irradiation, and the development of hemorrhagic diathesis during acute and subacute stages of the atomic bomb injuries was one of the prominent findings pointed out by many investigators. However, the question of whether hemorrhagic diathesis has been observed as a delayed effect has not been adequately answered, and only a few reports can be found dealing with this problem. Among these, a survey made by Kono (1957) seems to be valuable in this respect; hematological findings with Hiroshima survivors were compared to those with nonexposed individuals 11 years after the atomic bomb explosion. He studied the bleeding and clotting time, thrombocyte count, capillary resistance, plasma prothrombin time, and serum calcium content of 49 individuals who showed hemorrhagic diatheses. All of them were under 55 years of age, and those who showed signs of hypertension, familial disposition, apparent clinical abnormalities, or who had a history of hemorrhagic diathesis prior to exposure were excluded from his survey; 40 out of 49 cases studied (81.5%) were exposed at less than 2000 meters from the hypocenter and 38 cases

(75.5%) had acute radiation syndrome. Subcutaneous petechiae were found on the extremities and trunk in 28 cases of which 18 showed a slight prolongation of bleeding time; of 11 with thrombocytopenia, the bleeding time was also prolonged in 8 cases. As to the coagulation time, a slight prolongation was demonstrated in 4 out of 28 exposed individuals, while it was within normal range in 10 nonexposed controls. Capillary fragility was noted in 15 out of 28 cases who had apparent petechiae. Only 2 cases showed a slight prolongation of the whole plasma prothrombin time. The serum calcium content were normal in all examined cases.

From the above-mentioned results, Kono (1957) concluded that hemorrhagic diathesis observed among Hiroshima survivors 11 years after exposure to atomic radiation might be attributable either to thrombocytopenia or capillary fragility, or to a combination of both, with some exceptions the cause of which has not yet been established.

IV. Injuries of Japanese Fishermen Caused by a Hydrogen Bomb Test in Bikini Atoll

A. Introduction

An enormous explosion took place in the Bikini atoll in the Southern Pacific in the early morning of March 1, 1954. It was announced by the United States Atomic Energy Commission that it was due to a thermonuclear test explosion. A Japanese fishing boat, the 5th *Fukuryu-maru*, with a crew of 23, who were fishing at the time of the explosion, was located about 140 km away from the hypocenter and was covered with radioactive ashes produced by the explosion. The falling of the ashes on the boat began 3 hours after the explosion and lasted for about 5 hours. The falling ashes stuck to the body surfaces of all crew members, especially on exposed portions. They gave up fishing immediately and returned to their home port, Yaizu (approximately 160 km west of Tokyo) 2 weeks after the accident. They were unaware of the dangerous effect of the ashes. According to a physical assay, the ashes contained about 30 diverse nuclear fission products and small amounts of induced radioactive substances (Tsuzuki, 1956). The radioactivity of the ashes at 7.00 A.M. of the day of explosion was estimated to be approximately 1.4 curies/gm by a calculation of Kimura (1956).

Radiation injuries observed among the crew might have been induced by various modes, such as (a) external irradiation due to the ashes on their body surfaces (mainly beta-irradiation); (b) external irradiation due to ashes on the deck and other parts of the boat (mainly gamma-irradiation); and (c) internal irradiation due to radioactive substances that entered the body through the respiratory tract, alimentary tract, wounds, or ingestion of contaminated drinking water and food (mainly beta- and gamma-irradiation).

B. CLINICAL COURSE

According to an excellent review of Tsuzuki (1956a), some of the crew complained of the development of acute radiation syndromes (nausea, vomiting, anorexia, headache, or painful eyes) on the day of exposure. In 3 days, some of them noticed the development of reddish lesions with swelling on their faces, necks, and hands, that had been exposed to the ashes, and some complained of itchy sensations and small vesicles. In the next few days, the color of the lesions became darker and the vesicles eroded. Many of them also complained of lassitude, fever sensations, diarrhea, or epilation. Some of them developed hemorrhagic diatheses with gingival bleeding. After their arrival, all members of the crew were admitted to leading Japanese hospitals and were treated by specialists. The symptoms gradually lessened with occasional complaints of anorexia, fever, insomnia, and diarrhea or loss of weight in some cases. However, one of crew died on September 23, 1954, that is, 207 days after the exposure to the radioactive ashes; examination revealed severe damage to the liver and other tissues (Ohashi et al., 1955; Miyake and Ohashi, 1956). It has been reported that the rest of the crew have been in good health in recent years.

C. HEMATOLOGICAL CHANGES

Several detailed reports on clinical, hematological, and pathological findings are available (Mikamo et al., 1956; Shimizu et al., 1956; Tsuge and Ohi, 1956), and only brief hematological findings will be described here.

The most conspicuous change was observed in the leukocyte count. Progressive decrease of the leukocyte count occurred after admission, and reached a minimum approximately 1 month following exposure. Some cases showed less than 2000 white cells with the lowest value being 800, and all of the cases had fallen at least once to less than 4000. The leukopenia gradually ceased and a normal level with some fluctuation was reached about 1 year after exposure. In the early period, a shift to the left of neutrophils, which was accompanied by the occasional appearance of metamyelocytes or myelocytes, was noticed in the peripheral blood. Monocytosis was seen in almost all the cases, and eosinophilia was noted in some.

There were mild or moderate anemias, with erythrocyte counts of less than 400×10^4 during the early period. The minimum value was seen in the third month, followed by gradual recovery and a return to normal by the seventh month, with some subnormal cases.

Thrombocytopenia with mild hemorrhagic diatheses and prolongations of bleeding or clotting times developed in the critical period. The recovery from thrombocytopenia was not vigorous.

The bone marrow was completely aplastic during the critical period with a depletion of parenchymal cells and a proliferation of plasma cells and reticular cells. The nucleated cells in the bone marrow had fallen to approximately 10,000 or less in most cases. The depletion was protracted, and most of the cases were still below normal even 1 year after exposure. As to the morphological changes in the blood cells, various degenerative signs were noted in every element of the peripheral blood. Morphological abnormalities in immature granulocytes and erythroblasts were also seen in regenerating bone marrow.

Although all of the Bikini victims, except the one fatality, have been restored to health and no obvious delayed effects have been observed, they should be kept under strict medical supervision, as are the Hiroshima and Nagasaki survivors, in view of the fact that they have received heavy internal irradiation.

Not only the Japanese fishermen, but also the Marshallese on Rongelap atoll (64 persons), Ailinginae atoll (18 persons), and Utirik atoll (157 persons), and the Americans on Rongeric atoll (28 persons) were exposed to fallout from the hydrogen bomb of the same test explosion, and they were examined by an American investigation team (Cronkite *et al.*, 1956); they have been under follow-up observations since then.

V. Conclusion

Hematological studies of human beings exposed to atomic bomb radiation are of major significance for two reasons. In the first place, since hematopoietic tissues are extremely sensitive to radiation, it is natural that radiation effects are immediately and precisely reflected in hematopoietic tissue. Consequently, the study of hematological changes is important in clarifying the mechanism of the somatic effect of radiation. In the second place, in order to elucidate the mechanism of radiation carcinogenesis, hematological investigations have been considered essential. In other tissues and organs, follow-up studies of early radiation injuries that precede the development of neoplasms are extremely difficult. At the present time, with the exception of persons exposed to the atomic bomb, only fragmentary knowledge about radiation injuries, including radiation carcinogenesis, in human beings is available. Therefore, hematological investigations of the population exposed to ionizing radiation of the atomic bomb should contribute very much to the welfare of the human population as a whole. However, we are aware that much remains to be done before we can draw definite conclusions.

REFERENCES

Amano, S. (1953). *In* "Genshibakudan Saigai Chosa Hokokushu," Part II, pp. 895–949. Nihon Gakujitsu Shinkokai, Tokyo.

Amano, S. (1956). *In* "Research in the Effects and Influences of the Nuclear Bomb Test Explosions," pp. 1725–1766. Nihon Gakujitsu Shinkokai, Tokyo.

Atomic Bomb Casualty Commission (1955). Semi-Annual Report, January–June 1954, Part I.

Bender, M. A., and Gooch, P. C. (1962). *Radiation Res.* **16**, 44.

Bloom, M. A. (1948). *In* "Histopathology of Irradiation from External and Internal Sources" (W. Bloom, ed.), Natl. Nuclear Energy Ser., Div. IV, Chapter 6, pp. 162–242. McGraw-Hill, New York.

Clemedson, C., and Nelson, A. (1960). *In* "Mechanism in Radiobiology" (M. Errera and A. Forssberg, eds.), Vol. II, Chapter 2, pp. 95–205. Academic Press, New York.

Court-Brown, W. M., and Doll, R. (1957). *Med. Res. Council Spec. Rept. Ser.* **295**, 1–135.

Court-Brown, W. M., and Doll, R. (1960). *Proc. Roy. Soc. Med.* **53**, 761.

Court-Brown, W. M., Doll, R., and Hill, A. B. (1960). *Brit. Med. J.* **2**, 1539.

Cronkite, E. P., Jacobs, G. J., Brecher, G., and Dillard, G. (1952). *Am. J. Roentgenol.* **67**, 796.

Cronkite, E. P., Bond, V. P., and Dunham, C. L. (1956). *In* "Some Effects of Ionizing Radiation on Human Beings," pp. 1–106. U. S. Atomic Energy Comm., Washington, D. C.

De Bruyn, P. P. H. (1948). *In* "Histopathology of Irradiation from External and Internal Sources" (W. Bloom, ed.), Natl. Nuclear Energy Ser., Div. IV, Chapter 8, pp. 348–445. McGraw-Hill, New York.

Dobson, B. I., and Chupp, M. M. (1957). *Proc. Soc. Exptl. Biol. Med.* **95**, 360.

Dunlap, C. E. (1942). *Arch. Pathol.* **34**, 562.

Folley, J. H., Borges, W., and Yamawaki, T. (1952). *Am. J. Med.* **13**, 311.

Ford, D. D., Paterson, J. C. S., and Trueting, W. L. (1959). *J. Natl. Cancer Inst.* **22**, 1093.

Furth, J. (1934). *Proc. Soc. Exptl. Biol. Med.* **31**, 923.

Furth, J. (1946). *Physiol. Rev.* **26**, 47.

Furth, J., and Furth, O. B. (1936). *Am. J. Cancer* **28**, 54.

Furth, J., and Lorenz, E. (1954). *In* "Radiation Biology" (A. Hollaender, ed.), Vol. I, Chapter 18, pp. 1145–1201. McGraw-Hill, New York.

Furth, J., and Upton, A. C. (1954). *In* "Leukemia Research" (G. E. W. Wolstenholme, ed.), pp. 146–161. Churchill, London.

Furth, J., Seibold, H. R., and Rathbone, R. R. (1933). *Am. J. Cancer* **19**, 521.

Furth, J., Upton, A. C., and Kimball, A. W. (1959). *Radiation Res. Suppl.* **1**, 243.

Haigh, M. V., and Paterson, E. (1956). *Brit. J. Radiol.* **29**, 148.

Harada, T., and Ishida, M. (1960). *J. Natl. Cancer Inst.* **25**, 1253.

Hatano, S., and Watanuki, T. (1953). *In* "Scientific Reports of Research on Casualty of Atomic Bomb," p. 621. Japan Society for the Promotion of Science, Tokyo.

Heineke, H. (1903). *Muench. Med. Wochschr.* **50**, 2090.

Henshaw, P. S. (1944). *Radiology* **43**, 279.

Henshaw, P. S., and Hawkins, J. W. (1944). *J. Natl. Cancer Inst.* **4**, 339.

Heuper, W. D. (1934). *Folia Haematol.* **52**, 167.

Heyssel, R., Brill, A. B., Woodbury, L. A., Nishimura, E. T., Ghose, T., Hoshino, T., and Yamasaki, M. (1959). *ABCC Tech. Rept. Ser.* **02–59**, 1.

Hibino, S. (1956). *Sogo Kenkyuhokoku Shuroku Igaku Oyobi Yakugakuhen* **30**, 249.

Hibino, S. (1957). *Sogo Kenkyuhokoku Shuroku Igaku Oyobi Yakugakuhen* **31**, 209.

Hirose, K., and Fujino, S. (1950). *Acta Soc. Ophthalmol. Japon.* **54**, 449.

Hirose, F., Yamada, A., and Yamamoto, T. (1954). *Acta Haematol. Japon.* **17**, 307.

Jackson, D. P., Cronkite, E. P., Jacobs, G. J., and Behrens, C. F. (1952). *Am. J. Physiol.* **169**, 208.

Jacobson, L. O. (1954). *In* "Radiation Biology" (A. Hollaender, ed.), Vol. I, pp. 1029–1090. McGraw-Hill, New York.

Kageura, N., and Tomonaga, M. (1955). *Sogo Kenkyuhokoku Shuroku Igaku Oyobi Yakugakuhen* **29**, 418.

Kageura, N., Tomonaga, M., and Takamori, M. (1956). *In* "Research in the Effects and Influences of the Nuclear Bomb Test Explosions," pp. 1523–1525. Nihon Gakujitsu Shinkokai, Tokyo.

Kageura, N., Osajima, S., and Tomonaga, M. (1960). *Acta Med. Nagasakiensia* **5**, 1.

Kajitani, T., and Hatano, S. (1953). *In* "Genshibakudan Saigai Chosa Hokokushu," Part I, pp. 522–601. Nihon Gakujitsu Shinkokai, Tokyo.

Kaplan, H. S. (1952). *Acta Unio Intern. Contra Cancrum* **2**, 849.

Kaplan, H. S. (1954). *Cancer Res.* **14**, 535.

Kaplan, H. S. (1959). *In* "Radiation Biology and Cancer," pp. 289–302. Univ. of Texas Press, Austin, Texas.

Kaplan, H. S., Nagareda, C. S., and Brown, M. B. (1954). *Recent Progr. Hormone Res.* **10**, 293–338.

Kikuchi, T. (1957). *Sogo Kenkyuhokoku Shuroku Igaku Oyobi Yakugakuhen* **31**, 209.

Kikuchi, T., and Kimoto, S. (1953). *In* "Genshibakudan Saigai Chosa Hokokushu," pp. 1580–1642. Nihon Gakujitsu Shinkokai, Tokyo.

Kimura, K. (1956). *In* "Research in the Effects and Influences of the Nuclear Bomb Test Explosions," Part I, pp. 491–495, 497–519, 521–527. Nihon Gakujitsu Shinkokai, Tokyo.

Kono, Y. (1957). *Acta Haematol. Japon.* **20**, Suppl. 160.

Krebs, C., Rask-Nielsen, H. C., and Wagner, A, (1930). *Acta Radiol. Suppl.* **10**, 1.

Lange, R. D., Moloney, W. C., and Yamawaki, T. (1954). *Blood* **9**, 574.

Lewis, E. B. (1958). *Science* **125**, 965.

Liebow, A. A., Warren, S., and DeCoursey, E. D. (1949). *Am. J. Pathol.* **25**, 853.

Lorenz, H., Heston, W. E., Eschenbrenner, A. B., and Deringer, M. K. (1947). *Radiology* **49**, 269.

Loutit, J. F. (1957). *In* "Advances in Radiobiology" (G. C. DeHevesy, A. G. Foessbery, and J. D. Abbat, eds.), pp. 388–396. Oliver & Boyd, Edinburgh and London.

March, H. C. (1944). *Radiology* **43**, 275.

March, H. C. (1950). *Am. J. Med. Sci.* **220**, 282.

Mashimo, S., Kikuchi, T., and Funaoka, S. (1953). *In* "Genshibakudan Saigai Chosa Hokokushu," Vol. II, pp. 769–804. Nihon Gakujitsu Shinkokai, Tokyo.

Masuda Y. (1956). *Ganka Rinsho Iho* **50**, 245.

Mikamo, Y., Miyoshi, K., Shimizu, K., and Ishikawa, K. (1956). *In* "Research in the Effects and Influences of the Nuclear Bomb Test Explosion," Part II, pp. 1313–1331. Nihon Gakujitsu Shinkokai, Tokyo.

Miyake, M. (1953a). *Rinsho* **6**, 38.

Miyake, M. (1953b). *Ketsuekigaku Togikai Hokoku* **5**, 375.

Miyake, M., and Ohashi, S. (1956). *In* "Research in the Effects and Influences of the Nuclear Bomb Explosions," Part II, pp. 1767–1789. Nihon Gakujitsu Shinkokai, Tokyo.

Miyake, M., and Sugano, H. (1956). *In* "Research in the Effects and Influences of the Nuclear Bomb Test Explosions," Part II, pp. 1767–1789. Nihon Gakujitsu Shinkokai, Tokyo.

Miyake, M., and Sugano, H. (1962). *Kenkyu Hokoku Shuroku Hoshasen Eikyohen Showa 36 Nendo* 65.

Moloney, W. C. (1959). *In* "Radiation Biology and Cancer," pp. 310–321. Univ. of Texas Press, Austin, Texas.

Moloney, W. C., and Kastenbaum, M. A. (1955). *Science* **121**, 308.

Moloney, W. C., and Lange, R. D. (1954). *Blood* **9**, 663.

Murray, R. G. (1948). *In* "Histopathology of Irradiation from External and Internal Sources" (W. Bloom, ed.), Natl. Nuclear Energy Ser., Div. IV, Chapter 7, pp. 243–347. McGraw-Hill, New York.

Nakao, K. (1953a). *Rinsho* **6**, 87.

Nakao, K. (1953b). *Ketsuekigaku Togikai Hokoku* **5**, 361.

Nishida, S. (1956). *J. Hiroshima Med. Assoc. Original Ser.* **4**, (8B), 886, 917.

Nishida, S. (1957). *J. Hiroshima Med. Assoc. Spec. Ser.* **10**, 35, 64.

Ohashi, S., Hashimoto, K., and Fukushima, N. (1955). *Iryo* **9**, 46.

Ord, M. G., and Stocken, L. A. (1953). *Physiol. Rev.* **33**, 356.

Oughtersen, A. W., and Warren, S. (1956). *In* "Medical Effects of the Atomic Bomb in Japan," Natl. Nuclear Energy Ser., Div. VIII, Chapter 6, pp. 191–284. McGraw-Hill, New York.

Patt, H. M., and Brues, A. M. (1954). *In* "Radiation Biology" (A. Hollaender, ed.), Vol. I, Chapter 15, pp. 959–1028. McGraw-Hill, New York.

Pifer, J. W., Toyooka, E. T., Murray, R. W., Ames, W. R., and Hempelmann, L. H. (1963). *J. Natl. Cancer Inst.* **31**, 1333.

Prosser, C. L., Painter, E. E., Lisco, H., Brues, A. M., Jacobson, L. O., and Swift, M. N. (1947). *Radiology* **49**, 299.

Shigeto, F. (1955). *Sogo Kenkyuhokoku Shuroku, Igaku Oyobi Yakugakuhen* **29**, 2442.

Shimizu, K., Ishikawa, K., Saito, K., and Nakamura, K. (1956). *In* "Research in the Effects and Influences of the Nuclear Bomb Test Explosions," Part II, pp. 1333–1351. Nihon Gakujitsu Shinkokai, Tokyo.

Shirabe, R. (1953). *Gakujitsu Geppo Bessatsu Shiryo* **41**, 16.

Simpson, C. L. (1959). *In* "Radiation Biology and Cancer," pp. 336–346. Univ. of Texas Press, Austin, Texas.

Simpson, C. L., and Hempelmann, L. H. (1957). *Cancer* **10**, 42.

Simpson, C. L., Hempelmann, L. H., and Fuller, L. M. (1955). *Radiology* **64**, 840.

Sinskey, R. M. (1955). *Am. J. Ophthalmol.* **39**, 285.

Stewart, A., Webb, J., and Hewitt, D. (1958). *Brit. Med. J.* **1**, 1495.

536 SUSUMU WATANABE

Tabuchi, A. (1956). *Sogo Kenkyuhokoku Shuroku Igaku Oyobi Yakugakuhen* **30**, 256.

Tamagawa, C. (1950). *Trans. Japan Pathol. Soc.* **39**, 300.

Tamagawa, C., Sasaki, T., and Yokoyama, K. (1951). *Gann* **42**, 163.

Töppner, R. (1941). *Z. Ges. Exptl. Med.* **109**, 369.

Tomonaga, M. (1952). *J. Japan Soc. Internal Med.* **41**, 393.

Tomonaga, M. (1953). *Shindan To Chiryo* **41**, 38.

Tomonaga, M. (1956). *In* "Research in the Effects and Influences of the Nuclear Bomb Test Explosions," Part II, pp. 1531–1533. Nihon Gakujitsu Shinkokai, Tokyo.

Tomonaga, M. (1957a). *Konnichi no Igaku* **36**, 64.

Tomonaga, M. (1957b). *Sogo Kenkyuhokoku Shuroku Igaku Oyobi Yakugakuhen* **31**, 209.

Tomonaga, M. (1958). *Sogo Kenkyuhokoku Shuroku Igaku Oyobi Yakugakuhen* **32**, 129, 479.

Tomonaga, M. (1962). *Bull. World Health Organ.* **26**, 619.

Tomonaga, M., Amamoto, K., and Watanabe, B. (1956). *In* "Research in the Effects and Influences of the Nuclear Bomb Test Explosions" Part II, pp. 1527–1529. Nihon Gakujitsu Shinkokai, Tokyo.

Tomonaga, M., Itoga, T., and Watanabe, B. (1959a). *Acta Haematol. Japon.* **22**, Suppl. (2), 834.

Tomonaga, M., Brill, A. B., Heyssel, R., and Itoga, T. (1959b). *ABCC Tech. Rept.* **1159**, 1.

Tsuge, Y., and Ohi, T. (1956). *In* "Research in the Effects and Influences of the Nuclear Bomb Test Explosions," Part II, pp. 1309–1311. Nihon Gakujitsu Shinkokai, Tokyo.

Tsuzuki, M. (1951). *In* "Scientific Reports of Researches on Casualty of Atomic Bomb," Summary Part, pp. 1–49. Japan Society for the Promotion of Science, Tokyo.

Tsuzuki, M. (1954). "Atomic Bomb Injury from Medical Point of View." Igaku Shoin, Tokyo.

Tsuzuki, M. (1956a). *In* "Research in the Effects and Influences of the Nuclear Bomb Test Explosions," Part II, pp. 1287–1304. Nihon Gakujitsu Shinkokai, Tokyo.

Tsuzuki, M. (1956b). *In* "Research in the Effects and Influences of the Nuclear Bomb Test Explosions," Part II, pp. 1463–1467. Nihon Gakujitsu Shinkokai, Tokyo.

Upton, A. C. (1959). *In* "Ciba Foundation Symposium on Carcinogenesis, Mechanism of Action" (G. E. W. Wolstenholme and M. O'Connor, eds.), pp. 249–273. Churchill, London.

Upton, A. C., Kimball, A. W., Furth, J., Christenberry K. W., and Benedict, W. H. (1960). *Cancer Res.* **20**, 1.

Valentine, W. N. (1951). *Pamphlet Box, D#1, Atomic Bomb Casualty Commission.*

Wada, N., Yamada, A., and Hirose, F. (1957). *Acta Haematol. Japon.* **20**, 297.

Wakisaka, G. (1153). *Ketsuekigaku Togikai Hokoku* **5**, 346.

Wald, N. (1957). *Acta Haematol. Japon.* **21**, Suppl. 152.

Wald, N. (1958a). *Proc. 6th Intern. Congr. Haematol., Boston, 1956* p. 382.

Wald, N. (1958b). *Science* **127**, 699.

Watanabe, S. (1953a). *Kotsu Igaku* **7**, 1.

Watanabe, S. (1953b). *Ketsuekigaku Togikai Hokoku* **5**, 402.

Watanabe, S. (1955). *Acta Haematol. Japon.* **18**, 508.

Watanabe, S. (1957a). *Sogo Igaku* **14**, 924.

Watanabe, S. (1957b). *Gazz. Sanit.* **10**, 507.

Watanabe, S. (1957c). *Gakujitsu Geppo* **10**, 57.

Watanabe, S. (1957d). *Trans. Japan. Pathol. Soc.* **46**, 183.

Watanabe, S. (1958). *Pathol. Biol.* **34**, 1833.

Watanabe, S. (1960). *Proc. 7th Intern. Congr. Haematol., Rome, 1958* p. 245.

Watanabe, S. (1961). *J. Radiation Res.* **2**, 131.

Watanabe, S. (1962a). *Proc. 8th Intern. Congr. Haematol., Tokyo, 1960* p. 19.

Watanabe, S. (1962b). *Proc. 8th Intern. Congr. Haematol., Tokyo, 1960* p. 444.

Watanabe, S. (1964). *Proc. 9th Intern. Congr. Haematol., Mexico City,* in press.

Watanabe, S., and Hirose, F. (1963). *In* "Nihon Ketsuekigaku Zensho" (S. Amano, ed.), Part 5, pp. 523–542. Maruzen, Tokyo.

Watanabe, S., and Ito, T. (1959). *Acta Haematol. Japon.* **22**, 272.

Watanabe, S., Wago, M., and Ito, T. (1958). *Acta. Haematol. Japon.* **21**, 301.

Watanabe, S., Ito, T., and Matsubayashi, Y. (1960). *J. Radiation Res.* **1**, 81.

Yamada, A., Yokoro, K., and Wada, N. (1956). *Acta Haematol. Japon.* **19**, 248.

Yamamoto, T. (1957). *Acta Haematol. Japon.* **20**, 59.

Yamamoto, T., and Anderson, R. E. (1963). *Acta Haematol. Japon.* **26**, 373.

Yamamoto, T., Hirose, F., and Himeno, T. (1953). *Acta Haematol. Japon.* **16**, 89.

Yamawaki, T. (1953). *Ketsuekigaku Togikai Hokoku* **5**, 387.

Yamawaki, T. (1954). *Acta Haematol. Japon.* **17**, 345.

Yokoro, K., Hirose, F., and Yamamoto, T. (1955). *Acta Haematol. Japon.* **18**, 254.

Yokoro, K., Yamada, A., and Hirose, F. (1958). *Acta Haematol. Japon.* **21**, 285.

Author Index

M

McCall, M. S., 107, *132*
MacCarter, A., 45, *53*
MacComb, W. S., 382, *434*
McConey, W., 450, *453*
McCready, P. B., 350, *356*
McCulloch, E. A., 461, *481*
McCutcheon, M., 428, *439*
McDevitt, N. B., 61, 64, 66, *86*
MacDonald, E., 305, *335*
McDonald, M. K., 351, *356*
McDonald, T. P., 47, *52*, 122, 124, *131*
MacDuffee, R. C., 308, *336*
MacEwan, A. M., 44, *52*
MacFarlane, R. G., 224, 238, *261*, 389, 421, *434*
McGluskey, H. B., 392, *433*
MacGowern, J. J., 312, *335*
McGregor, D. D., 294, *333*
McGuire, J. A., 35, 37
Macheboeuf, M., 241, *262*
MacIntyre, W. J., 13, 22, 30, *38*, 145, 163, *169*
Mackay, I., 340, 341, *354*
McKinley, T. W., Jr., 472, *479*
MacKinney, A. S., 195, *258*
McKinney, G. R., 207, *258*
McLaughlin, M. M., 388, 403, *439*
McLeod, R. M., 219, *258*
McNulty, W., 475, *482*
McPherson, S. D., 364, *374*
McWhirter, R., 351, *356*
McWilliam, J. M., 351, *356*
Madden, S. C., 276, 280, 286, *337*
Madsen, C. B., *52*
Maduror, B. P., 35, *37*
Maebara, S., 33, *37*
Mäkelä, O., 188, *190*
Magee, M. Z., 387, 388, *436*
Maggioni, L., 420, 421, 422, 431, *434*
Magyar, S., 429, *441*
Mahoney, J. F., 312, *331*
Maier-Leibnitz, H., 144, *168*, *169*
Maisin, H., 475, 477, *481*
Maisin, J., 475, 477, *481*
Maissonet, M., 276, 280, 283, 286, 290, 291, 292, 297, 300, 301, 302, 310, *334*, 342, 351, *353*
Makinodan, T., 340, 344, *353*, *354*, 464, 476, 478, *479*, *480*, *481*, *482*

Malamos, B., *439*
Maldague, P., 477, *481*
Mallet, L., 409, *439*
Maloney, M. A., 111, *131*, 179, *190*
Maloney, W. C., 209, 217, *258*
Manaker, R. A., 61, 69, 83, *84*
Mandel, P., 287, *335*, *336*
Maney, B. E., 217, *258*
Mannick, J. A., 463, 471, *480*, *481*
Manstein, B., 447, *454*
Maraini, G., 32, *36*, 179, 180, *190*, 216, 217, *256*
March, H. C., 373, *376*, 511, 526, *534*
Marchesi, V. T., 62, *86*
Marcovici, I., 61, *85*
Marcus, J., 349, 350, *354*
Marcus, S., 346, 347, 349, 350, *352*, *355*
Marder, S. N., 368, *375*
Mardersteig, K., 276, *335*
Margen, S., 35, *37*
Marinelli, L. D., 152, *169*
Markowitz, H., 242, *262*
Marks, E. K., 266, 267, 269, 273, 276, 278, 297, 308, 327, 330, 331, *334*, 359, 360, 375, 385, 395, 404, 426, *437*, 459, 462, 464, 466, 472, 476, 478, *480*
Marks, P. A., 101, *127*
Maroteaux, P., 289, 303, 330, *335*, 342, 343, 351, *354*
Marques, P., 382, 411, 412, *435*
Marrack, J. R., 340, *354*
Marsh, J. C., 115, *131*
Martin, H., 118, *127*, 210, *255*
Martin, S. P., 112, *129*, 213, *256*
Martland, H. S., 392, *433*
Marx, R., 61, *85*
Masek, B., 210, *260*
Mashimo, S., 503, *535*
Masan, W. B., 326, *334*, 365, 366, *375*, 397, 398, 401, 402, *437*
Mason, R. G., 64, 66, *86*
Masuda, M., 33, *37*
Masuda, Y., 496, *535*
Mathé, G., 276, 277, 278, 279, 280, 281, 283, 286, 289, 290, 291, 292, 295, 296, 297, 300, 301, 302, 303, 305, 306, 307, 308, 309, 310, 311, 312, 313, 316, 317, 318, 319, 320, 324, 325, 326, 328, 330, *332*, *334*, 335, 336,

Subject Index

A

Acanthosis, 320

Accelerator globulin, labile factor, Acb, 390

Accelerin, 291

Accidental irradiation
atomic laboratories, 497
atomic plants, 497

ACD *see* Anticoagulant acid citrate dextrose

Acetylphenyl hydrazine, 144

Actinomycin, 182, 187
D, 99

Adenine, 214

Adenosinase, 112

Adenosine diphosphate (ADP), 65, 225, 247

Adenosine monophosphate (AMP), 225

Adenosine triphosphate (ATP), 108, 139, 201, 221, 227, 234, 247

ADP *see* Adenosine diphosphate

Adrenalectomy, 368

Adrenergic stimulation, 270

Adrenocortical steroids, 310

Adrenocorticotropic hormone (ACTH), 203

Aerobic glycolysis, 205

AET *see* 2-Aminoethylisothiouronium bromide HBr

Agglutination, 341

Agglutination techniques, 27

AGL *see* Leukemia, acute granulocytic

Ailinginae atoll, 532

DL-Alanyl-glycinase, 235

Albumin
extravascular, 35
intravascular, 35

Alexine, 342

ALL *see* Leukemia, acute lymphocytic

Alpha-radiation, 5, 24, 383

Americans on Rongeric atoll, 532

Amino acids, 211–214

Aminocaproic acid, 309, 425

2-Aminoethylisothiouronium bromide HBr, 6

Amino oxides, 6

p-Aminopropiophenone (PAPP), 6

AML *see* Leukemia, acute monocytic

AMP *see* Adenosine monophosphate

Amphibian limbs, 94

Amylase, 112

Anemia, 287, 358, 411, 528
aplastic, 14, 507
Cooley's, 67, 160
diagnosis of, 14
with Fe^{59} and Co^{60}, 14–17
hemolytic, 14
chronic congenital, 160
experimentally induced, 62
hyperchromic, 510
hypochromic hypersideremic, 67
iron-deficiency, 67, 510
normochromic, 360
pernicious, 3, 14, 16, 160
pregnancy, 444
severe aplastic, 510
sickle cell, 67
sideroachrestic, 67

Anhydroerythromycine-*N*-oxide, 6

Anion, Cl^-, 247

Anisocytosis, 503

Ankylosing spondylitis, 370

Anorexia, 493, 531

Anoxia, 98
anemic, 98
anoxic, 98
histiotoxic, 98

Antibiotica, 451

573